KU-405-382

THE PLANT CELL-WALL

by

Professor Dr. Pieter A. ROELOFSEN

Techn. Hogeschool, Delft/Holland

With 215 figures and 68 plates

1959

GEBRÜDER BORNTRAEGER · BERLIN-NIKOLASSEE

With the co-operation of Prof. C. E. B. BREMEKAMP
for the translation of the Dutch manuscript.

Alle Rechte, auch die der Übersetzung,
des auszugweisen Nachdrucks, der Herstellung von Mikrofilmen und der photomechanischen Wiedergabe,
vorbehalten.
© 1959 by Gebrüder Borntraeger, Berlin-Nikolassee
Druck: Felgentreff & Co., Berlin SW 61
Papier: Papierfabrik Scheufelen KG., Oberlenningen
Printed in Germany

G.88439

V

CONTENTS   Page

INTRODUCTION

It would be out of place in this work to draw the attention to the various ways in which the cell-wall is of importance to man. As to the part it plays in the life of the plant, it will be sufficient to point out that it would be impossible for an ordinary cell, i.e. one that is not provided with a special device for the excretion of water, to maintain itself in an ordinary, i.e. a hypotonic medium, were it not for the presence of a cell-wall, and that it is only because of the presence of the cell-walls that the aerial parts of land plants can withstand the stress exerted on them by the force of gravity. It is also worth remembering that it are the cell-walls that give the cells their shape and the tissues their texture, which means that they are responsible for those features of the plant that form the object of study of the plant anatomist.

The character of the cell-wall depends not only on the chemical and physical properties of its constituents, but also on their structure. Both these aspects have already been considered in the first edition of this part of the "Handbuch der Pflanzenanatomie" (van WISSELINGH, 1925), and in the present edition too they will receive due attention.

Since the appearance of the first edition both aspects, but especially the chemistry of important cell-wall constituents, have extensively been studied, and the literature on the cell-wall has increased so enormously that it would be impossible to discuss it here in detail; even a complete list of the titles would occupy too much space. For this reason we will confine ourselves to a sketch of the present state of our knowledge, with special emphasis on those aspects that are of interest to the botanist. For the older literature we will, as a rule, refer to works dealing with special parts of the subject, and direct references will be given to the more recent publications only. This will suffice to enable the reader to find the literature he should wish to consult. Direct references to the older literature will be inserted where a historical survey of the development of part of our knowledge is given, or when there appear to be discrepancies between older data and more recent ones, occasionally also when a question of priority has to be decided; to this kind of problems, however, no undue attention will be paid.

From what has been said, it will be clear that we do not strive after completeness, as was done in the first edition, but that we will content ourselves with a critical exposition of the present state of our knowledge.

1. The Cell-wall Constituents

A survey of the various constituents found in cell-walls of different origin is given in Table 1. The chemical character of these constituents will be discussed further on.

Table 1. Chemical constitution of cell-walls of various origin

Cell-wall of:	cellulose	hemicellulose	pectic subst.	chitin	lignin	suberin or cutin	lipids	protein
Avena coleoptiles...... (Bishop et al., 1958)	25	51	1	—	+	+ ?	4.2	9.5
Growing cotton hair[1] .	32	19	21	—	—	3.5	8	14
Full-grown cotton hair.	96	1 ?	0.9	—	—	0.3	0.6	1
Ceiba hair[2])	37	40	1 ?	—	12	1.5 ?	2.5	+ ?
Linum fibres (unretted)	85	9	4	—	0–6	—	2–5	+ ?
Corchorus fibres	60	26	+	—	11	—	1	+ ?
"Cambium"[3])	25	26	24	—	—	—	+	+ ?
Wood	41–48	25–40	0.5–1.5	—	25–30	—	+	+ ?
Petasites collenchyma[2])	20	35	45	—	—	—	?	+ ?
Quercus cork..........	2–11	+ ?	+ ?	—	12–20	40–60	5–15	+ ?
Phycomyces sporangio-phore	—	40	—	27	—	—	25	+ ?
Saccharomyces cerevisiae	—	70	—	1–3	—	—	8.5	7 ?

—: not present; +: present, but quantity unknown or very variable; + ?: presence probable, but not strictly proved. [1]) calculated from figures given by Tripp et al. (1954) and Kursanov (1952); [2]) own determinations; [3]) calculated from figures given by Allsop and Misra (1940) by assuming that the protein and lignin found by them are contaminations and may therefore be left out of consideration.

This table shows in the first place that the cell-walls of growing cells contain less cellulose and more hemicellulose and pectin then those of full-grown cells of similar origin. Growing cells never contain lignin; the lignin recorded as occurring in "cambium", is derived from adjoining xylem cells. Full-grown cell-walls may show important differences in their composition; those of cotton hairs consist for the greater part of cellulose, those of collenchyma and of *Ceiba* hairs of other carbohydrates, those of cork cells of fatlike substances. Lipids and proteins are probably present in all cell-walls, although in strongly varying amounts. The cell-walls of fungi differ considerably from all of them by the absence inter alia of lignin, pectin and cellulose, and by the presence of chitin (there are, however, exceptions to this rule), whereas their hemicelluloses are of a different nature.

11. Cellulose

111. OCCURRENCE IN THE ORGANIC WORLD

Cellulose is universally present in the cell-walls of the *Cormophyta*, although not in every layer of their cell-walls, for it is absent from the cuticle, the suberin layers and the middle lamella. In many cell-walls, however, it is present in such small amounts and so thoroughly enveloped by non-cellulose e.g. by hemicellulose, lignin or cutin, that it is impossible to demonstrate its presence by means of the ordinary reagents; under these circumstances it has first of all to be chemically purified. In order to appreciate its great importance, we should realize that the faculty of producing cellulose must have been one of the most valuable agents in the development of the land flora. It is also worth noting that more than a third of the amount of material produced by plants consists of cellulose, and that this is more than there is of any other substance. To man it is quantitatively the most important raw material of botanical origin.

Cellulose has also been found in many of the lower plants. The older literature on this subject has been discussed by VAN WISSELINGH (1925), TUNMANN-ROSENTHALER (1931: 1004), FRITSCH (1935, 1945) and others, but as the presence of this substance has often been inferred from the results of not fully conclusive reactions obtained with solvents and dyes, several of these records are either entirely erroneous, in contradiction with the observations of other investigators, or uncertain. The more recent literature is in this respect but little better. Moreover, as the observations are often hidden in publications dealing in the main with other subjects, a complete survey is difficult to obtain. For this reason we will have to confine our discussion to the main points and to part of the recent literature.

As to the *Algae*, cellulose may be regarded as universally present in the *Peridineae*, the *Conjugatae*, the *Phaeophyceae* (VIEL, 1939; PERCIVAL and ROSS, 1949, see however CRONSHAW et al., 1958), most of the *Rhodophyceae* (MORI, 1953, see however CRONSHAW et al., 1958), and part of the *Chlorophyceae*; among the latter it is found mainly in the *Cladophoraceae*, *Valoniaceae*, *Siphonocladaceae* and *Charales* (NICOLAI and PRESTON, 1952; HOUGH et al. 1952; AMIN, 1955; CRONSHAW et al., 1958). In some of the *Chlorophyceae* it appears in a form with a somewhat different crystal structure, viz. in that of the so-called cellulose II (NICOLAI and PRESTON, l.c.). In one of the *Rhodophyceae* too it is said to be present in this form (MYERS et al., 1956). In *Hydrodictyon* amorphous cellulose was found (KREGER, 1958 a).

Cellulose is very probably present in some of the *Cyanophyceae* too, at least in their heterocysts; in some others probably not (METZNER, 1955; FREY-WYSSLING and STECHER, 1954). In lichens the algal component is a facultative producer of cellulose; in some of them, therefore, it is present, in others not (HILPERT et al., 1937).

Among the *Fungi* cellulose has been found in the *Oomycetes*, in one of the *Chytridiaceae* (NABEL, 1939; see however FREY, 1950) and perhaps the *Monoblepharidaceae*.

Among the *Schizomycetes* it has been found in *Acetobacter xylinum* and related species (HIBBERT and BARSHA, 1931; MÜHLETHALER, 1949 a) and in *Sarcina ventriculi* (see section 113).

Dictyostelium discoideus is so far the only *Myxomycete* in which it has been found (MÜHLETHALER, 1956; GEZELIUS and RÅNBY 1957).

In the animal kingdom it is known only from some *Tunicates*. The "mammalian cellulose" detected in cattle hide (HALL et al., 1958) obviously consists of contaminating cotton fibres.

112. CHEMISTRY

(general literature, cf. OTT and SPURLIN, 1954/1955; surveys: TREIBER, 1957; RÅNBY, 1958; FREY-WYSSLING, 1959).

The *cellulose molecule* is a linear glucose-polymer, i.e. a long chain of glucose units connected by glucosidic bonds, cf. formula (1) in fig. 1. The glucosidic bond differs from the ordinary ether bond because a connection exists between one of the C-atoms (C_1) and a second O-atom, viz. the one that bridges the glucose molecule to a cyclo-semiacetal form, the pyranose ring. It should be noted that the O-atom of the glucosidic bond points in the same direction as the O-atom of the pyranose ring. This is the β-configuration, and since the glucosidic bonds connect C_1 with C_4, they are called β-1,4 glucosidic bonds. They are chemically less reactive than the α-1,4 bonds, which occur e.g. in starch. The greater stability of cellulose is to a large extent due to this difference in configuration.

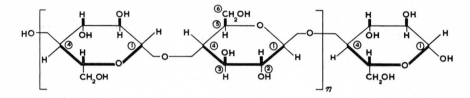

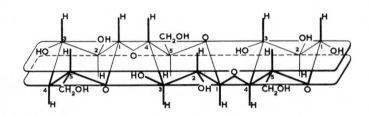

Fig. 1. (1) Structural formula of cellulose molecule; (2) Three-dimensional structure of cellulose molecule; (3) Atom model of cellulose molecule.

One of the consequences of the β-configuration is that the successive pyranose rings are alternately seen from the opposite sides. The two ends of the chain are different; at one end we have a free C_1-OH group with reducing capacity, whereas the other end is non-reducing.

It can not be doubted that the ordinary cellulose consists of unbranched chains only. It has been said, however, that the cellulose of bacteria consists of slightly branched chains, and that of animals even of strongly branched ones, just as the molecules of glycogen are more strongly branched than those of starch (VAN DER WIJK and SCHMORAK, 1953). These findings, however, have not yet been confirmed.

The structural formula (1) of fig. 1 shows that the H-atoms and the OH-groups are not located in the plane of the pyranose ring but project, more or less obliquely, above or below the latter. In reality the pyranose rings are not flat but show at each successive C-atom an upward or downward bent. These bents are slightly flexible, and theoretically eight so-called strainless configurations of the pyranose ring are conceivable. The pyranose rings of cellulose, however, must possess all of them the same configuration, as the chains are stretched, and as they are connected by means of the so-called H-bonds; this configuration is known as the "chair-form". It can be seen in schema (2) of fig. 1. In this schema as well as in formula (1) we note that each pyranose ring is, compared with the preceding one, turned the other way round. The glycosidic bridge by which they are connected, is but little flexible. The free molecules in a cellulose solution too are comparatively rigid, more or less like strips of rubber, whereas the molecules of several other polysaccharides behave as chains consisting of links. This explains why cellulose solutions are so strongly viscous, and why their molecules so easily stick together.

Some idea of the way in which the action spheres of the various atoms overlap, may be obtained by considering the model of parts of two adjoining molecules shown in (3). Here one sees very clearly how the OH-groups of the C-atoms 2, 3 and 6 project on the sides of the ribbon, whereas the ribbon itself is covered by H- and O-atoms. This is of importance for the establishment of H-bonds between the C_6-OH of the glucose monomers belonging to one of the cellulose molecules in the crystal lattice and the C_2-OH or C_3-OH group of the monomers in the adjacent one; these bonds give strength to the crystal structure. A glucose monomer has a diameter of circ. 5 Å, whereas its length (in the direction of the chain) is 5.15 Å.

The *degree of polymerization* (DP), i.e. the average number of glucose monomers per molecule, lies in native cellulose, according to most of the investigators, between 5000 and 10 000. This is a higher value than has been suggested so far for any other polysaccharide, but it is perhaps not high enough, for there are investigators who estimate it at some tens of thousands. Judging from its length we should be inclined to assume that a stretched cellulose molecule would be easily recognizable under the microscope (DP 5000 = 2.5 μ), but this is not so, as its diameter is far too small, even if we use a modern electron microscope.

The forms of cellulose with which we are confronted in daily life, e.g. cotton-wool, textiles, filtering paper, possess a lower DP, because in those products the chains have been broken in some places, either by oxidation or by hydrolysis. One investigator found e.g. a DP of 5000 for the cellulose of cotton fibres in a ripe but not yet dehisced cotton boll, but a DP of 3500 a few hours after dehiscence. In this case the decrease in the value of the DP is due to oxidation, the U.V. light of the sun acting as a catalyst. During the bleaching process used in the industry the DP once more undergoes a decrease, this time to a value of 1000 to 3000. The DP of cellulose that has been obtained from wood by applying a temperature of circ. 160° C, is of a similar order of magnitude, but here the depolymerization is due to hydrolysis. The cellulose that is used for manufacturing artificial silk, is purposely depolymerized by oxidation, and its DP has decreased to a value of 400 to 800. According to some authors (HESSLER et al., 1948; FREY-WYSSLING, 1954) the cellulose of the primary wall would have a lower DP than that of the secundary layers, but this is open to doubt, as the cellulose of the primary wall will have been mixed with a larger amount of hemicellulose. The inner layer of tension wood, at any rate, certainly has a lower DP (Bos, 1957).

In all cellulose preparations that so far have been studied, the DP showed a high degree of variability. Moreover, in preparations with the same average DP, the degree of variability proved to differ considerably. Owing to this circumstance their properties and their usefulness for industrial purposes differ; it also explains why with different measuring methods a different DP may be found. When the calculation is based on either the osmotic pressure or the reducing power of the solution, the size of the dissolved molecules is of no importance, and the degree of spreading therefore does not influence the average value calculated for the DP. Often, however, the DP is determined by measuring the viscosity of the solution, and as the latter is influenced more strongly by longer molecules than by shorter ones, it is clear that we will find a higher average DP in a preparation with molecules of strongly varying length than in a preparation consisting of molecules with the same average length but with less variability in length.

Starting from cotton wool, which in the raw state already contains 96% cellulose, a preparation with 99.8% cellulose has been obtained, but all attempts to arrive at a higher degree of purification have so far failed. Cellulose preparations obtained from wood contained never more than 99% cellulose. The *nature of the impurities* could be determined only by means of the recently introduced method of paper chromatography. They appeared to consist of xylose, arabinose, mannose, galactose and glucuronic acid. It is still a controversial point whether these sugars are attached to the cellulose chains in the form of side chains, whether they form an integral part of this chain, or whether they are present in the form of distinct polysaccharides, i.e. as rests of hemicellulose which remain firmly adhering to the cellulose molecules. The last-named supposition has the largest number of adherents, but there is no common opinion among them as to the way in which the hemicellulose adheres to the cellulose; this might be either purely mechanical inclusion assisted by adsorption on to the cellulose or a chemical binding.

Ordinary cellulose preparations contain also carboxyl groups, that can not be ascribed to the admixture of uronic acid derived from hemicellulose. However, by entirely excluding the possibility of an oxidation, the amount of the latter can be reduced to such a small value that it seems permitted to assume that native cellulose will be entirely free from them.

Some derivatives of cellulose, e.g. methyl cellulose and carboxymethyl cellulose, are soluble in water, other derivatives, e.g. cellulose acetate and nitrate, can be dissolved in organic solvents, but *cellulose itself is entirely insoluble*. It can, however, form associations with some highly hydrated ions, and the latter indeed dissolve in water; this will be discussed further on. The reason why cellulose itself is entirely insoluble, is to be sought in the ribbon-like, rather rigid structure of the chains, which adhere easily to each other, and form in this way bundles with the character of crystalline or partly crystalline material.

The principal binding forces between the molecules are the H-bridges which already have been mentioned; they are formed either between two OH-groups or between an OH-group and an O-atom in the pyranose rings. Notwithstanding the fact that the O-atoms are bound at two sides to C- or H-atoms, they still have two pairs of electrons which may exercise a certain attraction on the positively charged nucleus of an H-atom, in the same way as they do this in water, where it leads to the formation of di- and tri-hydrol complexes; di-hydrol is $H : O : H : O : H$.

$$\overset{\cdot\cdot}{H}$$

The OH-groups which in a glucose molecule are bound to C-atoms not only form bonds which connect this molecule with another one, but also with HOH, which in its turn can bind other water molecules; in this way a hydration layer is formed. In the presence of water there is therefore a certain competition for the H-atoms. In a crystal of glucose all the latter's OH-groups are mutually connected; in cellulose most of them. Glucose molecules at the periphery of a glucose crystal surrounded by water, nevertheless dissolve because their kinetic excitation suffices to burst the bonds with the other glucose molecules; the latter are already weakened because of the competition with the free electron pairs of the water molecules. A cellobiose crystal too dissolves rapidly, but when the chain length increases, the influence of the kinetic excitation decreases in comparison with that of the many H-bonds. Only so long as the chain consists of less than 20 units, the substance is soluble in water; such substances are the cellodextrines.

In solutions of certain bases, acids and salts the affinity between these molecules and the OH-groups of the cellulose appears to be greater than that between the latter and water. The dissolved molecules therefore form addition complexes with the cellulose, e.g. cellulose-OH $\cdot$ NaOH, and these complexes bind water to a far higher extent than cellulose itself does. In this way the limit between solubility and insolubility shifts to a higher DP. Above this limit the cellulose moreover shows a strong swelling. Ordinary cellulose dissolves in this way e.g. in 72—100% (w/w) sulphuric acid, 42% hydrochloric acid, 85—100% phosphoric acid. When the solution is diluted, the solubility of the cellulose decreases once more, and the cellulose is precipitated. It then appears to be strongly depolymerized, but this is a secundary effect and not responsible for the original increase in solubility, for it appears that a solution in phosphoric acid kept at 0° C shows almost no depolymerization at all.

At higher temperatures cellulose also dissolves in concentrated solutions of the halogenic and rhodanic salts of Li, Ca and Zn, and e.g. of K_2HgCl_4, and in these solutions too a depolymerization is noted. In solutions of other salts it only comes to a swelling of the cellulose, and the degree to which this faculty to cause swelling is developed, proves to be in agreement with the position of the salts in the lyotropic series; the stronger the hydration, the stronger the swelling, thus $Zn > Li > Ca > Mg > Na > NH_4 > K$ and $CNS > J > PO_4 > Br > Cl > NO_3 > SO_4 > ClO_3$.

With the strong bases NaOH, KOH, LiOH and tetra-alkylammonium hydroxide the maximum power of dissolving cellulose is reached at a 2 N concentration and at a low temperature, i.e. at 0° C or lower, but in order to be dissolved, the cellulose must have a DP below 400. Native cellulose probably contains little or nothing of this fraction, but in cellulose preparations obtained from wood it is always present. By extracting a cellulose preparation with such an alkali it is possible to determine how much depolymerized cellulose and hemicellulose, for the latter too is dissolved, it contains. Cellulose that is not or less far broken down, does not dissolve in alkali, but it swells, assuming at the same time a new crystal structure, viz. that of an alkali cellulose. In this form the crystal lattice contains not only cellulose and alkali but also water. This is the "mercerized" cellulose.

When by drying and pulverizing cellulose in a colloid mill it has been brought in an amorphous condition, it becomes soluble in alkali, because in this case little or no binding between the molecules is left.

The best of the so-called solvents of cellulose are the complex bases which ammonia and the amines form with cupric hydroxide. The solution of cupric hydroxide in ammonia (cuoxam, cuprammonium, SCHWEITZER's reagent) is the most commonly used one, and was discovered already a century ago by SCHWEITZER and MERCER. This fluid can dissolve 4.5% cellulose, and so long as no oxygen is present, there is no depolymerization. The formula of this reagent is $Cu(NH_3)_4^{++} \cdot (OH^-)_2$. Like several other metals the bivalent Cu can bind not only the ordinary two anions but in addition also four other groups. The latter must possess, like NH_3 or an amine (RNH_2), an extra pair of electrons. The complex Cu-ion formed in this way can exchange two of its NH_3-groups against two OH-groups of a sugar, but to this end it is necessary that the two OH-groups are attached to two adjoining C-atoms and that they project in the same direction (there may be an angle of at most 60° between them, REEVES, 1951). These two conditions are fulfilled in mannose, where the OH-groups are attached to C_2 and C_3 in the cis-position. It is also possible in glucose, although formula (1) of fig. 1 shows that here the OH-groups are found in the trans-position; however, as the atom model (3) of fig. 1 shows, their direction nevertheless differs but slightly. In the 1,4-polymers of glucose and mannose too the conditions for the exchange of the OH-groups are therefore fulfilled, but this is not so e.g. in the 1,3-polymers. Another excellent solvent belonging to this group is cupri-ethylene-diamine. It is not like cuoxam sensitive to oxygen and light, though the dissolved cellulose remains, as it would do in every other basic medium, subject to oxidation. Recently also complexes of alkyl amines and metals like Co, Cd, Ni and Zn have been introduced as solvents of cellulose. An advantage of the last-named one is that it has no colour (JAYME and NEUSCHÄFFER, 1955, 1957).

The attraction between the OH-groups of the polysaccharides and water explains the eagerness with which *water is absorbed by dry cellulose*, at least when the latter is not in the crystalline state (OTT and SPURLIN, 1954: 393; WISE and JAHN, 1952: 691). In order to eliminate the last traces of water from a moist cellulose preparation it is therefore not sufficient to dry the latter at 105° C in ordinary air, but this should be done in air that has been passed over P_2O_5. When the first amounts of water are taken up, the temperature rise is, because of the binding of free OH-groups, considerably higher than it would be if it were merely due to condensation.

The free OH-groups are only found in those parts of the cellulose preparation that are not crystalline. Other polysaccharides are, as a rule, more strongly hygroscopic, as they possess a lesser degree of crystallinity.

The same difference in structure is responsible for the fact that *cellulose is chemically less reactive than other polysaccharides are*. This difference in reactivity is seen e.g. when these substances are oxidized or hydrolysed. When cellulose is oxidized, aldehyde and carboxyl groups are formed at the C-atoms 2, 3 and 6, and the glucose monomers are partly broken down, so that the DP decreases. In a dry atmosphere and at a low temperature this process proceeds but very slowly, but the ruinous state of the linen that has been found in Egyptian tombs shows that nevertheless in the long run the oxygen in the atmosphere achieves its end. Moisture, high temperatures and light, especially U.V.-light, accelerate the process, and this can be said also of metals like iron and copper, and of alkali. It need hardly be emphasized that oxidizing agents, like the chromic acid which in the botanical laboratory is frequently used for the purpose of macerating tissues, as also perchlorate, H_2O_2, and chlorite, have the same effect. As wood-cellulose preparations have, as a rule, been treated with chlorine in order to remove the lignin, they always contain carboxyl groups. The latter convert the cellulose into a cation-exchanger, as their H-ions can be exchanged against Na, K, Ca, etc., which in their turn have to be removed by means of an acid when we wish to obtain a cellulose free from ash. This explains why slightly oxidized cellulose can, in a neutral medium, be stained by means of dyes in which the cation is responsible for the staining. Such dyes are methylene blue, neutral red and, in case the oxidation has proceeded further, ruthenium red. Staining, however, is not possible in an acid medium, as in that case the dissociation of the carboxyl groups is pushed back by the presence of the H-ions of the medium. The amount of methylene blue that is absorbed, enables us to estimate the number of carboxyl groups in the cellulose. It need not be emphasized that the amount of methylene blue bound by cellulose is always smaller than that bound by a substance like pectin.

Whereas alkali depolymerizes cellulose in the presence of oxygen only, acid accomplishes the same result no matter whether oxygen is present or absent. This is due to the fact that acid hydrolyses the glucosidic bonds. As the β-bonds present in cellulose are, in comparison with the α-bonds of substances like starch, of a more resistent nature, and also because of the high degree of crystallinity of the cellulose, the latter is not so easily hydrolyzed as most of the other polysaccharides are. Nevertheless, even traces of acid are in the long run sufficient to produce a certain effect. For this reason historical documents and textiles decay more rapidly in a town, where traces of SO_2 are present in the atmosphere, than elsewhere. When plant material is boiled for a short time in diluted acid, e.g. in a solution containing less than 5% sulphuric or hydrochloric acid, in order to purify it, this will cause a certain degree of hydrolysis, but not to such an extent that microscopical or electron-microscopical study reveals any change in its structure. However, when the temperature is raised, such changes may become readily noticeable. In order to break cellulose down to glucose we may e.g. heat the cellulose in 5% sulphuric acid to a temperature of 130 to 180° C. Even without the addition of acid the DP of moist cellulose undergoes at temperatures above 100° C a slight decrease. This is noticed e.g. when cellulose is prepared from wood. Concentrated mineral acids, as has been stated, cause already at room temperature a strong hydrolysis of the dissolved cellulose. In the hydrolytic method, which is the one that is used most often for analysing cellulose preparations, the cellulose is first of all dissolved in 72% sulphuric acid, which subsequently is diluted to 1%, and boiled. In the industry hydrolysis is effected by means of 40% HCl at 15° C.

In the world of the living, cellulose can only be broken down after it has first been *hydrolyzed by means of the enzyme cellulase* to cellobiose and subsequently by means of the enzyme cellobiase to glucose (cf. SIU and REESE, 1953; TRACEY, 1953; FÅHRAEUS, 1958). For the maintenance of the carbon cycle it is therefore essential that these enzymes are produced in a sufficient amount: responsible for the production are a large number of bacteria, fungi and invertebrate animals.

Cellulose can be preserved by substituting an H-atom or an OH-group in every monomer as this protects the glucosidic bonds against the action of the cellulase. Several of these resistant esters and ethers of cellulase are nowadays used for the fabrication of synthetic fibres, laquers and adhesives. Incompletely substituted celluloses, e.g. some water-soluble ethers, remain partly hydrolysable, and are used as a substrate in experiments with cellulase.

In the higher plants cellulase is usually present in small amounts. The results of its activity are recognizable in the perforation of the transverse walls of xylem and phloem vessels, and sometimes also in the dissolution of cell-walls (KÜSTER, 1956: 725).

113. PHYSICAL STRUCTURE OF CELLULOSE

This subject is of so eminent importance to everyone who wishes to obtain a good idea of the structure and of various other features of the cell-wall that it will have to be treated at some length.

The earliest information with regard to the physical structure of cellulose was obtained by means of the polarization microscope, i.e. by the study of its birefringence. After 1920 X-ray analysis came to the fore, and after 1940 electron-microscopic investigation.

Already as early as 1849 EHRENBERG pronounced the opinion that starch grains on account of their birefringence, should be regarded as crystal aggregates, and NAEGELI, who in 1860 studied the birefringence of starch as well as of cellulose, was of the same opinion. He thought that the birefringence proved that these substances consisted of *microscopically invisible, rod-like crystals with a parallel orientation*, dispersed in amorphous material. Although birefringence does not implicitly involves crystallinity, NAEGELI's view was confirmed later. Afterwards he introduced for these supposed crystals the name *micelle*. This term has been taken over by the chemists, but it is used by them for all electrostatically charged and eventually hydrated particles that are present in a colloidal suspension, no matter whether they are of a crystalline structure or amorphous. Most biologists, however, still use it in the original meaning. We will follow FREY-WYSSLING's (1953: 79) proposition to drop the condition that the particles should be crystalline; the term micelle will be used as well for amorphous as for crystalline or partly crystalline particles. In this work for the crystalline particles and for the crystalline part of micelles the term "crystallite" will be used. A micelle therefore may but need not contain a crystallite.

At first NAEGELI believed that his micelles were surrounded by fluid, or at least plastic material more or less as the bricks of a wall are embedded in mortar. Afterwards (see FREY-WYSSLING, 1953: 79) he understood that this is irreconcilable with the mechanical properties of gels and of cellulose as well as with the swelling anisotropism, for he then supposes "dass sie (i.e. the micelles) sich beliebig, bald baumartig (i.e. with a distinct orientation), bald netzartig (i.e. without orientation) aneinander hängen", and also that there are "Micellar-Reihen, in denen die Micelle miteinander verwachsen sind".

It were especially AMBRONN and his pupils who, in the period between 1858 and 1925 (cf. FREY-WYSSLING, 1953: 76), have defended the micellar theory against adverse criticism, and who finally succeeded in establishing its fundamental correctness. They did this by demonstrating that the birefringence of these substances is the resultant of the interaction of two different birefringent systems; it rests in the first place on the intrinsic birefringence of the total mass of crystallites and oriented amorphous cellulose molecules and in the second place on the birefringence which is due to the difference in refraction between the substance of the rodlets and the substance which fills the spaces between the latter. The second kind of birefringence is the so-called rodlet-birefringence. In pure dry cellulose the spaces between the rodlets are filled with air, this was proved by the fact that the value of the rodlet-birefringence could be changed at will by imbibing the preparations with fluids with a different refraction index (MOEHRING, 1922; VAN ITERSON, 1933; FREY-WYSSLING and SPEICH, 1936). Since then it has appeared that the rodlets are microfibrils, so that the spaces between them should be called interfibrillar spaces.

In the years round 1930 the micellar theory was accepted for cellulose by SEIFRIZ, MEYER, MARK, and others. They seemed to be aware only of the theory in its original form, which means that the micelles were thought not to be interconnected. Their only addition to that theory was that the micelles were given the structure that had been revealed by X-ray analysis. Soon the shortcomings of the conception that the micelles would be comparatively short and non-cohering, again became apparent. Such a model could e.g. not explain the resistance against extension of cellulose fibres, nor could it make clear why on swelling in alkali the fibres increase in diameter but never in length; in strong alkali they even shrink.

Far more satisfactory was the view at which ABITZ, GERNGROSS and HERRMANN arrived by elaborating NAEGELI's modified conception, viz. that of the interconnected micelles. This view too was published in 1930. They dealt with a gelatin gel, and assumed that this consisted of *"fringe micelles"*. These micelles were supposed to be rod-shaped crystallites connected with each other by means of molecule chains that projected from their surface in the form of a fringe. When the rodlets are oriented parallel to each other, their coherence must be strongest in the longitudinal direction, and then swelling can take place perpendicular to the axis only.

When the chemists discovered that the cellulose molecules were longer than the fringe micelles were supposed to be, the presence of a *reticulum of long microfibrils* was suggested. BONNER (1935) thought that these microfibrils were provided with "Haftpunkte" by the aid of which they could temporarily be connected. FREY-WYSSLING (1937c) suggested the two structures that are shown in fig. 2. In one of them there are anastomosing microfibrils whereas in the other one the anastomoses are absent. Although the model with the anastomosing threads has to this moment its defenders (FREY-WYSSLING, 1953: 105; VOGEL, 1953) and has found its way into recent books (ESAU, 1953: 52), the other one is at this moment more generally preferred.

We will now return to the year 1913 in order to consider *the results obtained by the X-ray analysis of cellulose*. In that year, i.e. in the year following LAUE's discovery of X-ray diffraction in crystals, the Japanese NISHIKAWA and ONO obtained X-ray diagrams from closely aligned fibres from various plants, and they drew from them the correct conclusion, viz. that cellulose contains small rod-shaped crystals that are placed lengthwise in the fibres, but that for the rest may have every kind of position.

The botanists NAEGELI and AMBRONN had already, as stated above, arrived at a similar conclusion on account of their observations on the birefringence shown by cellulose, but the confirmation of their conclusion brought by the work of the Japanese investigators remained unnoticed in Europe. AMBRONN,

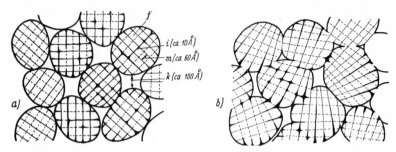

Fig. 2. Transverse sections through a cellulose fibre showing the two submicroscopic structures suggested by FREY-WYSSLING (1936—1937); i: intermicellar space, m: micelle, f: microfibril, k: interfibrillar space.

who in 1916 heard a lecture delivered by SCHERRER on X-ray powder diagrams, persuaded the latter to investigate also cellulose and starch by the aid of his method, but SCHERRER, who apparently was not much interested in these substances, had no success, and published two years later a negative report. In the meantime the crystalline structure of cellulose had been noticed once more by another investigator, viz. by HULL in 1917, but this paper too passed unnoticed. AMBRONN was not satisfied with SCHERRER's results, which to him seemed irreconcilable with his own observations on the birefringence of the two substances, and he pressed him to repeat his investigation. SCHERRER did this, and now obtained a positive result, which however was not published until 1920. In that year also R. O. HERZOG and JANCKE published the ring and spot diagrams that they had obtained respectively from powders and fibres in their study of lignified and unlignified fibres. That the diagrams of the two kinds of fibres appeared to be identical, led them, moreover, to the conclusion that wood can not be regarded as a mixture of cellulose and lignin molecules, as had hitherto been assumed.

POLANYI (1921, 1922) calculated from HERZOG's spot diagrams the dimensions of the so-called unit cell of the crystal lattice; this is the smallest possible three-dimensional unit of identity in the lattice. He also pointed out that this unit cell need not be identical with the cellulose molecule, but that the latter might well be much longer. Just at that time FREUDENBERG arrived by chemical considerations at the conclusion that the cellulose molecule indeed must have a considerable length. The American botanist SPONSLER (1926) developed for the first time a model of a crystal structure based on such long chain molecules, and calculated by means of BRAGG's atom diameters and HAWORTH's formula of glucopyranose the number of glucose monomers that are incorporated in a unit cell.

Also because the methods for obtaining X-ray diagrams in the meantime had been improved (cf. fig. 3), MEYER and MARK (1929) could construct a unit cell which differed but in one respect from that of MEYER and MISCH (1937) which is shown in fig. 4. In the model of 1929 the C_1-atoms are in all chains turned either upwards or downwards. In fig. 4 the orientation in the four peripheral chains differs from that in the central one. The proportion in reality is 1 : 1 as becomes apparent in fig. 5, where the glucose units are shown in projection on the horizontal (ac) - plane of the unit cell. This projection therefore is a parallelogram. It is clear that the OH-groups occupy positions at the margin of the ribbon - like cellulose molecule. The OH-group of C_6 of one glucose unit is always found near the OH-groups of C_2 and C_3 of the glucose unit which lies next to it in the (ab)-plane. Between these groups H-bonds are formed. The connection in the a-direction proves to be far more resistant than that in the c-direction, but in both directions it is less resistant than in the b-direction, i.e. in the direction of the axis of the molecule.

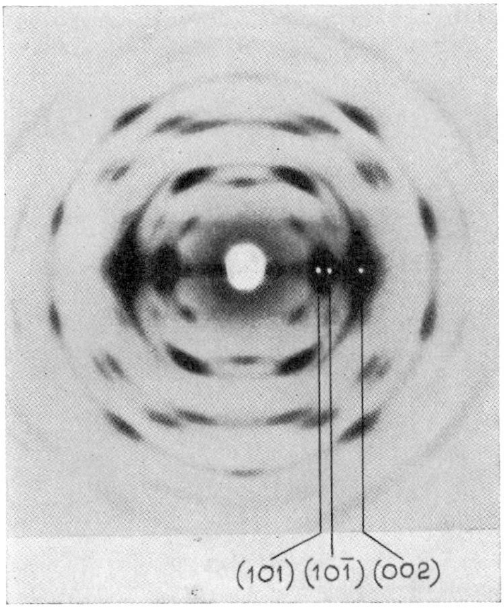

In fig. 5 the horizontal sections of the more important (vertical) lattice planes 002, 101 and 10$\overline{1}$ too are indicated; the reflections of these planes are shown in fig. 3.

(101) (10$\overline{1}$) (002)

Fig. 3. X-ray diagram of oriented ramie fibres.

The first of the three figures by means of which each of the three lattice planes is indicated, refers to the a-axis, the second to the b-axis, and the third to the c-axis; 0 means that the axis lies in the lattice plane, 1 means that adjacent planes of the same type intersect the axis at distances equal to the dimension of the unit cell in the direction of this axis, 2 means that adjacent planes intersect the axis at distances half of the dimension of the axis.

The calculations carried out by MEYER, MARK and MISCH in order to arrive at the crystal structure have

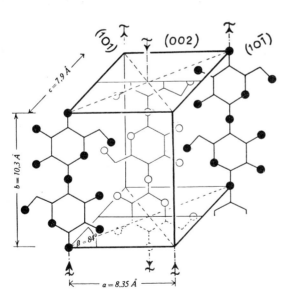

Fig. 4. Unit cell of native cellulose (cellulose I) according to MEYER and MISCH (1937).

more than once been subjected to a critical examination (GROSS and CLARK, 1938; VAN DER WIJK and MEYER, 1947) and compared with other possible solutions (PEIRCE, 1946), but their model has passed these examinations unchanged and is therefore regarded as the one that agrees best with the obser-

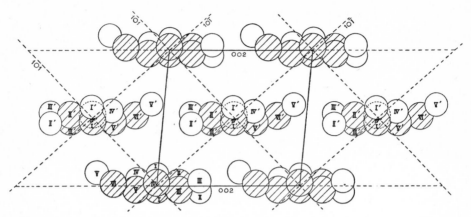

Fig. 5. Basal plane of the unit cell of native cellulose, according to MEYER and MISCH (1937).

vations. The model of MEYER and MISCH (1937) is the generally accepted one, but that of MEYER and MARK (1929) is also in agreement with the X-ray diagrams.

The real structure may be slightly different from that shown in the models as indicated by HERMANS et al. (1943), SEN and ROY (1954), FREY-WYSSLING (1955), PETITPAS and MERING (1956), CARLSTRÖM (1957), HONJO and WATANABE (1957). The slight change proposed by FREY-WYSSLING (l.c.) will be discussed further on and then we will also expound the biochemical grounds on account of which we prefer the model proposed by MEYER and MARK.

When the crystalline structure of native cellulose is destroyed e.g. by extensively grinding dry fibres and when the amorphous material is subsequently wetted, it crystallizes once more, but the crystal lattice now is different

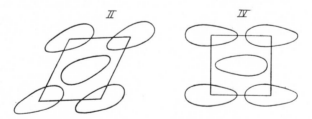

Fig. 6. Basal plane of cellulose II and IV.

(at least when the wetting is performed at room temperature). This is the so-called *cellulose II*, the native product being cellulose I. The change can also be brought about e.g. by dissolving the cellulose and subsequently precipitating it, or by letting it swell in acid, in alkali or in solutions of certain salts and afterwards washing it. The cellulose in rayons and in cellophane and other kinds of regenerated cellulose all belong to this form. Its unit cell is shown in fig. 6; it contains just as that of cellulose I, four glucose monomers, has the same b-axis (10.3 Å), but a more oblique and somewhat larger basal plane, and the plane of the pyranose rings is not parallel to plane 002, but to $10\bar{1}$. This structure is less resistant; it can absorb a few water molecules in its lattice, and its chemical reactivity, swelling power and solubility are greater.

Since as was mentioned, cellulose II is formed, e.g. by coagulating cellulose from a solution, one must assume that about half of the molecules in a crystallite will point upward with their reducing ends, the other half downward. In the construction of the unit cell it was assumed that this alternation occurs according to a definite pattern, the four molecules at the corners of the cell pointing in one direction the central molecule in the opposite one. However, a random distribution of upward and downward chains is conceivable too, and in fact seems more likely as the coagulation process, e.g. when artificial fibres are made, takes place very rapidly.

In view of the biosynthesis of cellulose microfibrils, which will be discussed later, we wish to point out here that it is not known whether the X-ray diagram of cellulose II would be different if the molecules in every fibre of the sample used would all point in one direction with their reducing ends. Nevertheless, MEYER and MISCH (l.c.) discarded the MEYER and MARK model of the crystal structure of cellulose I, solely because the X-ray diagram of mercerized native fibres proved to be identical with that of artificial fibres. Later VAN DER WIJK and MEYER (1947) doubted the solidity of this conclusion and admitted that both models are in agreement with the known X-ray data. This implies that in their opinion cellulose II crystallites with identically oriented molecules will give the same diagram as crystallites consisting of differently oriented chains.

Still another crystal structure of cellulose has been described. It is called cellulose IV; the basal plane of this substance too is shown in fig. 6. It arises when cellulose II is heated in a moist atmosphere to a temperature of 140—300° C or when amorphous or dissolved cellulose crystallizes at such a temperature. It is very similar to cellulose I, and according to some authors it should not be regarded as really distinct, but merely as having a somewhat lesser degree of order.

We should not have mentioned the different structure of cellulose II, were it not that there are indications that it does occur occasionally in cell walls of lower plants. VAN ITERSON (1936) found that the cell-wall of *Halicystis Osterhoutii*, a marine alga belonging to the *Valoniaceae*, assumes a blue colour in a solution of JKJ, i.e. that it behaves like regenerated cellulose. Shortly afterwards SISSON (1938, 1938a) found in the ring diagrams obtained from the cell-walls of three *Halicystis* species the same main interferences as in the ring diagram of cellulose II, whereas when the preparations were heated, the diagram of cellulose IV appeared. ROELOFSEN et al. (1953) confirmed SISSON's conclusion as to the cellulose II diagram, but they added that their chemical analysis seemed to point to the presence of a polymer containing not only glucose but also xylose. NICOLAI and PRESTON (1952) found similar diagrams for the cell-walls of nine other genera of *Chlorophyceae*, and could in one instance obtain conversion into cellulose IV by heating (but strange enough, also in hot diluted acid). MYERS et al. (1956) found the cellulose II diagram as well as the conversion into cellulose IV in the *Rhodophycea Griffithsia flos-*

culosa. CRONSHAW et al. (1958) obtained similar diagrams in this alga and in some other ones, but doubt whether it is really due to cellulose II, see section 242. MÜHLETHALER (1956) thinks that the cellulose of the *Myxomycete Dictyostelium discoideum* too might be cellulose II, but more convincing are the observations of GEZELIUS and RÅNBY (1957) showing that only a minor part of it might be cellulose II, the main part being cellulose I. In X-ray diagrams, obtained from mechanically cleaned walls of *Sarcina ventriculi* too cellulose II interferences have been observed (KREGER, private communication); this bacterium has long been known to stain blue with chlor-zinc-iodine (VAN WISSELINGH, 1925: 43).

According to some authors *cellulose would occur in the walls of living cells in the amorphous form*. BERKLEY and KERR (1946) came to this conclusion because they did not find X-ray interferences in fresh cotton fibres, though it could easily be demonstrated in fibres that had been dried and rewetted. Earlier investigators, however, had already found X-ray interferences of cellulose in fresh cell-walls (HEYN, 1934; HESS et al., 1936; see also PRESTON, 1952). The real cause of the difference in behaviour noted by BERKLEY and KERR is that the fresh fibres contain much more water than the rewetted ones, and that hence the interferences in the diagrams of the former were masked by a more conspicuous diffuse background blackening. That amorphous cellulose would be present and that it would be transformed by drying into crystalline cellulose, is moreover improbable for the following two reasons. In the first place there is hardly any difference in birefringence between fresh cotton fibres and dried ones that have been moistened. In the second place the cellulose of the latter is not cellulose II but cellulose I.

Other investigators are of opinion that the cellulose of primary cell-walls as well as that of lignified ones is partly amorphous and that this part crystallizes when non-cellulosic constituents are removed, but the correctness of this view too has not yet been proved; further on we will return to this question.

That in *Hydrodictyon reticulatum* the cellulose, at least the main part of it, is present in the amorphous state, as KREGER (1958a) assumes, rests on better grounds; it is dispersed in a nearly equal amount of mannan, and when the wall is treated with hot acid the cellulose crystallizes in the form of cellulose II (see section 2413).

The X-ray analysis has also given us indications as to the *dimensions of the crystallites*. A lattice plane gives a more sharply pronounced interference (narrower when measured in the radial direction), the larger the number of lattice planes that are present in each of the crystallites, i.e. the thicker the latter are in the direction perpendicular to that plane. The diagrams obtained from larger crystallites, in which a larger number of irregularities occur, may, however, be as unsharp as those of small but more regularly developed ones. When this source of error is left out of consideration, the mean diameter of the crystallite may be estimated at 50—80 Å, and its length at more than 600 Å (R. O. HERZOG, 1926; HENGSTENBERG and MARK, 1929; FREY-WYSS-LING, 1937a); entirely arbitrary is the assumption, often found in literature, that the length would amount to 1000 Å. When the irregularities in the structure are taken into account, the diameter may be estimated at ca. 100 Å.

Cellulose obtained from wood as well as that obtained from primary cell-walls give wider interferences than e.g. that from cotton; this points either to a smaller diameter of the crystallites, which in that case would be ca 50 Å, or else to a less regular crystal structure (CLARK et al., 1930; HESS et al., 1939; WARDROP, 1949, 1954b; STERLING, 1957a). In tension wood, which contains cellulose of lower DP, the crystallites must be either thicker or more regularly developed (WARDROP and DADSWELL, 1955). This is consistent with the common experience that shorter molecules crystallize better than longer ones. Relatively thick crystallites seem to occur in the cellulose of *Valonia* (RÅNBY, 1952a). On the base of the electron-diffraction diagram the diameter of the crystallites would in this alga lie between 100 and 500 Å (BALASHOV and PRESTON, 1955).

The diameter of the crystallites can also be estimated by means of another feature of the X-ray diagrams, viz. the extent of the blackened zone near the centre, the so-called small-angle scattering, see figure 111. For cellulose the estimates vary in this case between 30 and 150 Å, which means that they are of the same order of magnitude as those obtained in the other way (KRATKY et al., 1942, 1951; HEYN, 1949, 1950, 1955; WARDROP, 1949; ADAM, 1951; HEIKENS et al., 1953, 1958; BAYLEY et al., 1957).

X-ray analysis of cellulose II has shown that here the *crystallites are wider in the 101-direction* than they are in the 002- and in the $10\bar{1}$-direction (KRATKY et al., 1942, 1949; HERMANS, 1949). Their shape would be similar to that of a ruler, and they would show a tendency to split parallel to the 101-plane i.e. parallel to the flat surface of the ruler. X-ray analysis of cellulose I did not lead to positive results as to the shape of the crystallites, but study by the aid of the electron microscope of the cellulose micelles obtained by partial hydrolysis in acid has revealed that they too are flat, just like those of cellulose II (MUKHERJEE and WOODS, 1953; VOGEL, 1953). This, however, is no fully convincing proof, as the micelles of cellulose I may have obtained this shape on account of the way in which they were formed by hydrolysis and partial dissolution. These processes might have proceeded more rapidly in the direction perpendicular to the 101-plane. VOGEL (1953) observed similar ruler-shaped particles and threads as a result of mechanical desintegration, but he seems to interpret them as splitting products and hence the shape of the original crystallites remains doubtful. Nevertheless, although there is as yet no definite proof, it does seem likely that also the crystallites of cellulose I are flat. That the microfibrils too, as we will see further on, are probably flat, may be regarded as a corroboration of this view.

There are several reasons for assuming that the cellulose is not throughout crystalline, but that there is also *semi-crystalline and amorphous cellulose*. In the first place, the specific weight of cellulose, even when determined with the aid of gaseous helium or with fluids that penetrate into the finest pores, proves to be lower than that which can be calculated for cellulose crystals on account of the dimensions and the contents of the unit cell. In the second place, cellulose is hygroscopic, but this can not be due to a faculty of absorbing water within the confines of the crystal lattice, for in that case the X-ray diagram of dry and moist cellulose would be different which is not so. Thirdly, the X-ray diagram shows more diffuse background-blackening than could be expected from a product consisting entirely of crystals. Fourthly, there are several chemical indications for the presence of amorphous cellulose, viz. cation-exchange, reaction without a decrease of the crystallinity, faculty to absorb stains, etc.

Although the differences between the actually observed values and those that could have been expected from a completely crystalline substance are not the same for all criteria, it seems permitted to conclude from them that ca $^2/_3$ of the substance must be more or less crystalline and ca $^1/_3$ more or less amorphous (cf. i.a. OTT and SPURLIN, 1954: 265; HERMANS, 1949: 311, 517; PRESTON et al., 1950; TARKOW, 1950; BERGMAN and JOHNSON, 1950; HEATH and JOHNSON, 1950; CLARK and TREFORD, 1955; MANN and MARRINAN, 1956). The transition between crystalline and amorphous is undoubtedly gradual, and the ratio between these two amounts will be found different when different methods are applied. Crystalline areas with a diameter of less than 20 Å for instance will contain but a few cellulose molecules, and there will therefore be no X-ray interference, but nevertheless part of the OH-groups will not be available for the binding of water and for chemical reactions.

BALASHOV and PRESTON (1955) assume, on account of electron-diffraction diagrams, that the *Valonia* cellulose possesses a much higher degree of crystallinity, viz. ca 100%. In chemical respect this cellulose is said to show a remarkable resistance (PRESTON, 1951; RÅNBY, 1952a). The X-ray diagram of purified *Valonia* cellulose in fact is more sharp than of purified cotton cellulose (PRESTON and CRONSHAW, 1958). The lower degree of crystallinity found earlier (PRESTON et al., 1950), viz. 70%, applies to non-purified cell-walls, which contain 25% non-cellulose material.

The cellulose of the primary walls would, according to various authors, not only contain smaller crystallites, but it would also be for a smaller part crystalline (HEYN, 1934; HESS et al., 1939; WARDROP, 1949; PRESTON, 1952; FREY-WYSSLING, 1954). In dry condition they contain only about 30% cellulose. When the other substances have been removed, the interferences that were already visible, become more easily distinguishable, and some other ones are now seen for the first time. In wood the cellulose was found to behave in the same way when the lignin was removed (WARDROP, 1957a, cf. diagram in PRESTON, 1952: 42). These facts led to the view that the crystallites under these circumstances increase in size. Originally the amorphous cellulose molecules would have been surrounded by non-cellulose in such a way that the contact between them was insufficient to allow crystallization. PRESTON (1952: 195) supposes that the primary walls contain a cellulose-protein complex, whereas WARDROP (1957a) is of opinion that the phenomenon that he observed in wood, indicates the presence of chemical bonds between the lignin and the amorphous cellulose at the periphery of the microfibrils.

It is, however, still uncertain whether it is allowed to assign quantitative value to differences in distinctness and in width of the X-ray interferences in cell-walls that contain besides cellulose such large amounts of amorphous substances. BJÖRKQUIST et al. (1954) found that in mixtures of cellulose II and amorphous cellulose no interferences could be found when the proportion of the first-named substance sank below 20%, and the investigators who are of opinion that there is no proof that amorphous cellulose has passed into the crystalline form when other substances were removed, may therefore be right (SISSON, 1937; ASTBURY et al., 1935). If a cellulose II diagram were to appear, as happens in *Hydrodictyon* (KREGER, 1958a), there would be a distinct indication of crystallization, but this diagram has hitherto not been found in higher plants (cf. STERLING, 1957a). However, the adherents of the view that crystallization really takes place, might argue that crystallization takes place in the form of cellulose I because there are already crystals of this kind which act as seeds.

The crystallinity of the purified cellulose of primary walls would, according to FREY-WYSSLING (1954), be no more than 34—37%, but STERLING (1957a) found a higher value, viz. 55—60%. When we take into account that hemicellulose remnants will probably have been present, the figures of STERLING would indicate a normal degree of crystallinity. Not in line with the supposed lower degree of crystallinity is FREY-WYSSLING's statement (1959: 119) that the microfibrils in primary walls have a more compact structure. It was deduced from the failure to stain blue with chlor-zinc-iodine, but this is obviously due to the presence of non-cellulose since cleaned primary walls stain very well.

By the aid of the same methods with which the crystalline fraction of native cellulose I was estimated at ca $^2/_3$, a value of ca 40% was found for regenerated celluloses, such as rayon and cellophane. This lesser degree of crystallinity can not be due to a less regular orientation of the molecules in these substances, for when ramie fibres are mercerized under tension, so that there can be no change in the orientation of the molecules, they too appear to possess a crystallinity of no more than 40%. The real cause of the decrease is still unknown. What position the amorphous and the crystalline fraction of native cellulose occupy with regard to each other, will be discussed further on.

It was originally thought that a large number of crystallites were united, as shown in fig. 2, into threads, which eventually might anastomose. These threads were called microfibrils. The *microfibrils would be separated from each other by wide interstices* filled with air, water or some other substance, whereas the crystallites themselves would be separated from each other by narrow fissures.

For the assumption that interstices must be present, convincing grounds could be adduced. When the specific weight of cellulose was pycnometrically determined by the aid of helium gas or of a fluid of which it might be supposed that it would penetrate into eventually present interstices, it proved to be higher than when it was determined by the aid of a fluid that penetrated only into the lumen of the fibre. On account of the difference between these two values the amount of air in the wall of a dry ramie fibre could be estimated at 10%, and that in the wall of a cotton fibre at even more than 20% (cf. HERMANS, 1949: 197).

The fact that part of the birefringence of cellulose appeared to be due to rodlet birefringence that could be changed by injecting fluids with different refractive indices, also proved the presence of interfibrillar spaces. It appears that even colloidal substances like congo-red penetrate easily into the cellulose structure.

Still another reason to assume the presence of interstices between the cellulose elements is that in some types of cell-wall, incrusting substances occur between the cellulose, e.g. lignin, cutin and silica. These substances cannot be truly mixed with the cellulose molecules since they do not change the birefringence and the X-ray diagram of the cellulose.

Attempts have been made to estimate the size of the intermicellar spaces in fibres by filling them with crystals, e.g. of gold or silver, that were obtained out of their salts by reduction and determining the size of these crystals. This could be done by measuring the width of the gold and silver interferences shown by the X-ray diagrams (FREY-WYSSLING, 1937a; KRATKY and SCHOSSBERGER, 1938). When the crystals were formed rapidly, they proved to measure on the average 55—80 Å; when they were formed more slowly,

2*

100 Å or more. The X-ray diagram revealed moreover that the crystals must be cubical, but this did not agree with the fact that the colour of the fibres varied with the direction of polarization of light passing them, e.g. in the direction of the axis or perpendicular to the latter. This led to the conclusion that the cubical crystals must be arranged in longitudinal rows, and that the intermicellar spaces must be lengthened in the direction of the axis. FREY-WYSSLING (1937b) has calculated from the values that were found for the light dispersion caused by these conglomerates, that they must have a width of at least 100 Å and a length of at least 1000 Å. Some of them, however, proved to be much larger, and might even be microscopically visible. It is clear therefore that the spaces may eventually undergo an increase in size. For this reason this method of calculating the size of the interstices can not be regarded as fully reliable (WARDROP, 1954c).

Nevertheless the sketch of the cellulose structure which FREY-WYSSLING drew for us twenty years ago, does not appear to be much different from the one at which we now have arrived by the aid of the revelations of the *electron microscope*.

In 1940 H. RUSKA and KRETSCHMER investigated by the aid of the first electron microscope (constructed in the factory of SIEMENS by E. RUSKA and VON BORRIES) the structure of cotton fibres that had been subjected to a vigorous treatment with acid. They found that the wall of these fibres consisted of bundles of very long threads, of which the thinnest ones had a diameter of

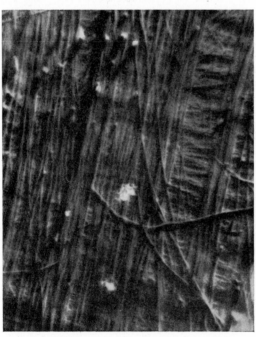

7a

50 Å. In the next years several investigators in Europe and in America found in mechanically disintegrated fibres as well as in bacterial cellulose similar threads with a diameter of 50—200 Å, but the images as yet remained vague.

Much clearer images were obtained by the application of the method of the "metal shadow-cast", which was perfected in 1944 by WILLIAMS and WYCKOFF. It consists in spraying vaporized metal at a low angle on the object. The first photos of more or less intact cell-walls that were obtained by the aid of this method, were published in 1948, and are produced in fig. 7a and b. The greater contrast obtained with the shadow-cast method is obvious by comparison with fig. 8.

The *Valonia* cell-walls are untreated, whereas that of maize root parenchyma has been freed of most of the hemicellulose and pectin by heating in dilute

acid and alkali. In *Valonia* we see crossed layers with closely and perfectly
aligned microfibrils which tend to form bundles. In the primary parenchyma
wall an intricate network of microfibrils is visible which reminds one of the
structure of felt or of paper as seen under an ordinary microscope. In primary

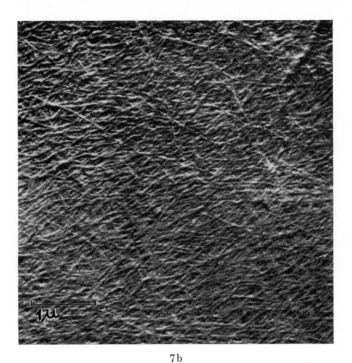

7b

Fig. 7. The first electron-micrographs of cell-walls with shadow cast.
a: cell-wall layers of *Valonia* obtained with a replica-method (PRESTON et al., 1948).
b: primary cell-wall from the parenchyma of the *Avena* coleoptile (FREY-WYSSLING et al.,
1948).

cell-walls that are somewhat desintegrated mechanically, and in the cellulose
of some slimes of botanical origin one can see that the microfibrils reach a
great length, viz. up to 10μ, and show a tendency to form ribbons (section 227,
fig. 18, see also FREY-WYSSLING, 1951, and JAYME and HUNGER,1958). Their
ends, which for this reason are but rarely seen, prove to be not frayed but
obtuse (MÜHLETHALER, 1950c). It is now rather generally believed that the
microfibrils do not anastomose. VOGEL (1953), however, is still of opinion
that, at least in the ramie fibre, the microfibrils consist of and are interconnected
by thinner elements, which he calls elementary fibrils, and that the microfibrils therefore do anastomose. Convincing arguments or figures, however,
are, in the reviewer's opinion, not brought forward.

Howsoever this may be, the fibrillar structure at any rate makes it clear 1°
that interfibrillar spaces must be present; 2° that a fibre whose microfibrils
run for the greater part in the direction of the axis, will swell easily in the
transverse direction, but hardly in the longitudinal one; 3° that it will show
rodlet-birefringence; 4° that the interfibrillar spaces may increase in size
when they become filled with crystals that are formed out of an imbibed

fluid, and 5° that hemicellulose and lignin may be deposited in the inter-fibrillar spaces without altering the general structure of the microfibrils.

The values that have been recorded for the *diameter of the microfibrils* vary. This appears to depend not so much on the object as on the investigator, and may be due to differences in the methods that have been applied in order to obtain the shadow casts, and also to differences in the resolving power of the special type of electron microscope that has been used. Estimates of the diameter with an error of $\pm$ 50 Å are easily obtained, but for real measurements magnifications of ca 100,000 times are required. The measurements carried out by RANBY (1952a, 1954) on such widely differing objects

Fig. 8.
More recent electron-micrographs of a single layer of *Valonia* cell-wall, but not shadowed (from WILSON, 1951).

as cotton fibres, *Acetobacter xylinum,* wood cellulose, cell-walls of *Valonia* and cellulose of *Tunicates,* lie between 70 and 120 Å, on the average therefore at ca 100 Å. Estimates carried out on the cell-walls of *Valonia* (WILSON, 1951), wood (RIBI, 1953; HODGE and WARDROP, 1950), cambium (PRESTON and RIPLEY, 1954) and cortical fibres (STERLING and SPIT, 1957) are of the same order of magnitude. Nearly the same diameter was found for the microfibrils of the substance that in *Halicystis* (ROELOFSEN et al., 1953; RANBY, 1952a) and in *Dictyostelium* (MÜHLETHALER, 1956) is supposed to be cellulose II.

Other investigators, especially FREY-WYSSLING and MÜHLETHALER and their collaborators report for the same objects, estimates varying between 100 and 300 Å. VOGEL (1953) measured in ramie fibres after a strong mechanical disintegration a width of 110—320, on the average 200 Å and a thickness of 25—100, on the average 30 Å. The thickness could be calculated from the width of the shadow, as the angle at which the vaporized metal was deposited, was known. PRESTON (1951) reports for the microfibrils of *Valonia* cellulose a width of 150—490 Å and a thickness of 50—350 Å; on the average they proved to be 3—7 times as wide as thick. The exceptionally high values which he sometimes found for the thickness, are ascribed to a torsion of the microfibrils. According to MEYER et al. (1951) the microfibrils of animal cellulose are also ca 200 Å in width, and they too are flattened. The same applies to the micro-fibrils of *Griffithsia* (MYERS et al., 1956) and other Algae (CRONSHAW et al. 1958), which would be about 200 Å wide and 100 Å thick. As the microfibrils, because of their crystallinity, can contain but a small amount of water, it is impossible that their ribbon-shape would be due to shrinkage on desiccation.

Suppositions as to the *position which the crystallites and the amorphous fraction occupy* with regard to each other in the microfibrils depend to a large extent on the value which is accepted for the thickness of the latter, and also on the way in which the amorphous fraction is defined. RÅNBY (1952a) points out that cylindrical microfibrils with a diameter of 100 Å must contain 240 cellulose chains, of which 50 will be found at the periphery; the latter will be free, at least at the outside, and may therefore be regarded as amorphous. This is in agreement with the 30% at which the amorphous fraction has been estimated and with a diameter of the crystallites of at least 50—80 Å that was calculated from the X-ray diagram. The inner part of the microfibrils therefore would be homogeneous. Later RÅNBY (1958) accepted that microfibrils are flat and he suggested the structure shown in fig. 9a.

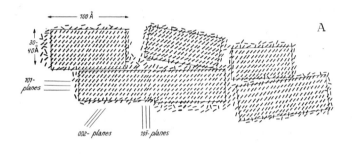

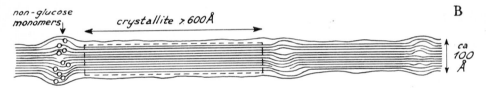

Fig. 9. Structure of cellulose microfibrils as seen in cross section (A) (according to RÅNBY, 1958) and in axial section (B).

A different conception of the fibrillar structure is that of FREY-WYSSLING (1953a, 1954, 1959:17), of which fig. 10 gives a picture. FREY-WYSSLING assumes that each microfibril with a diameter of 100×200 Å consists of four so-called elementary fibrils or micellar strands with a diameter of ca 50×100 Å. Following RÅNBY he supposed that the elementary fibrils would consist of a crystalline core with a diameter of 30×70 Å and a semiamorphous sheath. Inside the microfibril spaces with a diameter of ca 10 Å would be present. In cases of mechanical disintegration a microfibril would be split up into the four elementary fibrils. In this way he tries to explain the fact that VOGEL (1953) observed anastomoses, and that RÅNBY and others measured, after ultrasonic disintegration, diameters of circ. 100 Å.

However, this hypothesis does not explain how other investigators could find diameters of this order of magnitude in preparations of *non disintegrated* cellulose. It seems more probable therefore that the thick anastomosing threads in reality are bundles of two or more microfibrils. Their strong tendency to adhere and to align themselves in bundles is quite obvious and generally accepted. We will in this work therefore not use the term elementary fibril, but only the term microfibril. With this we mean non anastomosing threads of 60—200 Å thickness. Many electronmicroscopists use the terms fibril and microfibril for the same thing, although microscopists have used the term fibril already since long for microscopically visible threads or striations in cell-walls. We will therefore not use the term fibril at all. For microscopically visible structures we use the name thread, striation or microfibril bundle.

In the preceding considerations we have repeatedly mentioned the presence of amorphous and crystalline fractions in the microfibrils, and we have already noted that it is often difficult to distinguish between the two, because very small, supposedly crystalline fractions behave with respect to one criterion as amorphous material, whereas with respect to another criterion they are recognized as crystalline. It should be added that according to some authors the difference between the two is small, the amorphous fraction not being truly amorphous but merely containing a larger number of irregularities in the crystal lattice. It should

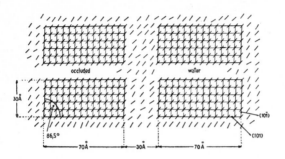

Fig. 10. Transverse section through the hypothetical microfibril of Frey-Wyssling (1954).

be realized that even in the most perfect crystals some dislocations may be, present.

Howsoever this may be, there is reason to assume that the amorphous cellulose is not confined to the peripheral part of the microfibrils or, eventually, of the elementary fibrils, but that it is present in other parts of them too. It was already remarked that when cellulose fibres are boiled in 10% sulphuric acid until ca 10% of the glucosidic bonds are broken, a colloidal suspension is obtained which appears to consist of flat rodlets with a length of 200—1000 Å (Husemann and Carnap, 1943, 1944; Ranby, 1952a; Mukherjee and Woods, 1953; Vogel, 1953). To explain the origin of these rodlets, it has rather generally been accepted that certain less well crystallized regions of the microfibrils, which would occur in intervals of 300—1000 Å, are more rapidly hydrolysed than the other parts. In these more easily hydrolysable parts of the microfibrils the molecular chains might contain the already mentioned abnormal monomers (carboxyl, other sugars). On this supposition the model shown in fig. 9b is based.

A periodically returning change in the structure of the microfibrils is indicated also by the periodical change in electron density along the length of microfibrils and of bundles of these, which has been observed after staining with iodine (Hess et al., 1957) and after staining or shadowing with metals (Kinsinger and Hock, 1948; Hodge and Wardrop, 1950). Although metal-shadowing may under certain conditions and with high magnification produce a similar granular structure in completely homogeneous substrates, e.g. in the supporting film, it appears that the structure observed in the cellulose micro-fibrils can not be regarded as an artefact. This was demonstrated convincingly by Hess et al. (l.c.), but as yet only for synthetic cellulose fibres or mercerized native fibres. However, Hess privately informed us that the same effects have lately been observed also with microfibrils of native fibres, such as cotton. He believes that the structure of adjacent microfibrils is interdependent, the "crystalline" and "amorphous" parts occurring in the same pattern, even throughout the whole fibre. The problem therefore is probably related to that of certain transverse markings in fibres described by several oldtime microscopists, to WIESNER's dermatosome theory, "chemical sectioning" etc. We refer to section 2341.

Indications for the flatness of the crystallites had already been obtained long before the electron microscope came into use. MARK and SUSICH (1929) took X-ray photos of pieces of cellulose obtained from *Acetobacter xylinum* and from the Tunicate *Phalusia*. The membranes had been allowed to desiccate on a glass plate, and had assumed therefore the form of films. When the X-rays fell perpendicularly on these films, no interference was noted in the 101-lattice plane, but when they passed the film tangentially, the interference due to this plane became visible. This proved that the christallites must have oriented themselves with their 101-planes perpendicular to the direction of shrinkage. A similar behaviour has been observed in many other cases, e.g. in cell-walls from *Valonia, Chaetomorpha, Cladophora, Rhizoclonium* and *Halicystis*, and in gels of regenerated cellulose. SISSON (1936) could show conclusively that the deformation orients the crystallites, for he proved that the same result may be obtained by mechanical flattening. He also experimented with deformation of the cellulose membranes in a tangential direction, and every time the 101-plane was found oriented perpendicular to the direction in which the deformation took place. Because of these findings the crystallites were supposed to be ruler-shaped with the 101-plane parallel to the flat side.

After it had been recognized that cellulose consists of microfibrils, it was generally assumed that the latter too would be flat, for if they were cylindrical, it seemed difficult to explain how deformation would lead to an orientation of the flat crystallites in a definite direction. However, cylindrical microfibrils might have a tendency to align into flat bundles with their 101-planes pointing in the same direction and the orientation of the crystallites can therefore not be accepted as necessarily involving a flattened shape of the microfibrils. If these were cylindrical, the bundles into which they are united, might all the same be flattened, for if the adhesion between them attained its highest value in that part where the 101-planes are exposed on the surface, the bundles would be flattened perpendicular to that plane. In case of deformation the crystallites in these flattened bundles would behave in the same way as the crystallites in flattened microfibrils would do. However, now that the microfibrils have also been studied by means of the electron microscope, their flattened form may be regarded as very probable.

It may be asked why the microfibrils should be flattened parallel to the 101-plane. If we start from the supposition that they are formed by the bundling of cellulose molecules, the flattened shape would according to FREY-WYSSLING (1955), mean that the mutual binding and the affinity between the cellulose chains would reach its highest value in the direction parallel to this plane. As we have to think here in the first place of H-bonds, and as, at least in the crystal model of MEYER-MISCH, the free OH-groups are found in the 002-plane, we should expect that not the 101-plane, but the 002-plane would be directed parallel to the flattened side of the microfibrils. The changes in the lattice spacings accompanying chemical reactions on cellulose also indicate the presence of more H-bonds in the 101-plane than there are according to the model.

The contradiction mentioned in the preceding paragraph, has led FREY-WYSSLING to the supposition that the OH-group of C_6 would occupy another position in the crystal lattice than MEYER and MISCH have assumed. Its position ought to be such that more H-bonds are formed in the 101-plane than in the 002-plane.

In this connection it is noteworthy that, according to KREGER (1957b), in the wall of desiccated strands of one *Spirogyra* species the 002-plane was found parallel to the surface, whereas in another species the 10$\bar{1}$-plane was found in this position. Following FREY-WYSSLING's reasoning these findings would mean that in native cellulose the OH-group of C_6 may occupy three different positions!

FREY-WYSSLING's explanation of the origin of flatness is of course hypothetical. To our mind it is at variance with the fact that cellulose II crystallites too are flat parallel to the 101-plane (HERMANS, 1949a), although here most H-bonds are to be expected in the 10$\bar{1}$-plane (see fig. 6).

The orientation of the crystallites that we have discussed above, has not been met with in all dried cell-walls. In ramie and cotton fibres all attempts to find it, have failed (ECKLING and KRATKY, 1930; SISSON, 1935). The a- and c-axes of the unit cell prove to differ widely in position, though the mean orientation of the b-axis is found in the direction of the fibre. This would mean that the flat sides of different microfibrils may be turned in different directions or also that they are twisted. This may be so because the relatively small deformation caused by the desiccation of these cell-walls with their high cellulose content is insufficient to bring the microfibrils in the same position.

It is still unknown whether there is any preference for a distinct position in the orientation of the a- and c-axes in the cellulose of the *living* cells in those lower organisms in whose cell-walls after deformation, as we have seen, a definite orientation was observed. PRESTON et al. (1948) were of opinion that they had found such a preference in *Rhizoclonium*, for if the X-rays passed the wall of a living cell in a radial direction, they found no 101-interference just as when they used dry walls. This finding, however, requires confirmation, not only because the reproductions of the diagrams in their paper show little detail, but also because we ought to know whether the 101-interference is visible when the X-rays pass the fresh wall in a tangential direction. It is possible that here too the interference will be invisible because the walls contain much water and a large amount of amorphous noncellulose. The interference of the 101-plane is known to be more sensitive to these factors than interferences of other planes; this was observed e.g. by PRESTON and WARDROP (1949) in non-purified cambium.

If a tangential orientation of the crystallites would be found in living cells, it might after all in this case too be due to deformation, viz. by the pressure exercized on the cell-wall by the turgescent protoplast. FREY-WYSSLING and MÜHLETHALER (1951) believe that differences in hydrophilic property of the different surfaces of the microfibrils might determine the orientation it acquires when deposited by the cytoplasm. However, this apparently seems not to apply to higher plants.

114. BIOSYNTHESIS OF CELLULOSE

It is unknown how and where cellulose molecules are synthesized by the protoplasm, and how and where the microfibrils arise from the molecules. Only of a few polysaccharides the manner in which and the materials out of which the molecules are formed, have been detected (STACEY, 1954). Of amylose, the linear component of amylum, it is known that it is formed by the aid of amylophosphorylase in this way that the glucose from glucose-1-phosphate is many times in succession linked with its C_1-atom to the C_4-OH-group at the non-reducing end of the growing amylose chain. Each time this happens, phosphoric acid is liberated. Nothwithstanding the fact that energy is required for the formation of the glucosidic bond, the reaction can proceed because the breaking of the bond in the phosphate ester liberates a similar amount of energy. Some other polysaccharides are synthesized from disaccharides by using the energy present in the glycosidic bond. Dextran for instance is formed out of saccharose under liberation of fructose. The formation of a polysaccharide by reversion of the hydrolysis, such as that of cellulose out of glucose with liberation of water would be, has never been observed, and is in a physiological environment unconceivable on thermodynamic grounds. Such a formation has nevertheless been regarded as a natural thing by some botanists who tried to explain the structure of cellulose microfibrils.

Some years ago HESTRIN and SCHRAMM (1954) demonstrated the production of cellulose by dead cells of *Acetobacter xylinum*, and recently COLVIN (1957) showed that this also occurred in a homogenenate of these bacteria, but the isolation of the enzyme system has not been effected so far (SCHRAMM et al., 1957). According to GLASER (1957) the immediate precursor of cellulose is uridine diphosphoglucose.

How and when the microfibrils are formed out of the cellulose molecules, is as yet an unsolved mystery; it is even uncertain whether they really are formed out of cellulose molecules or directly from the cellulose precursor. MÜHLETHALER (1949a, cf. also KAUSHAL et al., 1951) found by means of the electron microscope that in very young cultures of *Acetobacter xylinum* the cells are surrounded by a slimy substance in which indications of an orientation may become apparent and that subsequently long microfibrils become visible. On account of these observations he supposed that the cellulose molecules are formed by means of an extra-cellular enzyme, which polymerizes the slime and that subsequently the molecules aggregate to microfibrils. The chemical nature of the slime itself, however, was not cleared up.

This view of the formation of microfibrils seems to us at variance with another observation of MÜHLETHALER (1950c), viz. the formation of fibrous structures as a result of a similar aggregation process observed in flax-seed slime (see fig. 19) after treatment with hot acid. The process was supposed to demonstrate the way in which microfibrils are formed, but the great difference between native microfibrils and the threads formed in MÜHLETHALER's experiment is, in our opinion, that the latter anastomose frequently and vary greatly in thickness. This process probably applies to what occurs when cellulose II coagulates from a solution, but native cellulose seems to be quite different.

Moreover, COLVIN et al. (1957), when repeating MÜHLETHALER's observation on the formation of cellulose by *Acetobacter xylinum*, could not detect slime or aggregated slime as pre-stages of microfibrils but observed instead the direct appearance of short microfibrils which increased in length, not in thickness. According to these authors, the slime observed by MÜHLETHALER must have arisen from colloids occurring in the beer that was used as culture medium for the bacteria.

In higher plants too, short threads, which might be young microfibrils, have been observed, viz. on the inner surface of the wall of beet root parenchyma, fig. P 11. We must remark, however, that these walls had not been freed from protein, so that the threads might have been protein particles. Bundles consisting of similar short threads and rodlets were observed in remnants of the cytoplasm. Moreover the beet roots used, were mature and probably did no longer synthesize cellulose. In fact the particles of the so-called yellows virus disease of beet are rod-like. However, these rodlets have been observed in the leaves only, and moreover, in a much smaller quantity.

The structures shown in fig. 12 on the other hand are doubtless microfibrils, adhering to particles of cytoplasm. They were obtained by PRESTON and RIPLEY (1954) from the supernatant fluid when cambium was disintegrated in water. It seems unlikely that the short threads represent pieces of broken microfibrils pulled out of the wall. Star-like arrangements of microfibrils comparable to those shown in fig. 12, have also been found in *Nitella*, fig. P 198.

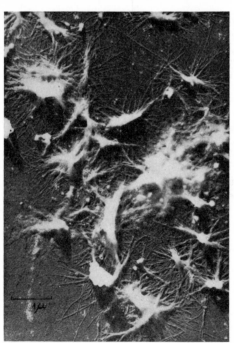

Fig. 12. Particles of cytoplasm with microfibrils adhering to them, obtained from desintegrated cambium cells of *Populus* (from PRESTON and RIPLEY, 1954).

Especially in *Valonia* the inner surface of the wall has been studied microscopically (FARR, 1949) and electron-optically (PRESTON et al., 1951, 1953) in search of indications with regard to the biosynthesis of the microfibrils. FARR believed to have observed long coiled threads of cellulose within the chloroplasts. However, PRESTON et al. found that the microfibrils are formed in the same place where they are deposited (fig. P 182). Once an outer cytoplasmic layer was observed, obviously oriented in the direction in which the microfibrils of a new wall layer were to be deposited (fig. P183). No structures comparable to those found in cambium were observed, which shows that if this really is the way in which microfibrils are formed in cambium, it certainly can not be regarded as the only way in which they are formed.

It has been postulated (FREY-WYSSLING and MÜHLETHALER, 1951; PRESTON, 1952: 195) that in primary walls protoplasm is present in the wall itself, and that microfibrils therefore might be produced not only on the surface of these walls but also in the interior of the latter. This view is partly based on the observation that especially the primary cell-wall may contain a fairly large amount of protein, in cotton hairs e.g. 14% (TRIPP et al., 1951), cf. section 181. Another argument that has been adduced in favour of this assumption, is that the microfibrils in the primary wall are so strongly intertwined, as this makes it difficult to believe that they would have arrived there by apposition.

These arguments look plausible, but they are nevertheless not convincing. The cell-walls of bacteria may consist for the greater part of protein, but in this case this is certainly no protoplasm nor wholly enzymatic protein, and this might also apply to the protein found in other cell-walls. The impression that the microfibrils are too much twisted around each other, is but a superficial one, it is not based on exact topographic observations. However, even if the impression of an extensive intertwining would prove to be correct, it would not definitely prove that the microfibrils are formed within the wall. Intertwining is also seen in paper, where the fibres have been deposited by sedimentation, which is a process comparable to apposition.

The observation of BAYLEY et al. (1957) that distinct layers of microfibrils occurring in the peripheral part of the outer epidermal wall of growing *Avena* coleoptiles do not become thinner but retain their thickness or even increase in thickness, looks more convincing. Recently SETTERFIELD and BAYLEY (1958a) demonstrated by means of the isotope technique the synthesis of cellulose within the wall and on the inner surface.

It seems beyond doubt that at least the main part of the cellulose is not formed within the wall, but by apposition onto it. This certainly applies to secondary thickening, but very probably also to the growing wall. In the latter case conclusive proofs have only been given for lower plants, most convincingly in *Nitella* (GREEN, 1958). In higher plants it is strongly indicated by differences between the fibrillar texture of the inner and the outer surfaces of the growing wall (cf. section 22823). It also appears from the findings of SETTERFIELD and BAYLEY (l. c.).

BOSSHARD (1952) believes that the microfibrils in the walls of cambial cells grow in thickness. In the walls of the cambium cells of *Fraxinus excelsior* they were found to be half as thick as those that are present in the *secondary* walls in the wood. However, he does not seem to have measured the thickness of the microfibrils in the *primary* walls of the wood and therefore did not prove their increase in thickness.

The rather constant thickness and the individuality of the microfibrils has obviously intrigued several authors. BALASHOV and PRESTON (1955) have drawn attention to the fact that the thinner elements in fibrillar proteins as well as inorganic fibres like those of asbestos also have a diameter of 100–300 Å, and they regard the constant thickness of microfibrils in cellulose therefore as a thermo-dynamical necessity, not as the result of a biological process. MÜHLETHALER (1956) sees in the fact that the microfibrils of both the extracellular and of the intracellular cellulose of *Dictyostelium* are of the same diameter an argument for believing that their shape and dimension are determined by physico-chemical factors but more recent electronmicroscopical observations have revealed that all cellulose in *Dictyostelium* is in fact extracellular.

The reviewer (1958) is of opinion that the microfibrils can not be formed out of the molecules in a purely physico-chemical way. Firstly because if that were so, it should be expected that the native cellulose would be cellulose II and not cellulose I, as it usually is. Secondly, the microfibrils would be threads of varying size and thickness connected by anastomoses as is found in disintegrated artificial fibres and not long threads of a uniform thickness without any anastomoses at all. The tips moreover should be frayed and not obtuse. For these reasons we assume that there is no previous formation of cellulose molecules, but that both molecules and microfibrils grow in length at the same time and at the same point, viz. at a tip of a microfibril. Here one or more molecules of the cellulose synthesizing enzyme are supposed to be engaged in detaching glucose-monomers from some high-energy precursor and in transfering these monomers to the ends of the molecules. This special way of microfibril synthesis would explain not only the formation of a special type of cellulose, viz. cellulose I, but also the uniform thickness of the microfibrils, the absence of anastomoses, and the fact that the natural end of the micro-fibrils is obtuse and not frayed (MÜHLETHALER, 1950). The enzyme might be localized with *Acetobacter* on the outside of the cell-wall and perhaps free in the medium; with higher plants on the inside of the wall and in primary cell-walls probably also in the interior of the wall.

For the formation of cellulose II and of entirely amorphous cellulose, prob-ably two different enzymes would be required. The enzymes that synthesize the various hemicelluloses might act in a similar way as that which is respons-ible for the formation of entirely amorphous cellulose. Nearly all these hemi-celluloses appear to be wholly amorphous, but some are fibrillar, e.g. certain mannans in higher plants and certain glucans in lower plants. These differences within the groups of cellulose and hemicelluloses would be difficult to explain if the formation of the microfibrils were a purely physico-chemical process.

The author (l.c.) also remarked that if tip growth is accepted for microfibrils, this would imply that they can only grow at one end and that all molecule chains in a microfibril must point in the same direction, just as they do in the unit cell proposed by MEYER and MARK (1929). The reason for this postulate is that if the molecules in a microfibril would alternate in direction as is assumed in the MEYER and MISCH model of the crystal structure (fig. 4), then, reducing as well as non-reducing molecule ends would be found at the growing tip. This would obviously imply that cellulose occupies a unique position, for it would be the only polysaccharide molecule that is synthesized by addition of monomers as well at the reducing as at the non-reducing end. No doubt this would require the help of two enzymes, each with its own cellulose-precursor, since it is inconceivable, at least unknown so far, that one and the same enzyme would be able to attach monomers to C_4-atoms as well as to C_1-atoms.

Of course, the author's tip-growth theory does not require that the molecules in the different microfibrils of a fibre are oriented in the same direction. This might be the case, but they might also in different microfibrils point in different directions. Both possibilities are in as good agreement with the X-ray data as the MEYER and MISCH model is. This was pointed out by VAN DER WIJK and MEYER (1947) as was already remarked in the previous section.

115. ISOLATION, PURIFICATION AND IDENTIFICATION OF CELLULOSE

1151. Isolation and estimation

From cell-walls such as those of the cotton fibre, that are not lignified and contain but little hemicellulose, it is not difficult to obtain nearly pure cellu-

lose, and to estimate its amount by weighing. After the material has been
extracted with hot alcohol and boiled in water, it is extracted in the absence
of air in order to prevent oxidation, with 1% NaOH at a temperature of
100° C in order to remove wax, cutin, protein, pectin, hemicellulose and low-
polymeric cellulose, and subsequently washed and dried (cf. WARD, 1955: 19;
DORÉE, 1950). The preparation obtained in this way from cotton fibres,
contains 98.9% cellulose; the rest, which could be identified only after hydrolysis, consists mainly of uronic acid and pentoses. Whether these substances
are enclosed in or attached to cellulose chains, or occur in the form of distinct
polymers, is still open to controversy.

When we wish to isolate cellulose from cell-walls which contain a higher
percentage of other substances, we have to apply more vigorous measures. In
this case we may take as guide the directions which already for a long time
have been followed when the so-called raw-fibre content had to be estimated
(cf. VAN WISSELINGH, 1925: 98; KLEIN, 1933: III, 29; A.O.A.C. 1955: 372).
Best known among them is the method of WEENDER, in which the raw material
is boiled first for half an hour in 1.25% sulphuric acid and then for the same
time in 1.25% NaOH. It can not be doubted that the cellulose is in this way
somewhat depolymerized and oxidized. The methods for extracting hemicellulose out of holocellulose which we will describe further on, may also be
used. Care should be taken that the acid concentration, the temperature and
the duration of the treatment are kept as mild as possible.

When the amount of cellulose in lignified cell-walls is to be estimated, we
should apply the methods that so carefully have been elaborated for the
isolation of cellulose from wood (cf. WISE and JAHN, 1952: 1138). They begin
with the extraction of the substances that do not belong to the cell-wall
proper, viz. lipids, tannins, sugars and proteins; after that the lignin is removed, which leaves us the so-called holocellulose, and when the latter has
been freed as far as possible from hemicelluloses, cellulose is left. By weighing
the material after each step, the value of the various fractions can be quantitatively estimated.

The extraction of lignin may be effected either by means of sodium chlorite
in acetic acid solution or by alternately chlorinating and extracting the
resulting lignin chloride by means of an alcoholic ethanolamine solution.

The extraction of the hemicellulose is carried out at room temperature in a
nitrogen stream either in two steps, viz. first with 5% and subsequently with
24% KOH, or in one step, viz. with 17.5% NaOH. In this way the so-called
a-cellulose is obtained as the residue. It still contains a comparatively large
amount of hemicellulose. Coniferous wood usually gives 62—71% holocellulose
and 51—57% a-cellulose; of the latter 44—47% is true cellulose. The wood
of deciduous trees gives less a-cellulose, but an equal amount of true cellulose.

The hemicellulose may also be removed by hydrolysis of the holocellulose
with diluted acid at a high temperature. In that case care should be taken
that the cellulose is not too strongly attacked. The best hydrolytic reagent
for hemicellulose, which gives least destruction of the monomers, is 3% nitric
acid; it should be heated to 100° C and allowed to act for about 4 hours (cf.
PAECH and TRACEY, 1955: 201). The hemicellulose may also be hydrolysed in
other ways e.g. by boiling the material 1—4 hours in 5% sulphuric acid.

When it is not intended to collect the cellulose, but merely to estimate its
amount, the holocellulose fraction, i.e. what is left after the lignin has been
removed, may also be completely hydrolysed.

The only satisfactory method for hydrolysing holocellulose or cellulose is by dissolving these substances in 72% (w/w) sulphuric acid; the acid is diluted to 1% and the hydrolysis is completed by boiling the material with the dilute acid (cf. PAECH and TRACEY, 1955: 205). The sugars that are obtained in this way are then separated, and quantitatively determined (cf. e.g. PAECH and TRACEY, 1955: 197). We may assume that practically all glucose has been derived from the cellulose.

Micro-estimations of cellulose have been described by SCHRAMM and HESTRIN (1954), DEARING (1957) and HALLIWELL (1958).

1152. Purification of cell-walls

It is sometimes necessary to separate the cell-walls from the cell contents. When this should be done, e.g. in micro-organisms, fungi or algae, the material is first crudely desintegrated, e.g. with a blender or, in the case of micro-organisms, with a kind of micro-ballmill, which is a shaking apparatus provided with small glass pearls. After that the material is repeatedly mixed either with pure or with slightly alkaline water and slowly centrifuged; as the protoplasm remains in suspension, it can in this way be removed.

The methods for the separation of cellulose or of raw fibre that have been mentioned above, are used also for macerating tissues, or for preparing a suitable substrate for carrying out reactions on cellulose, or for studying the structure of cellulose by the aid of the electron microscope. Several other prescriptions of this kind are to be found in the works of VAN WISSELINGH (1925: 98 and 137) and of TUNMANN-ROSENTHALER (1931: 49, 969 and 985). The following treatments are specially recommended.

If we are dealing with unlignified material, pectin and hemicellulose may be removed:

a. by boiling for ½—1 hour first with 2% sulphuric acid and then with 2% NaOH, or with NaOH alone; higher concentrations may also be used, but then the temperature should be lower; more than 10% acid causes too much hydrolysis, and more than 10% alkali mercerizes the cellulose and causes a strong deformation;

b. by a treatment for some hours at a temperature of 40—60° C with 3—10% H_2O_2 to which some ammonia has been added (KISSER);

c. by keeping the material for half an hour at room temperature in a solution of 5% chromic acid and 5% nitric acid (JEFFREY);

d. by heating for some hours with tri- or mono-ethanolamine; the temperature may, according to the object, be raised to 160° C;

e. (when the tissues are very frail) by keeping the material from a few hours to some days at 20—70° C in one of the following media:

1. 1% ammonium oxalate;

2. 0,1 m ethylene diamino tetra acetic acid at pH 10;

3. diluted ammonia;

4. one of the enzyme preparations that are prepared from cultures of fungi and contain pectinase and "hemicellulase", and are sold under such names as pectinol, pectasin, luizym, filtragol, etc., or cultures of certain bacteria (bacterial maceration, SKOSS, 1955).

These treatments should take place in pointed centrifuge tubes, in which the material is afterwards cleaned by decanting and by repeatedly shaking in water followed by centrifugation; for study by means of the electron microscope only glass-in-glass distilled water should be used.

In lignified material all non-cellulose may be removed:

a. by keeping the material for 1—20 hours at 60° C in a solution consisting of 2 volume parts perhydrol (30% H_2O_2) and 1 volume part acetic anhydride;

b. by keeping it at room temperature in a mixture of equal parts of dry potassium chlorate and conc. nitric acid (SCHULZE);

c. by the use of the above described mixture of JEFFREY, which here, according to the object, should be applied for 2—20 hours at a temperature of 30—60° C;

d. by heating for one hour to 250° C either in tri-ethanolamine or in glycerol;

e. (rapidly but rather destructive) by boiling clippings either in trichloroacetic acid (solid) or in solid phenol to which some conc. hydrochloric acid has been added, then cooling to tepid, adding alcohol, seaving, and shaking in water.

When it is lignin alone that has to be removed, the material is best treated during 1—3 hours at 85—90° C with 1—4% acetic acid and 2—14% sodium chlorite ($NaClO_2$) in a small flask with a reflux cooler (SPEARIN and ISENBERG, 1947). In this way more hemicellulose is removed than by the aid of the method by which, for analytical purposes, holocellulose is prepared; the latter process, moreover, takes more time.

In order to remove suberin and cutin (and part of the hemicelluloses) the material may be boiled for some hours in alcoholic alkali (12 g. KOH, 12 ml. water, alcohol up to 100 ml.). If we wish to remove the greater part of the hemicelluloses at the same time, we may use either concentrated alkali and a moderate heat, or glycerol at 250° C, but in this manner the cellulose is often deformed. Moreover, heating above 100° C must take place in sealed tubes, see section 123.

1153. Identification of cellulose

X-ray diagram. A critical method for demonstrating the presence of cellulose I in dried cell-wall material rests on the latter's characteristic X-ray diagram with its strong interferences corresponding to the lattice spacings of 6.1, 5.4, 3.9 and 2.6 Å, of which the 3.9 Å one is the most prominent. (In cellulose II the strongest reflections correspond to lattice spacings of 7.4, 4.4, 4.0 and 2.6 Å). A drawback of this method is that it requires a special elaborate apparatus (cf. section 213), and it has therefore but rarely been applied.

A great advantage of the X-ray analysis is the circumstance that amorphous admixtures, although they may decrease the clearness of the diagram, do not entirely obscure it, at least so long as the cellulose content does not sink below 20%. If there is any uncertainty, the other substances should be removed first. That this is highly desirable, appears from the discrepancies in the conclusions regarding the presence of cellulose in certain algae that were arrived at by different investigators using the X-ray method (cf. section 2413).

Until quite recently it was generally assumed that the most reliable method for identifying cellulose was that by means of the X-ray diagram. This is undoubtedly so when a sufficiently sharp and complete X-ray diagram can be obtained. However, if only the two or three strongest interferences are recognizable, no definite conclusion is possible, because the strongest interferences that are obtained with other polysaccharides may be practically

identical. Especially if we wish to demonstrate the presence of cellulose II,
this proves to be a serious drawback, as was experienced by CRONSHAW et al.
(1958) when they investigated the cell-walls of various kinds of algae, and
also by ROELOFSEN et al. (1953) in their study of *Halicystis*. The necessity
to supplement in such cases the results of the X-ray analysis by a chemical
investigation, becomes ever more apparent.

Birefringence. Cellulose molecules, no matter whether they are free or
connected into a crystal lattice, are positively birefringent, which means
that they have a higher refraction index for rays that are vibrating in the axial
plane than for rays that vibrate transversely to that plane (cf. section 212).
The birefringence is equal to the difference between these two refraction
indexes. In pure cellulose that has been dried and in which all the microfibrils
are oriented nearly parallel to each other, e.g. in the ramie fibre, the birefringence is $1.601 - 1.530 = 0.071$. In cellulose without orientation or in oriented
cellulose in non-polarized light, the refraction index has an average value
of 1.554 (cf. HERMANS, 1949: 214 et seq.).

In ordinary cell-walls of higher plants no other birefringent constituents
are present. For this reason it has sometimes been assumed that all birefringent
cell-walls must contain cellulose and that optically isotropic walls are free of
cellulose, but this is not so. In the absence of cellulose, a cell-wall may show
this peculiarity e.g. in fungi because of the presence of chitin, in the ivory
nut because of the presence of mannan, in lichens because of the presence
of lichenin, in algae because of the presence of as yet unidentified carbohydrates, in the cutinized and suberized cell-walls of *Cormophyta* because of
the presence of waxes. A cell-wall may also show a rodlet-birefringence (cf.
section 212) in the absence of cellulose.

In the second place it should be realized that the birefringence of the
cellulose needs not always be visible. This happens when it is compensated
by the birefringence of another substance, as e.g. by that of wax in the walls
of cork cells and in cuticular layers. Another possibility that should be borne
in mind, is that the cellulose microfibrils may be arranged at random within
the plane of the wall; then the wall will be optically isotropic in surface view.
The birefringence will also be hidden if the wall consists of two (or more)
layers of equal thickness, in which the orientation of the cellulose microfibrils
differs 90° or if the upper and the lower wall of a cell show such a difference.
However, in these instances the birefringence will become visible in light
which passes the cell-wall in a tangential direction, as there is always an
orientation of the microfibrils parallel to the surface. Portions of cellulose,
e.g. a coagulum, in which the molecules are oriented at random in all three
dimensions, will be optically isotropic no matter in which direction they
are studied.

In the greater part of the cell-walls of the *Cormophyta*, however, cellulose
appears to be the only birefringent constituent, and as rodlet-birefringence
due to other constituents plays no part either in these walls, the presence of
birefringence may in this group of plants usually be accepted as proof of the
presence of cellulose. The degree of birefringence is no measure of the amount
of cellulose since this also depends on the degree of orientation of the cellulose,
but in one and the same sample changes in the cellulose fraction, e.g. by
dissolution or chemical reaction, are, of course, reflected in concomitant
changes in the degree of double refraction, and such changes therefore may

be used to follow the course of the process. Some chemical changes, e.g. nitration, not only change the degree of birefringence but even its sign.

Chemical identification of cellulose has played an important part in the past. One method is based on the production of the octa-acetate of cellobiose, which is recognizable by its crystals. Intermediate products are acetylated triose, tetra-ose, etc. Another method starts with methylating the cellulose. By hydrolysing the methyl cellulose that is produced in this way, we must obtain 2, 3, 6 -trimethylglucose, since the units in cellulose are 1—4 linked. However, there are cell-wall constituents, e.g. amyloid (section 141), that produce octa-acetate and 2, 3, 6-trimethylglucose because they consist of a cellulose chain provided with branches which consist of other monomers that are easily split off.

The presence of glucose in a cell-wall hydrolysate has often been considered to prove the presence of cellulose in the cell-walls but there are several other glucans (cf. section 133, 141) which also yield glucose. It must be admitted that amyloid and non-cellulosic glucans do not occur in the normal cell-walls of higher plants, and until recently wood chemists therefore were of opinion that the glucose in a hydrolysate of holocellulose is derived entirely from cellulose, but this view can no longer be upheld since recently in spruce wood a heteropolymer containing glucose was discovered, viz. glucomannan, a substance already known to occur in certain seeds (cf. section 133).

In order to avoid such pitfalls, it has become customary to postpone the chemical analysis until other polysaccharides have been removed, as far as possible, by dissolution or hydrolysis.

Microscopical identification. In the identification of cellulose under the microscope colour reactions and solvents have, especially in the past, played an important part (the term "microchemical reaction" is in this case better avoided, because chemists use it in a different sense, viz. for reactions that require but a small amount of substance; the observation of such reactions, however, does not necessarily require the use of a microscope).

When a cell-wall entirely or partly dissolves as a result of the application of one of the earlier described purification methods, we may be sure that it contains no cellulose. However, it should be borne in mind that the amorphous cellulose, which is sometimes found in lower plants, dissolves more easily than the ordinary form of cellulose, and that insolubility does not necessarily mean that the substance really is cellulose, as e.g. chitin and yeast glucan do not dissolve either.

After the material has been purified, we may try whether it *dissolves in one of the cellulose solvents*. The one that is most often used to this end is ammoniacal cupric hydroxide (cuoxam, cuprammonium, SCHWEIZER's reagent). Directions for the preparation of this reagent are to be found in all handbooks of botanical microscopy (STRASBURGER-KOERNICKE, 1923; MOLISCH, 1923; TUNMANN-ROSENTHALER, 1931), whereas in case the solvent should be used for analytical purposes, handbooks for the study of cellulose (OTT and SPURLIN, 1954—1955: 1376) should be consulted[1]). The ammoniacal cupric hy-

---

[1]) A rarely mentioned, but very convenient way of preparing this reagent for qualitative purposes is to take dry cupric hydroxide powder and dissolve it up to saturation in conc. ammonia (the cupric hydroxide is obtained by adding a just sufficient amount of cold ammonia to a cold 15% solution of $CuSO_4$; the precipitate is sucked dry on a filter, and washed consecutively with: previously boiled dist. water, 96% acohol, absolute alcohol and ether; finally it is dried in vacuo.

droxide solution can be kept for some days when it is stored in stoppered bott-
les of brown glass in the cold, but even so it is oxidized; a cupric ethylene-
diamine solution keeps longer, and is just as good.

The material may either previously or simultaneously be stained with
0.2% ruthenium red; in the latter case the stain has to be added to the solvent;
it secures a staining of some of the insoluble constituents, e.g. of lignin, pectin
and cytoplasm. The reagent is sometimes diluted with conc. ammonia, viz.
when we wish to restrict the effect to a mere swelling; this may be desirable
either because it brings out the fibrillar structure, or because it permits us
to identify certain textile fibres.

That a cell-wall dissolves in cuoxam, certainly does not prove that it
consists of cellulose, and that it does not dissolve, does not mean that this
substance is entirely absent. For reasons that have already been set forth,
cuoxam dissolves all polysaccharides of which the monomers are provided with
two OH-groups bound to contiguous C-atoms in such a way that their distance
is small. This group comprises all 1—4 linked polymers of glucose, xylose and
mannose, e.g. xylan, mannan and lichenin. The cell-walls of some algae must
be treated with cuoxam before their cellulose stains with chlor-zinc-iodine;
in this case apparently some constituent occurs in interfibrillar spaces, which
is dissolved more rapidly than cellulose (cf. section 241).

Cellulose does not dissolve in cuoxam when the interfibrillar spaces contain
a comparatively large amount of lignin, pectin, hemicellulose or cutin, nor
does it dissolve when it is enclosed between layers that consist of such insoluble substances. Lignified cell-walls stain blue in cuoxam, which means
that this penetrates them to some extent, but the cellulose does not swell or
dissolve; even when the wood is pulverized, the amount of cellulose that goes
into solution, is very small indeed. Cuticular layers may stay for weeks in
cuoxam, but the amount of cellulose that is contained in them, does not
diminish. With collenchyma, of which the cell-walls contain 20% cellulose,
and in which the latter is protected by pectin, it takes some weeks before the
cellulose in dissolved. The progress made by the dissolution may be controlled
by studying the birefringence; to this end the material has to be washed in
diluted acid.

The slow dissolution of cellulose in the walls of *Valonia* and some other
algae has been ascribed to an uncommonly high degree of crystallinity (FREY-
WYSSLING, 1939; PRESTON, 1952; PRESTON and CRONSHAW, 1958).

The product which is formed when cellulose dissolves in cupric hydroxide
has a rather low diffusion coefficient, and in sections treated with cuoxam
some of it therefore may be left behind in the cell lumen. This product can be
precipitated, as GILSON has described, in the form of sphaero-crystals, by
washing the material with ammonia. The crystals show a weak birefringence,
various cellulose reactions, and the X-ray diagram of cellulose II (MOLISCH,
1923; TUNMANN-ROSENTHALER, 1931: 902; ROELOFSEN and KREGER, 1951).
The formation of these sphaero-crystals might perhaps be used as an additional
reaction on cellulose. It is, however, a drawback that they are not always
formed. Moreover, it is not excluded that other substances may form crystals
that react, in certain respects, in a similar way.

There are several other reagents in which cellulose dissolves (TUNMANN-
ROSENTHALER, 1931: 903). It can be dissolved e.g. in alkali after xantho-
genation (BALLS, 1919), in water or acetone after etherifying or esterifying,
but as nothing definite is known with regard to the way in which other con-

stituents of the cell-wall behave when subjected to the same treatment, these reactions have so far no diagnostic value.

Probably the best known reaction on cellulose applied in plant microscopy, is *the blue, violet or purple colour it assumes with iodine* in the presence of a swelling agent. For the latter purpose sulphuric acid and zinc chloride are most often used, but phosphoric acid, $CaCl_2$ and $AlCl_3$ may serve in special cases, viz. with relatively pure cellulose.

For unlignified cell-walls with high cellulose-content the concentration of the sulphuric acid should be 63% (by weight, which is 50% by volume when 98% sulphuric acid is used). Higher concentrations involve too much swelling and above 72% (w/w) dissolution. With fresh sections, however, often 66—77% (by weight, which is 53—66.7% by volume) sulphuric acid has to be used since these cell-walls usually contain much hemicellulose or pectic substances and sometimes in addition lignin. The reagent moreover, is often locally diluted by water contained in the section or adhering to it. Part of the acid is sometimes replaced by glycerol; the equivalent of the 63% sulphuric acid reagent is a mixture consisting of 3 parts by volume of concentrated acid with 1 water and (subsequently) 2 glycerol.

The most suitable concentration of zinc chloride is 60% (w/w), here too with a lower concentration the colouring is weaker, and with a higher one the colour disappears in course of time. For cell-walls containing little cellulose it is less suitable than sulphuric acid because it does not produce a sufficient swelling. It therefore takes a longer time, and occasionally even a pre-treatment with more effective swelling agents, e.g. with cuoxam, may be required.

As is customary with sulphuric acid, zinc chloride is sometimes added to the material, subsequent to the treatment with a solution of potassium triiodide. The latter substance readily decomposes so that the solution behaves like one containing free iodine. Usually, however, iodine, potassium iodine and zinc chloride are applied simultaneously in the form known as chlor-zinc-iodine. Directions for preparing this reagent are to be found in all handbooks of microscopical plant anatomy. Weaker forms of the reagent produce all kinds of gradations between red and blue, and are used for this reason for distinguishing between various kinds of cellulose of commercial importance. Directions for their preparation and use have been given in the fullest way by GRAFF (1942).

The value of iodine as a staining reagent depends, just like the value of cuoxam as a solvent, on the presence or absence of other cell-wall constituents. If pectic substances and hemicellulose are the only admixtures, it is almost certain that the reaction will be obtained in the long run, be it in a weakened form. In this case it is advisable to use sulphuric acid as a swelling agent, as this acts more vigorously than $ZnCl_2$. In suberized and cutinized cell-walls however, no reaction at all is obtained.

In lignified cell-walls, on the other hand, the reaction shows itself already after a rather short time in places where the wall has been damaged, e.g. along a cutting plane. Elsewhere the colour of the cell-wall changes in the long run from yellow to greyish yellow. The reaction becomes more clearly visible when we use polarized light by inserting the polarizer (not the analizer). Then all cell-walls in which the cellulose microfibrils (or their projections in the horizontal plane) lie in the vibrating plane of the polarized light will be greyish-blue, whereas they become pure yellow when the stage is turned 90°. This is due to the dichroism of the iodine; the molecules of the latter are adsorbed in a definite position to the oriented cellulose, and are therefore also oriented. The iodine molecules in the lignin point in all directions, and show therefore no dichroism.

When pure cellulose is stained with iodine, and when the microfibrils are, as in the bast fibres of *Linum* and of *Boehmeria,* all ideally parallel to each other, dichroism appears in the opposition of very dark blue to colourless, but when the arrangement is less regular, the contrasting colours are dark blue and light blue; this is seen e.g. in cotton fibres. When the arrangement is entirely irregular, as it is in the cell-walls of equidimensional cells when seen in surface view, the colour remains blue in all positions. The study of the dichroism is therefore a suitable and very simple means for obtaining information with regard to the arrangement of the cellulose microfibrils.

Iodine crystals too are dichroitic and for this reason the dichroism shown by cell-walls that have been stained by iodine was ascribed by AMBRONN to the presence of numerous small rod-shaped iodine crystals all pointing in the same direction. However, as BION (1928) could find no iodine interferences in the X-ray diagram, the explanation is now sought in an adsorption of the iodine molecules in a definite direction on the cellulose molecules. In addition there is a kind of dichroism that, in analogy to rodlet-birefringence, might be called rodlet-dichroism (FREY-WYSSLING, 1930). It is, in our opinion, nevertheless not entirely excluded that iodine crystals are present, but so minute ones that they do not produce interferences in the X-ray diagram, or at least did not in those obtained with the apparatus that was in use thirty years ago. This situation in fact applies to congo-red (see further on).

When potassium triiodide is used, the cellulose doubtless absorbs a sufficient amount of iodine, but the colour appears only after the cellulose has been permitted to swell. If the crystallites would swell, this would doubtless involve the loss of their crystalline structure. In fibres that had been treated with chlor-zinc-iodine and that subsequently had been washed and dried, BION (l.c.) in fact observed a change in the X-ray diagram, but he paid no attention to the possibility that this might have been caused by the formation of cellulose II. When repeating this experiment we did not find any change at all, which indicates that at least with the reagent we used (viz. that of BEHRENS) the major part of the crystallites was not destroyed, and that the colouring must have been restricted mainly to amorphous parts or to the surface of the microfibrils.

Why the cellulose must first of all swell, is still entirely unknown. It may be added that the blue colour of starch, and especially of the amylose fraction of the latter, is supposed to be due to iodine molecules that are oriented in the axis of the spirally twisted starch molecules. Here too the iodine colouring proved to be dichroitic, but so slightly that it is not noticeable in the starch grains. This seems to be the result of lack of orientation in the grains for the blue colour of synthetic amylose fibres is dichroitic.

The cellulose reaction with iodine can not be regarded as specific. A blue colouring, sometimes even a dichroitic one, may be obtained even with less vigorous swelling agents in other cell-wall substances, e.g. in the mannan B of the ivory nut, in amyloid, in some not yet identified cell-wall constituents of fungi (e.g. of *Pythium* and of *Phytophtora*) and of algae (R. FREY, 1950; NICOLAI and PRESTON, 1952). MOLISCH (1923: 336) even noticed it in inorganic substances.

Of some *other staining methods,* like that with congo-red or that with haematoxylin, it has in the past been assumed that they were typical for non-lignified cellulose, but this is entirely wrong, as the generally present hemi-celluloses and even chitin are also stained by them. More characteristic is that the staining of cellulose (and of chitin) with congo-red, benzo-azurin and other substantive diazobenzidine dyes, is strongly dichroitic provided of course that the cellulose has a preferred orientation. As with the iodine staining this peculiarity may be used in order to determine the mean orientation and even the mean angular dispersion of the cellulose microfibrils in the cell-walls (cf. section 212).

As the solutions of these stains are colloidal, and as the cellulose does not swell in them, we may assume that the particles of the stain are not deposited between the cellulose molecules, but on the surface of the microfibrils. According to Wälchli (1945) the particles of congo-red are ruler-shaped ($10 \times 20 \times 100$ Å), and they are deposited parallel to the microfibrils as shown in fig. 13. According to Frey-Wyssling (1947) congo-red molecules may even be bound between the cellulose molecules of the crystal lattice in the outer layer of the microfibrils. The particles are supposed to contain 10—20 molecules, and to possess a crystalline structure, but they would be too small to cause interference of X-rays. The absorption in green (and accordingly their red colour) is strongest in light that vibrates parallel to the longitudinal axis of the particle, and therefore parallel to the axis of the microfibrils too. When they are rotated with their axis through an angle of ninety degrees, they cease absorbing light, and the fibres therefore lose their colour. In an acid medium the absorption is highest in yellow instead of in green, and the fibres therefore do not look red but blue; rotated through an angle of ninety degrees they once more become colourless. With benzoazurin the dichroism is the same as with congo-red in an acid medium. With magdala-red the dichroism is, because of a different structure of the molecules, reversed.

An advantage of the dichroitic stains, and this applies also to iodine, is that they increase the birefringence to a marked degree. Because of this they are very suitable when cell-walls with a very slight birefringence, e.g. primary cell-walls, are to be investigated.

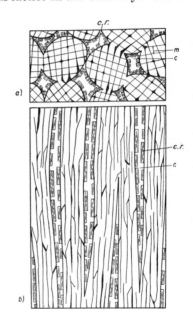

Fig. 13. Model of congo-red (cr) deposits in the interfibrillar capillaries (c) of cellulose according to Wälchli (1945) (according to Frey-Wyssling's concept of 1937, anastomosing multi-micellar microfibrils are supposed to be present).

Cellulose II is, as we have stated already, considerably more reactive than cellulose I, presumably because it contains more fractions consisting of irregularly disposed molecules, and because it has a less firm crystal structure and a lower degree of polymerization. This makes it possible to separate one from the other by means of certain solvents, e.g. by means of 10% NaOH at $-5°$ C, of 15% $CaCl_2$ in 85% formic acid at 40° C, of conc. $Ca(CNS)_2$ at 100° C, and of 60% H_2SO_4 (cf. LUNIAK, 1953). The lower DP is probably the main cause of the difference between the two kinds of cellulose, for depoly- merized cellulose I reacts in several respects in the same way as cellulose II (HERMANS, 1949: 147). The physical condition is doubtless of importance, for freshly prepared cellulose II is easily dissolved in 10% NaOH at room tem- perature, but after some time this becomes more difficult, and drying makes it almost impossible.

Cellulose II swells already in a strong solution of potassium tri-iodide (obtained e.g. by dissolving 4% iodine in 6% KJ, or 2 g. iodine in 10 ml. saturated KJ) to a sufficient degree to be stained blue. In this reagent the colour of pure cellulose I as well as that of pure cellulose II is very dark, but when cellulose II is washed with water, it retains for a long time a steel-blue colour, whereas the colour of ordinary cellulose under these circumstances changes to yellow, and disappears in a short time altogether. This staining of cellulose II is not specific either, as e.g. amyloid, a fraction of lichenin, and unidentified carbohydrates occurring in the cell-walls of fungi, also stain blue with potassium tri-iodide.

12. Chitin

121. OCCURRENCE

As early as 1811 BRACONNOT discovered in fungi a substance which he called "fungine". In 1894 this fungin was rediscovered and recognized as identical with a substance that was known already from the *Arthropoda* since 1823, and which had received the name chitin.

There are many reports on the presence or absence of chitin in lower plants (cf. VAN WISSELINGH, 1925: 186; TUNMANN-ROSENTHALER, 1931: 1004; ZECH- MEISTER and TOTH, 1939; BRIAN, 1949), but several of them are untrust- worthy, as the chitosan-iodine staining method that was used for its iden- tification, is not sufficiently specific, and as the reaction was sometimes carried out with insufficient amounts of material. It is perhaps worth mentioning that the interest in the presence of chitin was partly due to the speculations on its phylogenetic significance that were developed by F. VON WETTSTEIN (cf. R. FREY, 1950).

In fungi it is, with a few exceptions, always present. Exceptional are the *Oömycetes*, where the cell-wall undoubtedly contains cellulose, a substance whose presence appears to exclude that of chitin (R. FREY, 1950), and it is probably also absent in another group where the cell-wall seems to contain cellulose, viz. in the *Monoblepharidaceae*.

Some species of the *Chitridiaceae* are said to have cellulose and no chitin in their cell-walls (e.g. *Olpidiopsis* according to MC LARTY, 1941), though some other species have no cellulose but chitin (NABEL, 1939; MANGENOT, 1953). *Rhizidiomyces bivellatus* is the only species of which it has been reported that it contains both cellulose and chitin (NABEL l.c.), but this statement rests on the use of unspecific staining reactions. The fact that R. FREY (l.c.) obtained positive results when he applied the same two reactions to the walls of *Oömycetes*, which certainly do not contain chitin, casts considerable doubt on NABEL's conclusions regarding *Rhizidiomyces*.

In one genus neither chitin nor cellulose could be found viz. *Schizosaccha- romyces* (ROELOFSEN and HOETTE, 1951; KREGER, 1954).

Chitin has sometimes been said to be present in other lower organisms too, e.g. in *Cladophora* (cf. Astbury and Preston, 1940), bacteria and *Cyanophyceae* (cf. van Wisselingh, 1925:188), but these reports have never been confirmed. R. Frey (1950) denied its presence in *Cladophora*. It is true that with some bacteria hydrolysis of the cell-walls yields glucosamine, but this is not derived from chitin, but from certain hetero-polymers. The latter are found regularly in animals, and are known as mucopolysaccharides. It can therefore hardly be doubted that chitin is confined to yeasts and fungi, and that it is not found in all of them. Moreover, the greater part of the cell-wall of these organisms does, as a rule, not consist of chitin, but of other polysaccharides (cf. section 243).

That chitosan, which in the laboratory can be obtained from chitin by removing, either entirely or for the greater part, the acetyl-groups, occurs in living organisms too, viz. in *Phycomyces*, has only recently been discovered (Kreger, 1954). It will probably prove to be more generally distributed, and in that case the fact that it has been overlooked so far, is easily explainable. The material is, as a rule, purified with acid, and as chitosan dissolves in acid, it is removed before the analysis starts.

122. CHEMICAL AND PHYSICAL PROPERTIES

These properties have been dealt with at some length by Zechmeister and Toth (1939), and also by Klein (1932, III: 69) and by Whistler and Smart (1953).

Plant and animal chitin have the same chemical structure (Diehl and van Iterson, 1935; Meyer and Wehrli, 1937). When slowly hydrolysed, it yields acetylglucosamine, but when hydrolysed more vigorously, equivalent amounts of glucosamine and acetic acid are obtained; this proves that it is a polymerized acetylglucosamine (N-acetyl-2-amino-2-desoxy-D-glucose). The monomers therefore consist of glucose in which the OH-group of the C_2-atom has been substituted by $-NH-CO-CH_3$. Further chemical research has revealed that the monomers are linked in the same way as in cellulose by β-1,4-bonds, and that here too they form a straight chain. The preparations are never so pure that the percentages of N and of acetyl ($-CO-CH_3$) fully agree with the theoretically expected ones, but the deviations are but small, e.g. 22.10% acetyl instead of 22.17%, and 6.83% N instead of 6.9%. We have therefore no reason to assume that monomers with another constitution would be present too. It is true that in *Phycomyces*, one of the objects analysed, chitosan is present, but as the latter was removed before the chitin analysis began, the acetyl content nevertheless showed a close ap-

Chitin

proximation to the expected value. The DP of chitin is, like that of cellulose, very high.

Chitin dissolves in highly concentrated strong acids, but the required concentration proves to be lower than it is for cellulose, viz. 24—40% hydrochloric acid, 45% nitric acid (cellulose does not dissolve at all in nitric acid), 45—85% phosphoric acid, 65—98% sulphuric acid, water-free formic acid, and a mixture of formic acid and hydrochloric acid. At higher temperatures it disperses in the concentrated solutions of some salts that serve also as solvents of cellulose, viz. LiCNS, Ca(CNS)$_2$, CaJ$_2$. In the dissolved condition a considerable degree of depolymerization is effected; this is revealed by the decrease in viscosity. In disperged condition the depolymerization is but slight.

Chitin does not dissolve in cuoxam, and at room temperature or in the cold it remains unaffected by alkali, no matter what the latter's concentration may be; in these fluids its behaviour therefore is different from that of cellulose At higher temperatures, however, alkali causes depolymerization and de-acetylation, thus forming chitosan. After 40 hours in 50% (w/w) NaOH at 100° C but 6% of the original amount of acetyl is left, and the DP has sunk down to 15 (MEYER and WEHRLI, 1937). In 60% KOH at 160° C the same effect is obtained in 15 minutes. A less vigorous effect was obtained when the material was left for 24 hours in 5% alkali at 150° C, or when it was kept for 18 hours at 140° C in 20% alkali, or for 18 hours at 100° C in 40% alkali (RIGBY, 1936); nevertheless in all these cases a product was obtained that proved to be soluble in diluted acid.

Chitosan dissolves by binding acid in 2—10% HCl, HBr, HNO$_3$ and organic acids. In H$_3$PO$_4$, H$_2$SO$_4$ and chromic acid this takes place at higher temperatures only. In concentrated acids it dissolves already, just as chitin, at room temperature. When chitin is to be identified in the form of chitosan, the latter is precipitated from a solution in sulphuric acid in the form of its salt. When the solution has been obtained by the use of diluted acid at a high temperature, the precipitate is obtained by cooling; when it has been obtained by means of concentrated acid, by diluting.

Chitin is just as cellulose apt to be oxidized in an alkaline environment. This is the reason why in the long run it dissolves entirely in NaOCl at room temperature.

Hydrolysis of the glycosidic bonds with acid is in chitin even more difficult than it is in cellulose. Nevertheless, even after 1 hour at 65° C in 1.5% HCl some result is already noticeable. A complete hydrolysis can be obtained with concentrated acid at higher temperatures; under these circumstances the total amount of acetic acid too is liberated (PAECH and TRACEY, 1955: 268).

A hydrolysis that is not accompanied by a de-acetylation, can be obtained only by means of the enzyme chitinase, which is most easily prepared out of *Lycoperdon* (TRACEY, 1955; PAECH and TRACEY, 1955: 271). It depolymerizes chitin completely, but chitosan in part only. The enzyme is in living organisms not as common as cellulase, but has been found e.g. in several kinds of bacteria (VELDKAMP, 1955), in the culture liquid of fungi, and in gastric juice of snails (cf. ZECHMEISTER and TOTH, 1939).

The *crystallinity* of animal and plant chitin was discovered in 1924 by means of X-ray analysis, and since then the sharp spot diagrams that could be obtained by means of the well-oriented chitin in the tendons of *Crustacea* have been studied by several investigators. The strongest interferences proved to correspond with distances of 9.6, 4.6 and 3.4 Å. The crystal structure at which MEYER and PANKOW (1935) arrived, and which is reproduced in fig. 14, is at present generally accepted. Recently a slight change in this structure has been postulated by CARLSTRÖM (1957) which seems to be well-founded. The unit cell proves to be nearly twice as large as that of cellulose, and contains twice as much, viz. eight, monomers. The pyranose rings are here too parallel to each other, and supposed to run alternately upwards and downwards. The unit cell of chitin measures in the b-direction, i.e. in the direction of the axis of the molecule, 10.4 Å, which is the same value as has been found for the unit cell of cellulose; this means that chitin has the same configuration (chair position with β-1,4 bonds). The basal plane of the unit cell is a rectangle, and not a parallelogram as in the unit cell of cellulose. Just as in cellulose, the crystal lattice has no room left for the absorption of water.

From the width of the interferences a diameter of the crystallites of 90—100 Å, and a length of more than 600 Å has been calculated. What percentage of the material may be regarded as crystalline, has not yet been determined, but from the fact that the X-ray diagrams show but little background blackening, we may conclude that it will be a high one. This seems to follow also from the value found for the specific weight, which is 1.415, whereas theo-

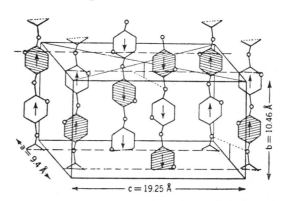

Fig. 14. Unit cell and crystal structure of chitin (MEYER and PANKOW, 1935).

retically that of the crystallites is 1.43; in cellulose I the corresponding values are 1.55 and 1.59.

The molecules in the crystal lattice are linked by means of H-bonds, but the latter are found not only between O-atoms and OH-groups, as in cellulose, but also between one amide group (-NH-CO-) and another one, as in proteins (DARMON and RUDALL, 1950).

Besides the α-chitin that has been dealt with above, and which is the one occurring in plants (KHOUVINE, 1932; VAN ITERSON et al., 1936; HEYN, 1936) and in most animals, there is also β-chitin, which has the same chemical constitution, but another crystal form and which has been found in some animals, viz. in the internal shell of the cuttle-fish and in the chaetae of annelids (LOTMAR and PICKEN, 1950). By treating it with 45% nitric acid it is converted into α-chitin. RUDALL (1955), who studied the occurrence of the two forms of chitin in various groups of animals, has found that the unit cell of β-chitin is more spacious than that of α-chitin, that its crystal structure is less firm, that the distance between its lattice planes may increase somewhat by the absorption of water, presumably because there is a smaller number of amide-groups that are linked to each other, and that its reactivity is larger, so that it dissolves e.g. in concentrated formic acid, which α-chitin, as a rule, does not. The degree of crystallinity too is thought to be less. The differences are therefore of a similar nature as those that have been recorded between cellulose I and II. However, when dissolved chitin is precipitated, not β- but α-chitin is formed.

That in chitin submicroscopical interstices must be present, follows from the fact that it shows a marked rodlet-birefringence. By the use of various imbibition liquids a rodlet-birefringence curve was found in plant as well as

in animal chitin, first by MOEHRING (1922), afterwards by DIEHL and VAN
ITERSON (1935), CASTLE (1936), SCHMIDT (1936) and PICKEN and LOTMAR
(1950). It appears that the positive birefringence of oriented chitin is, in
contrast to that of cellulose, not due to intrinsic birefringence, but to rodlet-
birefringence.

According to most of the investigators the chitin molecules and
crystallites themselves would be negatively birefringent, which means that
the highest refraction-index would be oriented perpendicular to the axis of
the molecule and the crystallite. CASTLE (l.c.), on the other hand, thinks that
the negative birefringence observed in the lowest point of the rodlet-birefringence curve may not be due to the chitin itself but to oriented adsorption
of the imbibition liquids. It will, at any rate, have to be admitted that with
various kinds of liquids rather strongly differing curves are obtained.

Whether the birefringence of the chitin itself is negative or positive, it will,
at any rate, be very small. This is due to the strong resonance possibility in
the transversely projecting acetylamine groups, which, although they are but
short, will nevertheless almost entirely compensate the resonance possibility
in the direction of the axis of the molecule.

As with cellulose the presence of interstices in chitin is indicated by the
possibility to stain it by means of colloidal dyes, e.g. with congo-red. Here too
the staining is dichroitic and the birefringence is increased.

The study of chitin by the aid of the electron microscope has fully confirmed the presence of interstices. It appears that there are, just as in cellulose,
microfibrils and interfibrillar spaces. The microfibrils in plant chitin are even
indistinguishable from those seen in cellulose (cf. section 243). Here too we see
very long, non-anastomosing threads with a diameter of 150—250 Å (FREY-
WYSSLING and MÜHLETHALER, 1950; ROELOFSEN, 1951 c).

Whether the microfibrils may be broken up by chemical means into fragments, a phenomenon which might be interpreted as indicating periodicity in
their crystalline or molecular structure, has not yet been investigated. Nor is
it known whether the microfibrils are flattened or not. An indication of a
flattening of the microfibrils (or may be the bundles in which these are aggregated), may be seen in the tangential orientation of the crystal plane
containing the pyranose rings, which HEYN (1936) found in dried sporangiophores of *Phycomyces*. The same orientation was found by FRAENKEL and
RUDALL (1940) in dried or flattened skins of maggots and, after the protein
had been removed, in the skin of fly pupae.

In yeasts chitin would, according to HOUWINK and KREGER (1953) be
present, at least partly, in amorphous condition, but it would crystallize and
the crystals would form aggregates when other cell-wall constituents are
removed; by the aid of the electron microscope no microfibrils could be detected
in these purified cell-walls, but only granules and rodlets, cf. fig. P 215.
In the X-ray diagrams chitin interferences are not noticeable before the purification, but only afterwards.

In the sporangiophores of *Phycomyces* too a large part of the chitin does
not seem to be completely crystallized (KREGER, 1954). The cell-walls of this
fungus are the only ones in which so far chitosan has been found; it seemed
to be amorphous, and not deposited in the form of microfibrils. Artificially
produced chitosan has a crystalline structure which was studied by CLARK
and SMITH (1936).

Very little can be said about the biochemical synthesis of chitin. Recently GLASER and BROWN (1957) succeeded in synthesizing it with the aid of a fungal homogenate using uridine-diphospho-N-acetylglucosamine as precursor. The hypothesis of the author (1958) regarding enzymic formation of cellulose microfibrils (cf. section 114) may also be applied to explain the development of chitin microfibrils.

123. ISOLATION, ANALYSIS AND IDENTIFICATION OF CHITIN

Chitin is always accompanied by other substances, in plants mainly by carbohydrates belonging to the group of the hemicelluloses, by proteins and by lipids. As the removal of these substances always causes some depolymerization and deacetylation and is seldom complete, the percentages found for N and for acetyl are, as a rule, not in full agreement with the expectation.

In order to purify the material, the following procedure is frequently applied:

1) the material is reduced to small particles, preferably without previous drying;
2) when chalk is present (in animal material), this is dissolved in $2-10\%$ HCl at room temperature, which takes $1-3$ days;
3) the material may first be boiled for $\frac{1}{2}-1$ hour in diluted (e.g. 2%) HCl, but then it should always be boiled for $\frac{1}{2}-24$ hours in $2-10\%$ alkali; for qualitative analysis not too impure material may, according to VAN WISSE-LINGH, be purified by heating it for a short time in glycerol at a temperature of $250-300°$ C, which has to be done in sealed tubes (cf. TUN-MANN-ROSENTHALER, 1931: 999);
4) if necessary, the material may further be bleached and purified by a treatment with acidified 2% $KMnO_4$, followed by one with 2% $NaHSO_3$, or better still, by one with 2% sodium chlorite at pH 5 and $85°$ C during at least one hour, after which it has to be washed; it has been said that a treatment at room temperature with diaphanol (i.e. 50% acetic acid saturated with ClO_2) when continued for some days would make the measure mentioned under 3 superfluous, but this is not so, and as this is an oxidizing agent, the long continued treatment causes a considerable decomposition;
5) if a final purification is desired, this can be obtained by dissolving the material rapidly in e. g. 30% HCl at $0°$ C, rapidly filtering through glass wool or glass filter, and precipitating the chitin by diluting with ice water or cold alcohol; the material dissolves most rapidly when it is pulverized and when the powder is first moistened with aceton or alcohol; this method of purification, however, causes depolymerization, and is therefore unsuitable for quantitative work.

When chitosan is present, this dissolves in the HCl used in the treatments 2 and 3, and can be regained by weakly alkalizing the solution.

Methods for the analysis of chitin, e.g. hydrolysis by means either of acid or of an enzyme, and estimation of actyl, glucosamine and acetylglucosamine, have been described by ZECHMEISTER and TOTH (1939), KLEIN (1932), and PAECH and TRACEY (1955, II). The estimation of the DP by means of the viscosity has been described e.g. by MEYER and WEHRLI (1937).

For the *identification of chitin* too it is desirable that the material should be purified to some extent.

The most conclusive method of identification is that by means of the X-ray diagram (KHOUVINE, 1932; VAN ITERSON et al., 1936; HEYN, 1936; R. FREY, 1950; HOUWINK and KREGER, 1953; KREGER, 1954; BLANK, 1953, 1954; RUDALL, 1955). When crystallized chitin is present in a mixture with amorphous carbohydrates at least 2% of the mixture must, according to KREGER (unpublished), consist of chitin, otherwise the interferences of the (non-oriented) crystals remain unrecognizable, but when the chitin is not completely crystallized, the percentage should be much higher. This is the reason why the X-ray diagrams of the cell-walls of *Phycomyces* sporangio-phores, which, according to KREGER (1954), contain ca 27% chitin, show but vague interferences. Purification of the material is the more desirable as it may in addition cause crystallization of the amorphous fraction of the chitin. That FREY (l.c.) did not always succeed in identifying the chitin in his diagrams, even where it certainly must have been present, is doubtless due to insufficient purification.

Chitin may evidently be identified also by means of chemical methods. The splitting of chitin by means of the press juice of *Lycoperdon*, which contains the enzyme chitinase, and the subsequent identification of the acetyl-glucos-amine that is produced in this way (cf. PAECH and TRACEY, 1955: 268), is much more satisfactory than the use of acid hydrolysis (THOMAS, 1928, 1942, 1943), although in theory there is still the possibility that this press juice contains other enzymes by whose activity acetyl-glucosamine may be split off from other cell-wall substances.

Of the other chemical reactions (cf. MOLISCH, 1923; TUNMANN-ROSEN-THALER, 1931; KLEYN, 1932; ZECHMEISTER and TOTH, 1939) only two are still in use, although in a slightly modified form (cf. PAECH and TRACEY, 1955: 266).

The first of these two reactions is based on the staining of chitosan with potassium triiodide in dilute acid. It is called the GILSON-VAN WISSELINGH test because it was first described by GILSON, and has further been elaborated by VAN WISSELINGH. Chitosan is obtained by VAN WISSELINGH by heating the material for 15 minutes at 160° C in a saturated solution of KOH (60 g. in 50 ml. water). He used to this end, just as he did when purifying the material with hot glycerol, sealed glass tubes, but it is safer to enclose the material in tinned iron tubes provided with screw valve and red copper washer (ROELOFSEN and HOETTE, 1951). It is also possible to boil the material for half an hour in concentrated alkali, but the most practical way is to put it with a small amount of alkali in a tube which is put with the basal part in a glycerol or oil bath at a temperature of 160° C (CAMPBELL, 1929). To avoid evaporation and entrance of air, the tube has in this case to be closed by means of a so-called BUNSEN valve, which consists of a piece of india-rubber vacuum-tube closed at its end and provided with a short longitudinal slit. Material con-taining a large amount of protein or fat should be purified beforehand, as already indicated; the simplest way to do this is by heating it in dilute alkali.

After the material has been allowed to cool, it is washed with water. When it happens to be finely divided (it may even be colloidally dispersed), the alkali has to be diluted with alcohol and the material centrifuged before it is washed.

When chitosan is present, it stains in a solution of 0.2% iodine in KJ to which 1% sulphuric acid has been added. The colour is either violet, purple or brownish violet, whereas most other cell-wall constituents that are able to withstand the treatment with alkali (!), e.g. cellulose, would assume a brown colour. When 70% (w/w) sulphuric acid is added, the chitosan dissolves and the colour disappears, whereas cellulose would under the same circumstances change its colour from brown to blue. Isolichenin and some as yet unidentified constituents in the cell-walls of fungi also stain violet with diluted potassium triiodide, but if these substances are present, they dissolve during the alkali treatment.

The test can nevertheless not be regarded as fully conclusive, for R. FREY (1950) records a positive effect for the cell-walls of *Phytophthora* and *Achlya*, which do not contain chitin. ROELOFSEN and HOETTE (1951) report that in yeast cell-walls treated with alkali the chitosan concentration may still be so low that the violet colour is not recognizable; under these circumstances the difference between the brownish violet colour due to the presence of chitosan, and the brown colour the material would assume if no chitin at all were present, may become too vague.

More sensitive and also more specific, though unsuitable for studying the localisation of chitin in sections by means of the microscope, is the reaction on chitosan by means of sulphuric acid, which yields crystals of chitosan sulphate. The latter had already been seen by GILSON in 1895, but BRUNSWIK (1921) was the first to use these crystals for the identification of chitin; it is therefore called the BRUNSWIK test. His method was subsequently improved by CAMPBELL (1929) and by ROELOFSEN and HOETTE (1951). After the chitin has been transformed into chitosan in the way described above, the material is mounted on a slide in 15% H_2SO_4 and covered; then the chitosan in it is dissolved by heating, and the solution is placed on a sand bath that has been given a temperature of 80° C, and allowed to cool slowly. In this way, flattened, in outline round or angular crystal aggregates are formed, which appear between crossed nicols as bright spots. They prove to be negatively birefringent sphaero-crystals, and to stain fast with 1% picric acid. The production of picrates is more or less typical for the NH_2-group, and is for this reason a reaction on proteins, alcaloids and similar substances. According to ROELOFSEN and HOETTE (1951) chitin is as far as known the only cell-wall constituent that is able to withstand the treatment with alkali, and which yields in this way negatively birefringent crystal aggregates that are stainable with picric acid.

The reaction with sulphuric acid comprises, at least when the material has not been purified by means of acid, chitin as well as chitosan, if the latter originally had been present. If we wish to prove the presence of preexistent chitosan, the transformation of chitin into chitosan should be avoided and the BRUNSWIK-test should be performed with the untreated material. Eventually the chitosan may first be concentrated and purified by extracting the material with hot acid, after which the chitosan is precipitated by neutralization and addition of alcohol. The identification of chitosan in the precipitate may be carried out in one of the three ways described above (by X-ray analysis, staining with iodine, or production of crystallized chitosan sulphate).

The reaction recommended by SCHULZE, viz. a transient staining with chlor-zinc-iodine after a pretreatment with diaphanol (TUNMANN-ROSENTHALER, 1931: 1001) is according to several investigators to be rejected, as it is unreliable.

13. Hemicelluloses

131. DEFINITION AND OCCURRENCE

Hemicellulose is the collective name for all those polysaccharides occurring in the cell-wall that dissolve either in cold or in hot alkali but are insoluble or only slightly soluble in cold and hot water. They are more easily hydrolysable in acid than cellulose is, and yield in this way hexoses or a mixture of hexoses and pentoses as well as a slight amount of uronic acid. Pure polyuronides like pectic substances and alginic acid are therefore excluded, not only because of their chemical constitution, but also because they are soluble in water at least if the pH is adjusted to neutral.

The exclusion of cell-wall polysaccharides that are soluble in cold or hot water, is somewhat artificial, as the low-polymeric fractions of hemicellulose are often soluble in water, and as part of the hemicelluloses become soluble in water after they have once been extracted with alkali.

On the other hand some fractions with a very high DP do not dissolve in alkali or dissolve very slowly. Nevertheless they are considered to belong to the hemicellulose group because their chemical constitution is the same as of the alkali soluble fractions. They can be extracted after pretreatment with some depolymerizing agent, e.g. with the one that is used to remove lignin from wood.

When SCHULZE introduced the term hemicellulose in 1891, he was thinking of the cell-walls of higher plants only, and nowadays too it is often used in this restricted sense, although this does not follow from the definition. When we include all cell-wall carbohydrates of the lower plants that are not cellulose, in the hemicelluloses, we may say that the latter are as far as known, present in all plants with the exception of the *Bacteria*.

The amount of hemicellulose varies considerably in different plants and also in different tissues of the same plant. Whereas the fullgrown cotton hair contains at the most 1%, the jute fibre contains 25%, wood 25—40%, collenchyma and growing cell-walls 35—50%, the cell-wall of the ivory nut more than 90%, that of the yeast cell 70%.

The hemicellulose content varies greatly even in different layers of the same cell-wall. In the middle lamella and the primary wall it usually is much higher than in the secondary wall. In wood, however, the percentage is nearly equal in all layers, but here too considerable differences are found after delignification for then it is about 60% in the outermost part of the walls and only 15% in the innermost part (ASUNMAA and LANGE, 1954; cf. also TREIBER, 1957: 259).

The term holocellulose is used only in connection with lignified cell-walls, and refers to the fraction that remains after the latter have been extracted with organic solvents and water, and after the subsequent removal of the lignin. It consists of cellulose, hemicellulose, pectins, and polyoses which because of the removal of the lignin have become soluble in water. The latter are usually also reckoned to the hemicellulose group.

132. SOME CHEMICAL AND PHYSICAL PROPERTIES OF THE HEMICELLULOSES, AND THE ESTIMATION OF THE HEMICELLULOSE FRACTION IN THE CELL-WALL

These subjects are extensively dealt with in WISE and JAHN (1952), OTT and SPURLIN (1954), POLGLASE (1955), and WHISTLER and SMART (1953).

The hemicellulose that is present in wood, has been studied far better than that from any other source. Table II shows the composition, after hydrolysis, of the holocellulose obtained from the wood of three different kinds of trees. Glucose appears to be the sugar that is best represented, but it has almost all been produced by the splitting of cellulose. This becomes clear when we begin by extracting the holocellulose with alkali in order to remove the hemicellulose, and hydrolyse the two fractions separately. The hemicellulose fraction appears to yield but a few percents of glucose, and even this small amount is probably derived in part from low-polymeric cellulose. The presence of the latter in the hemicellulose fraction was assumed to be demonstrable by means of X-ray analysis (RÅNBY, 1952a), but as in recent years other polysaccharides have been discovered with similar main X-ray interferences (CRONSHAW et al., 1958), it seems advisable to await further reports.

In spruce wood some glucose was found to arise from glucomannan (see further on). Much more glucose of non-cellulosic origin may occur in the walls of other cells e.g. in endosperms, further in callose and in the cell-walls of lower plants.

Table II. Percentage of different sugars and of some other substances found in hydrolysed holocellulose (from WISE and JAHN, 1952).

	Pinus sylvestris	*Larix sibirica*	*Populus tremula*
d-glucose	65.0	63.0	64.5
d-mannose	12.5	7.5	3.0
d-galactose	6.0	17.5	1.5
d-xylose	13.0	9.0	30.0
l-arabinose	3.5	3.0	1.0
uronic acid	4.1		3.5
acetyl	1.5		3.0

The difference in composition that is noticeable between *Pinus* and *Populus*, exemplifies a general dissimilarity in the nature of the hemicellulose found in the wood of conifers (softwoods) and in that of the deciduous trees of the temperate region (so-called hardwoods). In the hemicellulose obtained from the wood of the latter, xylose appears to play the dominant part, whereas in that obtained from softwood, mannose and galactose too occur in considerable amounts.

Hardwood hemicellulose appears to contain 70—80% pentosan, hemicellulose from the corn cob even as much as 94%, softwood hemicellulose only 30—35%. *Larix* hemicellulose is somewhat exceptional by its high galactose content. However, as the latter is derived for the greater part from a polysaccharide that is soluble in water, it ought not to be reckoned to the constituents of the hemicellulose.

A sugar that is not mentioned in the table, but of which, as a rule, a small amount is present, is l-rhamnose. The greater part of the uronic acid fraction does not consist of galacturonic acid, a derivative of pectin, but of methoxy-glucuronic acid, which in combination with an amount of xylose that is 3 to 20 times as large, originally formed a hetero-polymer. For a large part the methoxy-glucuronic acid is after the hydrolysis still bound to one or two xylose

units, which means that it appears in the form of aldobionic acid and aldotrionic acid. These substances, like all glycosidic compounds of uronic acid, are
difficult to split by hydrolysis.

When we wish to study the composition of the carbohydrate fraction in
wood, we should not try to hydrolyse it all at once, as that would leave a
large part of the more resistant polysaccharides intact. This applies also,
though in a minor degree, to the complete hydrolysis of holocellulose obtained
from wood and to that of non-lignified cell-walls. For this reason it is desirable
to begin with a gentle hydrolysis, which splits the hemicelluloses, and then
to treat the insoluble rest with a more vigorously hydrolysing agent, which
does away with the cellulose. It is also possible to separate hemicellulose
from cellulose by extracting the material with alkali in the way described
under cellulose, and to hydrolyse the two fractions separately. First of all,
however, pectin and the carbohydrates that are soluble in water should be
removed e.g. by the aid of hot ammonium oxalate or of highly diluted acid.
For methods of preparing holocellulose and of extracting it, of hydrolysing
hemicellulose as well as for analysing the component sugars we refer to WISE
and JAHN (1952), and PAECH and TRACEY (1955).

It appears from these works that the amount of hemicellulose in wood cannot
be determined by measuring the loss in weight caused by the extraction with
alkali. We obtain far too low values in this case. Some authors ascribe this
to a chemical cause, viz. to the presence of an insoluble compound of hemicellulose and lignin whereas according to others the cause may simply be
that lignin greatly hampers the diffusion of hemicellulose into the solvent.
The dissolved hemicellulose, moreover, would be polluted with lignin, and it
would be difficult to separate this lignin fraction from the hemicellulose.

The customary method, which starts from holocellulose and extracts the
hemicellulose with alkali, is much better but not entirely satisfactory either,
for the amount of hemicellulose that is found in this way remains 3 to 7%
short of the actual amount. There are two causes for this deficit; the first is
that part of the hemicellulose already dissolves in the liquid that is used for
the removal of lignin, and the second is that a badly soluble part of the hemicellulose remains firmly attached to the cellulose. The so-called α-cellulose
that is obtained in this way, proves to contain a few percents of non-cellulose.
These losses total more than 3—7%, but are partly compensated by a gain
that is caused by some low-polymeric cellulose which dissolves with the hemicellulose.

Table III gives an impression of the difference between the values that
should have been found for cellulose and hemicellulose and those that actually
have been found by means of the usual method of estimation.

Table IV shows the same differences diagrammatically.

Table III. Differences between the values that have been found for cellulose and hemicellulose and those that theoretically were to be expected; all values expressed as a percentage of the original wood weight (from WISE and JAHN, 1952).

	Pinus sp.	Quercus rubra
holocellulose	70	69
cellulose found	55	46
cellulose expected	46	44
hemicellulose found	15	23
hemicellulose expected	20	27

Table IV. Diagram of the true and the actually measured composition of the lignified cell-wall.

holocellulose (analytically found, contains traces of lignin)		lignin (analysis)
true cellulose	true hemicellulose	true lignin
α-cellulose (anal. found, contains hemicellulose), de-polymerized	hemicellulose (anal. found, contains low-polymeric cellulose and trace of lignin), depolymerized	lignin (anal. found, contains traces of hemicellulose)

Splitting hemicellulose in its monomers is a much simpler process than *the isolation of the different kinds of polysaccharides* of which the hemicellulose fraction is composed. The isolation of these compounds has as yet not proceeded very far. The reason why it proves so difficult to separate the various components, lies in the circumstance that they differ but slightly in their properties, and that each of them is polydisperse, i.e. contains molecules with a widely different degree of polymerization (DP). Low-polymeric molecules dissolve better and are more difficult to precipitate from their solutions. Fractionating therefore often does not lead to a separation of the various polysaccharides, but to a separation of molecules with a different degree of polymerization, and the fractions obtained in this way remain an inextricable mixture.

A method that has often been used when extracts containing hemicellulose have to be fractionated, starts with the neutralisation of the alkaline extract to pH 4.5. This causes the precipitation of the so-called β-cellulose. The rest of the neutralized extract may be precipitated by the aid of alcohol, and is called γ-cellulose. These two fractions look different under the electron microscope, β-cellulose consisting partly of granules, whereas γ-cellulose proves to be a structureless mass (RANBY, 1952a). As has already been mentioned, the X-ray diagram of the former looks like that of cellulose (in the II-modification), but whether it actually is cellulose, seems open to some doubt. The diagram of the γ-fraction is quite different. In the native wall these constituents are not crystallized.

Hemicellulose may also be fractionated by precipitating certain constituents from the alkaline solution by means of FEHLING's solution, BENEDICT's solution or some other solution of cupric hydroxide in NaOH or KOH, a method that was applied already in 1901 by SALKOWSKI. When cuprammonium reacts with cellulose, each Cu-atom combines with two OH-groups from one glucose-monomer, but here it are two pairs of OH-groups belonging to two different molecules which react with the Cu-atoms. Here too, the two OH-groups of each pair must be situated very near to each other. As a result the molecules of hemicellulose constituents that fulfil this requirement are combined into a network, and this leads to their being precipitated (DEUEL and NEUKOM, 1949b). As a rule, a polysaccharide that dissolves in cuoxam, will form a precipitate with FEHLING's solution. Instead of precipitating from a solution we may also extract alcohol-precipitated hemicellulose with FEHLING's solution; the latter will dissolve those fractions that would not be precipitated from a solution that is treated with the reagent.

Similar results as with cupric hydroxide are obtained with borax in an alkaline medium, as the latter too binds two pairs of OH-groups (DEUEL and NEUKOM, 1949 a).

Precipitation has to be repeated several times, as the precipitate always includes part of the dissolved hemicelluloses. From the hemicellulose contained in straw and in birch wood it has been possible to prepare in this way nearly pure xylan, from the ivory nut and from yeast cell-walls mannan was isolated, whereas in other instances the fraction that was not precipitated, yielded e.g. galactan and araban. As a matter of fact, a large part of the hexoses and pentoses that are present in hemicellulose form homopolymers. However, besides these homopolymers heteropolymers too are always present. The latter may contain e.g. glucuronic acid in ramified molecules with much xylose, but also arabinose, rhamnose and various hexoses. Only a few of these hetero-polymers, have so far been purified to some extent, and analysed (cf. WHISTLER and CORBET, 1955; BALL et al., 1956; GEERDES and SMITH, 1955).

NORMAN, one of the older cell-wall chemists, has introduced the term cellulosan for the first-named group of substances, that of the homopolymers, and for the second group the name polyuronide hemicelluloses. According to him the most important difference in "function" between the two groups would be that the first "forms a part of the cellulosic fabric" and "is oriented in the micellar structure", whereas the second group "interpenetrates and incrusts the cellulosic fabric" (cf. OTT and SPURLIN, 1954: 462). However, there seems to be no sufficient reason to assume that part of the hemicelluloses would not be present in the interfibrillar spaces, but in the cellulose micro-fibrils themselves. It is possible of course that hemicellulose molecules occur interspersed between the cellulose of amorphous regions of the microfibrils or that they are adsorbed on their surface. This might be the reason why it is so difficult to obtain pure cellulose from a cell-wall which in addition to cellulose contains a large amount of hemicellulose.

Attempts have been made to estimate the average degree of polymerization of the entire hemicellulose fraction and of some of its components. Although it can not be doubted that the hemicellulose is partly depolymerized during the delignification (TIMELL and JAHN, 1951), and although the estimates may not be entirely trustworthy, it can not be doubted that the DP is much lower than that of cellulose. The values that have been reported, vary between 50 and 300. This low DP is partly responsible for the greater facility with which the hemicelluloses, in comparison with cellulose and chitin, dissolve, are hydrolyzed and oxidized, and, in general, for their greater chemical reactivity.

The reactivity of hemicellulose is especially notable in fresh material; when stored, and especially when stored in a dry condition, the reactivity decreases.

Another particularity that is of importance for the chemical reactivity of the hemicelluloses, is that, with a few exceptions, they seem to be present in *amorphous condition*; if they possess "crystalline" areas, the latter are at any rate so minute that they do not give X-ray interference. The cell-wall of the higher plants shows the X-ray diagram of cellulose only, or in the epidermis and the cork-cells, that of various waxes. It is true that crystallization is obvious in precipitated hemicellulose, and some fractions, e.g. xylan, have even been isolated in the crystalline state, but always after extraction from the wall. Real exceptions are mannan in the ivory nut, a glucan in the cell-walls of fungi, and some polysaccharides of unknown composition in the cell-walls of algae; these are already in the natural condition at least partly crystalline. In agreement with the amorphous condition, the hemicelluloses, as far as known, show either no birefringence at all or but a very slight one.

In higher plants, so far, only one hemicellulose is known to have *a microfibrillar structure*, viz. mannan B of the ivory nut (cf. section 1332). In other native walls the hemicellulose usually appears under the electron microscope as a structureless or finely granular mass, fig. 11, P15 and P16. The cellulose microfibrils are embedded in this mass and they are often but vaguely visible or even not at all.

In the walls of some algae that do not contain cellulose I, microfibrils have been observed electron-optically, e.g. in *Halicystis* and some red and brown algae (cf. sections 2411 and 242). In some, probably in most cases, there are indications that these do not consist of hemicellulose but of cellulose II. In *Porphyra* they are undoubtedly hemicellulosic, but further details of the chemical constitution are as yet unknown.

In fungal cell-walls containing much chitin, the latter obviously constitutes the main part, if not all, of the microfibrils, but in baker's yeast part of the glucan evidently occurs in the form of thin short microfibrils (cf. section 243).

The *faculty to hydrolyse at least part of the hemicelluloses by means of enzymes*, is very common in bacteria, fungi and lower herbivorous animals, more common, in fact, than the power to attack cellulose or chitin. No enzyme preparations, however, are known, of which it has been proved that they cause a complete hydrolysis of the hemicellulose fraction. In view of the diversity of bonds and of monomers that are present in every kind of hemicellulose, and taking into consideration the substrate specificity of the polysaccharases, it is clear that such a preparation would have to contain quite a number of these enzymes.

In higher plants too hemicellulose hydrolysing enzymes are common, especially in seeds. Not only those with thick cell-walls containing "reserve cellulose", but also e.g. in barley and wheat. It is known that the enzyme activity increases during germination, so that it is in malt much greater than in barley. Literature on the morphological aspects of the way in which "reserve cellulose" is attacked may be found with Küster (1956: 725). Other parts of higher plants too contain hemicellulases; this is already evident from the fact that cell-walls may be perforated and that they may even disappear as they do in some ripening berries.

A *microscopical reaction* on the whole group of the hemicelluloses is the staining with acid fuchsin after oxidation of diol groups to aldehyde; this reaction succeeds more easily with hemicellulose than with cellulose. Asunmaa and Lange (1952, 1954) used this staining method to measure photometrically the distribution in sections of the wall.

Hemicelluloses stain only exceptionally with chlor-zinc-iodine or with sulphuric-acid-iodine; when a wall containing cellulose does not stain, this is usually due to the circumstance that the cellulose is enveloped by hemicellulose. The mannans of the ivory nut and of the date endosperm, however, do stain blue. The hemicellulose of unknown composition occurring in the coffee-bean, and some other seeds also seem to stain blue, but it is not excluded that in these cases the cellulose fraction may be responsible for the staining. That a hemicellulose stains blue with potassium triiodide alone is even more rare; it is seen in isolichenin and in amyloid, but these substances are soluble in water, and are therefore no true hemicelluloses.

Stainable with ruthenium red are especially the polyuronides, but as hemi-cellulose always contains uronic acids, these substances too are slightly stainable.

When cell-walls containing pentosan are heated for a short time in con-centrated hydrochloric acid, they yield furfural, which in a strongly acid medium combines with phenols like phloroglucinol and orcinol to produce brightly coloured substances. These reactions, which are used in analytical chemistry, have been applied by REEVE (1946) for the microscopical study of seedcoats containing pentosan. Xylan and araban would give with phloro-glucinol-hydrochloric acid a pink to lavender-blue colour, whereas hexoses, which must be heated for a longer time, yield hydroxymethylfurfural, which assumes a brown colour. BIAL's reagent, which contains orcinol and iron, gives other colours, but it seems desirable that these reagents should first of all be tested on cell-walls and preparations of known composition before con-clusions are drawn from the results obtained with them in cell-walls of unknown composition.

133. SOME OF THE BETTER-KNOWN COMPONENTS OF HEMI-CELLULOSE

1331. Xylans

This pentosan is found in all higher plants and also in some marine algae. Especially rich in xylan are the cell-walls in corn cobs (35%), in the glumes of cereals (40%), in straw and in wood of deciduous trees (20—25%); the wood of conifers, on the other hand, contains but 7—10%. In the first-named objects the hemicellulose itself contains 80—95% xylan. For this reason and also because of the possibility to purify xylan by precipitating it several times in succession by means of alkaline cupric hydroxide and dissolving the pre-cipitate in alkali (cf. PAECH and TRACEY, 1955; WHISTLER and SMART, 1953), pure xylan has been obtained from several objects. Study of the products obtained by hydrolysis of a methylated xylan from esparto grass led to the conclusion that it consists of straight chain molecules with β-1,4 bonds and with a DP of at least 100 to 200. Apart from the much lower DP and from the absence of the C_6-group, the chemical structure therefore shows a strong resemblance to that of cellulose. Besides this xylan, esparto grass seems to contain another xylan, which is said to be provided with side-chains con-sisting of arabinose units.

Already long ago a more or less crystalline xylan has been obtained (R. O. HERZOG and GONELL, 1924). A more complete crystallization of straw xylan can be obtained after treatment with diluted acid, which causes a slight degree of depolymerization, and lowers the DP to circ. 40 (YUNDT, 1951; ROELOF-SEN, 1954). The crystals are negatively birefringent, but differ widely in shape. The X-ray diagram is quite di-stinct from that of cellu-lose I or II.

Xylan

Other xylans occur either together with this one or alone. They are provided with a varying number of side-chains which usually consist of a single unit, viz. glucuronic acid, methyl glucuronic acid, rhamnose or arabinose. Instead of in the form of side-chains these units may also be found at the end of the main chain. Xylans of this type have been found in quite different objects, viz. in cereal straw, corn cobs, fibres of *Phormium tenax*, flax stalks, pears (GEERDES and SMITH, 1955; EHRENTHAL et al., 1954; ASPINALL and MAHOMED, 1954; ASPINALL and WILKY, 1956; WHISTLER and SMART, 1953). In *Porphyra*, a *Rhodophycea*, a low-polymeric xylan has been found with 1,3 and 1,4 bonds in its chain (PERCIVAL and CHANDA, 1950). This seems to have a fibrillar structure in the native wall (cf. section 2421).

1332. Mannans and substituted mannans

The cell-walls in the seed of *Phytelephas macrocarpa*, the ivory nut, have a mannan content of 90%; 6% is cellulose (MEIER, 1958).

Chemical analysis revealed that the mannan from the ivory nut consists mainly of unbranched molecules with β-1,4 bonds and, although it is partly depolymerized during the isolation, with a DP of at least 10—80. According to the most recent investigations (ASPINALL et al., 1958) no 1,6 bonds are present as was thought earlier, but some α-1,4 bonds and some glucose units. The low-polymeric fraction, called mannan A, which forms 60% of the wall, dissolves more easily in alkali than that with high DP (30%), which needs pretreatment with chlorite. Both fractions dissolve in cuoxam, are precipitated by FEHLING's solution and by borax. It is usually stated that they do not stain blue with iodine in sulphuric acid, chlor-zinc-iodine or potassium triiodide but according to MEIER (1958) mannan B does stain like cellulose. A similar mannan has been isolated from walnuts (HIRST and JONES, 1939).

Preparations of mannan with a crystalline structure have been obtained already long ago from the cell-walls of the ivory nut and from the wood of conifers (HERZOG and GONELL, 1924; KATZ, 1928; YUNDT, 1951). According to HESS and

Mannan

LÜDTKE (1928) these preparations give identical X-ray diagrams, which indicates an identical chemical constitution.

Native wall material of the ivory nut produces the same X-ray diagram as the isolated mannan A-fraction (MEIER, 1958, and observations in the author's laboratory). The residual mannan B is according to MEIER not crystalline although it is fibrillar. It is very similar to the mannan B of the date, shown in fig. 17b. The crystalline mannan A, on the other hand, appears to have a granular structure, similar to the date mannan A, shown in fig. 17a. This curious situation is unique since so far fibrillar cell-wall polysaccharides have always proved to be crystalline. It seems likely that in reality the microfibrils do have ordered regions but that the latter are too small to give interferences.

According to MEIER both mannan fractions are birefringent and the birefringence of the wall is certainly to be ascribed partly to the two mannans and partly to the cellulose. The preferential staining of the inner layer of the wall with chlor-zinc-iodine has generally been interpreted as indicating that the cellulose was mainly to be found here, but since MEIER (l.c.) has shown

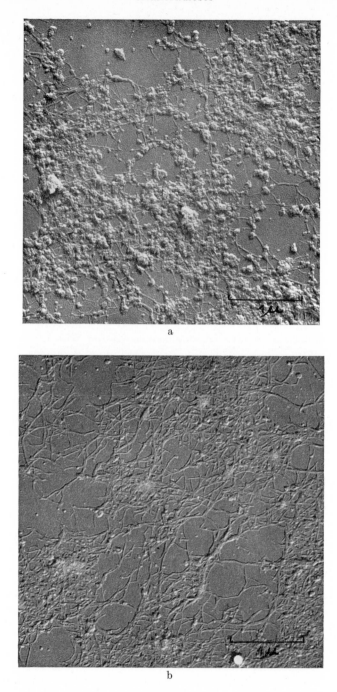

a

b

Fig. 17. Electronmicrographs of ultrasonically disintegrated endosperm of *Phoenix dactylifera*; a: native wall containing granular mannan A and fibrillar mannan B and also about 6% cellulose; b: mixture of mannan B and cellulose (± 15%) (from MEIER, 1956).

that mannan B too stains blue, this conclusion regarding the distribution of cellulose has to be discarded.

The chemical constitution shown by the wall of the date endosperm as well as the physical structure of the mannan fractions are, according to MEIER (1956, 1958), similar to the corresponding features in the ivory nut. Fig. 17 presents electronmicrographs of an ultrasonically disintegrated native wall (a) and of a mixture of cellulose and the mannan B fraction in the proportion of about 2 : 3.

Softwoods yield 7—15% mannose, hardwoods 1—3%. In spruce the whole amount of mannan seems to be incorporated in a glucomannan which contains 3—4 parts mannose against one part glucose (LINDBERG and MEIER, 1957; TIMELL and TYMINSKI, 1957).

The hard endosperm of *Iris ochroleuca* and of *I. sibirica* contains, according to ANDREWS et al. (1953), a glucomannan with 1,4-bonds in the chain, and perhaps with a few galactose units as side-chains; it is soluble in alkali. Gluco-mannans that are soluble in water, are met with in the tubers of *Amorpho-phallus*-species, but they do not form part of the cell-wall.

Coffee-beans would, according to observations made by SCHULZE in 1890 contain in addition to cellulose and pentosan, hemicellulose containing galactose and mannose. TÄUFEL and THALER (1935) also found much mannose in the hydrolysate of the alkali-soluble fraction. Later THALER (1957) stated that part of the hemicelluloses become soluble in hot water during the roasting of the beans, and this fraction was found to yield 70% mannose and 30% galactose after hydrolysis. It is apparently a mixture of polymers, for this proportion changed on further purification.

In the author's laboratory (unpublished results) cell-wall material of the raw coffee-bean yielded about 15% glucose, apparently derived from cellulose, while the hemicellulose yielded equal portions of galactose, mannose and arabinose, and to our surprise, only traces of xylose and no uronic acids at all. It was found that during consecutive treatments with hot water, chlorite and 5—24% KOH, respectively 6, 14 and 15% of the original amount of cell-wall material were dissolved. The residue, being 61%, still consisted of about three parts hemicellulose and one part cellulose. Here again we meet a hemicellulose which does not dissolve in the reagents that are used to determine hemicellulose in wood. No difference was found in the chemical constitution of the residue and the three different fractions, which seems to indicate that the three main monomers occur in one hetero-polymer which is heterodisperse.

The seeds of *Strychnos nux-vomica* contain, according to ANDREWS et al. (1952 a, 1954), most probably a mannan as well as a galactan; also the seeds of *Diospyros kaki* (HAYASHI and MIZUNO, 1952) very probably contain mannan.

Better known is the mannan which occurs in the *Rhodophycea Porphyra umbilicalis*. The molecule appears to be slightly branched, but is in other respects very similar to that of the mannan from the ivory nut (JONES, 1950). It was said that it did not form part of the cell-wall, but CRONSHAW et al. (1958) found that the material obtained after the wall had been extracted with hot water and cold 4n KOH was a mannan. In the electron microscope it appeared to be granular. The microfibrils that were originally present, had dissolved in the alkali together with amorphous material. After hydrolysis this solution yielded much xylose and less mannose and galactose, but which of them were derived from the microfibrils, remained obscure.

1333. Glucans

When hemicellulose from wood is hydrolysed, the product, as has been stated already, always contains a small amount of glucose, but this is most probably entirely derived from low-polymeric cellulose, and heteropolymers like glucomannan. Non-cellulosic glucans are rarely found. One of these is the *callose* occurring in the cystoliths of *Ficus elastica*. The latter contain, according to ESCHRICH (1954), 91.5% $CaCO_3$, 1.8% silica (in the stalk), 4.5% callose and 2.2% cellulose. The callose could be isolated by extraction with hot alkali, and appeared to be composed entirely of glucose units, but details with regard to its constitution are as yet unknown. It is insoluble in water and in cuoxam, dissolves in glycerol at a temperature of 250° C, is more easily hydrolysable than cellulose, stains yellow with chlor-zinc-iodine and with potassium triiodide, and is stainable with certain dyes, e.g. with resorcin blue.

The name callose was originally given to the substance of which the callus-cushions on the sieve-plates of the older sieve-tubes consist, and which behaves in the same way with regard to solvents and stains as the callose of the cystoliths. This substance too is a glucan. According to KESSLER (1958) the molecules are unbranched and the glucose monomers are, like in yeast glucan (v. infra), linked by β-1,3 bonds. It is, at least after it has been dried, present in the crystalline condition, but the crystals differ from those of yeast glucan (FREY-WYSSLING, EPPRECHT and KESSLER, 1957). According to ESCH-RICH (1956), callose is never birefringent, but this does not exclude the possibility that it may be present in the form of randomly arranged crystals.

Mainly on account of the faculty to stain with resorcin blue, which is considered to be a specific reaction, callose is said to be present also in certain plant hairs, pollen grains, latex tubes, root hairs, and lenticels, and also in *Chlorophyceae* and fungi (ESCHRICH, 1956). It is also produced by the *Allium* epidermis, when the latter is kept on a hypertonic sugar solution (ESCHRICH, 1957). Whether all these cell-wall constituents really may be regarded as identical, is uncertain; it is even uncertain whether it really are, like the callose of the cystoliths, glucans. ARNOLD recently (1956) found that very small amounts of sieve-tube callose are detectable by staining with a fluorochrom and observing the resulting fluorescence in U.V.-light. According to MÜHLE-THALER and LINSKENS (1956) the callose of pollen tubes shows no structure under the electron microscope.

Glucans have for a long time been known from fungi; they are represented here by the so-called yeast-cellulose, fungus callose, etc. The fungus glucans recently proved to be of various kinds, but that occurring in *Saccharomyces cerevisiae* is the only one of which the structure has been determined. The cell-walls of this yeast contain circ. 30% glucan (NORTHCOTE and HORNE, 1952; ROELOFSEN, 1953). In diluted alkali at boiling heat most other cell-wall constituents (mannan, protein, lipids) are dissolved, and this happens also with part of the glucan, but the rest, circ. 25% of the original weight of cell-wall, consists, apart from a small amount of chitin, entirely of glucan. This is therefore another alkali-insoluble substance which nevertheless is still included in the hemicelluloses. It appears to be provided with β-1,3 bonds, and one of each ten monomers has at the C_2-atom a side-chain with exactly the same structure as the main one. The degree of polymerization would only be circ. 40 (BELL and NORTHCOTE, 1950).

Yeast glucan appears to be, at least partly, in the crystalline condition (with interference zones corresponding to 13—17, 7—7.8, and 3.7—5.3 Å), and seems to be fibrillar, at least partly (cf. section 243). It does not stain with chlor-zinc-iodine or potassium triiodide, and does not dissolve in cuoxam, nor in cold 30% HCl. When boiled in 2% HCl, one half dissolves fairly rapidly, the rest very slowly; at the same time the degree of crystallization increases, and fibrillar aggregates are formed (HOUWINK and KREGER, 1953). This rest appears to dissolve easily in alkali. This solubility in alkali and the crystallization too might be due to a partial hydrolysis during the treatment with acid, but this is not certain. The crystalline yeast glucan which owes its origin to the treatment with acid, shows X-ray interferences of 13.4, 7.7, 6.7, 5.0, 4.5 and 3.9 Å, and this is in agreement with the interference zones of the original product. This diagram proves, and this is remarkable enough, to be nearly identical with that of the reserve carbohydrate "paramylon", which occurs in *Euglena* (KREGER and MEEUSE, 1952).

Another glucan, which goes into solution when the cell-wall in its original condition is treated with hot alkali, has been found in company of yeast glucan in the cell-walls of *Penicillium* and *Schizosaccharomyces*; it is also present in *Agaricus campestris*, where yeast glucan is absent (KREGER, 1954). Its structure is still unknown. *Polyporus betulinus* contains a glucan that chemically resembles yeast glucan (DUFF, 1952).

14. Polyoses that are Soluble in Water

The most recent survey of the chemistry of the substances belonging to this group is that of WHISTLER and SMART (1953); other aspects of certain representatives of the group have been dealt with by MANTELL (1947). Those polyoses that form very viscous solutions, are called gums or slimes; gums, when they are present in the form of an exudate which as a rule is produced only after a lesion or a necrosis; and slimes, when they are present under quite normal circumstances, remain inside the plant, and have therefore to be extracted. However, this difference is not always sharp and it is, moreover, not always adhered to.

Some slimes naturally occur in a slimy condition. These mostly form part of the cell-wall; the cell-sap is rarely slimy. In higher plants the production of slimes is confined to definite cells, often those of the epidermis, but also to other cells of seed-coats, tubers, or the phloem. In lower plants slimy cell-walls are very common, e.g. in *Cyanophyceae, Chlorophyceae, Flagellatae* and *Bacteria*. For details we refer to the summary given by TUNMANN-ROSEN-THALER (1931) and to the review by KÜSTER (1956).

Other water-soluble polyoses are not slimy in natural condition, but become so when extracted. These polyoses may be restricted to certain parts of the plant e.g. to the endosperm, but they may also occur more universally distributed in the plant.

A third group of water-soluble polyoses are not slimy at all, neither in the plant nor after having been extracted. This is due to their chemical constitution, and especially to the degree of polymerization. Not rarely they are merely the low polymeric fractions of true hemicellulose, which by definition dissolve in an alkaline medium only.

We will, of course, confine our discussion to those water-soluble polyoses of the three groups which are cell-wall constituents and we will therefore exclude the gums and the polyoses occurring in the cell fluid. The pectic substances and alginates are also water-soluble cell-wall constituents but these substances will be discussed in a separate section (15).

The extraction of the polyoses that are soluble in water, is, of course, a simple matter. It is performed with hot water, and the only precaution that has to be taken, is that the medium is kept approximately neutral, as otherwise hydrolysis and oxidation may take place. Sometimes it may be desirable to separate the cell-wall from the cell content, to remove lipids by the aid of benzene-ethanol mixture, and other substances by means of ethanol or aceton.

The polyoses are precipitated from the aqueous solution by dehydration; to this end either ethanol or aceton may be used. The preparations obtained in this way, contain many impurities, e.g. proteins, polyuronides, and eventually also amylum or other carbohydrates that are part of the cell content. The removal of these substances always leads to losses, and the separation is never quite complete. Amylum may be removed either beforehand or from the extract by means of salivary or pancreatic amylase (other enzyme preparations should be avoided, as they may attack the polyoses themselves). Protein too may be removed by the aid of enzymes, e.g. of pepsin or trypsin. The polyuronides may be precipitated separately in the form of salts by adding Ca, Ba, Al or Pb ions, or, after saponification of the pectin, by means of an acid; it should be noted, however, that part of the polyoses are precipitated at the same time.

The polyoses that are precipitated by alkaline cupric hydroxide, can be isolated satisfactorily by dissolving the precipitate and precipitating it again, a procedure that has to be repeated a few times. According to DEUEL and NEUKOM (1949b, 1954), yeast mannan, *Orchis* mannan, galactomannans and seed amyloid are precipitated by FEHLING's solution, whereas lichenin and the slimes in the seeds of *Plantago* and *Linum* are precipitated by a stronger alkaline cupric hydroxide. Agar and carrageenin can not be precipitated in this way.

The observations of DEUEL and NEUKOM (1954) with regard to precipitation with various salts, tannin, potassium triiodide, etc. may lead perhaps to additional methods of separation.

The hydrolysis of the polyoses and the analysis of the hydrolysate are carried out in a similar way as in the case of the hemicelluloses (cf. PAECH and TRACEY, 1955: 275; WHISTLER and SWART, 1953: 27). Monomers that may be present, are d-glucose, d- and l-galactose, d-mannose, d-xylose, l-arabinose, l-rhamnose, d-galacturonic acid, d-mannuronic acid, d-glucuronic acid; in marine algae also galactose sulphate and l-fucose (6-desoxy-l-galactose).

The principal representatives of the group of cell-wall polyoses that are soluble in water, will now be briefly discussed.

141. GLUCANS AND SUBSTITUTED GLUCANS

By extracting *Cetraria islandica* and other lichens with hot water various polyoses can be obtained. When the solution cools down, circ. 10% of the original dry weight of the lichen is precipitated. This is *lichenin*. Lichenin does not stain with potassium triiodide and chlor-zinc-iodine, dissolves in cuoxam, is not precipitated by FEHLING's solution but by a stronger solution of alkaline cupric hydroxide (DEUEL and NEUKOM, 1949b). The not at all or but slightly branched chains possess circ. 70% β-1,4 and 30% 1,3 bonds, whereas their DP would lie between 100 and 400 (CHANDA et al., 1957). It differs from cellulose in being amorphous, in the smaller size of the molecules, and in the 1,3 bonds, and in these differences lies the explanation of its solubility. Although it is present in the lichen itself in the amorphous condition, part of it can be made to crystallize; it has not yet been studied by means of the electron microscope. Neither do we know any reagents for its identification under the microscope. It is generally assumed that it is produced by the lichen fungus, but there is no actual proof of this. The amount in which it is present, and the aspect of the transverse section of the lichen under the microscope make it probable that it is indeed part of the cell-wall, but definite proof seems to be lacking.

A more or less similar glucan has been isolated from oat bran. It is present in an amount of 3.4%, and 65% of its bonds are 1,4 and the rest 1,3 (ACKER et al., 1955). It seems probable that the glucan fractions which have been isolated from the meal of other cereals, are of a similar nature. It is as yet uncertain whether it is a cell-wall constituent.

In view of the presence of the β-1,4 bonds it is no wonder that lichenin is partly split by cellulase. So long as we are not sure that this enzyme splits the 1,3 bonds too, it does not seem necessary to use the customary name lichenase.

From the polyoses that remain in solution when the hot water extract is cooled down, *isolichenin* has been isolated (CHANDA et al., 1957). Its molecules proved to be unbranched and to consist of circ. 40 glucose monomers linked by α-1,3 and α-1,4 bonds in the proportion of 3 to 2. An aqueous solution stains a greenish-blue with potassium triiodide. In the lichen itself the cell-wall as well as the cell content stain blue. Lichenin and isolichenin are certainly not present in all lichens. ASPINALL et al. (1955) found in *Cladonia vulgaris* (reindeermoss) quite different polysaccharides.

In view of the very different constitution of the cell-wall in various fungi, green algae and *Cyanophyceae*, it is to be expected that further study of the lichens will reveal important differences in cell-wall composition. To this end not only the fraction that is soluble in water should be analysed, but also that which dissolves in alkali.

Laminarin is the name of the glucan that can be obtained from *Laminaria sp.* to an amount of 10—30% and from *Fucus sp.* to an amount of 5—10% of the dry weight. It can be extracted by means of hot water, but better with diluted acid, because in that case it is not polluted with alginic acid (cf. PAECH and TRACEY, 1955). The amount varies according to the season, and it functions as a reserve carbohydrate. It consists mainly of unbranched chains, and the latter are composed of glucose with β-1,3 bonds, their DP is in the neighbourhood of 20. If glucose was the only constituent, laminarin would not differ much from yeast glucan, but the considerable difference in solubility in water and in alkali, and the differences in the X-ray diagram (KREGER and MEEUSE, 1952) indicate important differences in structure. In fact, besides 1,3 bonds also 1,6 bonds have been found, and besides glucose, mannitol proves to be present (PEAT et al., 1953, 1955). In the native condition it is not crystalline. It does not dissolve in cuoxam, and microscopical reactions are unknown. Some bacteria and fungi appear to be provided with a hydrolysing laminarase (CHESTERS et al., 1955).

Amyloids of seeds. That the cell-walls in seeds sometimes stain blue with diluted potassium triiodide, was discovered already in 1838. Afterwards it was observed that the cell-walls in other parts of the seedplants and also in some algae may occasionally be stained in the same way. The substance that was responsible for this reaction, but of which otherwise nothing was known, was called amyloid (cf. Molisch, 1923; van Wisselingh, 1925; Tunmann-Rosenthaler, 1931; Hopman, 1930; Klein, 1932 III: 274). In some algae it proved to be cellulose II; in seeds a substituted glucan; in other cases the chemical constitution is still unknown.

It appears from a study by Kooiman (1957) that amyloid occurs far more frequently in seeds than was formerly assumed. It can easily be extracted with hot water, and from the strongly viscous solution that is obtained in this way, it can be precipitated by means of alkaline cupric hydroxide. When it is hydrolysed, it yields glucose, xylose and galactose; for the proportion in which these three sugars appear, in different kinds of seeds the following figures were found: $3:2:1$, $4:3:1$, $4:3:2$. In the amyloid of the seeds of the *Anonaceae* the amount of xylose is probably much smaller.

The cotyledons of *Tamarindus indica* appear to contain 40—50% amyloid. Its chemical nature was elucidated more completely than that of other amyloids (White and Rao, 1953; Kooiman, 1957, 1957a, 1958). It appears to consist of a β-1,4 glucan chain similar to that of cellulose, but only every fourth monomer is free as in cellulose. The others are connected with their C_6-atoms to a xylose unit. Half of the latter are furthermore bound to a galactose unit. This structure explains why amyloid can be hydrolysed partly by cellulase with the production of several types of oligosaccharides.

The solubility must be due to the large number of branches, which prevent an aggregation of the molecules. The amyloids of other seeds have much in common with that of *Tamarindus* and may be supposed to have an essentially similar chemical structure.

Amyloid dissolves in cuoxam, stains blue with diluted potassium triiodide, and assumes a purple colour when afterwards 66.5% (w/w) sulphuric acid is added; it does not stain with chlor-zinc-iodine. In the cell-wall it shows bire-fringence, but there are hardly any X-ray interferences, although preparations obtained by precipitation may be crystalline (Kooiman and Kreger, 1957). The birefringence in the wall must be birefringence of aligned molecules or of very small crystallites (cf. section 212).

142. MANNANS AND SUBSTITUTED MANNANS

In yeast and in the tubers of orchids, mannans have been found that are soluble in water and which differ in structure too from the mannans with which we have dealt under the heading hemicelluloses. The mannan that can be extracted from *Saccharomyces cerevisiae* by the aid of hot water or better with diluted alkali, is provided with 1,2 bonds, and the main chain is provided with many side-chains which consist also of mannose units. This mannan too dissolves in cuoxam, and is precipitated by Fehling's solution. The yeast cell-wall appears to consist for about one third of this mannan (Northcote and Horne, 1952; Roelofsen, 1953), but it shows no X-ray interferences of this substance. The different constitution explains why it is so much better soluble than the mannan of the ivory nut. It certainly is no cell-wall constituent that occurs in all yeasts and it has so far not been found in molds (Garzuly-Janke, 1940; Kreger, 1954).

The mannan that is present in the tubers of various orchids is also soluble in water. Its chemical constitution is characterized by the presence of acetyl groups, and it has a high DP, viz. circ. 1600. The first-named feature would be responsible for its solubility in water, the second for the high degree of viscosity of the solution.

Galactomannans, i.e. mannans with side-chains consisting of galactose, are, as a rule, soluble in water. This as well as the solubility of yeast-mannan is to be explained in the same way as the solubility of amyloid, which, as we have seen, is a cellulose with side-chains consisting of xylose and galactose.

The strongly thickened cell-walls in the cotyledons of numerous *Leguminosae*, especially of those belonging to the tribes *Cassieae* and *Eucaesalpinieae*, contain 35—40% galactomannan, which functions as a reserve carbohydrate. It is in the main a mannan similar to that of the ivory nut, which means that it consists of mannose monomers with β-1,4 bonds, but the C_6 of either each second, each third, each fourth or each fifth monomer is linked with a galactose unit. The galactose content varies therefore, at least mostly, between 20 and 35%. In *Trigonella foenum-graecum*, however, no less than five of each six mannose monomers are provided with a galactose side-chain, and in *Medicago sativa* and *Trifolium* part of the galactose would even occur in the main chain (ANDREWS et al., 1952a, b). Recently a galactomannan has been found also in the seedcoat of one of the *Leguminosae*, viz. in that of the soybean (WHISTLER and SAARNIO, 1957).

The best-known representatives of the galactomannans are those of *Ceratonia siliqua* and of *Cyamopsis tetragonolobus*, that of the first with 20%, and that of the second with 35% galactose. The DP appears to amount to 1000—2000, which explains the high degree of viscosity.

Galactomannan has also been found in the soft endosperm of the palm *Borassus flabellifer* (SUBRAHMANYAN et al., 1956). This is so far the only definite instance of a galactomannan occurring outside the *Leguminosae*, but the constitution of the cell-walls in other palm seeds with soft endosperm, e.g.those of *Arenga saccharifera*, has not yet been studied. According to reports of SCHULZE dating from 1890, galactomannan would also be present in seeds of *Coffea*, *Phoenix*, *Elaeis* and *Cocos nucifera*, but this is with regard to the seeds of *Phoenix* undoubtedly erroneous (cf. section 1332), and with regard to the other seeds doubtful.

Galactomannans dissolve not only in water and alkali, but also in cuoxam, are precipitated by alkaline cupric hydroxide and by borax (DEUEL and NEUKOM, 1949a, b, 1954), and do not stain with potassium triiodide or iodine-sulphuric acid.

143. GALACTANS AND SUBSTITUTED GALACTANS

In all higher plants galactan, araban and pectin always occur together; when the pectin content increases, the amount of the two other substances increases, as a rule, at the same time. The three substances nevertheless occur in widely varying proportions. As the position of the OH-groups in the pyranose ring is in all three the same, it has sometimes been assumed that they are of common biochemical origin. At first it was generally assumed that the molecules were linked, but this does not fit in very well with the inconstant proportion. Commercial pectin preparations always contain considerable amounts of galactan and araban, up to circ. 20% of each. All three dissolve easily in water; pectin molecules, however, dissolve only when they are not mutually bound in the cell-wall by means of Ca- or Mg-atoms. The separation of the three substances is carried out by precipitating pectin in the form of

Ca-pectate, and adding a critical amount of alcohol to the filtrate; galactan
is in this way precipitated before araban. None of them dissolves in cuoxam,
nor are they precipitated by alkaline cupric hydroxide, so that in this way
no separation can be effected.

A sufficiently pure galactan preparation has been obtained from the seeds
of lupins, which are relatively rich in it. It appeared to consist of unbranched
chains of galactose units with β-1,4 bonds, and to have a DP of circ. 100. From
the seeds of *Strychnos nux-vomica* (ANDREWS et al., 1954) a similar galactan
has been obtained, but this one appeared to have a slight amount of galactose
(3%) in side-chains.

Araban and galactan may also be obtained, by extraction with hot water,
from coniferous wood, of which it is known that it contains but a small amount
of pectin (0.5—1.5%). The wood of *Larix*-species may even yield up to 20%
of a mixture of araban and galactan. The two could not yet be separated
in a satisfactory way, so that some authors assume that they are at least
partly present in the form of a hetero-polymer, an arabo-galactan. The
galactan is different from that of the lupin seeds, for it has β-1,6 bonds and
short side-chains.

Rhodophyceae always contain substituted galactans. A survey of the polysaccharides that are found especially in marine algae has been given by MORI
(1953). The most important polymers of galactose in these plants are agar
and carrageenin.

Agar is mainly obtained from species of *Gelidium* occurring in the Pacific,
which in the dry condition contain circ. 40% of this substance. The structure
is as yet incompletely elucidated, but it can not be doubted that it is in the
main an unbranched chain composed of at least some decades of d-galactose
units with β-1,3 bonds. One to each ten units is a l-galactose unit with a
1,4 bond and with the OH-group of C_6 esterified by sulphate; one valency of
the SO_4-group is linked either to Na or to Ca. The Ca-ion forms links between
the chains when the agar gelates; in an acid medium agar does not gelate
because the Ca is displaced by H.

Carrageenin comes from *Chondrus crispus*, which occurs especially in the
Atlantic Ocean. In dried condition it contains 70% of a substance that
produces a slimy solution in water; 47% of the latter dissolves already in cold
water and does not gelate. The fraction that dissolves in hot water only,
contains more Ca, and does gelate to some extent, but not so readily as agar
does. Both fractions would, according to recent investigations (BAYLEY, 1955),
contain two components, one with unbranched or but slightly branched
chains composed of galactose-sulphate with 1,3 bonds, and another one with
a chain composed alternately of two galactose-sulphate units and one galactose-
anhydride and to each six monomers a side-chain consisting of a single galactose
unit. The sulphate content of carrageenin is therefore considerably higher than
that of agar. It is noteworthy that agar as well as carrageenin contain d- as
well as l-galactose.

From the *Phaeophyceae* too a sulphate containing polysaccharide is known,
viz. *fucoidin*, a polymer of l-fucose-monosulphate (fucose itself is 6-deoxy-l-
galactose). It is a slimy substance which forms part of the cell-wall, and may
be seen when the fronds of these algae are broken. It is present in an amount
of 2—9%. It is usually obtained by extraction with diluted acid; in this way
pollution with alginic acid is prevented.

As the marine *Chlorophyceae* too are provided with sulphate-containing polysaccharides, whereas the fresh-water representatives of this group seem to be free of them, it may be that there exists a causal relation between the presence of these sulphate-esters and marine life. JONES and PEAT (1942) thought that this relation might be found in the mode of synthesis.

144. VARIOUS POLYOSES

Araban. That this polymer is very often met with in company of galactan and pectin, has already been mentioned. In order to separate it from galactan use is made of its greater solubility in diluted alcohol. The materials from which in the industry pectin is made, viz. apple pulp, *Citrus* peels, beet pulp, may also serve for preparing araban. Ground *Arachis* seeds that have been deprived of fat, are relatively rich in araban, and so is the wood of conifers.

The arabans from *Arachis* as well as those that have been isolated from pectin preparations, consist probably of l-arabinofuranose units with a-1,5 bonds and alternately provided with a single arabinose unit as side-chain.

Seed-coats. Some seed-coats become slimy on wetting. This is due to a cell-wall substance which is usually confined to the epidermis, and here it is, as a rule, found in the secondary layers, sometimes in those of the outer wall only, sometimes in all walls. The cell-lumen may have become very small or even inconspicuous. The substance that becomes slimy on wetting is present from the beginning; transformation of an originally normal cell-wall into a slime producing one has never been observed. When the seed comes into contact with water, the slime swells to such a degree that the enveloping outer layer bursts, and the slime oozes out. Slime-cells are usually readily recognizable by a structureless or but faintly lamellate hyalin mass. Exuded slime is difficult to see when the cells are lying in water. It becomes better visible when they are mounted in diluted Indian ink. The swelling may be prevented by immersing in diluted alcohol or in solutions, e.g. of sugar or of glycerol, with a high osmotic value. Various methods of staining and other kinds of reaction have been given by MOLISCH (1923) and by TUNMANN-ROSENTHALER (1931), but they do not tell us much about the chemical constitution.

Well-known slimy seeds are those of *Linum usitatissimum, Plantago arenaria, Cydonia vulgaris, Lepidium sativum, Cobaea scandens,* and *Salvia* species. Details with regard to the chemical constitution of the slime of the first three seeds are given by MANTELL (1947), and of all of them by WHISTLER and SMART (1953). The slime of *Linum usitatissimum* and of *Plantago arenaria* dissolves entirely in water, but that of the other seeds contains some cellulose; *Cydonia* slime 24%, *Lepidium* slime 18% on a dry weight basis. The microfibrils of the cellulose in these slimes are embedded in a structureless matrix of the slimy substance. They are quite clear when studied by the aid of the electron microscope, and they appear to be very long, of uniform thickness and provided with obtuse ends; they do not anastomose, and show a tendency to form flat bundles, as is common with cellulose microfibrils, cf. fig. 18. According to MÜHLETHALER (1950c), the microfibrils would sometimes already be oriented from the beginning, but it seems that this conclusion is not fully justified, as the preparation method was not so that an artificial orientation must be regarded as entirely excluded.

TREIBER (1953, 1957: 257) seems to be of opinion that the cellulose was precipitated within the slime, and that the X-ray diagram of this fraction is not identical with that of normal cellulose I. MEYER and MARK (1953: 493) apparently think that the cellulose-containing slimes consist of a mixture of

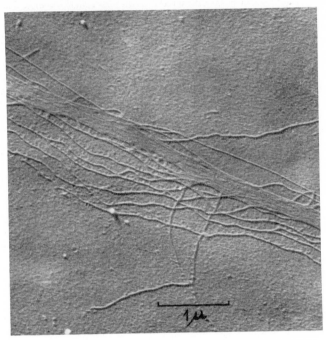

Fig. 18. Slime of *Lepidium sativum*, as seen under the electron microscope. Microfibrils of cellulose in a structureless mass (from MÜHLETHALER, 1950c).

cellulose molecules and molecules of a different kind, but it is not clear how they arrived at this conclusion.

In *Linum* slime, which does not contain cellulose, many oblong granules have been observed electronmicroscopically, fig. 19a.

On mild acid hydrolysis the structureless substance disappeared, and the granules aggregated to form a mesh of anastomosing threads of varying thickness, quite unlike a mesh of microfibrils, cf. fig. 19b. The process was considered illustrative of the formation of microfibrils, but the present author is of a different opinion (cf. section 114).

After complete hydrolysis *Linum* slime yields equal amounts of galacturonic acid, rhamnose, galactose and xylose, in addition to considerable amounts of aldobionic and of aldotrionic acid, substances that are not readily hydrolysed. The slime of *Plantago arenaria* (known as dark psillium) is also cellulose-free, but contains a much larger amount of xylose (HIRST et al., 1954). Other slimes too appeared to contain, as a rule, besides a uronic acid two or three pentoses (xylose, arabinose, rhamnose), and sometimes galactose and/or glucose. All these slimes are very probably mixtures of hetero-polymers (cf. e.g. ERSKINE and JONES, 1956).

Cereal "gums". From flour of wheat, barley, rye, rice and other cereals, polysaccharides could be extracted with water at room temperature, which are said to be cell-wall constituents, although there seems to be no good reason for this assumption. When they are subjected to hydrolysis, they yield besides glucose, mainly xylose and arabinose. These substances have received

a fairly good deal of attention, as they are supposed to play a part in the manufacture of bread, beer, etc. They are usually called "gums".

"Wheat gum" is probably a mixture of a strongly branched arabo-xylan and a glucan (GILLES and SMITH, 1956; MONTGOMERY and SMITH, 1955), and "barley gum" seems to be similar (PREECE and MACKENZIE, 1952). In malt the "gum" is further disintegrated than in barley, and malt itself contains hydrolysing enzymes. As stated above, oat contains a substance resembling lichenin (ACKER et al., 1955), and it seems probable that the glucans that are present in other cereal "gums" are of a similar nature.

Lower plants. With the exception of the slimes of the bacteria, the slimes of the lower plants have received but little attention (cf. WHISTLER and SMART, 1953; TUNMANN - ROSENTHALER, 1951). *Ulva lactuca* is said to contain a polysaccharide with sulphate groups; it would consist mainly of rhamnose, but monomers of another composition would be present too (KYLIN, 1946; BRADING et al., 1954). A similar polysaccharide with sulphate groups is known from

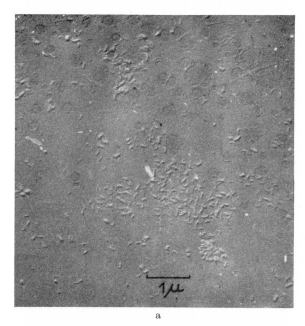

a

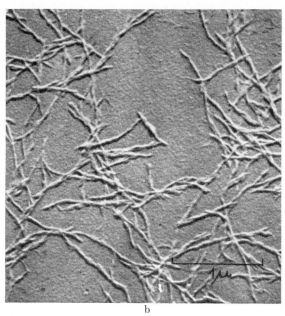

b

Fig. 19. Electronmicrographs of: a: seed-coat slime of *Linum usitatissimum*, showing granules of unknown constitution embedded in a structureless mass; b: as in a, after a mild hydrolysis, showing aggregation of the granules (from MÜHLETHALER, 1950c).

Cladophora rupestris, another marine alga (FISHER and PERCIVAL, 1955).

The slime of various *Cyanophyceae* has been studied by means of the electron microscope (FREY-WYSSLING and STECHER, 1954; METZNER, 1955; DRAWERT and METZNER, 1956; NIKLOWITZ and DREWS, 1956). In several instances the presence of microfibrils was noted; the latter strongly resembled the microfibrils of cellulose, and reacted in the same way to iodine reagents. The slime itself shows no structure. HOUGH et al.(1952) found in the hydrolysate of *Nostoc* slime rhamnose, xylose, glucose, galactose and uronic acid. Alkaline extracts of *Oscillatoria* have also been studied, but here it is unknown from what part of the cell the polysaccharides are derived.

15. Polyuronides

Polyuronides are polymers that consist either entirely or for the greater part of uronic acid. In the cell-walls of plants these substances are present only in the form of pectic substances and of alginic acid. The pectic substances are polymers consisting of galacturonic acid, whereas alginic acid is a polymer of mannuronic acid. Hetero-polymers which contain uronic acid, have been mentioned in the parts dealing with the hemicelluloses and with the polyoses that are soluble in water.

151. PECTIC SUBSTANCES

A very detailed review of the chemical and physical properties of the pectic substances, and of the analytical methods, preparation, industrial use, enzymatic decomposition, etc. is to be found in KERTESZ (1951); less detailed surveys in HOTTENROTH (1951), WHISTLER and SMART (1953), DEUEL and STUTZ (1958) and HENGLEIN (1958). PAECH and TRACEY (1955 II: 226) confine themselves to the methods of identification and estimation. In connection with their industrial importance the pectic substances have received a good deal of attention, so that we must confine ourselves here to a short summary of what is actually known.

Although there are gradual transitions, three groups are distinguished, viz. protopectin, pectin and pectic acid.

Protopectin is the cell-wall constituent that does not dissolve in neutral hot or cold water.

Pectin in the restricted sense is the cell-wall constituent that can be extracted with hot water and partly even with cold water. It is the soluble product that is used for making jams and jellies. Between one and three fourth of the acid groups are esterized with methanol. The name pectin, however, is often used for the whole complex of pectic substances.

Pectic acid has all its acid groups free or but a few of them esterized with methanol. It dissolves in water only in the form of pectate, and to this end needs therefore the addition of bases of e.g. Na, K or NH_4. It does not occur as acid in nature, but only as pectate probably as Ca- and Mg-pectate.

1511. Occurrence

In the *Cormophyta*, perhaps with the exception of the *Bryophyta*, pectic substances are like cellulose present in all cell-walls, but the amount differs in the various species, and in different tissues too. This is seen in the accompanying table.

Table V. Amount of pectic substances in various cell-walls.

Cell-wall in:	% of dry weight
wood	0,5—1.5
bark	7-30
cambium	24
cotton, pr. wall	9
cotton, sec. wall	0.7
Avena coleoptile	1
potato	14
apple pulp	15—25
beet pulp	25—30
Citrus peel (albedo)	20—50
Petasites, collenchyma	45

In lower plants pectic substances have not been identified with certainty. It is true that the older literature contains several positive statements (cf. van Wisselingh, 1925: 72), but the latter are all based on the observation that cell-walls can be stained with ruthenium red and with other cationic dyes, and eventually on the fact that the substance that is responsible for the reaction can be removed by heating in glycerol to a temperature of 200—300° C, but neither of these reactions can be regarded as conclusive evidence.

It seems very probable that pectic substances, and especially pectin itself, are not confined to the cell-wall, but that they may also be present in the form of solutes in the cell-sap, and perhaps even in the protoplasm too. This seems to follow from the presence of large amounts of pectin in the press-sap e.g. of fruits. This amount increases, as a rule, during the process of ripening. As the total amount of pectic substances does not increase at all or to a slight extent only, and as the amount of protopectin usually undergoes a decrease, it seems plausible to assume that the pectin in the vacuole is derived entirely or partly from the protopectin in the cell-wall. As a matter of fact, the cell-walls of e.g. overripe apples, in contrast to those of unripe ones, prove to be only faintly stainable with ruthenium red.

The pectic substances in the cell-wall are mainly confined to the middle lamella and to the primary walls. This follows from the fact that they are present in large amounts in the cell-walls of meristematic cells, from the localization in the cell-walls of the staining with ruthenium red and similar dyes, and from the fact that the connection between the cells can, at least in non-lignified tissues, be disrupted by means of an enzyme preparation which attacks protopectin. In epidermis cells too the primary wall is richer in pectin than the secondary layers; this follows from the fact that young cotton hairs contain much more of it than the full-grown ones (cf. table 1), from the high pectin content of the outer layer of root hairs, from the increase in pectin content and the decrease in cellulose content of the outer epidermal wall in outward direction, etc.

It is noteworthy that in full-grown cells protuberances consisting of pectin may appear in places where the cell-walls withdraw from each other in order to form intercellular spaces. They have been described by various investigators (cf. Küster, 1956: 702), but were figured for the first time by Carlquist (1956).

In the secondary layers pectic substances are often not or difficult to detect, but tissues that are rich in pectin, like collenchyma and the peel of the orange, form an exception to this rule. In collenchyma cells the various wall layers differ in their pectin content (ANDERSON, 1927a; MAJUMDAR and PRESTON, 1941; PRESTON and DUCKWORTH, 1946), and the same state of things is found in flax fibres (HOCK, 1942).

1512. Chemical and Physical Properties

All pectic substances contain as main constituent chain molecules composed of d-galacturonic acid with a-1,4 bonds and with an average DP which in the original condition reaches a value of some hundreds. Preparations have been obtained with a DP of 1800 (SCHLUBACH and HOFFMANN-WALDECK, 1949). This *pectic acid* has an acid reaction and is insoluble, but it gives soluble salts with e.g. Na, K or NH_4. In order to solve the pectic acid, it has therefore to be neutralized with bases which contain these ions. With some other metal ions, e.g. Ca, Ba, Mg, Al, Pb, Cu, Fe, insoluble salts are formed.

Pectic acid

In preparations that have not been chemically changed, part of the carboxyl groups of the pectic acid are esterized with methanol. If this has happened with about one fourth of them, which means that the CH_3O-groups constitute circ. 4% of the total weight, the substance may be called *pectin*, because in that case it proves to be soluble in water without previous neutralization. This is the so-called low-methoxyl pectin. Because of the large number of carboxyl-groups it does not dissolve in a strongly acid medium, e.g. at a pH below 3; at a higher pH it dissolves only if there are not too much metal-ions that form insoluble pectates, such as Ca and Mg. In solutions of low-methoxyl pectin gelation may therefore be brought about by addition of small quantities of e.g. Ca-ions.

Ordinary pectin as used for jams etc., also called high-methoxyl pectin, contains 8—12% methoxyl. As the theoretical maximum content is 16.3%, it is clear that in the ordinary pectin only 50—75% of the carboxyl-groups are esterized. Under certain circumstances, however, pectin with 15% methoxyl has been obtained (SCHLUBACH and HOFFMANN-WALDECK, 1949). High-methoxyl pectin dissolves as well in a strongly acid medium as in the presence of the metal ions with which low-methoxyl pectin forms insoluble salts; it dissolves the more easily the larger the number of methoxyl-groups. Some cell-walls contain a large amount of easily soluble pectin. GRIEBEL (cf. KERTESZ l.c.:265) described how in sections through ripe fruits, e.g. of *Pirus domestica*, especially near the intercellular spaces, globules of pectin are formed, which continually increase in size. In the ripening fruit of certain *Citrus* varieties the pectin in the albedo imbibes so much water that the cell-walls become gelatinous (cf. KERTESZ l.c.: 305). These swelling processes are perhaps of a similar nature as the swelling which cell-walls of marine algae undergo on loss of turgor (cf. section 2421).

High-methoxyl pectin gelates only when the two following conditions are fulfilled: the pH must have a value between 2.5 and 3.5, and the solution must contain 50 to 70% sugar, conditions which are fulfilled in manufacturing jam.

The chemical structure of *protopectin* is not precisely known, but the possibility to dissolve it almost quantitatively in the form of pectin by heating it e.g. with 0.2% HCl or with 1% ammonium oxalate is an indication that it consists of a network of pectin molecules that are united with each other by means of metal ions; these metal ions are removed by HCl, and form salts with the oxalate ion. As the cell-walls, and especially their middle lamellae, always contain Ca and sometimes also Mg and Fe, it is plausible to regard these ions as responsible for the transformation of pectin into protopectin. The pectin can be set free by other Ca-binders too, e.g. by citrate, polyphosphate, amino-tetra-acetic acid derivates and other substances which easily form chelates with metals. If acid is used for dissolving the pectin, it is desirable to add a Ca-binder, because otherwise small amounts of Ca-pectate are left behind.

Protopectin can also be dissolved completely by heating it with diluted alkali, e.g. with 0.05% NaOH or with 1% Na_2CO_3. In an alkaline medium the methylester bonds, and eventually also other ester bonds of the protopectin are rapidly hydrolysed. At the same time a depolymerization takes place, and Ca in the pectates is replaced by alkali ions; the resulting solution therefore contains low-polymeric alkali-pectate and further araban, galactan and hemicelluloses.

The possibility that the pectin molecules in protopectin may be united in other manners too, e.g. by ester or ether bonds, is not excluded. It has also been suggested that there may be ester bonds via phosphate (HENGLEIN et al., 1949). Most probably there are also bonds of this kind or at least H-bonds with hemicelluloses, especially with galactan and araban, which, as has been stated already in our discussion of the hemicelluloses, always accompany the pectin. The greater part of these substances can be removed by fractionated precipitation by means of alcohol (araban dissolves best in the latter); the pectin may be precipitated in the form of Ca-pectate. Hemicelluloses, however, are partly coprecipitated, and special methods are required to obtain a really pure pectic acid with more than 99% of the required carboxyl groups. The purity of this product proves that the earlier opinion according to which pectin would be a hetero-polymer of methyl-galacturonate, arabinose and galactose, is incorrect.

The protopectin which is present in lignified cell-walls, is probably linked to lignin, as it is very difficult to extract it directly from the wood, though it is easily obtained from the latter after delignification.

The protopectin network is broken down in a quite different way by the enzyme *pectinase* or polygalacturonase, which splits the glycosidic bonds. This too leads to a soluble product, but the solution is not so complete that this method can be used for estimating the amount of protopectin; to that end the extraction with acid or with alkali has to be used. The fact that the protopectin in ripening fruits gradually becomes more readily soluble, and that the mesocarp in this way disintegrates, is ascribed to the action of this enzyme. The presence of the latter has indeed been proved in certain fruits, e.g. in the tomato (cf. KERTESZ l.c.: 347) and in the avocado pear (McCREADY and REEVE, 1955), perhaps in the pear too (WEURMAN, 1954), but in numerous other fruits and in other objects the search has been in vain. Even its presence in malt, which had been regarded as fully established, has been denied (SLOEP, 1928), and in the medlar fruit (*Mespilus germanica*), the fruit that is known to undergo disintegration within the space of half an hour when the cells are killed by means that leave the enzymes intact (SLOEP l.c.), its presence could not be put beyond doubt (ROELOFSEN, 1954). It is true that OZAWA and OKAMOTO (1952) are of opinion that they have proved its presence in various objects in which others could not find it, but this requires confirmation. The explanation of these contradictory results may be firstly, that the pectinase is in many instances inactivated by the presence of inhibitors (WEURMAN, 1954), secondly, that the growth of microorganisms has not always been prevented sufficiently. In fungi, bacteria, and lower animals like snails, pectinase appears to be a very common enzyme.

The action of pectinase is, as a rule, confined to the splitting of bonds between those galacturonic-acid units that are not esterized. The methyl-ester groups have to be split off previously by another hydrolysing enzyme, viz. pectin-esterase, which usually accompanies the pectinase. It is rather remarkable that this enzyme is present in considerable quantity in nearly every tissue of the higher plants, also where no pectinase could be demonstrated and where no decomposition of pectin takes place. The main function of this enzyme perhaps lies in another field. In fungi a pectinase capable of hydrolysing bonds between esterified units has been found in addition to the normal type of enzyme. A recent review of the findings in this field is that of DEMAIN and PFAFF (1957).

Until recently it was generally believed that native pectin does not show birefringence, that it does not cause X-ray interference, and that it must therefore be regarded as amorphous. Until recently in most cell-walls of higher plants no other X-ray interference than that of cellulose was observed; and this applied even to the cell-walls of collenchyma cells, which contain 45% pectin (PRESTON and DUCKWORTH,1946). However, when the cellulose and at least the greater part of the hemicellulose from a collenchyma strand were removed, a pectin skeleton was obtained which ROELOFSEN and KREGER (1951) found to be negatively birefringent with reference to the axis of the cells of the strand. This negative birefringence, however, was seen only when the prepara-tion was immersed in a liquid with a refractive index between 1.5 and 1.6. In liquids with a lower or with a higher refractive index positive birefringence was noted. This means that the pectin molecules are negatively birefringent with reference to their axis, but that this remains usually hidden because of the presence of a stronger positive rodlet-birefringence.

These pectin skeletons moreover showed the distinct pectin X-ray diagram which was already known from artificial pectin fibres. The observation that at least one interference characteristic for pectin could also be detected in dried and even in semidried native collenchyma strands seems to be particul-arly important. It shows that the greater part of the pectin molecules in collenchyma cells must be oriented lengthwise and forms, at least partly, crystalline regions in a similar way as cellulose does. This implies that not only the pectin of pectin skeletons but also that of the native wall, at least in collenchyma cells, should exhibit birefringence. It is no wonder that this has never been observed, not even in cellulose-free pectin-rich layers such as the middle lamella, since the birefringence of the cellulose in the adjacent layers is so much stronger that diffuse light emanating from these layers, irradiates the cellulose-free ones so strongly that such faint optical effects remain hidden. Moreover in many cases the pectin molecules may lack orientation.

Electronmicrographs of the pectin skeletons revealed that they consist of tiny short microfibrils, cf. fig. P 20. The crystallinity of pectin in the native wall indicates that the microfibrils seen in the skeletons will also occur in the native wall. Here they will probably be aligned in a more nearly axial direction than they are in the skeletons, because the latter shorten considerably during the extraction of the cellulose.

The finding of microfibrillar crystalline pectin in collenchyma walls evidently does not prove that pectin is also fibrillar and crystalline in walls which contain a smaller amount of this substance or in which its molecules may lack orientation.

Already at an earlier date birefringence and crystallinity had been observed in artificial pectin fibres that had been obtained by squirting an aqueous solution into ethanol or when a solution had dried up in the form of a film (VAN ITERSON, 1933; WÜHRMAN and PILNIK, 1945; PALMER et al., 1945, 1947). In gels of Ca-pectate that were oriented in a different way these findings were confirmed by STERLING (1957 b). The rod-like crystallites possess a negative birefringence proper to the molecules, and a positive rodlet-birefringence that may be stronger. The rodlet-birefringence sinks down to its lowest value when the imbibition liquid has a refraction index of circ. 1.5, which is equal to that of pectin (that of pectic acid is 1.53). The negative intrinsic birefringence is due to the transverse orientation of the carboxyl- or ester-groups.

The X-ray interferences corresponding to 8, 4.2 and 3.1 Å that were found in pectin skeletons agree with those that were noted in artificial fibres (PALMER et al., l.c.). This means that the length of the b-axis of the unit cell (identity period along the axis of the molecule) is 13.1 Å, and that the unit cell, which would comprise 4 chains, contains in each chain three uronic acid units, i.e. 12 uronic acid units altogether. This structure is therefore entirely different from that which was found in cellulose. By absorption of water the distance between the chains may be increased.

With regard to the way in which the pectin molecules are formed in the plant, we are completely ignorant. As pectin occurs mainly in the cell-walls of meristematic cells, it has been suggested that it may have a function in the surface growth of the cell-wall. It might enable the cellulose microfibrils to glide along each other. It seems that at least in *Avena* coleoptiles this function may be taken over by hemicelluloses, since here the pectin content is small, cf. table 1.

1513. Isolation, Estimation and Identification

For the methods of preparing and purifying pectin that have briefly been mentioned in the preceding part, we may refer to KERTESZ (1951), PAECH and TRACEY (1955: 226) and HOTTENROTH (1951). In these works the various methods of estimation and analysis and their reliability are also dealt with. Not yet mentioned is the colorimetric method by the aid of carbazol (McCOMB and McCREADY, 1952).

For the identification of pectin in solutions a number of reactions described by KERTESZ (1951) may be used. None of these reactions is in itself sufficient when pectin is accompanied by other carbohydrates, but when several of them are applied, the result proves to be entirely satisfactory. The most suitable procedure is to split the pectin in galacturonic acid and methanol, and to react on these products. As the glycosidic linkage of the uronic acids is very resistent, hydrolysis by means of an acid may lead to considerable losses, as a large part of the uronic acid is decomposed. For this reason hydrolysis by means of an enzyme is to be preferred. An excellent method of identifying uronic acid is that by means of paper chromatography, but it does not differentiate between glucuronic acid, galacturonic acid and mannuronic acid (JERMYN and TOMKINS, 1950). There are, however, various reactions by means of which these acids may be distinguished (cf. PAECH and TRACEY, 1955: 49).

Very characteristic for pectin, but unfortunately very little sensitive, is the formation of a gel of calcium pectate by adding a plant juice that contains calcium and pectin-esterase, e.g. press juice of clover. This reaction has been applied already in 1840 by FRÉMY in order to demonstrate the presence of pectin-esterase.

Rather characteristic is the reaction with thorium nitrate according to BRYANT (cf. KERTESZ, l.c.; DEUEL and NEUKOM, 1954). McDOWELL (1955) describes a sensitive reaction by the aid of which dissolved pectate and alginate can be identified. According to McCREADY and REEVE (1955) a characteristic reaction on esterized pectin is the formation of an insoluble red compound after conversion in hydroxamic acid and addition of ferric chloride.

The reagent that is most often used for the identification of pectin in sections under the microscope is a solution of 0.02% ruthenium sesquichloride with a little ammonia; this reaction was discovered in 1889 by MANGIN. When the staining is completed, the section is washed with hot water. The reaction is not specific, and has to be supplemented by observations on the way the sections stain after the pectin has been removed, e.g. with ammonium oxalate (cf. KERTESZ, l.c.: 205), and after the non-pectin has been extracted, e.g. with cuoxam. Other substances like protein, lignin, hemicelluloses, slimes that contain uronic acid, alginic acid, and the polysaccharides that contain sulphate, are also stained with ruthenium red. Likewise e.g. yeast cell-walls after treatment with alkali, although these cell-walls certainly do not contain pectin. Very probably also the acidic precursors of cutin (cf. sections 171, 2362). However, if the walls do not stain with ruthenium red, we may be sure that there is little or no pectin. When much hemicellulose is present, as e.g. in some meristematic walls, the staining proceeds slowly and may remain faint (MERICLE and GORDON WHALEY, 1953).

The results obtained with the other stains that to this end have been recommended by MANGIN (cf. TUNMANN-ROSENTHALER: 931), do not prove that they are more specific. An intricate reaction on uronides in sections was described by KRAJCINOVIC (1954), but it has as yet not been sufficiently tested. This applies also to the reaction of McCREADY and REEVE that was mentioned above.

More or less characteristic is the fact that the pectin skeleton which is obtained with cuoxam, dissolves at room temperature in diluted ammonia, alkali and ammonium oxalate, as also the very slight negative birefringence which oriented pectin shows when mounted in a liquid with a refractive index of 1.5—1.6, but this seems of little practical value. Maceration of tissues by means of 1% ammonium oxalate, with a little toluene added to prevent the development of bacteria, may in our opinion be regarded as proof of the presence of middle lamellae containing pectin. Negative results however, do not mean that there is no pectin.

152. ALGINIC ACID

For the literature on this substance we refer to WHISTLER and SMART (1953), MANTELL (1947), and BLACK (1948).

Alginic acid is found only in the cell-walls of the *Phaeophyceae*. The amount varies between 13 and 45% of the dry weight, and depends not only on the species but also on the season. The most suitable sources for the isolation of this substance are *Macrocystis* and *Laminaria*; *Fucus* is much less suitable.

Alginic acid, like pectin, is mainly located in the middle lamellae and in the primary wall, which are here very strongly thickened. The secondary layers contain cellulose. It looks very probable that alginic acid too is insolubilized within the wall by means of Ca and Mg bridges, as by means of substances like Na-citrate a strong swelling and, at higher temperatures, even a dissolving can be obtained (ANDERSEN, 1955; Moss, 1948).

Alginic acid

Alginic acid consists of chains composed of d-mannuronic acid[1]) units with β-1,4 bonds, and has a DP which may reach a value of some hundreds. It is therefore very similar to pectic acid. It is likewise not directly soluble in water, but only after being converted into an alkali salt. When acid is added to the solution, it gelates at a pH of 3. For this reason the seaweeds are preferably extracted in a slightly alkaline medium, and the alginic acid itself is obtained from this solution by acidification. It proves to be nearly pure, in contrast to pectin, which is always accompanied by certain polysaccharides. With alkaline earths, Cu, Cr, Al, etc. it forms salts that are also insoluble; Mg-alginate, however, is, in contrast to Mg-pectate, soluble. These salts can be dissolved in alkali, to which preferably substances are to be added by which the metal ions are bound. Like all other uronides, alginic acid proves to be very resistant against hydrolysis by means of acid; the conditions have to be so severe, that a large part of the mannuronic acid that is set free, is destroyed. Alginases are known to occur in *Bacteria*, *Myxomycetes* (KOOIMAN, 1954; CHESTERS et al., 1955) and *Invertebrates* (OSHIMA, 1931), but not in fungi, nor in higher plants and animals.

Only a short time ago (ANDERSEN, 1955) it was found that the alginic acid in the cell-wall shows birefringence, and that the latter is, in contrast to that of pectic acid, positive with regard to the direction of the molecular axis. The effect of this intrinsic birefringence is increased by that of a rodlet-birefringence. A typical difference between the birefringence of the alginic acid in the middle lamella and in the primary wall and that of the cellulose in the secondary layers, is that the first increases when acid is added, and that it decreases when it begins to swell, e.g. under the influence of sodium citrate. This provides us with a means to study the localisation of the alginic acid. It is still unknown whether the latter is present in the cell-wall in a crystalline condition or not.

Artificial fibres of alginic acid and of alginates are crystalline and birefringent; the birefringence is positive, just as that of the alginic acid in the

---

[1]) and L-guluronic acid (cf. WHISTLER and KERBY, 1959)

cell-wall. The positive birefringence of these fibres is the more remarkable as artificial fibres of the very similar pectic acid are negatively birefringent. PALMER et al. (1947) and STERLING (1957c) have tried to explain this difference.

In order to estimate the amount of alginic acid the same methods are to be taken into consideration as in the case of pectin, viz. precipitation in the form of the calcium salt, colorimetry according to the carbazol method, and the estimation of the carbon dioxide that is formed when the material is boiled with concentrated hydrochloric acid. Just as in the case of pectin, the last-named method is the most reliable one (JENSEN and SUNDE, 1955).

The paper-chromatographic method that has been applied to hydrolysates of pectin, can be used also for the identification of alginic acid; differences in behaviour between the uronic acids have been reported by PAECH and TRACEY (1955: 49). McDOWELL (1955) describes a sensitive qualitative reaction on dissolved alginate; it rests on its precipitation with Ca-ions and the possibility to stain the precipitate by means of a basic stain. Pectate reacts in the same way, but the Mg-salt of the latter is insoluble, whereas Mg-alginate is soluble. DEUEL and NEUKOM (1954) describe its behaviour with regard to various salts.

For reactions under the microscope ruthenium red may be used, just as in the case of pectic acid and with similar restrictions. The optical method which we described above, can also be applied.

With regard to solvents too its behaviour is the same as that of pectin; it is therefore insoluble in cuoxam and in acid, soluble in alkali and in a neutral medium which is free of precipitating cations.

16. Lignin

In recent years a good deal of study has been devoted to the chemical and physical properties of lignin (the name is derived from lignum, i.e. wood), and to the way in which it probably is synthesized in the plant. Detailed reviews have been given by BRAUNS in a book (1952) as well as in chapters contributed by him to the works of WISE and JAHN (1952: 409, 1215) and of OTT and SPURLIN (1954: 480). FREUDENBERG has devoted special attention to the biosynthesis (1954); we also mention HÄGGLUND's book (1951).

Lignin is found in all *Pteridophyta* and *Anthophyta*; in the *Bryophyta* it has, if present, an aberrant structure (KLEYN, 1932 III: 267; TREIBER, 1957: 446). In lower plants it does not occur, although on account of results obtained with staining methods it has in the older literature been assumed that it would be present here too; in animals it is completely absent (VAN WISSELINGH, 1925: 132).

Lignin is known only as a constituent of the cell-wall; the largest amount is found in the middle lamella (60—90% in wood); the percentage decreases very strongly when we pass from the primary wall to the secondary layers, and in the latter it shows a further decrease towards the cell-lumen (down to 10% in wood; A. I. BAILEY, 1936; LANGE, 1954a; TREIBER l.c.). This is well shown by the entirely different way in which the various layers are attacked by fungi causing brown rot and by those causing white rot. The former preferentially attack the carbohydrates, the latter the lignin. This may e.g. be seen in the photos of MEIER obtained by means of the electron microscope (1955); they are reproduced in fig. 21, (cf. also ASUNMAA, 1955).

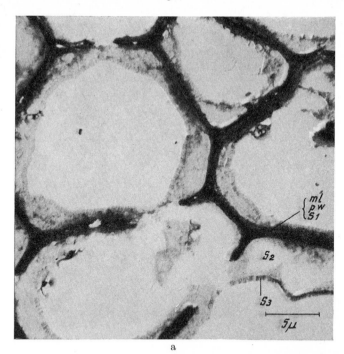

a

The *lignin content* of hardwoods is usually 19—25%, although in some tropical woods 30% and more has been found. Softwoods contain 25—30%. Spring wood contains more of it than summer wood, because it contains a smaller percentage of secondary layers. In the bark sometimes a much higher lignin content has been reported, but these figures are unreliable, as no sufficient attention has been paid to sources of error, like the presence of tannin, suberin, etc. In herbaceous plants the lignin content varies strongly, and depends to a large extent on the stage of development, as in the course of the latter an ever larger part of the tissues becomes lignified, e.g. the interfascicular parenchyma.

The native lignin is sometimes called *protolignin*, in order to differentiate it from the isolated lig-

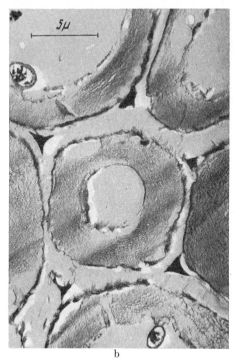

b

Fig. 21. Photos made by means of the electron microscope of birch wood attacked a: by *Merulius domesticus* (brown rot), and b: by *Trametes pini* (white rot), (from MEIER, 1955).

nin preparations which are probably, or at least possibly, different from the native lignin. The total amount of lignin that can be extracted in such a mild way that a change in its composition may be regarded as excluded, does not exceed 2% of the protolignin. This is called BRAUNS' lignin and it may be obtained by extracting ground wood either with aceton, with alcohol or with dioxane at room temperature. The amount of lignin that can be obtained in this way from wood which has been attacked by the brown-rot fungus, is larger (DE STEVENS and NORD, 1951; VAN VLIET, 1954). Although no definite chemical differences were found between this product and BRAUNS' lignin, it is not quite certain that the two really are identical.

According to BJÖRKMAN (1956) about half of the protolignin can be extracted with these solvents if the wood is first ground to a very fine powder by means of a steel ball mill. Probably the degree of polymerization of the protolignin is decreased as a result of this disintegration, but it still proved to be twice as high as that of BRAUNS' lignin (BJÖRKMAN and PERSON, 1957). This shows that the latter consists of the fraction with the lowest molecular weight.

That the composition of the lignin undergoes a change when the material is treated with the drastic chemical agents by means of which the whole amount can be extracted, has been demonstrated several times and is beyond doubt.

The insolubility of protolignin, and some other phenomena as well, have been explained by some authors by assuming that in the cell-wall the lignin is chemically bound to carbohydrates, especially to the hemicellulose which together with the lignin fills the interstices between the cellulose microfibrils. HARRIS (1953) and MEREWETHER (1957) have discussed this question in detail. It can certainly not be denied that the hemicelluloses become more readily soluble and more reactive after the lignin has been removed, and that the same applies to lignin when the carbohydrates are attacked, e.g. by brown rot. However, these differences in behaviour have also been explained by assuming that the components of this mixed system, viz. lignin and the carbohydrates protect each other, by preventing or at least retarding the entrance into the system of reagents that can attack only one of them. The recent isolation of lignin-carbohydrate complexes by BJÖRKMAN and PERSON (l.c.) however, is in favour of the former explanation.

Although the *chemical structure* of lignin is not yet completely known, it has, at least in broad outline, been elucidated, especially by the work of P. KLASON, K. FREUDENBERG and H. HIBBERT. It is a three-dimensional polymer consisting of various derivatives of phenylpropane (I); which are all provided with a phenolic hydroxyl group para to the propane chain and either one or two phenolic methoxyl groups adjacent to this phenolic group. The aromatic group therefore is either guajacyl (II) or syringyl (III); in most *Gymnosperms* guajacyl alone is present, but in the higher *Gymnosperms* and in the *Angiosperms* there is 30—50% syringyl and the rest guajacyl (TOWERS and DARNLEY GIBBS, 1953). That is why in the softwoods the methoxyl content of the lignin is 16%, in hardwoods ca 22%. In most of the monomers the propane group contains a hydroxyl, either a primary or a secondary one, and often a carbonyl group or a double bond. There undoubtedly are several different monomers in one lignin; it is a heteropolymer, that may contain e.g. coniferyl aldehyde (IV), sinapyl aldehyde (V) and other substances (VI). With regard to the way in which these monomers are combined into the polymers, we may assume with safety only two things, viz. that the phenolic OH-group is involved in it (VII) and that pyran (VIII) as well as furan (IX) rings are formed.

The *degree of polymerization* may vary widely; in the fractions which dissolve in alcohol, dioxane, pyridine, diluted alkali, etc. it has been estimated at some decades, whereas for the lignins dissolved under more severe conditions the estimates range from a few decades to several hundreds. However, these figures tell us little with regard to the DP of protolignin.

A *solution of lignin* (partly changed) may be obtained in various ways, some of which are of importance for the analytical estimation of lignin, whereas others are used in the industry, viz. for the delignification of wood and of paper pulp.

The best solvent is hot alkali. Part of the lignin dissolves already at room temperature and in diluted alkali; a higher amount is obtained from straw and from herbaceous plants than from wood. For the extraction of the entire amount temperatures of 160—180° C are required and a concentration of at least 4% of the alkali. Hot alcoholic alkali too may be used. After neutralization the lignin is precipitated together with a certain amount of hemicellulose. It may be purified by dissolving in dioxane, and precipitating once more.

When lignin is treated with alkali, phenolate is formed, which means that the heterocyclic rings are broken, and that depolymerization takes place; it is therefore an alkaline hydrolysis. In the industry part of the alkali is often replaced by Na_2S; OH-groups are in this case changed in SH and S, and the lignin therefore in thiolignin; the latter too dissolves after binding alkali. In the laboratory instead of alkali, mono- or tri-ethanolamine is sometimes used, but this requires a longer time or else a higher temperature.

Delignification can also be obtained by heating in slightly acid bisulphite solution at temperatures not exceeding 140° C. The lignin is partly depolymerized, and takes up 1 or 2 SO_2 groups per monomer. The ligno-sulphonic acid that is formed in this way, dissolves in the heat in a more or less colloidal form.

A third method, much in favour for analytical purposes, starts with a treatment with chlorine, chlorite or hypochlorite, by which the lignin is oxidized and converted into chloro-lignin fragments; the latter are subsequently dissolved in ethanol, ethanolamine, water or, most conveniently, in alkalized water. As lignin is sensitive to other oxidizing agents too, in the laboratory H_2O_2, chromic acid and chlorate may be used in order to obtain delignification (cf. section 1152).

Finally, the greater part of the lignin may be dissolved, also with partial changes, in a number of alcohols, thio-alcohols, phenol, dioxane, etc., at least in the presence of acid and at a higher temperature. We may use e.g. ethanol with 5% HCl or phenol with 0.2% HCl. The removal of lignin forms part of the purification of cellulose with phenol-hydrochlorid acid in the heat.

In order *to obtain solid lignin* we may precipitate it from the solution or we may also dissolve the accompanying substances in lignified material. The best-know method is to treat the material, after lipids, resins, tannins, proteins and such substances have been removed, with 72% (w/w) sulphuric acid at room temperature. Less often used are 42% HCl, HF, or mixtures of these acids. Powdered wood may also alternately be extracted with diluted acid in the heat and with cuoxam in the cold. The lignins that are obtained in this way are not unchanged either.

When we wish to have a measure for the degree to which the lignin in our preparations has been changed, we may make use of the methoxyl content. The latter varies in the lignin of softwood from 14 to 18%, in that of the wood of deciduous trees from 18 to 22%; in herbaceous plants it might be much lower (BONDI and MEYER, 1948). Only a small part of the methanol that can be gained from wood, is derived from other sources than lignin, viz from methylglucuronic-acid units which form part of the hemicelluloses.

With regard to the *physical properties* of protolignin, we will begin with a remark on its colour, which is not yellow, as is often assumed, but nearly white. The yellow colour of lignified material is due to the presence of other substances. By the aid of peroxides wood may be almost completely decolorized, whereas the lignin that is contained in it, is but slightly changed. It is, however, a noteworthy fact that protolignin shows a strong absorption for ultraviolet rays, especially below 250 mμ, and with a peak between 275 and 280 mμ; the latter is typical for the substituted aromatic ring. Protolignin shows a blue to blue-green fluorescence in longwave U.V. light (METZNER, 1930).

The physical property of protolignin which may be regarded as the most important one in the life of the plant, is its rigidity, which not only lends strength to trunks and branches, but also prevents the collapsing of the water-conducting elements. In this connection it is worth noting that lignin is almost entirely confined to land plants, and that it appeared on the scene at the same time as the first land plants. In higher plants that live submerged, like *Potamogeton* and *Zostera*, little or no lignin is found.

A property that is of importance e.g. to cabinet-makers, is its thermoplasticity in the humid condition, and allows us to change the form of steamed timber while it is still hot.

Isolated BRAUNS' lignin becomes softer between 80 and 120° C, and changes into a liquid at 140—145° C, but there is no definite melting point. The chemically changed lignin preparations are no longer thermoplastic.

Protolignin is much less hygroscopic than cellulose and hemicellulose; the last-named substance is the most hygroscopic one of the three (RÜNKEL and LÜTHGENS, 1956). The wood of deciduous trees, which contains somewhat

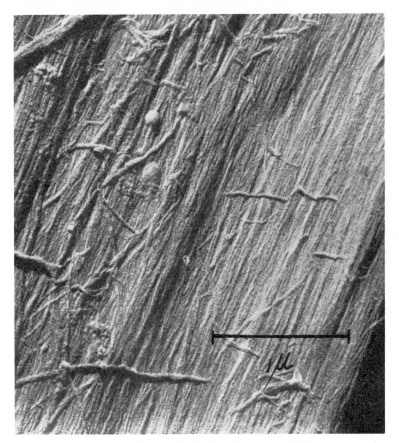

Fig. 22. Cell-wall from the wood of *Pseudotsuga taxifolia*, as seen under the electron microscope (HODGE and WARDROP, 1950).

more hemicellulose and somewhat less lignin than that of the conifers, has for this reason a somewhat higher water content, when the relative humidity of the air is the same.

Protolignin is undoubtedly an amorphous substance; lignified cell-walls show cellulose interferences only, notwithstanding the fact that they contain 20—25% lignin. Some investigators nevertheless are of opinion that their lignin preparations may to some extent be crystalline, but the majority is convinced that these preparations are always amorphous. Recently BECHERER

et al. (1955) have studied the X-ray diagram of lignin. With a very high magnification under the electron microscope, a granular structure has been observed in sections of lignin (Asunmaa, 1955), but it must be remarked that
this lignin had been attacked by a brown-rot fungus. The granules had a diameter of 20-30 Å.

Protolignin occurs in the form of an incrustation between the cellulose
microfibrils. This is seen clearly when we compare by the aid of the electron
microscope the structure of the cell-wall before and after delignification (viz.
figs. 22, P134 and P136 with P116, P122 and P138). It appears also from
the structure of the lignin skeleton (fig. 23), for where originally cellulose
microfibrils were found, we now notice the presence of interstice; the lignin
itself forms a continuous framework (Mühlethaler, 1949b; cf also Wardrop, 1957a).

The spongy structure of the lignin skeleton was already long known because
of the fact that skeletons of lignified fibres show different degrees of rodlet-
birefringence when immersed in different liquids (Freudenberg et al., 1929).

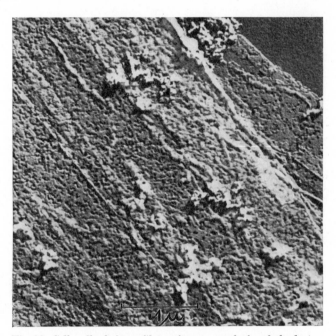

Fig. 23. Cell-wall of *Agave* fibre, after removal of carbohydrates,
as seen under the electronmicroscope (Mühlethaler, 1949b).

In liquids with a refractive index of 1.6, the specimens prove to be optically
isotropic, which means that this is the refractive index of the lignin itself (cf.
also Björkman and Person, 1957). As the refractive index of cellulose is
circ. 1.55, the rodlet-birefringence of the system cellulose-lignin may be
neglected. The phase-difference observed between crossed nicols in the same
object before and after delignification is the same, but the removal of the
lignin causes a shrinking, and for this reason the birefringence $(n// - n\perp)$ is
after delignification higher (Kanamaru, 1934; Preston, 1935). In sections

through lignified stomata FREY-WYSSLING (1928) found the same phase-difference in adjoining parts of the cell-wall that were either lignified or non-lignified.

When cell-walls are delignified in living tissues, as e.g. in the sclereid cells of *Cydonia*, the walls also decrease in thickness, and they thicken when they are lignified (A. FREY, 1926; ALEXANDROV and DJAPARIDZE, 1927; PRESTON, 1941, 1952: 141; PRESTON and MIDDLEBROOK, 1949). The interstices between the cellulose microfibrils are apparently widened when lignin is deposited in them. The shrinkage caused by delignification, however, is not visible in all objects (WARDROP, 1957a).

The specific gravity of lignin is circ. 1.40, that of the lignified cell-wall 1.45, as that of cellulose is higher, viz. 1.56. That wood floats on water rests exclusively on the presence of air in interstices in the cell-wall, in intercellular spaces and especially in the cell-lumina.

With regard to the way in which *lignin is synthesized*, several hypotheses have been brought forward. Those according to which pectins and hemicellulose would act as precursors, have now been discarded. For the hypothesis brought forward in 1897 by KLASON, according to which this part is allotted to coniferyl alcohol and coniferyl aldehyde, valuable arguments have been adduced in recent years (FREUDENBERG, 1954, 1955; MASON and CRONYN, 1955; REZNIK, 1955, 1956; SIEGEL, 1955; KRATZL and BILLEK, 1957; HIGUCHI, 1957; see also SCHUBERT and NORD, 1957 and various papers in TAPPI *40*: 262—285, 1957).

Cambium sap often contains glucosides of coniferyl alcohol, viz. coniferin, and of sinapyl alcohol, viz. syringin. Alcoholic extracts of coniferous wood always contain coniferyl aldehyde, those of the wood of deciduous trees moreover in addition to this, sinapyl aldehyde and syringyl aldehyde. After hydrolysis of the glucosides by means of β-glucosidase, which is present in the cell-wall of young xylem cells, the phenolic OH-group would be dehydrogenized by means of a peroxydase after which spontaneous polymerization would take place. An earlier precursor is supposed to be p-hydroxyphenylpyruvic acid and like other aromatic compounds in the plant, this is supposed to arise from shikimic acid (SCHUBERT and NORD, 1957; BROWN and NEISH, 1955). Whether the lignin precursors in secondary wood are produced by the cambium cells only, and diffuse in a centripetal direction, or whether they are produced by the lignifying cells themselves, is unknown. In any case lignification occurs in living cells only; it is not an impregnation of the wall of dead cells and therefore not comparable to the transformation of sapwood in heartwood.

Decomposition of lignin in the living plant is possible; but it is an exception, just as that of cellulose and hemicellulose. Examples are found in the delignification of stomatal cells and in that of stone-cells in ripening fruits, and further in the perforation of the transverse walls in xylem vessels (cf. KÜSTER, 1956: 687).

Several fungi, saprophytic ones as well as parasites, possess the faculty to decompose lignin, although they are less numerous than those that attack cellulose and hemicellulose. Some wood fungi nevertheless decompose lignin more rapidly than cellulose; they are responsible for the so-called "white rot". Those that decompose cellulose more rapidly than lignin, are responsible for the "brown rot" (cf. fig. 21).

6*

Decomposition of lignin by bacteria seems to occur only under exceptional conditions. Presumably it must take place under certain circumstances in the mud of ditches, but the attempts made in our laboratory to demonstrate the disappearance of lignin in powdered wood that was exposed half a year to conditions supposed to be comparable to those prevailing in mud, were inconclusive. Several authors have found a decrease of lignin in cereal straw in anaerobic cultures. As is well known, wood offers a great resistance to the attacks of anaerobic bacteria. This follows from the condition of the poles found in the remains of lake-dwellings and from the durability of piles that have been driven into a waterlogged soil.

Some aerobic thermophilic bacteria would, according to VIRTANEN (1946), decompose lignin. Attack by other bacteria too has been reported, but was afterwards denied (RAYNAUD et al., 1956). The literature with regard to the decomposition of lignin by microbes is discussed by GOTTLIEB and PELCZAR (1951) and by BRAUNS (1952: 599).

Some investigators are of opinion that the first step in the biochemical decomposition of lignin is an oxidation, which is supposed to be catalyzed by a phenol-oxidase. This enzyme in fact is secreted into the medium by those fungi that are able to decompose wood, but not by other ones (LINDEBERG, 1948; COOKE, 1957; LYR, 1958). The medium in which these fungi are cultivated, is said to oxidize BRAUNS' lignin (VAN VLIET, 1954), but it is possible that in these experiments not lignin but unknown phenols that were present as contaminants, functioned as substrate (own unpublished observation; HIGUCHI, 1956). The fungi liberate from the lignin e.g. coniferyl aldehyde, syringyl aldehyde and vanillin (HIGUCHI, 1955), but whether this is due to an oxidation, and if so by means of which enzyme it is effected, seem to us as yet unanswered questions.

The most important methods for the *estimation* of lignin have already been indicated. We may refer also to BRAUNS (1952), WISE and JAHN (1952: 214) and PAECH and TRACEY (1955 III: 499). Removal of lignin as a preliminary measure when we wish to study cellulose or holocellulose, has been dealt with elsewhere. A quantitative estimation of protolignin in the various parts of the cell-wall by means of ultraviolet microphotometry has been described by LANGE (1950, 1954; TREIBER, 1957: 259) It requires a very specialized physical apparatus. In recent years attempts have been made to separate lignin preparations in different fractions by means of paper chromatography (BLAND and GATLEY, 1954; SCHUBERT and NORD, 1955).

Qualitative reactions on lignin are known in a large number (WISE and JAHN, 1952: 414; BRAUNS, 1952; TUNMANN-ROSENTHALER, 1931; VAN WISSE-LINGH, 1925: 101). In a strongly acid medium lignin is brightly stained by various phenols, aromatic amines and heterocyclic compounds. The colour obtained by means of phenols varies between red, green and blue; that obtained with the amines between yellow, red and orange. It was soon recognized that these reactions rested on addition to an aromatic aldehyde, but it has long remained a controversial point whether the latter formed part of the lignin or had to be regarded as an admixture. At present it seems safe to assume that the reaction is due to the presence of a small number of free aldehyde-groups belonging to coniferyl aldehyde, and in the wood of deciduous trees also to the sinapyl aldehyde, that form part of the lignin.

The best-known reagent is that of WIESNER with phloroglucinol, which gives a cherry-red colour. Free coniferyl aldehyde and some other aromatic aldehydes that occur in plants, e.g. vanillin, give the same colour as lignin (BLACK et al., 1953). The same occurs with several exuded gums and resins. The red colour disappears when the lignin preparation is heated. In this respect it differs from the pink colour that is obtained when pentoses or pentosan are heated with WIESNER's reagent, in which case the heterocyclic aldehyde furfural is formed; this has been mentioned already in our discussion of the hemicelluloses.

The reaction with WIESNER's reagent is sometimes, on account of the fact that it is obtained also with some free aromatic aldehydes, condemned as unspecific, but as these substances are in the cell-wall either absent or present in very small amounts only, the reaction may nevertheless be regarded as specific for protolignin, especially when the cell-walls have previously been extracted with an organic solvent and with water. Modified lignin does not give the reaction, and in some cases protolignin itself does not react either (JOULIA, 1938; ULLRICH, 1955).

In some objects the lignin already assumes a red or violet colour when it is treated with hydrochloric acid alone. This is due to the presence of catechins or other derivatives of flavones which contain either a phloroglucinol or a resorcinol group; this renders the addition of phloroglucinol superfluous. Hydrochloric acid may therefore be used as a reagent for the detection of catechins in wood, although it is more common to use for this purpose a reagent that contains its own aromatic aldehyde, e.g. vanillin-hydrochloric acid.

Among the aromatic amines anilin is, as is well-known, the one that is most often used.

Another reaction on the aldehyde-group is that with thiobarbituric acid, which gives an orange-red colour with lignin. The same colour is given by suberized cell-walls (BERNHEIM et al., 1951) but this does not mean that the reaction should be regarded as unspecific, as the suberized cell-walls often contain lignin.

The red or red-brown colour which chloro-lignin assumes in an alkaline medium rests on an entirely different reaction. This reaction was described already more than a century ago by PAYEN, who treated wood first with chlorine and subsequently with ammonia. A similar reaction was obtained in 1893 by CROSS and BEVAN when they treated chloro-lignin with sodium sulphite. Best known, however, is the reaction in the form described by MÄULE in 1900, and which is now carried out in the modification introduced by CROCKER (1933). The object is treated successively with 1% $KMnO_4$, HCl, water, and ammonia. The $KMnO_4$ is reduced to MnO_2, which forms chlorine with HCl; after the chlorine has reacted with the lignin, free chlorine is washed out. The chloro-lignin assumes with ammonia in the majority of the *Angiosperms* a red, and in the *Gymnosperms* a brown-red colour; the difference in colour is due to the fact that the lignin of the *Angiosperms* also contains syringyl groups. When the lignin has been slightly decomposed, the reaction with phenols and with amines soon becomes negative, but the chloro-lignin reaction remains. However, in some plants this reaction may be negative, whereas the reaction with phloroglucinol gives a positive result (JOULIA, l.c.; ULLRICH, l.c.).

The reaction introduced by COMBES also seems to be fairly specific (JOULIA, l.c.). Lignin is treated successively with a hot $ZnSO_4$-solution, H_2S and sulphuric acid, and assumes as a consequence a red colour. COMBES himself used in addition JAVELLE solution (cf. WISE and JAHN l.c.). It seems to be unknown how the reaction is to be explained.

Lignin can be stained also with several basic stains like ruthenium red, methylene blue, malachite green, safranine, gentian violet, etc., but these staining methods are unspecific. They rest on the fact that lignin, by the presence of phenolic hydroxyl-groups, has the character of an acid.

Lignin reactions that are not mentioned in botanical handbooks, and which nevertheless deserve our attention, are that with silver according to COPPICK and FOWLER (1939), and the yellow colour lignin assumes after a treatment with concentrated nitric acid followed by one with triphenyl-amine (cf. JAYME and HARDERS-STEINHÄUSER, 1947). These reactions remain positive even when the lignin undergoes a modification.

The way in which a cell-wall swells and finally dissolves in cuoxam may, if critically studied, give in some cases valuable indications with regard to the lignin content (COPPICK and FOWLER l.c.). In our discussion of the cellulose we have referred to the dichroism of lignified fibres which had been stained with chlor-zinc-iodine.

17. Cell-wall Substances of Lipid Character

True lipids are usually defined as substances that can be extracted by the aid of "lipid solvents", but we will include here also cutin, suberin and sporopollenin, although these substances can not be extracted by the aid of these solvents. The literature has also been discussed by several authors in RUHLAND (1958) vol. X.

171. CUTIN

The outermost periclinal wall of the epidermis is in all *Cormophyta* as is well known, completely covered by a water-repellent layer, the cuticle proper. The latter consists of cutin, probably with an admixture of wax. It may be regarded as an extra layer secreted by the cell on the outside of the ordinary cell-wall. On its inside the cuticle is often lined with the so-called cuticular layer, which consists of cellulose, cutin and wax. Here the cutin is therefore not secreted on the outside of the cell-wall, but encrusted within a part of the latter. The complex layer comprising the cuticle and the cutical layer, we call in this work cuticular membrane.

A thin layer of lipid nature might also be present where cell-walls border on intercellular spaces (cf. section 2362), and even within the walls (cf. section 2364), but the chemical nature of these substances is very imperfectly known.

Whether cutin is present in lower plants, is unknown. The hyphae of fungi may be covered with a thin, easily detachable layer of a lipid nature (cf. section 243). MEVIUS (1923) found in algae a substance which shows some resemblance with cutin.

The *chemical constitution of cutin* is but imperfectly known. FRÉMY was the first to report between the years 1859 and 1885 that two acid fractions may be obtained from the cuticular membranes of the *Agave* leaf. One of these fractions, the "stearo-cutic acid" is solid at room temperature, the other one, the "oleo-cutic acid" is semi-liquid; the fractions appeared in the proportion 1 : 5. LEE (1925) stated that free as well as esterized fatty acids, aliphatic hydroxyacids, and higher alcohols are present. LEGG and WHEELER (1925, 1929) isolated from the detachable epidermis of *Agave* leaves 10% substances that proved to be soluble in water, 15% wax and 14% cellulose, whereas 57% dissolved under saponification in hot alcoholic alkali. The latter fraction contained e.g. "cutic acid", "cutinic acid" and „phloionic acid", but the last-named substance is the only one that may be regarded as unmixed; they were all recognized as hydroxyacids. ZETSCHE and LÜSCHER (1938) too assumed that in the cuticular membrane of the *Agave* leaf several saturated as well as unsaturated hydroxy-mono- and hydroxy-di-carbonic acids are present. HUELIN and GALLOP (1951) confirmed, in the cutin of the apple, the presence of compounds consisting of various hydroxyacids.

MATIC (1956) obtained more detailed data in a brilliant study devoted to the cutin of *Agave* leaf. He stripped the epidermis off from the leaf in the same way as LEGG and WHEELER had done, extracted the wax and the substances that are soluble in water and in alcohol, and removed the cellulose, as far as possible, with cuoxam. After saponification of the cutin that in this way was obtained, he could, by applying the most modern methods of analysis, isolate and identify several aliphatic acids, viz.

1. 9:10:18-trihydroxy-octadecanoic   %
   (phloionolic) acid $HO\text{-}(CH_2)_8\text{-}(CHOH)_2\text{-}(CH_2)_7\text{-}COOH$ 25

2. 10:16-dihydroxy-hexadecanoic acid
                               $HO\text{-}(CH_2)_6\text{-}CHOH\text{-}(CH_2)_8\text{-}COOH$ 9.7

3. 10:18-dihydroxy-octadecanoic acid
                               $HO\text{-}(CH_2)_8\text{-}CHOH\text{-}(CH_2)_8\text{-}COOH$ 10.3

4. 18-hydroxy-octadecanoic acid $HO\text{-}(CH_2)_{17}\text{-}COOH$ 0.3

5. 18-hydroxy-octadec-cis-9-enoic acid
                               $HO\text{-}(CH_2)_8\text{-}CH{=}CH\text{-}(CH_2)_7\text{-}COOH$ 2

All are therefore ω-hydroxy-monocarbonic acids, i.e. aliphatic acids provided with a terminal hydroxyl-group. The most important three are, moreover, provided either with a single or with two secondary-alcohol groups, and one possesses a double linkage.

As the portion of the cutin that could be identified in this way, amounts to 47% of the total amount, and as the latter, moreover, comprised 12% that proved to be unsaponifiable (in our opinion this may have been cellulose from the cuticular layer), and as the acids, of course, could not be isolated without loss, it seems safe to say that the principal building stones of cutin are now known. Because of the results recorded in the older literature, the presence of dicarbonic acids would have been expected, but the latter were not found by MATIC.

When hydroxyacids of the kind isolated by MATIC, are heated, they spontaneously form esters with each other, and these esters can in their turn be decomposed into the original hydroxyacids. It is therefore allowed to regard cutin as a poly-ester (estolide, etholide). On account of the presence of di- and tri-hydroxyacids, it seems probable that the molecules are strongly ramified. As no solvent for native cutin is known, we are unable to estimate its degree of polymerization. As the number of the OH-groups is larger than that of the COOH-groups, part of the OH-groups must be free; this is in good agreement with the fact that cutin can be acetylized.

Whether the living cell, or at least an enzyme, plays a part in the polymerization process, which as mentioned takes place also without enzymic
catalysis, is unknown. As the poly-ester is entirely insoluble, and a transport
therefore is excluded, the formation ought to be effected in the place where
the product is met with, but so far not even a protein has been found in the
cuticular membrane, and it is even difficult to see how such an enzyme, with
the water it requires, would be able to penetrate into the hydrophobic and
rather impermeable cutin. LEE and PRIESTLEY (1924) and ZIEGENSPECK
(1924) had already assumed that cutin owes its origin to spontaneous polymerization of the aliphatic hydroxyacids, which are much less hydrophobic
than cutin, and might therefore be more readily transportable. The unsaturated
aliphatic acids, moreover, might be oxidized when they come into contact
with air, and might accordingly more easily polymerize. MARTENS (1933)
reports that he has found indications for a semiliquid condition of the newly
formed cutin and LINSKENS (1952) also observed changes in the properties
of the cuticle in the course of time.

With regard to an *enzymatic decomposition of cutin* nothing is known. In
the plant itself it has never been observed, and when the epidermis is perforated by parasitic fungi, the cuticular membrane is ruptured mechanically.
Cutin certainly is one of the most resistant substances that are met with in
the organic world, and is present even in fossil material, although it occurs
there in a slightly modified form (cf. KLEIN, 1932, III: 307). In the soil,
e.g. in the mud of ditches, cutin nevertheless seems to be subjected to a slow
decay, but this has so far not been proved by means of experiments. Powdered
cuticular membranes added to anaerobic accumulation cultures (cf. section 172)
did not decrease in cutin content. FRITZ (1935) has remarked that the cuticular
layer becomes more easily stainable as a result of the action of bacteria, but
whether the cutin was attacked, remained obscure.

Of the five aliphatic hydroxyacids isolated by MATIC, phloionolic acid and
18-hydroxy-octadec-cis-9-enoic acid have been found also in suberin, though
they are not the main constituents of the latter. Cutin and suberin nevertheless
are certainly to be regarded as chemically allied substances. In some plant
waxes too estolides have been found. Another substance which reminds us of
cutin, is shellac, an excretion product of the *Aphid Tachardia lacca*; this
substance, however, is soluble in alcohol. It contains 30—40% trihydroxy-
hexadecanoic acid, a homologue of phloionolic acid. In addition there are
hydroxyacids with 18 C-atoms. Various synthetic lacquers and plastics too
are polyesters.

Apart from cutin, wax and, perhaps, pectin, the cuticular layer contains
resin-like and tannin-like compounds, and sometimes also anthocyanins
(SCHOCH-BODMER, 1938). LEGG and WHEELER (l.c.) and KARIYONE and
HASHIMOTO (1953) have found derivatives of triterpenes. The last-named two
authors found in cutin the triterpenoid ursolic acid and melissyl alcohol, but
as these substances are more or less general constituents of waxes, and as
they were present in very small amounts only, it is very well possible that
they were derived from a rest of wax. According to SKOSS (1955) in many
plants the cuticles contain about 20% wax, but the amount varies greatly
with different climatic circumstances.

The periclinal as well as the anticlinal walls of epidermis cells may, as is
well known, be lignified. This lignification may be confined to the stomatal
cells (FREY-WYSSLING, 1928) or it may be present in all cells (ULLRICH, 1955).

The cell-walls of many hairs too are lignified, e.g. those of *Ceiba* and of *Asclepias*; those of *Ceiba* contain circ. 12% lignin. KARIYONE and HASHIMOTO (l.c.) found in the epidermis of *Ilex* no less than 38% lignin, but the abnormally low methoxyl content of the latter suggests that it must have been mixed with other substances. There is no proof that lignin is ever present either in the cuticle or in the cuticular layer; it is always the subcuticular layer in which it occurs.

With regard to the *physical properties* of cutin, we may note in the first place that this substance is always amorphous; X-ray interferences have only been observed when the cutin contained wax. Owing to the presence of wax the cuticular layer is strongly birefringent, and the cuticle sometimes slightly so, at least when seen in tangential direction. When the wax is extracted, the cuticular membrane becomes nearly isotropic. The very slight residual birefringence is, according to ROELOFSEN (1952), partly due to small amounts of oriented, chemically bound wax molecules, and partly to a rodlet-birefringence which finds its origin in the anisotropic interstices that were left after the extraction of the wax (cf. section 2362).

In U.V.-light with a long wave-length the cuticular membrane fluoresces with a golden-yellow to greenish yellow shine (METZNER, 1930). Wax as well as cutin absorb U.V.-light (WÜHRMAN-MEYER, 1941), but the ecological significance of this absorption is mostly small in comparison to that of the absorption by substances that are dissolved in the cell-sap (LAUTENSCHLAGER-FLEURY, 1955) and by flavanone pigments sometimes found in the cuticular layer (unpublished work of BOLLIGER, quoted by FREY-WYSSLING, 1959: 58).

For the *isolation of cuticular membranes* we may often make use of the presence of a layer that is rich in pectin and which is intercalated between the cuticular membrane and the inner parts of the cell-wall. By the aid of one of the maceration methods which we have mentioned in section 115, it is possible to detach the cuticular membrane (ROELOFSEN, 1952; KISSER and SKUHRA, 1952; SKOSS, 1955; ORGELL, 1955; SCOTT et al., 1957). The use of hot alkali should, however, be avoided, as this may cause saponification of wax or cutin. The cuticle may also become detached in the natural course of events, e.g. in withering flowers (MARTENS, 1933; VAN ITERSON, 1937). In some instances it is also possible to strip off the epidermis, either directly or after a treatment with sulphuric acid or with zinc chloride. It is always desirable, but in the last-named cases it is necessary, to remove cellulose, hemicellulose and pectin by means of concentrated sulphuric acid or of cuoxam and diluted alkali. In this way it is, of course, possible to isolate the cuticular membrane from more voluminous parts of the plant.

When lignin is present, this too has to be removed, but this is more difficult. According to the prescriptions given for the procedure by KLEIN (1932, III: 1, II: 216) and by PAECH and TRACEY (1955, II: 392) the lignin may be dissolved by means of an oxidizing or chlorinating agent, when the material has first been treated with concentrated sulphuric acid in order to remove the carbohydrates. It would also be possible to remove the carbohydrates and the lignin at the same time by treating the material with sulphuric acid and H_2O_2. However, it has appeared to the author that the cuticular membrane from the leaf of *Clivia nobilis*, which contains no lignin, decreases considerably in weight even when, after wax and cellulose have been removed, it is subjected to a mild delignification, viz. by chlorination and extraction with ethanolamine.

The best way to *remove cutin* is by saponification with alcoholic alkali (12 g KOH, 12 ml water, ethanol to 100 ml; boiling for several hours or else heating for half an hour to 160° C). It leaves the cellulose of cuticular layers intact and does not cause much deformation. Waxes, lignin and part of the hemicelluloses may dissolve also during this treatment.

If it does not matter whether the skeleton of cellulose retains its original shape, the saponification can also be carried out with an aqueous solution of alkali or by heating with glycerol to a temperature of 250—300° C, according to VAN WISSELINGH's method. By these methods, wax, lignin, hemicelluloses and pectins are removed more completely.

The best-known *reaction on cuticular membranes* for use under the microscope is that with lipophilic stains, e.g. with sudan III or IV or with sudan black B, dissolved in alcohol-glycerol or in glycols (CHIPPELLE and PUTT, 1951). Previous bleaching with JAVELLE solution and removal of the excess stain with diluted alcohol are to be recommended. Native cutin containing wax as well as wax-free cutin are stained. Several other staining methods have also been recommended (TUNMANN-ROSENTHALER, 1931: 990). FRITZ (1935) advises magdala red to differentiate the cuticle from the cuticular layer. Ruthenium red has been used to detect pectic substances in the cuticular layer by this author and by ANDERSON (1928) but we suppose that this will stain acidic cutin precursors too.

Other well-known criteria for recognizing cuticular membranes are the temporary resistance against strong inorganic acids at room temperature, e.g. 75% (w/w) sulphuric acid, 85% phosphoric acid, 38% hydrochloric acid, 50% chromic acid, combined with a very rapid solution in hot aqueous alkali (15—50%) or alcoholic alkali. Concentrated nitric acid destroys cutin. Another recommendable characteristic is the negative birefringence of the membrane when observed tangentially; this birefringence disappears for the greater part when the wax is removed, and also when the membrane is heated for a short time in glycerol, but in that case it returns when the material is cooled down. After the removal of the wax, the thickness of the membrane proves to be reduced.

Characteristics by means of which cutin may be distinguished from sporopollenin and suberin are given in KLEIN (1932, III:1, II: 237).

172. SUBERIN

The presence of suberin is, like that of cutin, known with certainty from the *Cormophyta* only. It occurs mainly, as is well known, in the periderm, but it may be present also in other parts of the plant, e.g. in the exo- and endodermis, in wound tissue, in the abscission layers of leaves and seeds (chalaza), and sometimes also in the epidermis of the seed-coat, but in that case it is not found in the peripheral wall.

SCOTT (1950) described the presence of suberized layers in normal cell-walls but it is not certain that these layers really are suberized; the only thing that is known with certainty is that they are of lipid nature.

The literature with regard to the *chemical constitution* of stopper-cork and of suberin has been discussed e.g. by ZETSCHE (1932), STOCKAR (1948), RIBAS-MARQUÉS (1952) (cf. also TREIBER, 1957: 418). The constitution of stopper-cork proves to vary considerably in samples of different origin and with the age of the tree and the age of the sample.

By the aid of hot water 2—6% of the dry weight of this cork can be removed, and in a later stage of the analysis, viz. after the suberin has been saponified, in the same way another 13% can be extracted. The substances that are extracted in this way, are mainly tannins and other polyphenols, as well as glycosides and carbohydrates.

With organic solvents like hexane, benzene, chloroform, ethanol and pyridine the cork-wax which is interposed between the suberin, may be almost completely extracted, at least when the material is boiled in them for a very long time. The amounts of this substance that have been recorded, vary between 4.5 and 20%, but this wide range of variability is partly due to the use of solvents by which also non-lipids are extracted.

Of the remaining 70—85% more than half, viz. 40—60% of the original weight of the stopper-cork, can usually be hydrolysed and dissolved in boiling alcoholic alkali. This is the suberin. The insoluble part, 20—40% of the original weight, consists mainly of tannin-like compounds, cellulose and lignin. The values that have been recorded, vary a good deal, viz. for cellulose between 2 and 11%, and for lignin between 12 and 20% (FIERZ-DAVID and ULRICH, 1945; STOCKAR, 1948; RIBAS-MARQUÉS, 1952). These cell-wall constituents are not entirely derived from the cork-cells, but partly from sclereids and from the parenchyma found in the lenticels.

Although several investigators have occupied themselves with the chemistry of the suberin obtained from the cork of *Quercus suber* (cf. in addition to the authors mentioned already also JENSEN, 1950; JENSEN et al., 1954, 1957; MIGITA et al., 1951; MATIC, 1956), but a few of its constituents have as yet been completely identified; together they form less than half the total amount of the suberin. The substances that have been identified, and their amounts expressed as a percentage of total suberin are mentioned below. However, the amounts vary greatly in different samples.

$\%$

1. 22-hydroxy-docosanoic (phellonic) acid
$$HO\text{-}CH_2\text{-}(CH_2)_{20}\text{-}COOH \qquad\qquad 14$$
2. docosanedioic (phellogenic) acid
$$HOOC\text{-}(CH_2)_{20}\text{-}COOH \qquad\qquad 0.75$$
3. 9:10-dihydroxy-octadecanedioic
(phloionic) acid $\qquad HOOC\text{-}(CH_2)_7\text{-}(CHOH)_2\text{-}(CH_2)_7\text{-}COOH$ 12.7
4. 9:10:18-trihydroxy-octadecanoic
(phloionolic) acid $\qquad HOOC\text{-}(CH_2)_7\text{-}(CHOH)_2\text{-}(CH_2)_7\text{-}CH_2OH$ 2.5
5. cis- and trans-octadec-9-enedioic acid
$$HOOC\text{-}(CH_2)_7\text{-}CH\text{=}CH\text{-}(CH_2)_7\text{-}COOH$$
6. 18-hydroxy-octadec-cis-9-enoic acid
$$HOOC\text{-}(CH_2)_7\text{-}CH\text{=}CH\text{-}(CH_2)_7\text{-}CH_2OH$$

The hydroxyacids 4 and 6 have been found in saponified cutin too, but in the suberin to which the analysis pertains, other hydroxyacids are quantitatively more important, viz. phellonic and phloionic acid. In suberin, moreover, the dicarbonic acids (2, 3 and 5) play a prominent part, whereas such acids are lacking in cutin. Two of the acids contain 22 C-atoms, and acids with such a large number of C-atoms have not been found so far in cutin. DRAKE et al. (1941) have stated that these acids contain even no less than 24 C-atoms, but others (see RIBAS-MARQUÉS, l.c.) definitely discard this view (cf. also JENSEN, 1950). Lower aliphatic acids too are sometimes found, viz. octanedioic (suberic) acid and 8-hydroxy-octanoic (suberonic) acid, but these are supposed to be decomposition products of the native acids.

As a result of the saponification, not only acids but also glycerol is produced and this is another difference with cutin. The amounts that have been recorded, vary between 1.1 and 7%, but some investigators deny the presence of glycerol altogether. The glycerol, at any rate, can not have been derived from rests of protoplasmatic fat, as the amount of glycerol that can be obtained by means of saponification, proves to be the same before and after extraction of the material with fat-solvents. The cork-wax that in this manner is removed, therefore does not contain glycerol, and there are apparently no protoplasmatic fats and phospholipids.

That substances like phellonic acid polymerize spontaneously when they are heated above 70° C, and that they become in this way less soluble in fat solvents, although not so completely insoluble as suberin, has been known for a long time. When the polymerization product is saponified, the original acid is regained. On account of these findings, and also because of the close analogy existing between suberin and cutin in constitution and properties, it seems safe to assume that suberin too must be regarded as a poly-ester. It is, however, not excluded that other bonds are present too. It is also possible that part of the carboxyl-groups of the suberin form salts with the metals that according to the ash analysis must be present in cork to an amount of 0.5 to 2.5%. Carboxyl may also be linked to glycerol.

Other kinds of cork may have an entirely different constitution. Usually much lower amounts of suberin are found than in stopper-cork (ZETSCHE, l.c.). HERGERT and KURTH (1952) found in that of *Pseudotsuga taxifolia* similar amounts of cork-wax and suberin, but more tannins and sometimes a large quantum of the polyphenol dihydroquercetin. When the suberin was saponified, it yielded other acids, viz. 11-hydroxydodecanoic acid, hydroxyhexadecanoic acid, and quantitatively most important of all a still unknown phenolic acid which proved to be linked to an aliphatic hydroxyacid. We may add that the same investigators found in the wax that was present in this cork, a phenolic acid which proved to be identical with ferulic acid. In suberin obtained from the cork of *Picea* too a phenolic acid has been found as a building unit.

The suberin from the cork of *Betula verrucosa* contains, according to JENSEN and RINNE (1954), more phloionolic than phloionic acid, i.e. just the reverse of what was found in the suberin of *Quercus suber*. The marked diversity in constitution that we observe in the cork of different objects, therefore, seems to be present also in that of the suberin (cf. JENSEN and OSTMAN, 1954).

Although suberin and cutin are very similar in constitution, the two substances differ considerably in resistance against hydrolysing agents. ZETSCHE (l.c.: 237) gives a summary of these differences. Suberin dissolves more readily in hot glycerol, which takes place under hydrolysis. It is already at room temperature saponified by alkali and by cuoxam, at higher temperatures even by soda; whereas cutin does not react to any of these treatments. In boiling aniline suberin dissolves slowly, cutin not at all. Both substances, on the other hand, resist for some time the action of concentrated inorganic acids (see under cutin), with the exception of nitric acid.

With regard to *enzymatic decomposition of suberin* we are no better informed than we are with regard to that of cutin. It is well known that cork bottle-stoppers do not deteriorate even if they are kept for many years in the humid atmosphere of a cellar. DeBaun and Nord (1951) grew various wood-attacking fungi on a culture medium containing powdered cork, but they found that the lignin in the cork remained unattacked. The lignin is in this case apparently entirely enveloped by suberin, and the fact that it remains unattacked, was taken as indirect proof of the resistance offered by the enveloping suberin. In experiments made in the author's laboratory with anaerobic accumulation cultures containing bacteria that ferment cellulose and other bacteria that reduce sulphates, that were kept during a whole month at temperatures varying from 30 to 55° C, no decrease in the amount of suberin in the cork powder that had been added to the medium could be observed.

Prescriptions for a *quantitative estimation* or for further analysis of suberin may be found in the literature cited above, and in Paech and Tracey (1955, II: 394). The ordinary method of saponification by means of alcoholic alkali may also be used in order to remove suberin and wax from preparations when the cellulose skeletons are to be studied. The latter are less damaged with this method than by boiling in an aqueous solution of alkali or by heating, according to van Wisselingh's method in glycerol to temperatures of 250—300° C.

For the *identification* of suberin *under the microscope* usually the well-known stains are used that are soluble in lipids. We may also try to find out whether the material to be tested dissolves when it is heated e.g. in 10% alkali, alcoholic alkali or glycerol (to which eventually a slight amount of alkali has been added), and whether it may resist for some time the action of 75% sulphuric acid at room temperature. With chlor-zinc-iodine it assumes a brown colour; cuoxam needs a very long time in order to make its influence felt. A characteristic feature is the formation of sphaerites when the material is boiled for a moment with 50% KOH; these sphaerites are the potassium salts of aliphatic acids (cf. Molisch, 1923: 348). By the aid of 50% chromic acid a clear separation between the suberin layer and the primary wall is obtained (Tunmann-Rosenthaler, 1932: 987). The reaction obtained with a mixture of potassium chlorate and nitric acid rests probably on the presence of cork-wax. Mader (1954) gives a detailed description of the reaction with osmic acid; this substance is reduced by suberin because of the latter's unsaturated character, but according to Sitte (1955) the reaction remains mainly confined to the surface of the suberin lamellae.

Ordinary stopper-cork as well as cork that has been deprived of waxes, fluoresces with a faintly blue shine in U.V.-light (Metzner, 1930; Mader, 1954). According to Sitte (cf. Treiber, 1957: 431), the fluorescence of exhaustively extracted cork is, however, yellow-brown, whereas the wax solution, in contrast to the solid wax, fluoresces blue, as also does the original cork. From this, Sitte deduces that the wax causes the blue fluorescence of cork and that it occurs within the cork in mono- or bi-molecular oriented layers (cf. section 2364).

Characteristic for native cork is the negative birefringence which it owes to the presence of wax, and which is temporarily suppressed when the material is heated for a moment in glycerol.

That suberin is an amorphous substance, has been shown by means of X-ray analysis by PRINS (1934), SITTE (1955) and KREGER (1958). The last-named author is the only one who observed interferences of the crystalline cork-wax in X-ray diagrams of cork.

173. SPOROPOLLENIN

The outermost cell-wall layer of the pollengrains in the *Anthophyta* and of the spores in the *Pteridophyta* consists of a particularly resistant substance of lipid character, for which the name sporopollenin has been chosen. In the wall of fungus spores it has not been found. In pollen it forms 4—24% of the dry weight, but in the cell-wall itself the percentage is, of course, higher. Sporopollenin is even more resistant to attack by micro-organisms than cutin, and is accordingly often found in fossil material, although in that case its constitution proves to be slightly changed (KLEIN, l.c.: 307; FREUND, 1952).

With regard to its chemical constitution we know at present no more than ZETSCHE (1932) did. The bruto formula is $(C_{10}H_{16}O_3)n$, and it is further known that about half the number of the O-atoms is present in the form of OH-groups. ZETSCHE suggested that it may be a polyterpene, which means that it would be related to rubber and gutta-percha, but the latter substances are much less resistant to decay.

The higher degree of resistance makes it easy to distinguish sporopollenin from cutin and suberin (cf. ZETSCHE, 1932: 237). It can not be saponified by means of hot alkali, and only when it is melted with solid KOH decomposition takes place. Concentrated sulphuric acid changes its colour, but it attacks it very slowly. In boiling glycerol with or without alkali it remains unchanged. Concentrated nitric acid and chromic acid dissolve it, but this proves impossible when it has previously been chlorinated. The latter reaction makes it possible to gain sporopollenin from brown-coal and coal. It can be stained with sudan III and similar dyes. Sporopollenin may be stained by the presence of anthocyanin (GEITLER, 1934, 1937). The fluorescence varies in different objects (ASBECK, 1955).

Although as yet little studied, it seems clear that native sporopollenin and likewise preparations of it, are not doubly refractive and do not produce X-ray interferences (cf. SITTE in TREIBER, 1957). Highly magnified electron micrographs of sections revealed a granular structure, the granules having a diameter of about 60 Å. On the assumption that these granules are molecules, the molecular weight has been calculated (cf. STEFFEN, 1955).

174. WAX

Wax is probably present in all plants that are provided with a cuticle or with cork. Wax may be secreted on the outside of the cuticle, but it is always to be found in the cell-wall, viz. either in the cuticular membrane or in the suberin layer. The amount of wax in these layers may be 20% but varies greatly (cf. sections 171, 172). When expressed as a percentage of the epidermal wall as a whole, it is of course much less, e.g. 8% in the primary wall of mature cotton hairs and 0,7% when expressed as a percentage of the wall as a whole, 2,4% in *Ceiba* hairs.

Very probably all cell-walls of higher plants contain a slight amount of wax. TUPPER-CAREY and PRIESTLEY (1923) demonstrated the presence of lipids in meristematic walls, although these lipids can not be made visible by means of the well-known staining methods. GUNDERMANN et al. (1937) confirmed this by means of the X-ray method, whereas K. and M. WÜHR-MANN-MEYER (1939) demonstrated their presence in parenchymatic walls of *Avena* coleoptiles by means of the double refraction. They even arrived at certain conclusions regarding the shape of the wax crystallites and regarding their orientation in the wall, but this seems less well-founded (cf. section 2362).

Analysing whole maize-mesocotyls, WIRTH (1946) found 7—23% lipids (expressed on the total weight of the wall material), but an unknown part of this is of protoplasmic origin. As determined in the author's laboratory, washed and dried cell-walls of these mesocotyls contained 2% lipids.

As mentioned in section 2364, thin layers of lipids or at least of material containing lipids have been observed microscopically in all kinds of cells.

Lower organisms, like fungi and bacteria, that possess neither cutin nor suberin, still have lipids in their cell-walls. According to KREGER (1954) the walls of *Phycomyces* sporangiophores contain as much as 25% lipids, which are said to be chemically linked to other cell-wall material. Yeasts also contain lipids in their cell-walls (cf. section 243).

The literature on the chemical and physical properties of the waxes is treated in detail by WARTH (1956); PAECH and TRACEY (1955, II: 380) deal with the analytical methods; KÜSTER (1956: 701), TREIBER (1957: 432) and KREGER (1958b) give summaries of chemical and physical properties, and discuss the botanical aspects of the problem of wax secretion.

Plant waxes may contain one or more of the following compounds: esters of higher aliphatic acids and higher aliphatic or cyclic alcohols, the aliphatic acids and the various alcohols themselves, paraffin hydrocarbons, higher ketones and various cyclic compounds with wax-like properties. The aliphatic acids and the primary alcohols possess, as a rule, an even number of C-atoms varying between 24 and 34, the paraffin hydrocarbons, secondary alcohols and ketones frequently have an odd number, varying between 25 and 35. A wax consists as a rule of a mixture of these groups of substances, with long-chain aliphatic hydrocarbons, alcohols and esters as the principal constituents.

In exceptional cases the greater part of the aliphatic acids may be unsaturated, whereas lower aliphatic acids, e.g. with 16 C-atoms, too may be present; they may even be present in the form of glycerides, although in that case we should not speak of a wax but of a fat.

The polyester constituents of the wax that have been obtained from the needles of conifers, are especially noteworthy in connection with their resemblance to the cell-wall substances cutin and suberin. In this wax ω-hydroxy-acids, viz. 12-hydroxy-dodecanoic acid and 16-hydroxy-hexadecanoic acid, are present as monomers, but di- and tri-hydroxyacids, dicarbonic acids and di-alcohols have also been found. However, this is an exceptional case; as a rule, the main components of the waxes are entirely different from the monomers of cutin.

Cyclic constituents too may be of importance, viz. sterols and derivatives of terpenes. The wax from ordinary cork e.g. contains 20% cerin and friedelin, which are tri-terpene-ketones, and a small quantity of terpene-alcohols. Various aliphatic acids make up the main part of cork-wax.

Ursolic acid, another derivative of a tri-terpene, and for the first time found in the wax of *Arctostaphylos uva-ursi*, appears to occur in the epidermis of a large number of plants (KARIYONE and HASHIMOTO, 1953), e.g. in that of the apple, in which, however, aliphatic alcohols and paraffin hydrocarbons form the main part of the wax.

The wax from the cork of *Pseudotsuga taxifolia* has a quite different constitution; it contains a large amount of a C_{24}-alcohol and an aliphatic acid also with 24 C-atoms; the corresponding ester is also present, and further a considerable amount of ferulic acid, a phenolic acid, which may be present either in the form of an ester or free. The suberin of this tree too contains a phenolic acid, as we have already mentioned.

It is to be expected that the waxes occurring on the outside of the cuticle and within the latter will, at least in the same plant, differ but slightly, as they will in both places owe their origin to the same synthetic process inside the epidermis cells. A special study of this problem, however, has not yet been carried out.

The constitution of the various waxes differs so widely that a discussion has little meaning; the literature has been reviewed in detail by WARTH (l.c.).

The waxes excreted by the epidermis of many plants, as well as the waxes deposited in the cuticular membrane, in suberin-layers and in other layers of the cell-wall have, so far as they have been studied, always proved to be at least partly crystalline. As has been mentioned already, in meristematic walls their presence was discovered by means of their X-ray diagram. This method has been used extensively by KREGER (1948, 1958) in order to determine the chemical nature of the main component of cuticular waxes and of wax of stopper-cork. This study was based on the classic work of PIPER and CHIBNALL on the relation existing between the X-ray interference pattern and the chemical constitution. On crystallizing, the aliphatic constituents of waxes are all aligned in the same manner. The bases of the unit cells are all alike, fig. 24, and so are the interferences of those lattice planes that run parallel to the molecule axis, the so-called side spacings, group a in fig. 25. Differences between the X-ray diagrams of the different constituents appear only in the reflections of the long spacing which arise from the lattice planes which are normal to the molecule chains, group b in fig. 25. These differences permit certain conclusions both on the length of the molecules as determined by the number of C-atoms and on their chemical constitution: whether it is an aliphatic hydrocarbon with or without a functional group and whether the latter is a carboxyl, an esterized or non-esterized OH-group, or a carbonyl.

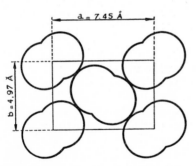

Fig. 24. Diagram showing the arrangement of the chains in a transverse section of the unit cell of a crystalline aliphatic long-chain wax component.

At least in cuticular layers and in suberin lamellae the wax crystallites so far have proved to be tabular, being oriented parallel to the surface of the cell-wall. Since the wax-molecules are always oriented normal to the plane of the wax-platelets and are positively birefringent with reference to the molecule axis, and since the double refraction of the wax usually is stronger than that of the cellulose, which is present

in these wall-layers, the latter usually are negatively birefringent with reference to their surface; the major refractive index is oriented normal to this
surface.

In these cell-walls the presence of waxes is therefore, as a rule, immediately
recognizable under the polarization microscope. This birefringence moreover,
disappears on extraction of the wax. When the spe-
cimen is mounted in glycerol and heated for a short
time, the negative birefringence disappears too, because the wax crystallites melt. On cooling the
birefringence returns. These points will be treated
in some more detail in sections 2362 and 2364.

On account of their lipid character waxes can,
of course, be stained by means of dyes that are
soluble in fats, e.g. by sudan III, but this is no specific reaction, as these dyes also stain a large
number of other substances, e.g. wax-free cutin
and suberin and intra- as well as intercellular
triglycerides, resins, essential oils and phosphatides.

A large number of organic substances may be
used for dissolving and extracting waxes, especially at higher temperatures. According to WEBER
(1942), alcohol is to be regarded as a bad solvent,
benzene and carbon tetrachloride as good ones, but trichloroethane and chloroform as the best ones. Boiling pyridin is recommended by M. MEYER (1938).
According to ROELOFSEN (1952), even if the cuticular membrane is boiled for
days in these liquids, this is not sufficient to extract all the wax. Part of it seems
to be chemically bound to the cutin (cf. section 2362).

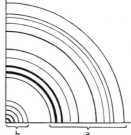

Fig. 25. Quadrant of the
X-ray diagram of aliphatic
long-chain wax compo-
nents; a: Side spacings, b:
several orders of the long
spacing.

As the birefringence of the cuticle proper is very weak in comparison with
that of the cuticular layer, and may even be entirely wanting, it has been
suggested (FREY-WYSSLING, 1953: 295) that the wax would occur mainly
or exclusively in the cuticular layer, but this assumption seems unfounded,
as the cuticle would also be optically inactive when the wax molecules were
not oriented. We do not know whether there are wax crystallites in the cuticle,
but if there are, they must be arranged at random.

18. Other Substances that may occur in the Cell-wall

181. PROTEINS

The question whether the cell-wall, apart from the plasmodesmata, contains
protein, has already for more than a century captivated the attention of
botanists. The answer may be of importance with regard to a more fundamental
problem, viz. the question whether the cell-wall is to be regarded as a living
or a non-living part of the cell. The idea that the cell-wall might be a living
element containing protoplasm, was born out of the difficulty the older
botanists experienced when they tried to explain its surface growth and the
phenomena that are related to the latter on the assumption that it is an
entirely passive structure. However, with the advent of modern biochemistry
it became possible to visualize synthesis of cell-wall material within the wall
without necessarily assuming the presence of living protoplasm. If precursors
and enzymes are produced in the protoplasm and diffuse into the wall, the

synthesis of cellulose and of other cell-wall constituents may take place within the wall in the absence of protoplasm. That this actually may occur, is indicated e.g. by the synthesis of cellulose around the cells of *Acetobacter xylinum*, cf. section 114. Also by the old findings of CORRENS, FITTING and others, according to which the walls of certain algae and of the megaspores of *Pteridophyta* may show growth in thickness although there is no contact with the cytoplasm [(cf. section 232). The proof of cellulose synthesis within the wall was given recently by SETTERFIELD and BAYLEY (1958a) in experiments with coleoptiles.

Presence of protein is, of course, no proof of the presence of living protoplasm or of enzymes; the cell-walls of micro-organisms and of animals may contain protein, and they may even consist for the greater part of protein, but the latter is a scleroprotein. Absence of protein, on the other hand, excludes the presence of protoplasm and enzymes, and would prove therefore that the cell-wall plays but a passive part.

Reviews of the older literature on the presence of protein in the cell-wall are to be found e.g. in KÜSTER (1956) and in TUNMANN-ROSENTHALER (1931). Originally, too much faith has been placed on the result of a few non-specific protein reactions, e.g. that with MILLON's reagent, which reacts not only with the tyrosine of proteins, but also with other phenols. The observations on the changes which the faculty to absorb certain stains as well as other physical properties undergo when the cell-wall is heated, and which were ascribed to the coagulation of protein, are not very convincing either. Typical for such observations are those of TUPPER-CAREY and PRIESTLEY (1923).

At present, however, it may be regarded as definitely proved that the primary cell-wall indeed contains protein, and that it is left behind in it when the secondary layers are deposited. The final proof was supplied by TRIPP et al. (1951), who in experiments with full-grown cotton hairs succeeded in separating the primary wall from the secondary layers by a mechanical device. The primary walls which could be collected in this way, proved to contain 1.9—2.8% N, which might correspond with circ. 12—17% protein. In fact, hydrolysis yielded amino-acids. Protein reactions (ninhydrine, MILLON's reagent, xanthoprotein) on this material, however, were indefinite, which casts doubt on the reliability of these reactions in cell-walls.

In the method used by TRIPP et al. the possibility that the protoplasmatic protein is not completely removed during the process of cleaning, and that a slight amount therefore may still adhere to the cell-wall, is entirely excluded. This can not be said of the methods applied by other investigators, who have reported the presence of protein e.g. in washed cleaned cell-walls of disintegrated cambium, coleoptiles, seedlings, etc. (cf. section 221). The cell-walls of unicellular organisms, like yeasts and bacteria, are perhaps somewhat more easily cleaned; the cells may be burst in a micro-ball mill, and the cell-walls separated from the cell contents by centrifuging, vigorously blending the sediment with water, centrifuging once more, etc. The amounts of protein found by different authors in the cell-wall of yeast, vary between 6 and 13% (ROELOFSEN, 1953; NORTHCOTE and HORNE, 1952; FALCONE and NICKERSON, 1956). The last-named authors are of opinion that the protein is linked to mannan and to glucan, which seems to exclude any protoplasmic or enzymic character. There are many similar findings with regard to the cell-walls of *Bacteria* and *Actinomycetes* many of which also contain scleroproteins (e.g. ROMANO and NICKERSON, 1956; SALTON, 1953).

In recent times too, just as formerly, still other arguments are adduced in favour of the opinion that the primary walls must contain protein, and even in favour of the existence of cellulose-protein complexes, but they are not convincing. That the X-ray diagram of cellulose in the cell-wall becomes clearer when the latter is extracted with alkali, has, for instance, been ascribed to the decomposition of a cellulose-protein (PRESTON, 1952:195), but the alkali, of course, decomposes and removes several other substances which might influence the clearness of the X-ray diagram. Furthermore it has been said that the apparent twisting of the cellulose microfibrils round each other implies that they are produced in situ, and hence that cytoplasm and cell-wall must interpenetrate (FREY-WYSSLING and MÜHLETHALER, 1951). It has also been supposed that the microfibrils grow in thickness, and that they must therefore be surrounded by cytoplasm (BOSSHARD, 1952), but this too is not proved. These points have also been dealt with in section 114.

In secondary layers protein has not with certainty been identified; if it be present at all in these layers, the amount must, at any rate, be much lower than that in the primary wall. In fully developed cotton hairs for instance the total amount of protein is 1%, but it is entirely confined to the cell-lumen and to the primary wall (TRIPP et al., l.c.).

182. EXTRACTIVE MATERIALS

The term "extractive materials" is used for substances that are present in the cell-wall, and can be extracted with water or with organic solvents with or without heating, but which can not be regarded as normal constituents of the cell-wall. The last-named restriction is necessary in order to exclude such substances as the soluble polyoses, the poly-uronides, the waxes and part of the lignin and of the inorganic cell-wall constituents. The latter are regarded as normal constituents, because they occur in large groups of plants, and if not in all kinds of cell-walls, then at least in cell-walls of a definite type. The extractive materials, on the other hand, vary considerably from species to species. As a rule, they appear in the cell-wall only after the protoplast has ceased to live, and this too indicates that they are not essential.

Most of the extractive substances that are known at present, have been derived from the cell-walls of wood. They are of a considerable diversity; a review has been given by WISE and JAHN (1952: 543). The principal groups are: essential oils, resins, tannins and related coloured substances, alcaloids, organic acids and glycosides. In order to extract all of them, various solvents have to be used, e.g. water, steam, alcohol and a mixture of benzene and alcohol. Some of these substances are of economic importance; they may e.g. increase the value of wood by lending it colour or an agreeable smell or by enhancing its power of resistance against rotting and against the attacks of insects, shipworm, and similar pests, or by influencing its combustibility and its weight. The amount in which these substances may be present varies in wood from almost nothing to circ. 30%.

In wood the extractive materials are produced by cells that remain for a long time alive, viz. wood parenchyma, tyloses, wood rays and cells of resin ducts. The substances are secreted by these cells either during their life or afterwards; in both cases the substances diffuse into the surrounding cell-walls. Not all the material that can be extracted from wood, is, of course, present in the cell-walls; part of it is derived from the desiccated contents of the cells.

7*

As mentioned in sections 171 and 172, cork and cuticular layers usually contain several extractive materials in addition to wax, cf. also KÜSTER (1956: 712). The cellulose-part of epidermal walls contains such substances more often than the walls of other living cells, which usually are free of extractive materials (except lipids). A peculiar situation is met with in the hairs of the so-called "green lint" cotton strains, where the secondary walls contain many thin lamellae, probably consisting of lipids with chlorophyll (HOCK, 1947). On exposure to the light of the sun the colour gradually disappears.

183. PHYTOMELANE

The most resistant product that is found in plants, is a black substance which is deposited in some *Compositae* in the middle lamellae and also intercellularly in certain layers of the pericarp. HANAUSEK has published detailed anatomical descriptions of these layers in the years 1902—1913. The substance has been studied chemically by DAFERT and MIKLAUZ (1912) and by DE VRIES (1948). The last-named author also dealt with the way in which it is produced, and with the circumstances which may affect its production. A discussion of its chemical properties is given by DAFERT (cf. KLEIN, 1933 III), and a detailed review of the literature by DE VRIES (l.c.). See also e.g. TUNMANN-ROSENTHALER (1931).

Apart from HJ, by which phytomelane is under certain circumstances slightly attacked, there is no reagent which influences it at room temperature. It can therefore be isolated from the pericarp by oxidizing the other organic constituents with a mixture of chromic acid and sulphuric acid at room temperature; at higher temperatures, however, the phytomelane too is attacked. Analysis of the product that is obtained in this way shows that the elements C, H and O are present in the proportion $3.7 : 2.1 : 1$; the carbon content proves to be more than 70%. As the elements H and O are present in the same proportion as in water and in carbohydrates, it has been suggested that phytomelane owes its origin to the dehydration of a carbohydrate; the empiric formula of phytomelane as well as that of a carbohydrate is $Cx(H_2O)y$. According to DE VRIES (l.c.), there are indications that phytomelane is at first semi-liquid, and that it gradually solidifies.

With regard to the physical properties and to the submicroscopical structure of phytomelane nothing is known.

In various other objects substances are present that may be related to the phytomelanes of the pericarp of the *Compositae*. The black substance in ebony (wood of *Diospyros ebenum*) is according to DAFERT and MIKLAUZ no true phytomelane, as it is attacked more readily by the mixture of chromic acid and sulphuric acid. However, as the true phytomelanes too are in the long run attacked, the black pigment in ebony may, according to DE VRIES (l.c.), after all be regarded as related to phytomelane; it would only be less strongly carbonized. Its C-content is 65%. From Coromandel ebony and from the stem of a tree-fern DE VRIES could isolate, by means of the mixture of chromic acid and sulphuric acid, substances that proved to be very resistant and of which the empiric formula proved to be $Cx(H_2O)y$, but which contained only 55% carbon (the carbon content of sugar is 40%). The darkly coloured substances that have been found in some roots and rhizomes may also be related to phytomelane. There may also be affinity to humin. The intensity of the black colour of all these substances is the higher, the higher the C-content.

The faculty to absorb light would be due to the presence of multiple bonds between the C-atoms.

184. INORGANIC SUBSTANCES

Literature on this subject is to be found in KÜSTER (1956: 705) and FREY-WYSSLING (1959).

In the ash of cell-walls two groups of inorganic substances are found, in the first place substances that originally were bound to organic cell-wall constituents, and in the second place inorganic incrustations.

To the first group belong e.g. the oxides of metals that were bound to the carboxyl-group of uronic and other acids, especially of Ca and Mg, and also the acid radicals that were linked to carbohydrates in the form of esters, viz. SO_4 and perhaps PO_4 and SiO_2. From this group perhaps Ca-oxalate merits special mentioning, because its presence in cell-walls is unexpected. Many cases are mentioned by KOHL (1889); OZTIG (1940) described the occurrence in the innermost layers of the stipe of *Acetabularia* and in xeromorphic *Mesembrianthemaceae*.

The main representatives of the second group are SiO_2, $CaCO_3$, and Fe- and Mn-oxides. Several other inorganic salts too may be present in the cell-wall either in undissociated or dissociated form, and either temporarily or permanently. This applies, for instance, to the epidermis, which, as is well-known, may excrete salts. The way in which these inorganic compounds may be identified, is described e.g. by MOLISCH (1923) and by TUNMANN-ROSENTHALER (1931).

The incrustation with $CaCO_3$, which is best known to the botanist, is that of the cystoliths, which are found in all *Urticales* and in part of the *Combretaceae*, *Acanthaceae* and *Cucurbitaceae*. The cystoliths are negatively birefringent, but this is not due to the presence of $CaCO_3$, but probably to that of the cellulose (FREY-WYSSLING, 1959: 49). There are several other deposits of calcium carbonate in or on plant parts; they have been reviewed by PIA (1934). With regard to the form in which the calcium carbonate is present, we mention that in *Corallinaceae* it is, according to BAAS BECKING and GALLIHER (1931), present in the form of calcite, whereas in some other *Rhodophyceae* it would occur in the form of aragonite (cf. FRITSCH, 1945). BRANDENBERGER and SCHINZ (1944) too found calcite in various *Thallophyta*, aragonite in other ones. According to BOLLMANN (unpublished, quoted by FREY-WYSSLING 1959:49) the $CaCO_3$ of cystoliths is also in the form of calcite crystals, having a mean diameter of $0,1\,\mu$.

In fresh-water plants deposits of $Fe(OH)_3$ and $Mn(OH)_3$ are frequently found in the walls, e.g. in iron-bacteria and in *Chlorophyceae*, but also in the reddish-brown teeth of *Elodea* leaves. Literature is cited by KÜSTER (l.c.), CHOLODNY (1922), TUNMANN-ROSENTHALER (1931: 195). With regard to the manner in which these substances are deposited, and with regard to their physical state nothing is known, except in iron-bacteria (W. VAN ITERSON, 1958).

Well-known is the phenomenon of cell-wall silicification, e.g. in *Silicoflagellatae*, *Diatomeae*, *Equisetales*, *Gramineae* and *Cyperaceae*, but which may occur in nearly all kinds of plants. It is observed mainly in the epidermis, sometimes equally distributed and sometimes locally in cystolith-like swellings. It is mainly present in the outer wall, but not rarely in the anticlinal walls too. In other tissues too the cell-walls may be silicified, e.g. in wood. For literature on this subject we may refer to KÜSTER (l.c.) and to FREY-WYSSLING (l.c.).

The manner in which silica skeletons may be obtained, has been described by
TUNMANN-ROSENTHALER (1931).

Silica is usually present in the form of a deposit between the organic cell-wall constituents. When the latter are removed by oxidation, a silica skeleton is obtained which shows rodlet-birefringence (A. FREY, 1926). The silica is usually amorphous, but in *Diatomeae*, the *Chlorophycea Chlorochitridion* and in the stalk of the *Ficus* cystolith, it occurs in the crystalline form, viz. as quartz (BRANDENBERGER and FREY-WYSSLING, 1947; ESCHRICH, 1954); see also LANNING et al. (1958). Silica deposits in the cell-lumen and in the intercellular spaces (NETOLITZKY, 1929) are beyond the scope of this work.

2. The Cell-wall Structure

As is already implicated in the title that has been chosen for this volume of Linsbauer's encyclopedia, this part of it too will deal only with the structure, especially the ultrastructure, of the cell-wall itself. The form of the cell will be considered only in those cases where there seems to be some relation between the latter and the cell-wall structure.

21. Some special Methods of Cell-wall Investigation

In dealing with the cell-wall structure it will appear again and again that beside the traditional mode of investigation by means of the ordinary microscope and the ordinary reactions and staining methods, other procedures have become indispensable, viz. polarization microscopy, X-ray analysis, and electron microscopy. It does not seem necessary to describe these methods here, as this may be found in the manuals that are dealing with them. We will confine our attention to the information that by the aid of these methods may be obtained with regard to the structure of the cell-wall (see also FREY-WYSSLING, 1959 and PRESTON, 1952).

211. MICROSCOPIC METHODS

Although the ordinary microscope is more suitable for the study of the structure of cells and tissues than of the cell-wall, and although the information it gives us with regard to the structure and constitution of the cell-wall does not extend to all aspects of the latter, this information nevertheless should not be neglected. As is well known, one may study the constitution of the cell-wall or of certain layers of the latter by means of specific reagents including stains. The reagents and solvents that are commonly used, have already been mentioned in the first part of this work. We may further refer to manuals of microscopical anatomy like STRASBURGER-KOERNICKE (1923), MOLISCH (1923), TUNMANN-ROSENTHALER (1931), JOHANSEN (1940). Prescriptions for the cutting of fibres with the normal microtome may be found in the works of LUNIAK (1953), A. HERZOG (1955), SCHWARZ (1934), and for wood e.g. in that of KISSER (1939). For the use of ultramicrotomes, see OSTER and POLLISTER (1956, vol. III).

We will restrict our discussion to those microscopical methods that are of importance to the study of the cell-wall, but which, as a rule, are not mentioned in handbooks.

Ballooning. Certain differences in structure between the various layers of a cell-wall may be made visible, when the cell-wall is treated with agents that cause a swelling of the cellulose, as the way in which these layers swell, proves to be different. Such differences are responsible for the so-called ballooning or beading. A necessary condition is that the outermost layer of the fibre, be it the primary wall or the outermost layer of the secondary wall, does not swell at all or, if it swells, either to a lesser degree or in a different way owing to the circumstance that the cellulose microfibrils are oriented in a more transverse direction as compared with those of more central layers. The ballooning of raw cotton fibres, as depicted and explained by NAEGELI more than a century ago, is the best known example, and it is also the easiest to obtain. The outermost layer of the cotton fibre is formed by the primary wall, and here the greater part of the microfibrils run in a transverse direction.

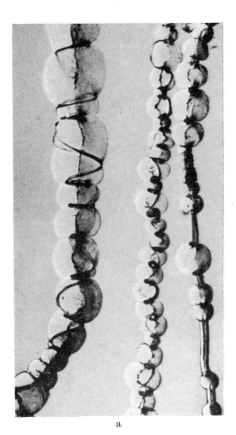

As this layer contains cutin, wax, pectin and hemicelluloses, it hardly swells at all, and the very slight swelling which actually occurs, moreover, does not take place in the direction of the microfibrils, which means that the diameter of this layer does not increase. The secondary layers, on the other hand, consist nearly

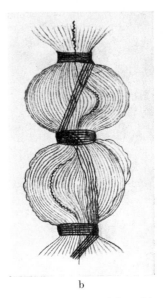

a   b

Fig. 26. Ballooning of, a: raw cotton fibre (from HERZOG, 1955); b: bast fibre of *Cannabis* (drawing by NAEGELI, 1864a).

entirely of cellulose, and the microfibrils are in this part of the wall oriented in a steep spiral; these layers therefore swell strongly in a radial direction. The primary wall is unable to withstand the pressure exercised on it by the swelling secondary layers, and is broken up into a great number of short cylinders, or rings, which are responsible for the constrictions between the beads formed by the protruding secundary wall, cf. fig. 26. When the primary wall has been scraped away in undried fibres, ballooning is no longer possible (KERR, 1946). When the non-cellulose has been removed from the primary wall, ballooning may still occur, although this happens but rarely (HOCK et al., 1941). This proves that the presence of non-cellulose is of importance but that the effect is caused by differences in the orientation of the cellulose microfibrils. This is in agreement with the fact that under certain conditions the strips by which the swelling is locally prevented, are not formed by the primary wall but by the outermost layer of the secondary wall. Since this layer has a spiral structure, no balloons are formed but a swollen helix, resembling a thick rope, cf. fig. 142.

Ballooning has also been observed in many other kinds of fibriform cells in which the outermost layer differs in orientation as also to some extent in chemical constitution from the subsequent ones. Figures have been published e.g. of bast fibres of *Linum* (ANDERSON, 1927 b; HOCK, 1942), *Boehmeria* (NODDER, 1922; ALDABA, 1927), *Edgeworthia* (HERZOG, 1955: fig. 879), *Asclepias* (ROLLINS, 1947) also of slighty lignified bast fibres like those of *Cannabis*, where the phenomenon was already noted by NAEGELI, cf. fig. 26 b. Delignified sclerenchyma fibres from the vascular bundles of various *Monocotyledones*, wood fibres and tracheids too show the phenomenon, cf. fig. P123. GRIFFIOEN (1935) has determined the relation between the dimensions of the balloon and the fibre diameter. A survey of literature is to be found with MANGENOT and RAISON (1942).

Although the consecutive layers of the cell-wall in all these examples indeed show differences in the orientation of the cellulose microfibrils, as we will show further on, ballooning in itself can not be regarded as a strict proof of such a difference, as it can also be obtained in fibres of which the microfibrils are all oriented in the same way in the axial direction, as in rayon fibres and even in natural silk, by treating the outermost layer with certain chemicals by which the faculty of swelling is reduced or destroyed (HALLER, 1935; OHARA, 1933).

In some fibres, e.g. those of *Pandanus*, *Andropogon*, *Arundo donax*, *Saccharum* and *Bambusa*, the difference between successive layers that is required for ballooning, does not occur once only, but more than once in the same cell-wall. Here, we find major beads, comprising the whole cell-wall, as well as minor beads, that are restricted to central wall layers, see fig. 112 b. There may even occur more than one small bead inside a bigger one. Sometimes part of the layers in these multi-layered fibres are expelled and produce telescope-like protrusions at broken ends of the fibres, a phenomenon that had been observed already in 1864 by NAEGELI. This phenomenon is to be ascribed to a much steeper orientation of the cellulose microfibrils in the inner part of each layer than in the outer part (V. D. HOUVEN VAN OORDT-HULSHOF, 1957; PRESTON and SINGH, 1950, 1952).

Lamellae. Ballooning and telescoping are due to differences between relatively thick layers. At least in the secondary wall each of these thick layers consists, as a rule, of a great many very thin ones. How many of the latter can be recognized under the microscope, depends on the latter's resolving power, the staining method, etc. These "lamellae" are usually studied in transverse sections of cell-walls that are swollen e.g. in diluted cuprammonium. A classic example are the tenths of daily growth-rings that are seen in the cotton fibre (BALLS, 1919), see fig. 27 and section 23441. In other hairs the lamellae are certainly not always daily growth-rings, cf. section 23442.

With cotton the lamellae probably differ in density only, but in other instances there are differences in orientation of the microfibrils, e.g. in another classic object, the cell-wall of the green alga *Valonia*, cf. section 2411. Sometimes from layer to layer differences in chemical constitution may be present, which are responsible for differences in swelling, e.g. in collenchyma cell-walls, which contain lamellae that are alternately rich in pectin and in cellulose, cf. section 23452. BAILEY and KERR (1935) give many other striking examples of lamellar structures resulting from differences either in orientation of the microfibrils or in chemical constitution.

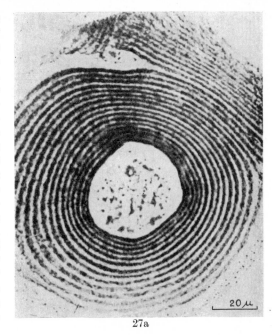

27a

Phase-contrast microscopy (BENNETT et al., 1951) is especially suitable for detecting lamellae in cell-wall sections; the refractive index of the mounting liquid should to this end be slightly higher than that of the section (MÜLLER, 1956).

Striations. As is well known, a great many fibres, tracheids and algal cell-walls are provided with microscopically visible striations, usually arranged in S- or Z-helices[1]. These striations are often easily observable, e.g. in bast fibres and in longitudinal sections of freshly cut wood, when the latter are studied in air, water or another liquid with a low refractive index. Sometimes two or even three sets of striations are visible in the same cell-wall, usually alternating in direction, and with different pitch.

The striations often become better visible or visible in a larger number, when the cell-wall is allowed to swell a little, see fig. P 28. Here too, phase contrast microscopy and special staining methods (BUCHER, 1957a) may be useful. With a pretreatment with NO_2 the outermost striations seem to become more easily distinguishable (ROLLINS, 1945).

Since the length of swelling fibres decreases, the pitch of the helices too undergoes a decrease. Pressure on the cover glass, a trick that is often applied to make the striation better visible, is another method to reduce the spiral

---

[1] When a Z-helix is placed vertical, i.e. in the direction N—S under the microscope, the part nearest to the observer is parallel to the middle part of the letter Z. The mirror image of such a helix is an S-helix. This designation has been introduced by textile scientists, and is recommended for wider use, since the terms right- and left-handed are apt to cause confusion. Geometricians, technicians and some botanists call a Z-helix right-handed, as it is found in a corkscrew, which has to be turned "to the right" to be driven in. However, other botanists call such a helix left-handed. In old German botanical literature a Z-striation has often been called "rechts ansteigend" or "süd-östlich" (from south to east), an S-striation "links ansteigend" or "süd-westlich". BREMEKAMP (1944) has introduced the terms helictic and antihelictic for Z-helices and S-helices respectively.

pitch. When the ends of fibres are not impeded in their movements, they will, in case a helical layer is resent, begin to twist. This also will change the pitch of the helix. Twists enforce a helical structure upon a layer that originally had no such structure at all. We should therefore be careful with the interpretation of helical structures if the latter are seen only in swollen cell-walls.

27 b

Fig. 27. Daily growth-rings in cotton fibre as seen in, a: swollen transverse section (outer-part ruptured) and in b: a swollen fibre (from KERR, 1937 and A. HERZOG, 1955).

Another method by the aid of which the striations, at least of superficial ones, may be made more easily distinguishable, is that of metal shadowing (i.e. by spraying the object in vacuo and under a low angle with some vaporized metal) after which the object is studied in a reflecting microscope (illumination from above) with a high-power objective. The shadowing emphasizes the striation, especially if its direction is perpendicular to that of the latter. This technique has especially been applied by EMERTON and GOLDSMITH (1956), see fig. P118.

The striations that are visible under the ordinary microscope always run parallel to the average direction of the cellulose microfibrils in the layer in question, but they can not be identical with them, as the latter are far too thin. The striations may be due to the presence of bundles of microfibrils or else to fissures between the latter.

There is still another method of making the direction of the cellulose orientation more conspicuous, that deserves our attention. It was introduced by BAILEY and VESTAL (1937a), but has rarely been applied by others, and consists in *encrusting the cell-wall with visible iodine crystals* by applying potassium triiodide and then sulphuric acid; (in our experience it is advisable to treat the material for a short time with 2% H_2O_2 before the sulphuric acid is added). These crystals prove to have their greatest dimension parallel to the direction of the microfibrils, probably because they are formed in fissures and in interfibrillar spaces, which subsequently are widened. Fig. 29 shows the striations in a tracheid of a conifer that has been treated in this way; two helical systems are visible. In other instances three different layers proved to be present, the inner and the outer one with an S- or Z-helix with a low pitch, the middle one with a high-pitch helix ascending in the opposite direction.

The same authors (1937b) directed the attention to the remarkable *corrosion figures* that are shown by lignified cell-walls as the result of an attack by certain fungi. These are either biconical cavities or cylindrical cavities with conical ends, which, as a rule run parallel to the main direction of the cellulose microfibrils, fig. 30 (compare also the figure shown on plate II of Esau, 1953). The way in which these cavities arise, is as yet uncertain. The explanation suggested by the present author (1956), who rejected an earlier explanation of Frey-

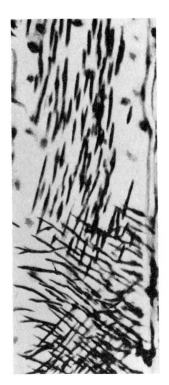

Wyssling, seems to be supported by the observations of Hess et al. (1957) regarding transverse structures in the wall of fibres (cf. section 113). This mode of corrosion is characteristic of certain fungi, but it has repeatedly been noted that in the first stage of an attack by other fungi and by bacteria the existing microscopically visible striations become more conspicuous.

Dimensional changes on swelling

There is a considerable amount of literature on the swelling of cell-walls. It started already in the 19th century with von Höhnel, Naegeli, Schwendener, Steinbrinck, etc. (cf. Dippel, 1898). More recent literature was reviewed by Mangenot and Raison (1942).

As has been stated already, swelling of the cell-wall may reveal the presence of different layers

Fig. 29. Cellulose orientations in the wall of a tracheid as revealed by encrusted iodine crystal-aggregates (from Bailey and Vestal, 1937a).

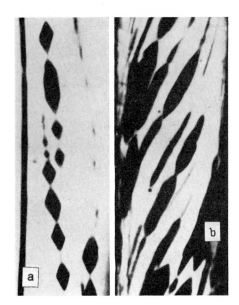

and of a helical structure. By studying the degree of swelling or shrinking in various directions we may obtain still more information. The swelling of cellulose may rest on two different processes, viz. an interfibrillar swelling, which appears e.g. in water and stronger in diluted alkali, and an intrafibrillar one, which takes place e.g. in concentrated alkalis and acids and diluted cellulose solvents. In

Fig. 30. Corrosion of a xylem fibre (a) and a tracheid (b) by a soft rot fungus (Bailey and Vestal, 1937b).

the first-named process it are the non-celluloses like hemicellulose and pectin that are mainly responsible for the swelling, whereas the cellulose microfibrils increase but slightly in thickness because of the swelling of amorphous parts of the microfibrils. In the second process the crystalline parts of the cellulose microfibrils too begin to swell, and this is accompanied by a loss of crystallinity. The microfibrils doubtless become much thicker. They will also shorten, because the chain molecules of which they consist, will, as soon as they are no more aligned in the crystallites, try to assume the statistically more probable, more or less zigzagged form.

Let us first consider *interfibrillar swelling*. This will always be strongest perpendicular to the plane of the cell-wall, as relatively the largest amount of interfibrillar space is found in that direction, the microfibrils being always oriented in the plane of the wall (uniplanar orientation). When the micro-fibrils are irregularly distributed in this plane (isotropic orientation), which means that they show no other kind of orientation, the swelling in this plane will also be entirely isotropic, i.e. equally strong in all directions, although, of course, less strong than in the direction perpendicular to this plane.

When the microfibrils, apart from their orientation parallel to the plane of the cell-wall, show in addition preference for a certain direction within that plane, e.g. for a more or less axial one as in the secondary layers of elongated cells, transverse interfibrillar swelling will exceed swelling in the axial di-rection, and this anisotropy of swelling will be the more pronounced the higher the degree of axial orientation. Tubular cells with a predominantly transverse orientation of the microfibrils, e.g. vessels and growing elongated cells, will, on the other hand, show a greater increase in length than in cir-cumference. Fibres with ideally aligned axially oriented microfibrils, like the bast fibres of *Boehmeria*, show practically no increase in length, but only in diameter, at least so long as there is interfibrillar swelling only.

Fibres with a helical structure of the various layers, will show a greater increase in length, the lower the pitch of the helix in the predominating layer. They will at the same time untwist, since with increasing diameter of the cell the path of the helically oriented microfibrils would have to increase, which is impossible. The direction in which the untwisting will take place, depends on the direction of the helix in the dominating layer, and is characteristic for the species. When the twisting is studied in bundles of fibres, the untwisting in the swelling bundles and the twisting in the shrinking ones are both easily observable, and such tests are therefore often applied when textile fibres of unknown origin are to be identified. REIMERS (1922) and NEWMAN and RIDDELL (1954) have described the outcome of this test for a large number of species. KERPEL (1938) described in what manner the twisting may be studied in a single plant hair, viz. of *Ceiba*. Cell-wall layers containing crossed fibrillar structures, may swell abnormally, see section 23433.

In *intrafibrillar swelling* the walls will likewise increase in thickness and very considerably so, but in other respects entirely different phenomena are observed. Pieces of cell-wall appear to shrink considerably in the plane of the wall. Very instructive was the observation of CORRENS (1893) that a piece of *Valonia* cell-wall (cf. section 2411) increased 300% in thickness, whereas the surface decreased 30—50% in various directions. This at first sight strange behaviour is not only due to the shortening of the fibrils, but also to the cir-cumstance that they have to run a more zigzag course since they overcross and intertwine and since their thickness increases. This shrinkage will be greatest in the direction in which most of the microfibrils are oriented, and by measuring the changes in length and breadth of free cells or of cell-wall fragments, one can therefore obtain indications with regard to the predominant orientation. The first to apply the anisotropy of dimensional changes during the intrafibrillar swelling as a method for studying cell-wall structures was VAN ITERSON (1937). In applying the method we should keep in mind the following complications. When the experiment is carried out with a fragment of the cell-wall like the piece of *Valonia* cell-wall used by CORRENS, there is no limit to the swelling whatsoever. The fragment may even become gelatinous and may eventually dissolve. With cells things are somewhat different, since there will always be some outer layer in which the microfibrils are oriented either in a transverse direction or in a helix with a low pitch. Such layers will offer some resistance to an increase in diameter of the cell, and will therefore direct the radial swelling towards the cell lumen. With thin-walled cells a heavy swelling perpendicular to the plane of the wall is possible before the lumen is entirely filled with the swollen mass. Therefore, parenchymatic cells are free to decrease in all dimensions as a result of the shrinkage in surface of the wall. Most fibres, however, have relatively thick walls and a small lumen, and these will begin to increase in diameter as soon as the lumen is filled up. As has already been mentioned, this will be counteracted by the outer layers, which have a more nearly transverse orientation. As this resistance will vary in strength locally as well as in different cells, all kind of things may happen; there may be a marked untwisting, constrictions may appear or it may come to ballooning and telescoping. The length of the fibres will allways decrease since the microfibrils are predominantly oriented in that direction, or at least in a spiral with a pitch of more than 45^0. In bast fibres the shortening may amount to more than 60%.

A quite different feature of the cell-wall, viz. the *shape of the pits*, also allows us to draw some conclusions with regard to the structure of the cell-wall. If they are oblong or split-like, the greater part of the cellulose microfibrils will be oriented parallel to the longer axis of the pit. This applies to ordinary pits as well as to the bordered ones, and to those in growing cells as well as to those in full-grown cells.

Attempts have also been made to correlate the mechanical properties of the fibres with the orientation of the cellulose microfibrils; a low-pitch helical arrangement, for instance, has been thought to indicate ductility (SONNTAG, 1909). It is, however, more probable that this property is determined by the non-cellulose by which the cellulose is incrusted (FREY-WYSSLING, 1952). Cotton fibres e.g., in which the pitch is lower than in bast fibres like ramie, flax and hemp, are not more extensible.

A strongly specialized microscopical method of cell-wall study is that by means of *microspectroscopy*. Here the absorption of rays of various wavelengths by the various layers in sections of the cell-wall is quantitatively estimated. The investigation can be carried out in visible as well as in ultra-violet light (BLOUT, 1953, 1954). LANGE (1950, 1954, see also TREIBER, 1957) was the first to study the chemical constitution of the various layers of a cell-wall, viz. that of conifer tracheids, by the aid of this method. He also introduced the *interference microscope* for the determination of the distribution of cell-wall components (see TREIBER, 1957: 279; LANGE and KJAER, 1957). HEYN (1957) and GREEN (1958a) used this new method for the study of other properties of the cell-wall.

212. POLARIZATION MICROSCOPY

For information with regard to the optical theory of birefringence and for descriptions of the methods that are applied in polarization microscopy we refer to the following manuals: AMBRONN and FREY (1926), PFEIFFER (1949), McCLUNG (1950) and FREY-WYSSLING (1959). The works of BURRI (1950), HARTSHORNE and SHOART (1950), and BEREK (1953) give more details, but are more specially intended for mineralogists. When the birefringence is very slight, which is not rare in biological objects, useful indications for its study are to be found in LAVES and ERNST (1943), SWANN and MITCHISON (1950) and INOUÉ and HYDE (1957). In such cases the birefringence may be enhanced by staining with dichroitic stains like congo-red, benzoazurin and chlor-zinc-iodine. The so-called interference colours that are seen in such preparations, are, of course, abnormal.

The nature of the information which can be obtained by studying the birefringence of the cell-wall, depends on the manner in which the birefringence is brought about.

The first condition that has to be fulfilled, is that the material has an anisotropic structure.

Crystals may, but need not, show so-called *crystalline birefringence*, viz. when the bonds between the atoms or molecules of which they are composed, differ in the three dimensions of the crystal lattice. Plane polarized light travels through a birefringent crystal with a velocity that depends on the orientation of the polarization plane. Higher velocity involves a lower refractive index, and a so-called index ellipsoid may therefore be constructed for elucidating the optical properties of the crystal. The indices are oriented in three mutually perpendicular directions, the smallest one is designated with the symbol ηa, $\eta \gamma$ is the highest one, $\eta \beta$ intermediate. When a crystal is placed on the revolving stage of the polarization microscope with e.g. ηa vertical, there will be extinction when the stage is brought in such a position that either $\eta \beta$ or $\eta \gamma$ coincides with the vibration plane. By these positions therefore we know the orientation of the indices. By using a suitable compensator, preferably a Red I plate, we can find out which is the major one, $\eta \gamma$ and which $\eta \beta$, and in this way the position of the index ellipsoid in the crystal is determined.

An aggregate like cellulose, containing a number of microscopically invisible crystals may, when these crystals are oriented more or less in the same way, also show birefringence, but not, of course, when they are distributed at random, because in that case the differently oriented crystallites compensate each other. It is an absolute condition that the material should be anisotropic.

Oriented molecules do not only produce birefringence when they are present in the form of crystals, but also when they occur in amorphous solids and even in liquids. This *molecular birefringence* is characteristic for all substances consisting of chain molecules. When plane polarized light is transmitted perpendicular to the axis of a straight-chain molecule like that of cellulose, the highest refractive index, $\eta \gamma$ in the accompanying scheme, will be found in the direction of the axis. It is the refractive index of light vibrating in a plane parallel to $\eta \gamma$. Light that vibrates in a direction perpendicular to $\eta \gamma$, may have two refractive indices, viz. ηa and $\eta \beta$, which differ in orientation with regard to the plane of the pyranose-ring. When $\eta \gamma$, the refraction index for light that is transmitted in the direction of the molecular axis is higher than $\eta\alpha$ and $\eta\beta$, as in cellulose, the molecular birefringence is called positive with reference to the molecule axis. In substances like cellulose nitrate and pectic acid $\eta\gamma$ proves to be lower than the mean value of $\eta\alpha$ and $\eta\beta$, and in that case we speak of negative molecular birefringence.

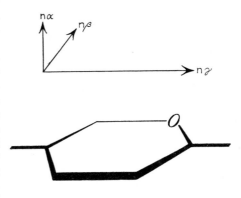

The birefringence of rodlike crystals, of microfibrils or of fibres, may in a similar way be defined as positive or negative with reference to the greatest dimension. Transverse sections of cell-walls, by which the light therefore is transmitted parallel to the surface, are called positively birefringent if the refractive index of the plane-polarized light vibrating in the plane of the cell-wall proves to be the higher one. For convenience sake one may speak of the "orientation of the highest refractive index" or of the "major extinction direction", although in reality orientation and direction apply to the plane of vibration, not to the refractive index. To avoid confusion of the refractive indices of the fibre as a whole with those of the cellulose microfibrils, for the first the signs n and n⊥ are often used.

Just like the birefringence of crystals the molecular birefringence is present only when the particles, in this case the molecules, are oriented. Such an orientation is obtained, for instance, when a solution dries up in the form of a film, for in that case the molecules will be prostrated in the plane of this film, so that the latter when viewed in light that is transmitted parallel to this plane, will show birefringence.

Orientation of molecules may also be realized in other ways, viz. by oriented adsorption: *adsorption birefringence*; when a solution consisting of elongated molecules flows in a thin film over a solid surface or through a thin tube: *flow birefringence*; or when an isotropic substance is subjected to mechanical stress: *strain birefringence*. Adsorption birefringence may appear, for instance, when certain objects are imbibed with certain liquids. Strain birefringence may occur in lenses and also in glass slides, especially when the latter are heated. It has been suggested that it might also occur in stretched cellulose (FREY-WYSSLING and SCHOCH-BODMER, 1938; SCHOCH-BODMER, 1939), but this has not been proved, and another explanation seems more likely (section 22823).

When a bundle of anisotropic molecules, like those of cellulose, crystallizes, the birefringence of the crystallites is the sum of two effects, viz. the molecular birefringence of the individual anisotropic molecules, and the birefringence due to the anisotropy of the bonds between the molecules in the crystal lattice. Whether the birefringence of a solid is crystalline or molecular, can best be detected by means of X-ray analysis. Molecular as well as crystalline birefringence are called *intrinsic*.

Obviously not intrinsic is the so-called *form birefringence*, which is neither due to the presence of a crystal lattice nor to that of anisotropic molecules. It occurs in heterogeneous aggregates consisting of elongated or flattened particles that are distributed in a more or less oriented manner in a medium with a different refractive index. The diameter of the particles furthermore must be small in relation to the wave-length of the light in which they are observed, at least in one direction. They may therefore appear in the form of filaments, rodlets or platelets, but it does not matter whether they are crystalline or amorphous. The medium in which they are dispersed, may be a solid, a fluid or even a gas. Form birefringence may also be present in solids with an anisotropic porous structure when the pores are filled with a substance with a different refractive index; this may be a gas, a fluid or a solid. The cell-walls belong to this category; the cellulose microfibrils and the bundles of these being surrounded by pores which may be filled with various substances, solids like hemicellulose and lignin, fluids like water and imbibing liquids, and in dried cell-walls air; or also solids in the small interfibrillar pores and water or air in the wider pores between the bundles of microfibrils.

Whether the form birefringence will reach a perceptible value, depends on the ratio of the two components, their degree of orientation, and the difference in their refractive index. A heterogeneous aggregate consisting of the components A and B, which shows form birefringence because the refractive index of A is different from that of B, will become isotropic when A is replaced by C, which has the same refractive index as B, provided, of course, that there is no adsorption birefringence, see curve 1 in fig. 31. However, the greater the difference in refractive index, the more light will be scattered, and this may become so serious that the study of the birefringence is impaired. It commonly occurs when the objects are studied in air.

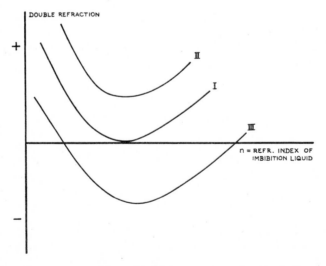

Fig. 31. General appearance of form birefringence curves, 1: when both components are isotropic, 2: when one of them is positively birefringent, 3: when one of them is negatively birefringent.

When either the particles or the medium or both have an intrinsic birefringence, the total birefringence will, of course, be the resultant of the two kinds of birefringence. This is shown in the curves 2 and 3 of fig. 31. According to BAAS BECKING and WAYNE GALLIHER (1931) the inclination of the axis of symmetry of the form birefringence curve would permit to conclude whether the particles or pores causing the form birefringence are tabular or rodlike. However, this seems to be doubtful (McCLUNG, 1950).

A more reliable way to detect the form of the particles and their orientation is to study the form birefringence when the object is viewed from different directions.

In the *Cormophyta* the birefringence of the cell-wall is, as a rule, almost exclusively due to the presence of cellulose, and since the cellulose microfibrils are always oriented in the plane of the wall, the birefringence of the wall is always positive with reference to this plane. However, in the cell-walls of cork and in the cuticular layer it is not due in the first place to the presence of cellulose, but to that of wax. The latter may play a part in other cell-walls too, especially in meristematic ones, but it is there of less importance. Its birefringence is always negative with reference to the wall. Positive birefringence in a cell-wall of a higher plant is therefore, although not a definite proof, at least a very strong indication of the presence of cellulose, and in this way the presence of the latter has in various instances for the first time been recognized, e.g. in the cell-plate and in meristematic cell-walls.

Birefringence of other cell-wall constituents has in higher plants but rarely been found, e.g. in seeds with reserve cellulose, where it may be due to the presence of mannan or of amyloid. In collenchyma cells, which besides cellulose contain a considerable amount of pectin, and where the molecules of the latter prove to be oriented, a very slight negative birefringence due to this substance must be present. However, it is completely dominated by the positive birefringence of the cellulose that is found in these cell-walls. In hemicelluloses and in cutin and suberin no birefringence has ever been observed. It is known, however, that films and threads that have been made from hemicelluloses, may be birefringent, and this indicates that the reason why these substances show no recognizable birefringence in the native cell-wall, must be sought in lack of orientation of their molecules and in the suppression of their small birefringence by that of cellulose.

The cell-walls of *Thallophytes* may contain constituents that are different from cellulose and which nevertheless cause a high degree of birefringence, e.g. alginic acid in *Phaeophyceae* and various as yet unidentified polysaccharides in the latter as well as in *Rhodophyceae* and in *Chlorophyceae*. Most fungi do not contain cellulose; in their cell-walls chitin is the most important birefringent constituent.

The birefringence of the cellulose is due to several causes; there is crystalline birefringence of the crystallites in the microfibrils, molecular birefringence in the more or less amorphous parts of the latter, and rodlet-birefringence in the aggregate formed by the microfibrils and the interfibrillar material. In pure cellulose the latter consists of water or of air, in most cell-walls of moist hemicellulose, pectin or lignin, in some other ones of cutin and wax. Apart from the rodlet-birefringence of pure cellulose, the contributions of these various factors have never been determined separately. The rodlet-birefringence of pure cellulose, however, is far weaker than the intrinsic birefringence, even in air. As it is, like the latter, positive with reference to the axis of the microfibrils, the two are additional.

Chitin behaves in this respect differently, for its intrinsic birefringence is negative and rather small, whereas its rodlet-birefringence is more pronounced and, of course, positive with reference to the axis of the microfibrils.

When a light beam passes an object containing a large number of birefringent particles which, like the microfibrils of the cell-wall, are of a very small size only, the birefringence of these particles is automatically averaged. Therefore, a simple determination of the extinction positions, supplemented by observations by means of a Red I plate, will reveal to us the mean orientation of the major index, and consequently of the microfibrils, at least when the latter are oriented parallel to the plane of the microscope stage, and when no other birefringent substances, like wax, are present.

The value of the birefringence, which is to be estimated by means of suitable compensators, may under certain conditions, be regarded as a measure of the degree of fibrillar orientation. The birefringence of the cell-wall in surface view will be relatively high when the greater part of the microfibrils is oriented parallel to each other, as they are in phloem fibres. However, with a small degree of orientation, as is found e.g. in tubular parenchyma cells, the birefringence produced by the same amount of cellulose will be much lower, and it sinks down to zero when there is no orientation at all as in most isodiametric parenchyma cells.

Things will be different, of course, when the cell-walls are not studied in light that passes perpendicular to their surface, but in light that is transmitted parallel to the latter. Under these circumstances all cell-walls will prove to be birefringent, since the microfibrils always show an orientation parallel to the surface. There is but one exception to this rule, viz. when the microfibrils are all oriented parallel to the direction of the light beam; this happens e.g. when an exactly transverse section of a phloem fibre with highly oriented microfibrils is examined, but even in such a section the isotropy is usually restricted to the main layer, as the microfibrils in the other ones will, as a rule, be oriented in a different way, e.g. transversally or helically. The birefringence of a cell-wall layer viewed parallel to its surface will be highest when the microfibrils are all oriented perpendicular to the direction of the light beam, a condition that is fulfilled in longitudinal sections of fibres with highly oriented microfibrils, and it will be lower when the microfibrils are less highly oriented, as they are in the walls of parenchyma cells, or, in a fibre with highly oriented microfibrils, when the fibre is not sectioned in the longitudinal plane but in some other direction.

The preceding exposition will have shown that a few simple observations by the aid of the polarization microscope are, as a rule, sufficient when we wish to determine the orientation of the cellulose microfibrils in the cell-walls of isolated cells or in the cell-walls seen in transverse or longitudinal sections through a tissue.

Complications arise when the microfibrils are helically oriented. As this orientation is of very common occurrence, we will pay some attention to these complications. For a more detailed treatment we must refer to the special works that have been enumerated above. That in cells with a helical orientation of the microfibrils in the cell-walls the birefringence that is actually observed, will simply be the average of the birefringence in the lower cell-wall and that in the cell-wall by which it is covered, is theoretically not entirely

correct, but may in many circumstances be regarded as a permissible approximation. If the angle between the thread of the helix and the longitudinal
axis of the cell is less than 45°, the major refraction index will be axial; when
this angle is more than 45°, it will be directed transversally; and when the
angle is just 45°, the two cell-walls will behave as if they were isotropic.

That the exposition given in the preceding paragraph, is not entirely
correct, was recognized already by NAEGELI, who studied the optical behaviour
of objects with a rather strong birefringence, like thin plates of mica when
they were placed one upon the other but in different directions (NAEGELI
and SCHWENDERER, 1877: 332 and DIPPEL, 1898: 246); the point was discussed
also by FREY-WYSSLING (1941, 1959:251). The position of the major refraction index is not exactly the average of the positions it occupies in the two
component parts, but in most cells, the deviation from that value is so small
that it may be neglected. That a deviation nevertheless is present, is seen
when a fibre with a helical structure of the cell-wall is placed in one of
the extinction positions (socalled orthogonal positions) and a Red I compensator plate is inserted. In that case the fibre will not show the same
colour as the Red I background, but it will look either more bluish (addition colour) or more yellowish (substraction colour); this depends on the
position of the microfibrils in the lower and the upper cell-wall with reference
to the vibration plane of the polarizer, and is therefore different for Z-helices
and S-helices.

When a fibre like that of *Linum* whose microfibrils are for the greater part
oriented in a steep S-helix, is placed parallel to the vibration plane of the
polarizer (N-S position) it will show a substraction colour. This is due to the
circumstance that the $\eta\gamma$ indices of the consecutive birefringent layers, viz.

the lower wall (1), the upper
wall (2), and the Red I
plate (3), occupy alternative
positions, see text figure.
In the same position a fibre
with a dominant Z-helix will
show an addition colour,
since the $\eta\gamma$ indices are in
consecutive position. When
the fibres are turned 90°
so that they arrive in the
other extinction position
(E-W), the one with a do-
minant S-helix will show
addition colour, the one
with a dominant Z-helix
will show substraction colour.

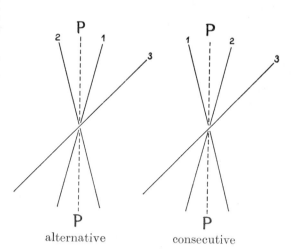

alternative   consecutive

Formerly, microscopists,
e.g. NAEGELI, DIPPEL and HERZOG, placed a Red I plate underneath the object instead of in or on the tube as is done in modern polarization microscopes, and in their publications therefore exactly opposite results are
mentioned.

From NAEGELI's experiments with mica plates one would furthermore
anticipate that fibres showing interference colours of the second order, like

8*

the bast fibres of *Boehmeria*, should behave differently from fibres with a lower double refraction (ROELOFSEN, 1951 b). This however, is not so, which indicates that a single wall of such a fibre does not behave like a single birefringent plate. In fact there are always at least two differently oriented helical layers in the secondary thickening of a single cell-wall. If these layers are thick enough to act as birefringent plates (FREY-WYSSLING l.c.) a cell will not be comparable with two, but with four superposed plates. In that case it is the sign of the helix in the outermost layer which appears to determine the optical behaviour of the whole fibre. In the opinion of the present author this evidently applies to the cotton fibre and to the phloem fibre of *Cannabis* (cf. section 23441 and 2341). We have discussed this point at some length since it is generally tacitly accepted that the optical behaviour of a fibre is solely determined by the cell-wall layer with the greatest birefringence, which usually is the thickest one.

The phenomena described above have been used already for a long time to distinguish e.g. the phloem fibres from *Linum* from those of *Cannabis*. The behaviour of the cotton fibre is unique. Firstly the helical structure is so pronounced that this fibre has no extinction positions and lights up even in the orthogonal ones. Secondly the direction of the spiral reverses frequently along its length, so that the fibre shows a frequent alternation of substraction and addition colours when it is placed in one of the orthogonal positions with the Red I plate inserted, see fig. 143.

A more direct method of detecting the presence of a helical structure and of determining the direction of the helix is that of determining the extinction position of a single cell-wall. The structure of the cells offers sometimes an opportunity to apply this method e.g. in isolated tracheids of *Pinus*, where some pits are so large that it becomes possible to observe a single wall; in this case we have only to determine whether this is the upper or the lower one.

When we have to deal with large isolated cells, like those of filamentous algae, hairs or unicellular sporangiophores, it is often possible to make oblique cuts under the preparing miscroscope, and to flatten the cells after turning them a little so that at one end a diamond-shaped piece of single wall appears. In this piece the direction of the extinction can be determined, and after it has been decided whether the wall is seen from the outside or from the inside, we will know whether the microfibrils are arranged in a Z- or in an S-helix.

When the cells are small, for instance when we have to deal with young cotton hairs or with a suspension of macerated parenchyma, they may be disintegrated by means of a blendor, and then we may search the slide for cells with one of the walls partly missing, so that the opposite one is uncovered. It is, of course, also possible to section a tissue obliquely, and then to separate the cells in the sections from each other by maceration, or to section a thick suspension of cells in gelatin by means of the freezing microtome, etc. Another method is to bring a suspension of cells on a glass slide coated with gelatin, e.g. on a photographic plate, there let it dry, and then scrape off the upper cell-walls of the cells. With thin cells this may be done with a fine needle, with thicker cells by scraping off the slide with the sharp edge of a microtome knife (PRESTON, 1934).

Along the edges of oblique sections through non-macerated tissue too protruding pieces of single cell-wall will be present. However, one can never be sure that such a piece really belongs to one cell only, and does not contain portions of the wall of the adjacent cell, with which it is united by means of the middle lamella. When studying non-macerated tissue the only reliable way out of the difficulty is to cut sections of equal thickness but a different angle to the direction of the cell axis, and to compare the values that are found for the birefringence in the same relative position throughout the whole series of sections. The birefringence will be least in the section perpendicular to the average orientation of the microfibrils and it will be maximal in the section which is parallel to the average orientation of the microfibrils. Hence both the sign and the pitch of the helix in a cell-wall or in a thick cell-wall layer can be determined. This elaborate, but sometimes indispensable method was introduced by WARDROP and PRESTON (1947, 1951). They did not recognize, however, that the direction of the spiral could be determined in this way and unnecessarily stipulated that the helices in the different layers of a wall should be of the same sign.

Since most single cell-walls, even many primary cell-walls, consist of layers in which the microfibrils are differently oriented, the direction in which extinction is found need not be identical with the actual mean orientation of the microfibrils in any of these layers. Theoretically it is even possible that within a single wall the birefringence of two or more layers with helically oriented microfibrils will compensate each other in such a way that there is no oblique extinction at all.

In order to give an impression of the results that are to be obtained by the study of the optical properties, we have developed a number of schemata which illustrate the orientation of the cellulose in various cell types; they are reproduced in fig. 32. The microfibril directions are indicated by means of lines, long lines when the microfibrils run parallel to the plane of drawing, shorter ones when they include an angle with the latter, and dots when this angle reaches a value of 90°. The degree of birefringence and the position of the major refractive index are indicated by means of index ellipses.

Drawing a represents the so-called fibre texture (Faserstruktur), b a fibre texture with helically oriented microfibrils. When the microfibrils are less regularly oriented, we may speak of a fibroid texture (faserähnliche Struktur); this is represented in the drawings d and e. Most fibres, however, show combinations of the two kinds of textures; an example of such a fibre is given in l.

The drawings c and f represent so-called tubular textures (Röhrenstruktur), c with helical, f with predominantly transverse orientation. In cells with such a tubular texture the part that stands perpendicular to the direction of the light beam (surface view) is always separated by an isotropic zone from that which is parallel to the latter (seen in optical section). The structure shown in f is the one that is usually found in growing tubular cells and in full-grown sieve tubes, latex vessels and wood vessels. In the former often a more complex structure is met with, the so-called multinet structure shown in h; here too, however, the predominant structure is the one shown in f.

Drawing g represents the so-called foliate texture (Folienstruktur); it owes its name to the fact that unstretched films (folia) which are left when the solution of a polysaccharide is evaporated on a flat surface, show this structure, a uniplanar orientation of the chain molecules. The longitudinal axis of the microfibrils in the wall lies in the plane of the wall, but they are arranged at random. When such a cell-wall is observed in surface view, it is isotropic, but sections prove to be birefringent since the microfibrils are seen in optical

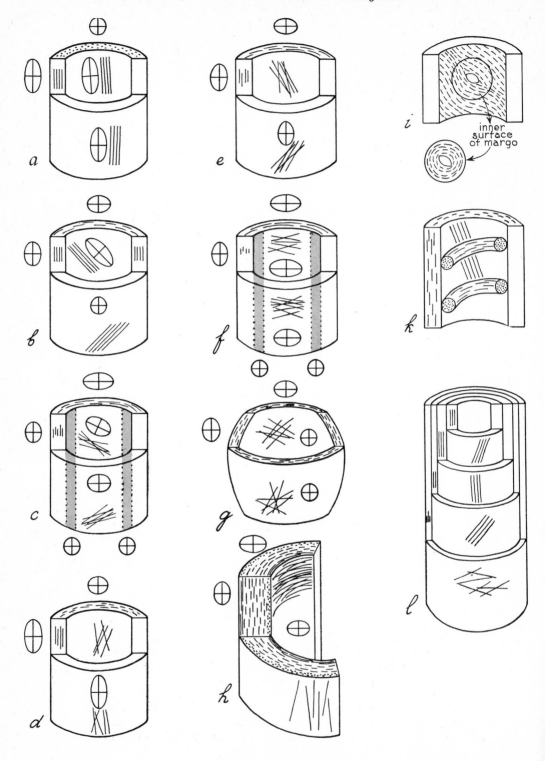

projection on the horizontal plane. It is the structure found in the walls of all isodiametric cells of higher plants.

The drawings i and k show the situation that is found respectively round bordered pits and in the spiral thickenings of tracheids and of xylem vessels.

The *dichroism* of cell-walls stained e.g. by chlor-zinc-iodine, congo-red or benzoazurin may supply important information of an additional nature. In cell-walls that have been stained with one of these substances and which are observed in surface view the light, or at least a certain part of it, is absorbed most strongly when its plane of vibration coincides with the direction of the greater part of the microfibrils, and least when it is perpendicular to that direction (cf. section 115). This applies to chitin too. It means that a cell-wall stained with chlor-zinc-iodine, congo-red or benzoazurin will look black, red or blue when the microfibrils in the cell-wall are oriented parallel to the polarization plane and normal to the beam of light, whereas it will be nearly colourless when they are oriented perpendicular to the former. So, at least, it is with structures like the one shown in a of fig. 32.

The dichroism of fibres with a cell-wall structure like that shown in the figures b, d and e is less strongly marked; with chlor-zinc-iodine the contrasting colours are black and bluish, with congo-red dark red and pink, and with benzoazurin dark blue and light blue. The optical properties of dichroitically coloured single cell-walls will enable us to separate those whose structure corresponds to that shown in b from those whose structure is of the type e. This is not possible when only the major extinction direction is determined. When in the study of entire cells dichroism is taken into consideration, it is possible to discern cells with structures like a and d from those with structures like b and e. When only the double refraction is considered, it is impossible to distinguish textures of the types a, b, d and e from each other, unless the birefringence is quantitatively estimated and the cellulose content as well as the thickness of the cell-wall are known. FREY-WYSSLING (1942a) has applied both methods for calculating the mean degree of deviation of the microfibrils from their mean orientation, the so-called angular dispersion (cf. also PRESTON, 1952; WARDROP and DADSWELL, 1952a; BÖHMER, 1958).

Another advantage of the dichroitic stains is that they increase the birefringence, which is especially valuable when the latter is very small.

The so-called quadrant dichroism, which appears when dichroitically stained objects consisting of two or more layers with different orientation are studied between crossed nicols, may also be of importance. It is visible already when the overcrossing layers are so slightly birefringent that their

---

Fig. 32. Schemata illustrating the orientation of the cellulose microfibrils in various kinds of cells; the microfibrils are indicated by lines, the character of the birefringence by index ellipses. a: nearly ideal uniaxial orientation, so-called fibre texture, positively birefringent; b: Z-helix orientation, isotropic in surface view, since the pitch is 45°; c: Z-helix orientation with low pitch, negatively birefringent in surface view with isotropic zones; d: fibroid structure; e: same as d, but with helical orientation; f: tubular structure, negatively birefringent with isotropic zones; g: foliate structure, i.e. random orientation but parallel to the plane of the wall, isotropic in surface view; h: so-called multinet structure, i.e. dense transverse orientation on the inner side of the cell-wall, gradually passing into a wide-meshed longitudinal orientation on the outer side, negatively birefringent; i: structure round bordered pit in the wall of a tracheid; k: structure of spiral thickenings in a xylem vessel; l: compound structure consisting of a primary wall and a three-layered secondary wall as is usually found in fibres and tracheids.

presence can not be distinguished by means of the earlier described method (OORT and ROELOFSEN, 1932; ROELOFSEN, 1951).

The study of form birefringence may sometimes supply information with regard to the form and the orientation of *submicroscopical interstices* that eventually may be present in the cell-wall. Already long before the presence of microfibrils in the cellulose was demonstrated by means of the electron microscope, it was proved in this way that the cell-wall must contain long and slender interstices, whereas the rodlet-birefringence observed in cell-walls out of which the cellulose had been removed, i.e. in lignin skeletons of tracheids and silica skeletons of epidermal cells, had led to the conclusion that the cellulose must consist of particles with the form of rodlets. The shape of the interstices in the cuticular layers that are filled with wax, could also be determined in this way, at least approximately. The reader is referred to sections 113, 122, 16, 174, 2362 and 2364.

213. X-RAYS

X-rays may be used for the study of the crystalline parts and for determining the mass of the cell-wall through which they are passing.

For the theory of X-ray diffraction in crystalline materials and for the procedure that is to be followed in this kind of investigations we refer to the works written by CLARK (1940) and PEISER et al. (1955) and to the reviews in OSTER and POLLISTER (1956) and WEISSBERGER (1949). For its application to cell-wall research the works of FREY-WYSSLING (1959) and of PRESTON (1952) should be consulted.

X-ray analysis of cell-walls adds valuable evidence to the results obtained by means of the polarization microscope. In the first place it is possible to find out *whether crystalline materials are present* or not, and under favourable conditions the pattern of interferences shown in the diffraction diagram may allow a conclusion with regard to the chemical nature of the crystalline substance. When two crystalline components are present, it may yet be possible to recognize both of them, but as a rule a separation will have to be effected by extracting one of them; after that the extract is evaporated, and the residue as well as the extracted cell-wall are investigated separately; when three or more crystalline components are present, such a previous separation is absolutely necessary. However, it should be realized that the extraction of one of the components may lead to the crystallization of substances that originally were present in the amorphous condition, and that in the residue from the extracts too previously amorphous substances may have crystallized. In our discussion of the chemical nature of the cell-wall constituents several examples of this type of results obtained by means of X-ray analysis have been given. They have been obtained mainly with cellulose I, cellulose II, chitin and lipids.

The X-ray diagrams offer us also the opportunity of estimating the *amount of crystalline material* in proportion to the amount of amorphous substance. To this end the blackening located in the interferences should be compared with the diffuse blackening of the background. This method was developed by HERMANS (1949, 1949a).

The *dimensions of the crystallites* can approximately be determined from the breadth of the interferences in radial direction. This was first applied with cellulose in 1926 (cf. section 113) and has since been used for this and other substances by several authors. To this end also a new X-ray method has been developed which is based on so-called small-angle scattering or small-particle scattering, fig. 111 (see GUINIER and FOURNET, 1955 and section 113). Under certain conditions the size of the crystallites or of amorphous particles is determined; under other conditions the distances between the particles (HEYN, 1955; HEIKENS et al., 1953, 1958).

In the past the conventional X-ray analysis has also been used to determine the mean distance between the crystallites of cellulose, that is the mean dimension of the interfibrillar pores. To this end the fibres were imbibed with aqueous solutions of substances that crystallized within these interstices. Subsequently an X-ray diagram was made, and the mean size of these crystals was determined from the breadth of the interferences. However, there is a great danger that the crystals will not stop growing at the right moment, and that the interstices therefore will be artificially enlarged (see section 113).

From the location and the density of the interferences in a diagram, preferably in one obtained on a moving film from a fibre with well-oriented microfibrils or from a single crystal that is rotated or oscillated, not only the unit cell, but also the spatial location of the atoms in the crystal lattice may be deduced. This application is of great importance for *determining molecular structures* of organic and inorganic crystallized substances, but it has little bearing on cell-wall structure.

By far the most important feature of the X-ray diagram in the study of the cell-wall structure is the arrangement of the interferences, as this shows *how the crystalline material is oriented*. It leads to similar conclusions as were arrived at by means of the polarization microscope and by ordinary microscopical study, and is sometimes a valuable confirmation of the latter. With objects like the bast fibres of *Boehmeria*, in which the microfibrils are ideally oriented in the direction of the axis, sharp spot diagrams may be obtained like that shown in fig. 3.

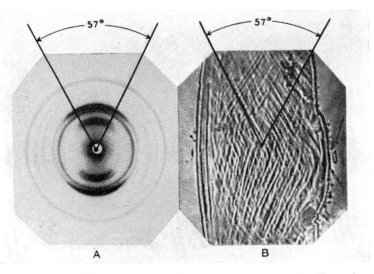

Fig. 33. Comparison of X-ray diagram with fibrillar orientation. A: X-ray diagram of mature cotton fibre. B: photomicrograph of cotton fibre swollen in phosphoric acid, showing fibrillar structure (SISSON, 1938a).

In fibres in which the orientation of the cellulose microfibrils varies to some extent (fibroid texture of fig. 32d), or when the latter are oriented in a steep helix so that the orientation in front of the cell differs from that at the back, the interferences become sickle-shaped (fig. 33). From the length of the sickles the angular dispersions can be calculated. The "spiral diagram" has especially been studied by PRESTON (1952) and LINDGREN (1958). When the microfibrils are arranged in a helix with a pitch of e.g. 45°, or in a single piece of cell-wall consisting of layers in which the microfibrils are oriented in e.g. two directions, two superposed diagrams are obtained (fig. 34). Especially suitable for the study of these cases is the small-angle scattering method.

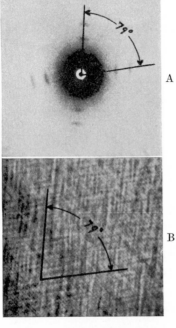

As a rule, the crystallites of cellulose and chitin are oriented only with one of their axes, the longitudinal one. Sometimes, however, they prove to be oriented with the other axis too; this appears from the fact that the interferences of certain lattice planes are lacking when the object occupies a certain position with regard to the direction of the light beam. In fig. 34 the interferences of the 101-planes are absent, although they are present in diagrams obtained by directing the X-ray beam parallel to the surface of the cell-wall. In our discussion of the cellulose we have pointed out that this phenomenon, which owes its origin to the desiccation of the preparation, is probably due to the flattened shape of the microfibrils.

To the plant anatomist a disadvantage of the X-ray method is that we can not study a single cell-wall, but that we have to use a large number of cells. It is true that there are micro-cameras for making X-ray diagrams of objects with a diameter as small as 20 μ (ECKLING and KRATKY, 1930; PRESTON, 1934, 1952: 50; KREGER, 1948), but the use of these cameras has several disadvantages and 20 μ is still a considerable distance in microscopical anatomy.

Fig. 34. X-ray diagram (A) and photomicrograph (B) of a piece of *Valonia* cell-wall taken perpendicular to the surface, showing the orientation of microfibrils and crystallites (SISSON, 1938a).

Another disadvantage is that small amounts of crystalline substances, e.g. less than 5—20% (depending on the degree of crystallinity), often fail to give recognizable interferences. It is, moreover, impossible to detect in this way the presence of a small amount of substance with a different kind of orientation. In the beginning, when investigators were inclined to overestimate the value of the X-ray diagram on a-priori grounds, and when the restrictions of the method had not yet been recognized, there has been much misinterpretation of results with regard to both cell-wall constitution and cell-wall structure (cf. sections 2341 and 2343).

It should also be realized that no interferences can be obtained from very minute crystallites, e.g. those of cellulose, with a diameter of less than 20 Å;

in general a crystal plane must be represented more than four times in each crystallite. In such cases one is apt to conclude that a substance is present in the amorphous condition, whereas in reality it is at least partly crystal-lized.

Recently it appeared that the location of the main interferences in the X-ray diagrams of various polysaccharides may be very similar, and this was another deception, as for this reason too the diagnostic value of the X-ray diagram proved to be less than had been expected a few years ago (cf. section 242).

X-rays may also be used for the *determination of the mass* of an object, as the absorption of the rays is determined by the latter; the extent of absorption is, of course, entirely independent of the physical state of the object. In the study of the cell-wall X-rays have been used to this end by LANGE, viz. in trans-verse sections of wood cells. He applied this method in order to determine the localisation of lignin, cellulose and hemicellulose (cf. sections 132, 16). It is to be expected that it will soon be possible to use a more precise technique, viz. when the X-ray microscope, which is now being developed, will be avail-able (cf. COSSLETT et al., 1957). With a special method a resolving power of 0.1 μ may be obtained. The images are silhouettes based on differences in mass; with biological objects staining with "heavy" substances or shadow-casting with metal will therefore often be necessary, just as in electron microscopy.

With amorphous material X-rays produce very diffuse diffraction rings. The latter may reveal some particularities of the molecular structure. Among the amorphous cell-wall constituents lignin is the only one that so far has been studied in this way (BECHERER et al., 1955).

214. ELECTRON RAYS

Electron rays can, like X-rays, be used in microscopy as well as in the study of the crystalline state.

The first electron microscope was constructed about twenty years ago by E. RUSKA and VON BORRIES in Siemens' laboratories in Germany. A beam of electrons is focussed on the object in much the same way as visible light is focussed in an ordinary light microscope, a magnetic field acting as a kind of lens. With other magnetic lenses the image is enlarged. Modern versions of the electron microscope as well as the special methods for preparing the objects that are to be studied, are described e.g. by HALL (1953) and in less detail in OSTER and POLLISTER (1956, I, III).

An electron ray is at the same time a corpuscular ray and a wave ray; in the latter function it is comparable to rays of visible light and X-rays. The wave-length depends on the velocity of the electrons; with the ordinary 50 KV electrons it amounts to circ. 0.05 Å. The resolving power of the electron microscope is not so large as might perhaps be expected from this exceedingly short wave-length. This is due to the defects of the magnetic lenses, which require the use of very narrow bundles of electrons with apertures ranging from 0.001 to 0.003. With most of the microscopes now in use the resolving power is at best 30 Å; with some of them it may with favourable objects be brought down to circ. 10 Å. This is nevertheless a very important achieve-ment, as the resolving power of these instruments is about a hundred times as high as that of the light microscope and the U.V. microscope.

The small size of the aperture involves a large focal depth, which in fact is about a thousand times as large as the resolving power, whereas with the light microscope these two are of the same order of magnitude. In electron microscopy only very thin objects can be used; in fact, they must be distinctly thinner than the focal depth, and they are therefore throughout in focus. This explains why the image gives us the impression of a much denser structure than in reality exists. However, the great focal depth facilitates the focussing on the fluorescent screen; the latter is temporarily inserted in order to make the image visible. After that an electron micrograph is made on a photographic film, and when the micrographs are very good, they may subsequently be enlarged to such an extent that a magnification of 50.000 to 200.000 is obtained.

Electron rays have a very small penetrating power, e.g. only 0.2 mm in ordinary air, and therefore the whole path of the rays in the microscope, the object and the photographic film included, must lie in a very high vacuum, viz. of the order of 0.0001 mm of mercury or less. Hence the object will be completely desiccated, as liquids, and solids with a measurable vacuum pressure too, will under these circumstances evaporate or sublimate. Moreover, the rate and the extent of this process are considerably increased because the temperature of the object increases owing to the energy it receives from the absorbed electrons. When an organic object is more than 0.2μ thick, the amount of electrons that are absorbed, becomes so large that the object is charred; this, however, does not matter very much, as such an object is, at any rate, so thick that it completely absorbs or scatters the electron rays, and hence does not show any structural details. The heat that is produced in the object, is transmitted by the thin film (100—200 Å) of nitrocellulose, cellulose acetate or polyvinyl formal on which the object usually rests, to the metal grid which supports the film. But although the heat is rapidly dispersed by this metal grid, artefacts due to incipient charring nevertheless may be produced, even in objects of the appropriate thickness of 100—500 Å.

The image does not owe its origin to the absorption of electron rays but to the fact that the latter are partly scattered by the object, the deflected rays being screened off by a narrow diaphragm. The deflection is larger in those parts of the object that are thicker or which possess a denser structure, and the corresponding parts of the image therefore will look less bright on the fluorescent screen, and less dark on the photographic film.

Insufficient contrast is often a serious handicap in the study of biological object. To enhance the contrasts, heavy atoms may be introduced, either in the interior of the object as a kind of dye, e.g. by the use of osmic acid or of phosphotungstic acid, or on its outside by the method of metal shadowcasting. In the latter case a metal, usually U, Pd, Pt or Cr, is vaporized in a high vacuum and in such a position that the vapour strikes the object at a small angle (circ. 15°). In this way the ridges on the surface of the object are coated with a layer of metal two to several atoms thick on the side that is turned towards the oncoming metal vapour; on the other side no metal at all is deposited. When a positive is made from the micrograph, the object is seen in three dimensions; the print, in fact, looks like a landscape illuminated by a rising or sinking sun. The great increase in contrast that is obtained by means of the metal-shadowcasting method is clearly seen when we compare fig. 7a with fig. 8.

The length of the various shadows can be taken as a measure of the height of the object as a whole and of the ridges on its surface in particular. However, on account of the high surface forces that act upon small wet particles, and also on account of the shrinkage due to the desiccation of non-rigid particles, the objects are often flattened in the direction of the film on which they rest. In such cases the true form can only be preserved by quick freezing on the film and freeze-drying. Another difficulty with which we are confronted in taking the length of the shadow as a measure of the height, is due to the circumstance that the film on which the object rests, is not flat, but sags between the bars of the metal grid, so that the slope of corresponding parts will vary from place to place.

Once it was thought that the heat of the metal vapour produced artefacts in thin cell-walls (FREY-WYSSLING, MÜHLETHALER and MOOR, 1956); but JAYME and HUNGER (1958) showed that the artefacts were not caused by heat but resulted from the bundling of microfibrils during the desiccation of the specimen.

When the two opposite primary walls of a single cell have been freed from non-celluloses, they are together $0.1—0.2\ \mu$ thick, which means that they are sufficiently thin to resist the damaging effect of the electron rays. Cells of this type may be obtained by macerating meristematic tissues. Chemical maceration combined with mechanical disintegration have often been used in order to separate the cells more completely or to obtain single cell-walls, but it should be realized that in this way we always run the risk of producing artefacts, such as a wider meshed fibrillar network and oriented or disoriented microfibrils.

After secondary thickening has set in, even single walls are usually much too thick for investigation. It is possible to cut them into sections with a thickness of 100—500 Å by using ultramicrotomes and by applying special embedding and cutting techniques. The results, however, are disappointing when the cellulose structure is dense, as in that case the orientation of the microfibrils is obscured. Sometimes it is fortunate that the cell-walls are swollen during the polymerization of the methacrylate used for embedding before sectioning. Sometimes it is necessary to enhance the swelling in some way.

In thick objects the structure of the surface can be studied in casts, usually called replica's. Several methods of preparing such casts have been described in the works enumerated above. Casts can, of course, also be made from cells at the surface of thick sections.

The surface structure of thick objects can also be studied by means of the shadowcasting technique and by using electron rays at glancing incidence and photographing the object from a direction which includes with the surface of the latter but a small angle too (cf. EMERTON et al., 1956), but this method does not offer much advantage in comparison with the ordinary cast technique.

In the following sections many examples will be given to illustrate the considerable achievements that have been obtained in the study of cell-wall structure by means of electron microscopy.

With crystalline materials electron rays produce similar *diffraction patterns* as can be obtained by the use of X-rays. Most electron microscopes are adapted for this purpose too. Electron rays are sometimes more suitable than X-rays because in this case but a very small amount of material is required. This makes it possible to obtain a diffraction diagram and an electron micrograph of the same object, and to compare them. HURST (1952) seems to have been the first to do this with cell-walls, viz. in his study of the lipids occurring in yeast cell-walls. PRESTON and RIPLEY (1954) applied the method to the cellulose in the wall of *Valonia*. A disadvantage of the method is that the specimen is easily overheated, but HONJO and WATANABE (1957) applied the method with great success by simultaneous cooling of the specimen.

Electron rays may, like X-rays, also be used for determining the geometric structure of molecules, but so far this procedure has not been applied to the constituents of the cell-wall.

22. The Primary Cell-wall of the Anthophytes and its Surface Growth

As the structure of the primary cell-wall is quite different from that of the secondary one, it will be treated separately. The difference in structure obviously implies differences in function and in physiological behaviour. One of the most important features of the primary wall is that its surface growth is not accompanied by a marked increase in thickness; the secondary wall, on the contrary, increases in thickness, but does not grow in area.

The primary wall and the middle lamella are now commonly defined in the manner proposed by BAILEY and KERR (1934). The wall by which the meristematic cell is enclosed, is called the primary wall, and for the inter-cellular layer by which a cell is connected with the adjoining cells, the name middle lamella is used. The secondary wall consists of the cell-wall layers that are deposited after the cell has ceased its growth. However, we will see that some cells are provided with walls that already increase in thickness before the growth of the cell has been completed; for the walls of cells of this nature we will use the term "thickened primary walls", which was introduced by MAJUMDAR and PRESTON (1941).

The primary wall can be studied in meristems, primary or apical ones as well as secondary ones, viz. cambium and phellogen, and also in the out-growths produced by some epidermis cells in aerial parts as well as in roots, and in pollen tubes. In the meristems the walls consist, of course, of a middle lamella covered on both sides with a primary wall, whereas in the epidermis of the aerial parts the outer walls are either encrusted with or covered by cuticular material.

The primary wall has been studied in various kinds of mature cells too, sometimes after isolating it from the rest of the cell-wall and sometimes by observing isolated cells from the outside.

221. THE CHEMICAL CONSTITUTION OF THE GROWING CELL-WALL

Although the study of the structure of the growing cell-wall has remained confined so far to the cellulose part, the composition of the wall as a whole can certainly not be regarded as immaterial, as the cellulose fibrils form but a small part of the total mass. They may be compared to the iron bars that are present in reinforced concrete, although it should be realized that they are flexible, and that the non-cellulosic mass in which they are embedded, is at least more or less plastic.

With regard to the *water content of the wall* in the meristematic cell we are but very imperfectly informed. As to our knowledge no serious attempts have been made to determine it, we have tried to fill this gap by estimating it at least in one object, for which we chose the mesocotyl of the corn seedling (unpublished). The mesocotyls were to this end ground in a mortar, disintegrated by means of a blender in a 0.01 m citrate buffer at a pH of 6.5, and centrifuged at a rather low speed in order to separate the cell-walls from the cell content, the latter remaining suspended in the fluid. This process of desintegration and purification was repeated a few times. Finally the cell-walls were pressed between filter paper in order to remove adhering water; to this end we applied a pressure of 4 atmospheres, i.e. a pressure of the same order of magnitude as that which is exercized on the cell-wall by the turgescent protoplast. The water content now appeared to be 60%.

When the mesocotyls were merely ground and after that immediately pressed, i.e. when the plasm was not removed, a water content of 63% was found. These figures are in good agreement with the observation that primary walls shrink to about one third their original thickness when they are desiccated (BONNER, 1935). A much higher figure was given by FREY-WYSSLING (1959:7), viz. 92.5%, but this estimate was based on the, in our opinion very improbable, supposition that the percentage of water in the growing cell-wall is equal to that in the entire coleoptile in fresh and turgescent condition.

With regard to the *chemical composition of the dried cell-wall* we are somewhat better informed. WIRTH (1946) analysed "corn coleoptiles" (presumably mesocotyls). His results, as well as those obtained by NAKAMURA and HESS (1938) with the same object and by THIMANN and BONNER (1933) with *Avena* coleoptiles, are reproduced in Table VI. However, the analytical methods applied by these authors are out of date and not sufficiently specific, so that their figures can not be regarded as more than a first approximation. More reliable are the recent data from BISHOP et al. (1958). The table also contains the analytical results obtained in the author's own laboratory with corn mesocotyls, and figures relating to cotton hairs and cambium cell-walls, which have been recorded already in Table I.

Table VI. Principal constituents of the growing cell-wall, expressed as a percentage of its dry weight.

	cellu-lose	hemi-cell.	pec-tin	li-pid	pro-tein	cu-tin
Zea mays, coleoptiles						
and 9 mm [1]) 37	37	45	10	7 ?		
mesocotyls 32 mm [1]) 33	33	34	10	23 ?		
[2]) 40	40	32	?	10 ?		
[3]) 30	30	50		2	3	
Avena coleoptiles [4]) 42	42	38	8		12	
Avena coleoptiles [5]) 25	25	51	1	4.2	9.5	
Cotton hairs (cf. Table I) 32	32	19	21	8	14	3.5
Pinus cambium [6]) 25	25	>26	24		(unknown: 26)	

[1]) According to WIRTH (1946); [2]) according to NAKAMURA and HESS (1938); [3]) according to an analysis carried out by the present author; [4]) according to THIMANN and BONNER (1933); [5]) BISHOP et al. (1958); [6]) calculated on protein- and lignin-free basis from figures given by ALLSOP and MISRA (1940).

The figures given in Table VI prove that only about one third of the dry weight of the cell-wall consists of cellulose, and that the total amount of the hemicelluloses is of the same order of magnitude; according to Bishop et al. (1958) it is in *Avena* even twice as high; the rest consists of pectin, proteins and lipids. Apart from the cellulose, all the constituents are, as has already been mentioned, at least for the greater part amorphous. They form the continuous phase of a heterogeneous system in which the discontinuous phase is formed by the cellulose. This conclusion is in full agreement with the observation that primary walls do not readily react to cellulose reagents when they have not been purified previously, and also with the fact that purified and non-purified primary walls look entirely different under the electron microscope, for whereas in the purified walls the cellulose microfibrils are easily distinguishable, their presence is in the non purified ones but faintly indicated, which means that they must be completely enveloped by the continuous phase (fig. P 16 and 70).

Purified cell-walls, in fact, are to be regarded as cellulose skeletons. In electron micrographs these skeletons look rather compact, but this should not lead us astray. That they impress us in this way, is partly due to the fact that the layer of which the electron microscope gives us a sharp image, is comparatively thick, and partly to the circumstance that the cell-wall has shrunk considerably, both by desiccation and by the removal of the other constituents.

According to Frey-Wyssling (1959), who calculates his values on the basis of a water content of 92.5%, the cellulose in the primary wall of coleoptiles would constitute no more than 2.5% of the total weight or about 2% of its volume. At an earlier occasion (1936) the same author had estimated the water content of the same object at $^2/_3$ of the total weight, and the cellulose content at 14%. The same value for the water content was assumed by Wardrop and Preston (1947), who estimated the cellulose content of cambium cell-walls at 8%. If this value is correct, the mean distance between the cellulose microfibrils must be about four times their diameter, which may be estimated at 100 Å. When we base our calculation on the values for the water and cellulose content determined by the present author, we find that the cellulose occupies 9% of the volume.

As the cellulose microfibrils are for the greater part crystalline and contain therefore but very little water, the water content of the other cell-wall constituents (the lipids excepted) must be higher than that found for the cell-wall as a whole, and may be estimated at circ. 72%.

222. THE CELL-PLATE

The initial stage of the partition wall between two daughter cells is called cell-plate. The literature on the way in which the latter arises, has been surveyed in detail by Tischler (this Encyclopedia Vol. 2, part 2: 215 et seq.). More summarily treatments are found in all textbooks dealing with plant anatomy, e.g. in Esau (1953).

The cell-plate arises in the equatorial plane of the fibrous spindle which connects the two daughter nuclei, the so-called phragmoplast. The phragmoplast as well as the cell-plate usually show a gradual expansion by which they finally reach the cell-wall. It is commonly assumed that this is not due to an equal expansion of the material of which the cell-plate consists, but that new material is deposited along its circumference. In some instances the cell-plate first reaches one side of the old cell-wall, and then grows out in the direction of the other side. In the cells of the vascular cambium the cell-plate occupies an oblique position, and is seen to expand gradually in the direction of the upper and of the lower end. In pollen mother-cells, in cells of the endosperm and in those of Thallophytes no cell-plate is formed, but the cells are partitioned by circular ridges arising from the plasmatic lining of the existing cell-wall and gradually advancing towards the middle of the cell.

Before the cell-plate is formed, we observe, as a rule, the development of semi-fluid particles, perhaps of the nature of vacuoles, in the protoplasm. These particles seem to coalesce, and either to constitute or to secrete the cell-plate. The latter is considered to consist partly, or perhaps mainly, of pectin, as it can be stained with ruthenium red but not with plasma stains. However, as pectin is by no means the only substance that stains with ruthenium-red, the chemical evidence for this view appears to be rather meagre. The cell-plate usually is isotropic between crossed nicols, but NAKAMURA (1937) observed in fixed preparations of dividing pollen mother-cells birefringent lamellae. This may be due to the presence of uniplanarly oriented pectin, which in fact is negatively birefringent, but it may be caused also by the presence of lipids or by adsorption birefringence.

Later, i.e. after the cell-plate has begun its growth towards the cell-wall, it becomes, with respect to its plane, positively birefringent (BECKER, 1938). This can be taken as proof that cellulose is being deposited, most probably by the protoplasmic membranes on either side of it. From now on the cell-plate therefore consists of three layers, viz. the middle lamella and two primary walls. All three thicken visibly before the growth phase of the cell sets in.

There are two different opinions with regard to the way in which the two primary walls and the middle lamella of the cell-plate are adjusted to the primary wall and the middle lamella of the mother-cell. The view advanced by GILTAY in 1882, according to which the daughter-cells form a new, completely continuous primary wall, finds support in observations made by PRIESTLEY and SCOTT (1939), MARTENS (1937, 1938), ELLIOT (1951) and WARDROP (1952). In full-grown tissue thin, feebly birefringent membranes, presumably the remains of the primary wall of the parent-cells, were found to traverse the intercellular spaces, cf. fig. 35.

FREY-WYSSLING and MÜHLETHALER (1951) gave a description of the process based on electron micrographs obtained from dividing cells of *Avena* coleoptiles (cf. fig. P 36), which is at variance with GILTAY's view. These authors are of opinion that the microfibrils of the primary wall of the parent-cell are gradually broken down, perhaps by enzymatic action, and that other microfibrils take their place and become interwoven with the microfibrils of the primary wall which covers the cell-plate.

It seems to us that the electron micrographs of FREY-WYSSLING and MÜHLETHALER do not prove their interpretation. We regard it as more probable that the connection between the primary wall of the cell-plate and that of the parent-cell is mainly brought about by the deposition of new fibrils. The microfibril bundles that were present at the boundary line between two daughter-cells, may easily have been disrupted when the tissue was macerated and disintegrated, even though the cells themselves were not separated from each other, fig. P 36 a. Images such as that shown in fig. P 36 b, make it probable that at least part of the microfibrils from the primary wall of the parent-cell are left behind in the form of a sheath round the new primary wall of the daughter-cell. In cells like those of the cambium, where there is little or no longitudinal growth, these sheaths will retain their original thickness and afterwards, when intercellular spaces are formed, they may become

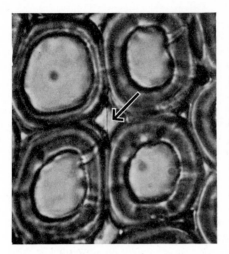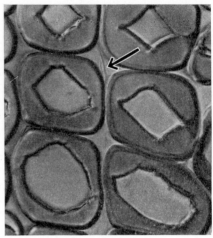

Fig. 35. Parts from the wall of the parent-cell, presumably the primary wall, traversing the intercellular spaces in compression wood of *Pinus pinaster*, before (left), and after (right) delignification (from WARDROP and DADSWELL, 1953).

separated from the rest of the wall, as is shown in fig. 35. In coleoptiles, however, where the cells undergo a marked increase in length, the sheaths will presumably be weakened considerably, and disappear almost entirely.

The observations made by HOUWINK and ROELOFSEN on the stellate cells which are found in the medulla of the leaves of *Juncus effusus*, confirm the supposition that the wall of the daughter-cells is surrounded by a sheath derived from the primary wall of the parent-cell (fig. P 37), but here no disrupted bundles of microfibrils were found. It appears that these microfibrils undergo a reorientation, on account of the stress to which they are exposed during the growth of the cells, and change their transverse position into an axial one. Such axially oriented microfibrils are indeed clearly distinguishable on the outside of the cells shown in fig. P 36 b. This reorientation is a phenomenon of general occurrence, to which we will return when we are discussing the so-called multinet growth.

Very often the cell-plate develops into an ordinary wall which is no longer discernable from the other walls by which the cells are surrounded. This applies e.g. to isodiametric parenchyma cells and also to cambium cells. In other instances, e.g. in the tips of roots and shoots and in coleoptiles, the cells are arranged in longitudinal rows (fig. 41), and the partition walls between the cells of such a row appear to be much thinner and provided with a much larger number of plasmodesmata than the other walls.

The development of partition walls of this kind in the parenchyma cells of growing tips of *Cucurbita* shoots is shown in the electron micrographs reproduced in fig. P 38. At first we note a very thin and sparse network of

microfibrils. This network is provided with at first angular, afterwards
rounded pores, which in the beginning were most probably filled with protoplasm; as on all sides of them microfibrils are deposited, they gradually
lose their angular shape. Afterwards secondary thickening sets in, and then
part of the pores seems to be closed, but this stage is not represented in the
figure.

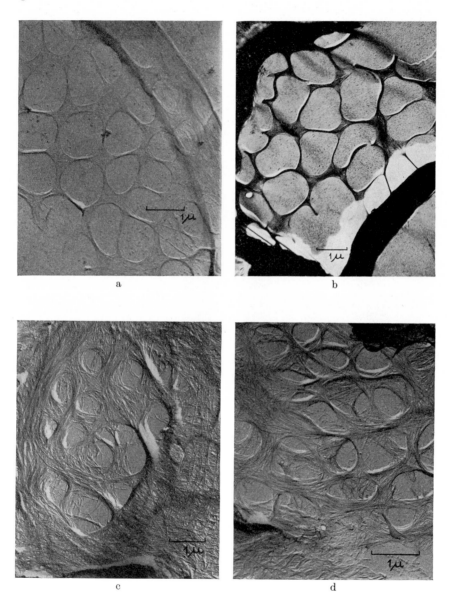

Fig. 40. Differentiation of sieve plates in the apex and in the young internodes of *Cucurbita* shoots; in every figure two primarywalls are represented; in *b* the latter are slightly
displaced; *a* youngest, *d* oldest stage (from FREY-WYSSLING and MÜLLER, 1957).

9*

In cells which continue to grow nearly to the end of their life, e.g. in those of the hairs on the *Tradescantia* stamens, neither the partition walls nor the other walls undergo secondary thickening. These partition walls (fig. P 39), retain a structure resembling that shown in fig. P. 38 b. They contain circ. 800 pores, each with a diameter of circ. 0.1 μ, i.e. just below the resolving power of the ordinary microscope. In the meristems of coleoptiles and roots (SCOTT et al., 1956) similar partition walls are found.

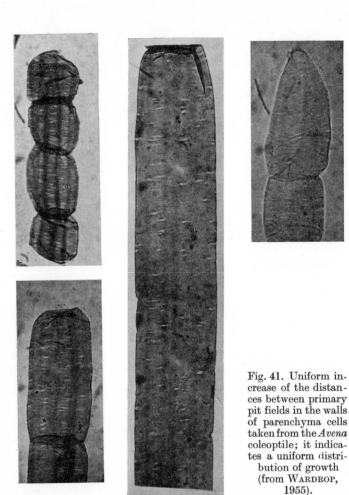

Fig. 41. Uniform increase of the distances between primary pit fields in the walls of parenchyma cells taken from the *Avena* coleoptile; it indicates a uniform distribution of growth (from WARDROP, 1955).

The development of the much larger pores in the sieve plates is shown in fig. 40, which refers to the sieve tubes of *Cucurbita*. It is similar to that of the small pores. According to FREY-WYSSLING and MÜLLER (1957) the pores are probably from the first filled with plugs of cytoplasm, which increase in diameter, so that the parts of the wall by which they are separated from each other, are compressed; in this way these parts are reduced in surface, but increased in height.

223. PROOFS OF ACTUAL GROWTH

Before entering into a discussion of the structure of the growing cell-wall, it seems desirable to make sure that this wall actually increases in surface. It was postulated already in 1848 by NAEGELI and as an explanation he proposed his intussusception theory. It seems superfluous to review the extensive literature on this topic, in the first place, because this has been done in several of the older works (i.a. by VAN WISSELINGH, 1925), and secondly, because until quite recently there were no fully convincing proofs that the supposed extension of the cell-wall really occurs, and that the increase in surface is not due to addition of entirely new cell-wall areas.

CASTLE (1955) marked small parts on the surface of growing *Avena* coleoptiles with CuO dust, and by studying the changes in the relative position of these dust particles he came to the conclusion that the rate of growth is nearly the same in all parts of the cell's surface.

WARDROP (1955), SCOTT et al. (1956) and WILSON (1957) studied, respectively in *Avena* coleoptiles, onion roots and *Elodea* internodes, the increase in distance between all primary pit fields which they noted in the youngest cells, and found that this increase occurs everywhere cf. fig. 41.

Finally WARDROP (1956), GORHAM and COLVIN (1957), SETTERFIELD and BAYLEY (1957) and BÖHMER (1958) fed *Avena* coleoptiles and onion roots with sugars that had been labelled with ^{14}C, and made autoradiographs of macerated cells that were obtained either from the epidermis or from the parenchyma. The autoradiographs revealed that cellulose had been deposited uniformly over the whole surface of these cells, which ruled out the possibility of a bipolar tip growth as well as that of a growth localized around the primary pit fields. According to BÖHMER (1958) this applies also to the cell-wall growth in xylem and phloem cells.

By means of a similar technique, viz. by feeding cotton plants with labelled carbon dioxide, O'KELLEY (1953) could show that the growth of the seed hairs is accompanied by a deposition of cellulose along the whole length of the wall. This proves that the growth of these hairs can not be restricted to the tip.

The autoradiographs do not only prove that the cell-wall grows over its whole length, but also that this growth is not confined to a mere stretching, but that it involves a deposition of cell-wall material. This appears also from the increase in weight of the cell-wall material in each cell, a point to which we will return in section 2281.

There are, on the other hand, many examples of cells where the growth does not extend over the whole length, but is confined, either permanently or during a certain period, to a definite zone situated either at the tip or somewhere else. Apical growth was noted for the first time in 1843 by SCHMITZ in the hyphae of Fungi, and has been recorded from some Algae, from pollen tubes and from some kinds of hair by NAEGELI, and from root hairs by HABERLANDT, WORTMANN and REINHARDT. Recent literature on the growth of pollen tubes is to be found in a paper by SCHOCH-BODMER (1945), on that of root hairs in one written by LUNDEGÅRDH (1946). ZIMMERMANN described already in 1893 various instances of cells in which growth is not localized in the top, but in some other part of the cell, e.g. the stellate cells that are found in the medulla of some plants, the mesophyll cells of pine needles and epidermal cells. HABERLANDT (1887) noted in hairs of *Geranium sanguineum* a growth which at first extended over the whole length of the cell, but which subsequently receded to the top and the base, and which in the final stage proved to be restricted to the latter. Other examples are given by Küster (1956: 788).

Noteworthy is the apical growth of phloem and xylem fibres and of tracheids, because it allows these cells to force a way for themselves between cells that have already completed their growth (Schoch-Bodmer and Huber, 1951 and 1952; Wardrop and Dadswell, 1952; see also Esau, 1953: 88).

From observations made by Tammes (1908) in flax, by Aldaba (1927) in flax and ramie, and by A. D. J. Meeuse (1941) in a number of other phloem fibres which develop from long initial cells, it was already known that the apical parts of these fibres are still growing when in the other parts secondary thickening has set in and has advanced already to a considerable extend in the basal part. Shorter phloem fibres as well as the cortical and perivascular fibres of Monocotyledones would, according to Meeuse, not show this apical growth, but a growth extending over the whole length.

The initials of the cambium too show apical growth (Bannan, 1950 and 1956), but whether their growth is confined to the top, is not certain.

When we are going to study the structure of the growing cell-wall in a new object, we should first of all make sure whether, at the moment the cell was fixed, the part of the cell-wall that we have before us, had not yet ceased to grow. As we will show in section 2282, it is most unsafe to conclude from the structure of the cell-wall whether the latter is full-grown or not.

As we will confine our attention here to the structure of the cell-wall, we will not enter into the problem of the interrelations existing between the growing cells of a tissue, i.e. whether there is sliding growth as visualized by Krabbe in 1886, symplastic growth in the sense of Priestley, or partly symplastic, partly intrusive growth as postulated by Sinnott and Bloch in 1939. Our present knowledge of cell-wall structure and growth agrees very well with the last-named view, for which recently additional evidence has been advanced by Schoch-Bodmer and Huber (l.c.). The latter authors speak of interposition growth because they believe that the cell which forces its way between the other cells, does not grow along its whole length, and that its wall therefore does not slide along the walls of these cells, but that it grows at the extreme tip only, so that it is a new part of the wall which is pressed against the walls of the cells that are pushed apart.

224. MICROSCOPICAL OBSERVATIONS ON THE STRUCTURE OF THE PRIMARY WALL

Dippel had observed already in 1898 in the cell-walls of young tubular cells, which he studied in various objects, the presence of slitlike "primary pit fields" (i.e. pits in the primary walls), which were oriented transversely to the direction of growth, cf. fig. 41. Similar observations have been made by several other investigators, but Söding (1932 and 1934) and Diehl et al. (1939) were the first to see the connection between the shape and the orientation of these pit fields and the ultra-structure of the cell-wall. They recognized that the direction of these slitlike pit fields coincided with the average direction of the cellulose micelles. In the walls of isodiametric cells, on the other hand, the cellulose micelles are oriented at random, and here the pit fields prove to be more or less circular in outline. In order to make the pits more easily recognizable, it is recommended to stain the cellulose with iodine and rather concentrated sulphuric acid (66 vol %), eventually after removing the non-cellulosic constituents of the cell-wall. In the primary pit fields themselves there is but little cellulose, and the latter is embedded in so much non-cellulosic material that little or no colouring is effected (GORDON WHALEY et al., 1952).

In the literature many examples are given of primary walls which show a striation. The latter may be visible already in the original condition or else after the walls have been treated with reagents on cellulose. The striation has often been regarded as founded in the structure of the cell-wall, but, as a rule, no connection between the two proved to be present. This applies e.g. to the transverse striations that are sometimes seen on the epidermal and hypodermal cells of *Avena* coleoptiles. It appears that they owe their origin to minute folds which arise when the coleoptiles are sectioned; at that moment the tissue tension disappears, and the cell-walls contract (HEYN, 1933; SÖDING, 1934). Minute folds of a similar kind may also arise when the cells lose their turgescence.

In thin cell-walls these minute folds are visible only between crossed nicols, so e.g. in growing cotton hairs, in the growing region of the sporangiophores of *Phycomyces* and in the hairs on the *Tradescantia* stamens (ROELOFSEN, 1951; ROELOFSEN and HOUWINK, 1951). This easily explainable optical effect has often led to incorrect conclusions with regard to the orientation of the cellulose micelles in the cell-wall, cf. section 225.

In cutting sections too we may obtain artefacts, especially in the epidermis. It are dislocations of the cellulose structure, which, when the walls are stained with chlor-zinc-iodine, appear in the form of rather conspicuous but irregularly distributed striations (B. J. D. MEEUSE, 1938 and 1941).

In the cuticle too we observe in some objects striations which have nothing to do with the structure of the wall, but owe their origin to the growth of the cells, e.g. in the hairs on the stamens and in the petals of *Tradescantia* (MARTENS, 1937; VAN ITERSON, 1937) and in the sporangiophores of *Phycomyces* (ROELOFSEN, 1950 b).

However, not all observations made by means of the microscope need be discarded in this way. Those pertaining to changes in the dimensions caused by interfibrillar or intrafibrillar swelling, which have already been dealt with in section 211, give valuable indications. It was found e.g. that growing cotton hairs, and growing tubular cells in general, show on desiccation (interfibrillar shrinking) a decrease in length amounting to 20—30%, but that their diameter decreases but very slightly (BERKLEY, 1942). This indicates a predominantly transverse orientation of the microfibrils.

By studying the shrinkage caused by intrafibrillar swelling in concentrated alkali, we arrive at the same conclusion. In this case the diameter of the young cotton hairs proves to decrease more considerably than their length. The same phenomenon had already been observed by VAN ITERSON (1937) in the hairs of the *Tradescantia* stamens, and by DIEHL et al. (1939) in parenchyma cells of growing hypocotyls of *Helianthus*.

Another phenomenon which may throw light on the structure of the primary wall, is its behaviour in cells that are torn in two under the preparing microscope. In some kinds of cells the two parts remain connected by a narrow ribbon which unwinds from one or from both sides in a helical fashion (cf. fig. 42). This was observed in *Cladophora* cells (ASTBURY and PRESTON, 1940), in sporangiophores of *Phycomyces* (ROELOFSEN, 1950 b) and in the cells of the hairs on the *Tradescantia* stamens (ROELOFSEN and HOUWINK, 1951), and has been adduced as evidence for the presence of a helical structure.

The behaviour of full-grown hairs and fibres in reagents causing intra-fibrillar swelling often give still more indications regarding the structure of the primary wall. We may refer here to the ballooning of hairs and fibres

Fig. 42. Spiral unwinding of a strip torn from the wall of a cell of a staminal hair of *Tradescantia* (from ROELOFSEN and HOUWINK, 1951).

discussed in section 211, cf. fig. 26. It may be due to a predominantly transverse orientation of the cellulose in the primary wall, e.g. in cotton hairs. However, the fact that raw cotton hairs show the phenomenon much more frequently than dewaxed ones, shows that the incrustation of the primary wall with cutin, wax and polysaccharides other than cellulose, can not be without importance. As mentioned before, ballooning has been observed in several other kinds of tubular cells too, e.g. in phloem fibres of *Linum, Boehmeria, Edgeworthia* and *Asclepias*, in sklerenchyma fibres of *Cocos, Agave, Musa, Bambusa* and *Saccharum*, and in the tracheids and wood fibres of many plants, though in the lignified elements only if an adequate part of the lignin is removed.

Although the cellulose of the primary wall is very probably in all these objects transversely oriented, ballooning does not really prove the presence of a primary wall of this kind, as it may also be due to the presence of a flat spiral structure in the outermost layer of the secondary wall. In fact, the ballooning of Conifer tracheids (BUCHER, 1957a) as well as the so-called spiral ballooning of cotton hairs (KERR, 1946) are to be ascribed to the presence of such an orientation of the microfibrils in the outer layers of the secondary wall.

The inability to produce ballooning, on the other hand, does not prove that no layers with a transverse orientation of the cellulose are present. The swelling may be insufficient, either because the cell-wall is too thin or because it contains too much lignin or hemicellulose. It is also possible that the primary wall is so thin and fragile that it does not offer enough resistance. Finally the orientation of the cellulose in the secondary wall may be transverse instead of longitudinal.

225. POLARIZATION OPTICAL OBSERVATIONS ON THE STRUCTURE OF THE PRIMARY WALL

The earlier microscopists, like NAEGELI and DIPPEL, were already well aware of the fact that in transverse sections of such cells as fibres and tracheids the outermost layer of the cell-wall is often more strongly birefringent than the main part of the secondary wall. They regarded this as proof of a transverse orientation of the particles of which the primary wall was thought to consist. However, as in the outermost layer of the secondary wall the cellulose is, as we now know, oriented, as a rule, in a flat spiral, and as this layer, moreover, contains a larger amount of this substance than the primary wall, its birefringence will, as a rule, be much stronger than that of the latter, and as the primary wall, moreover, is not discernable as a separate layer, it appears that the conclusion of the earlier microscopists with regard to the orientation of the particles in the primary wall, although right, was not justified.

In order to arrive at a fully warranted conclusion with regard to the orientation of the particles in the primary wall, the observations will have to be made on preparations in which apart from the primary wall no cell-wall layers are present.

A more thorough study of the optical properties of the growing cell-wall set in after the publications of A. FREY-WYSSLING had drawn the attention of the botanists towards the possibilities which the study by the aid of the polarization microscope offers, i.e. after the year 1930. In the following years cell-wall growth became an object of special interest to the botanical world.

The first investigation was carried out in 1932 on the growing region in the sporangiophores of *Phycomyces* (cf. section 2431). It was followed in rapid succession by a whole series of studies on the growth of the cell-wall in Vascular Plants. A general conclusion to be drawn from these studies is that, like all cell-walls containing cellulose, the primary wall always appears to be positively birefringent when viewed in the plane of wall, i.e. in optical section. In surface view it may be isotropic, viz. with isodiametric cells (cf. fig. 32g), but in growing tubular cells it is, with very few exceptions, negatively birefringent with reference to the axis of the cell. Removal of the non-cellulose influences the optical properties but slightly or not at all.

The optical properties of the primary wall proved that the main part of the cellulose micelles must be oriented either transversely (fig. 32f), or else in a helix with low pitch (fig. 32c). This was at a later date fully confirmed by the results of X-ray analysis and of electron microscopical investigation, which will be reviewed in the two following sections.

It seems worth while to list here in chronological sequence the publications on the objects in which the primary wall was found to be negatively birefringent, i.e. of tubular texture, as well as those in which it showed a different optical behaviour and where the texture proved to be predominantly axial. Since observations of this nature are but rarely considered of sufficient importance to devote a special paper to them, they are easily overlooked and we do not claim therefore that the list of authors is strictly in accordance with priority. Neither is the list of objects complete, as we have on the whole restricted it to those that have also been studied by other methods, e.g. by means of the electron microscope, or which, for some reason or other, will be discussed in one of the other sections.

Examples of tubular texture	*Authors*
1. Epidermis and parenchyma from the seta of *Pellia*	OVERBECK (1934)
2. Meristems of coleoptiles, mesocotyls, hypocotyls, leaves, stems and roots	SÖDING (1934), BONNER (1935), RUGE (1938), DIEHL et al. (1939)
3. Cambium initials	VAN ITERSON (1935)
4. Hairs from *Tradescantia* stamens	VAN ITERSON (1937)

Examples of tubular Texture	*Authors*
5. Grass stamens	FREY-WYSSLING and SCHOCH-BODMER (1938)
6. Growing as well as full-grown cotton hairs; in the latter case the primary wall was isolated	WERGIN (1937)
7. Phloem fibres from *Linum* and *Cannabis*	A. D. J. MEEUSE (1938 and 1941), KUNDU and PRESTON (1940)
8. Cortical and perivascular fibres from the leaves of Monocotyledones	A. D. J. MEEUSE (1938)
9. Medulla of *Juncus* leaves	MAAS GEESTERANUS (1941)
10. Hairs from *Ceiba* and *Asclepias*	ROELOFSEN and HOUWINK (1953)
11. Cortical fibres from *Asparagus* shoots	STERLING (1957a)
12. Growing tips of root hairs	see text
Predominantly longitudinal texture	
13. Outer wall of epidermis in *Avena* coleoptile	HEYN (1933)
14. Same of *Helianthus* hypocotyl	BONNER (1935)
15. Collenchyma of *Heracleum*	MAJUMDAR and PRESTON (1941)

A few notes may be added to this list (the numbers at the beginning of the paragraphs correspond to those of the list).

1. In the cells of the seta of *Pellia*, cell-wall material is deposited during growth, but the amount that is deposited is entirely insufficient to compensate the decrease in thickness caused by the extension of the wall. In fact, according to OVERBECK (1934), the thickness of the wall decreases from 6.5 μ to 0.65 μ.

2. The parenchyma cells of *Avena* coleoptiles retain their tubular texture, as BONNER (1935) observed, when the coleoptiles are kept at a temperature of 2° C. At this temperature they still lengthen, but there is no synthesis of cell-wall material.

According to PRESTON (1938) the negative birefringence that was observed in *Avena* coleoptiles, would not be due to a transverse orientation of the cellulose micelles, but to an orientation in a spiral with low pitch. He based his conclusion on the oblique major extinction which he noted in single walls; the latter were obtained by sticking the cells to a glass slide, and by scraping the free wall off. However, the cells which were used by him, were probably, as we will show in section 23451, full-grown, and in such cells the primary wall may already be covered by a secondary one. The study of the optical properties by BAYLEY, COLVIN, COOPER and MARTIN-SMITH (1957), which was carried out on a series of oblique sections, as well as the observations of other authors by means of the electron microscope, do not leave the slightest doubt as to the transverse orientation of the micelles.

The walls of the parenchyma cells of the *Avena* coleoptile are in the angles slightly thickened, and here the orientation of the micelles is not transverse but axial. This was demonstrated by MÜHLETHALER (1950b) by the aid of a dichroitic staining method. The presence of axially oriented micelles had already been stated by K. and M. WÜHRMANN-MEYER (1941), but their interpretation was wrong, for they ascribed it to secondary thickening. BÖHMER (1958) found a similar effect, but as he could find no secondary thickening, he interpreted it correctly. Like the outer wall of the epidermis in the *Avena* coleoptile, these angular thickenings of the primary wall of the parenchyma cells may be counted to the group of exceptions to the rule that in the primary wall of tubular cells the micelles are transversely oriented. In section 2271 we will see that in the side of the ribs that is turned towards the interior of the cell, the fibrils may be once more transversely oriented.

3. In the primary wall of the conifer tracheids too the micelles would, according to PRESTON (1947), not be oriented transversely, but in a spiral with a pitch of circ. 20°. He observed this orientation in wall pieces projecting from broken mature tracheids. However, since in cambium cells that were studied by means of the electron microscope no helical orientation of the microfibrils could be found, and since it is now known that such a structure is present in the outer layer of the secondary wall which like the primary wall tends to separate, it seems almost certain that PRESTON's aberrant result is to be ascribed to the presence of this layer in the pieces that were studied by him. It should furthermore be noted that cambium cells as well as their derivatives grow mainly at the ends. If we assume that they do not grow at all in the remaining parts, the transverse orientation of the micelles would be an exception to the rule that the latter are always oriented perpendicular to the direction of growth, and this would tend to shake our confidence in the validity of this rule. In fact, as we will discuss in section 228, it is very probably not the direction of growth, but the anisotropic wall tension which determines the orientation of the micelles. In tubular cells the tension in the wall is in the transverse direction about twice as large as in the axial one.

4, 5. It has been observed that the transverse orientation of the micelles in the primary wall of tubular cells may sometimes be retained throughout the period of rapid growth by which these cells attain their final length, even though there is, on account of the shortness of this period, no question of an equivalent amount of new wall material being deposited, and even though the cells during this interval may grow out to six times their original length. These observations have contributed materially to the solution of the problem why the micelles in the primary wall of such cells are so regularly oriented in a transverse direction. The first case, that of *Pellia*, has been mentioned already. The phenomenon was studied in more detail and explained by VAN ITERSON (1937) in his study of the hairs on the *Tradescantia* stamens. Under certain circumstances these hairs may show a rapid increase in length of 150%, which is made possible by the osmotic absorption of water (MARTENS, 1931 and 1938). FREY-WYSSLING and SCHOCH-BODMER (1938) found that in the filaments of grass stamens too the transverse orientation of the micelles in the cell-wall was retained during the short period in which the filaments grow out to several times their original length. In the filaments of *Anthoxanthum* these authors found that in the end the walls become positively birefringent. They interpreted this as the result of the tension to which the cellulose micelles were subjected, but this hypothesis looks improbable, and is also unnecessary, as the phenomenon can apparently be explained in a simpler way, see section 22823.

ROELOFSEN and HOUWINK (1951) claim to have found that the micelles in the primary wall of the cells of the hairs arising from the *Tradescantia* stamens are oriented in a flat spiral. They based their opinion on the spiral unwinding of strips torn from the wall (cf. fig. 42) and also on a study of the birefringence. The pitch of the spiral was found to be 5—13°, and the occurrence of S- as well as of Z-spirals was noted.

6. According to Balls (1923) and to several more recent investigators (see the review of Flint, 1950), the wall of young cotton hairs would not only contain transversely oriented cellulose micelles, but also crossed helical strands. They arrived at this conclusion, because they observed with the polarization microscope striations arranged in S- and Z-helices. Balls himself was not fully convinced of the correctness of his interpretation, because the helices were found to change their orientation with regard to the cell axis when the preparation was rotated under the microscope. Roelofsen (1951 a) observed this phenomenon in other objects too, and showed that it is caused by the presence of minute wrinkles, which light up when oriented more or less diagonally to the vibration plane. These wrinkles are formed when the cells lose their turgidity, and also when the walls are chemically cleaned and undergo a shrinkage on this account.

7. According to Kundu and Preston (1940) the transverse orientation of the micelles in the primary wall of young phloem fibres of *Cannabis* would afterwards be changed in an axial one, and this change is said to be the result of growth. However, no evidence is produced.

12. In root hairs, e.g. of *Zea mays*, *Lepidium sativum* and *Sinapis alba*, the present author often noted a small negatively birefringent area in and sometimes below the flattened hemispherical tip. It soon merged into an isotropic zone, which in its turn passed into the secondary thickened and therefore positively birefringent fullgrown part of the wall. In some instances, however, the whole tip proved to be isotropic. These findings are in agreement with the fact that the root hairs of land plants grow at their tip only. The root hairs of *Trianea bogotensis*, which is a water plant, are, on the other hand, negatively birefringent along their whole length. Whether these root hairs grow over their whole length or at the tip only, seems to be unknown.

The walls of the pollen tubes are, according to Vogel (1950) isotropic along their whole length. It seems to be unknown whether they undergo secondary thickening.

13, 14, 15. The objects mentioned in the list under these numbers, are exceptions to the, in our opinion, dubious rule according to which the greater part of the cellulose micelles in growing walls would always be oriented perpendicular to the dominating direction of growth. The edge thickenings of parenchyma cells are another exception. These walls and wall areas proved to be positively birefringent, which implies that at least the greater part of the micelles must be oriented parallel to the axis of the growing organ. Van Iterson (cf. Diehl et al., 1939) suggested that this would be due to an additional axial tension in the wall, of which the origin is to be sought in tissue tension. In this connection it is noteworthy that Majumdar and Preston (1941) are of opinion that the increase in length of the collenchyma cells is in the main a passive stretching. In growing collenchyma cells taken from petioles of *Apium graveolens* with a length of 10 cm or more, too a positive birefringence was observed by Beer and Setterfield (1958). In younger cells, however, the double refraction of the wall was very low, and its character, moreover, varied in different parts of the cell, which indicates a fairly random orientation.

In the primary walls of cells that grow more strongly in width than in length, like the segments of xylem vessels, short hairs and isodiametric epidermis cells, the orientation of the micelles has, to our knowledge, not yet been studied. The results of such a study will be of great interest because they will offer us a better insight into circumstances, such as wall tension and wall extension, which determine the orientation of the microfibrils. This problem will be discussed more fully in section 228.

226. X-RAY INVESTIGATIONS ON THE STRUCTURE OF THE PRIMARY WALL

Under this heading but few investigations can be recorded.

The first to study the primary wall by means of X-ray analysis was HEYN (1934), who worked with strips of the epidermis torn from *Avena* coleoptiles, and confirmed his earlier finding with regard to the orientation of the cellulose micelles in the thick outer wall, which dominated in his preparations. As he had found out already by means of the polarization microscope, these micelles are here oriented parallel to the direction of the axis of the coleoptile. BAYLEY et al. (1957), who studied the same object by means of the small angle scattering method, confirmed HEYN's conclusion.

In cotton hairs collected within twenty days from the date at which the flower opened, i.e. before the development of the secondary wall has set in, at first no orientation of the cellulose could be detected by means of X-ray analysis, although these hairs were studied by several investigators (cf. SISSON, 1938b, where the attempts of the other authors too have been recorded). Presumably because of a more thorough chemical cleaning of the hairs, and also because he was more successful in preventing the distention of the hairs during the process of drying, BERKLEY (1938), however, obtained X-diagrams in which he could recognize the transverse orientation of the micelles that had just been discovered by WERGIN (1937) in another way, viz. by means of the polarization microscope.

PRESTON and WARDROP (1949) studied the structure of the primary wall of cambium cells by means of the X-ray method, using to this end strips of cambium obtained from *Pinus sylvestris*. They could confirm the predominantly transverse orientation of the fibrils that had already been deduced from a study by means of the polarization microscope. However, they assume that the orientation was not exactly transverse, but that the fibrils were arranged in a helix with a pitch of somewhat less than 16°. In this way there would be a reasonable agreement between the results of this study and those obtained by PRESTON (1947) in his study, by means of the polarization microscope, of pieces of cell-wall that projected from the walls of mature tracheids and were supposed to be primary walls. However, as we have pointed out in the previous section, these pieces must have contained part of the secondary wall, and for this reason PRESTON's conclusion with regard to the orientation of the fibrils in the primary wall can no longer be accepted. The X-ray data obtained by PRESTON and WARDROP are consistent with a transverse orientation, when we make allowance for a mean deviation of the order of 16°.

The latest X-ray investigation that can be mentioned here, is that of the cortical fibres of *Asparagus* shoots, which was carried out by STERLING (1957a). Here again, in accordance with the results obtained by the aid of the polarization microscope, in the primary wall a predominantly transverse orientation of the micelles was found.

227. ELECTRON MICROGRAPHS OF THE PRIMARY WALL

The earliest attempt to study the structure of the primary wall by means of the electron microscope was that of BARNES and BURTON (1943). They worked with young cotton hairs, but as their preparations were not shadowed, the microfibrils remained invisible. The next publication, that of FREY-WYSSLING, MÜHLETHALER and WYCKOFF (1948), already contained excellent electron micrographs made by MÜHLETHALER in WYCKOFF's laboratory. It was followed by a whole series of papers emanating from the school of FREY-WYSSLING at Zürich and from that of PRESTON at Leeds, and also from other quarters. They will be discussed hereafter under various headings according to the kind of cell to which they refer.

As the primary wall, especially after the removal of the non-cellulose, is exceedingly thin, even an intact wall consisting of two primary walls and a middle lamella, may, as a rule, be used directly for the study by means of the electron microscope. Except when stated otherwise, the micrographs reproduced in this section, were made of walls out of which the non-cellulose has been removed, i.e. of "cellulose skeletons". It should be borne in mind that the cellulose, as was pointed out in section 221 forms, on the average, but 9% of the volume of the fresh wall, and only 30% of the dried one; by the removal of the non-cellulose and of the water the wall therefore shrinks considerably, not only in surface, but to an even greater extent in thickness, and the texture formed by the microfibrils is therefore in the preparations that are studied by means of the electron microscope, much more compact than it is in the original condition.

2271. Parenchyma cells

The objects that most often have been studied, are the parenchyma cells of *Avena* coleoptiles and those from the root tips of corn and onion. The structure of the wall was sometimes studied in sections and sometimes in cells that had been isolated by maceration. The latter have lost their natural angularity (cf. ESAU, 1953: 177), and have become barrel-shaped or tubular; however, when the cells are arranged in longitudinal files, those at the end of the file may go out into a conical tip, fig. 41. A conspicuous feature of the walls are the primary pit fields, which during the greater part of the growing period retain a slit-like shape and a transverse orientation. They are confined to the flat sides. A peculiarity of the ribs by which the flat sides are separated from each other, and of which there are usually six, is that they are thickened. As was stated in section 225, the study of the birefringence has revealed that the orientation of the cellulose micelles in these thickened ribs is predominantly axial, whereas it is predominantly transverse in the flat sides. So long as strongly growing tissue strips are investigated, the transverse orientation appears to be the dominant one.

The most important papers on the study of the *parenchyma of the Avena coleoptile* by means of the electron microscope are those by MÜHLETHALER (1950a and 1950b), WARDROP (1955 and 1956), SETTERFIELD and BAYLEY

(1957, 1958), BÖHMER (1958) and WARDROP and CRONSHAW (1958).

According to BÖHMER, the orientation of the microfibrils in the wall of very young, still approximately isodiametric cells is predominantly transverse, although there is considerable angular dispersion. When the cells begin to grow out, they also increase considerably in width, and as they do so, the transverse orientation of the fibrils becomes more pronounced.

In the transverse sections of the very young cells studied by SETTERFIELD and BAYLEY, on the outside as well as on the inside of the primary wall comparatively long pieces of microfibril were noted; the orientation of the latter, therefore, must have been approximatively transverse, see fig. 43a and P 44. In the ribs they noted that the microfibrils were axially oriented; microfibrils with this kind of orientation proved to be rare in the flat sides, fig. 43d and P 44.

In somewhat older cells transversely oriented microfibrils are restricted to the dense inner layer. The latter merges into a less dense and less well oriented central layer, and then, in the outermost layer, we note the presence of longitudinally oriented microfibrils which in sections appear in the form of very short segments, fig. 43b, P 44 and P 45. Underneath this layer sometimes a texture consisting of crossed microfibrils is present, fig. P 46 (see also fig. 1 on plate 5 of WARDROP, 1955). In the outermost layer some of the microfibrils appear to be bent round the pit fields, fig. P 46. At the rib edges, transversely oriented microfibrils from the inter-rib regions can be seen to change their direction and to weave into the axial texture of the rib.

In older cells the ribs are much thicker and also wider than in younger ones, as appears from a comparison between fig. P 44, fig. P 46 and fig. P 47. As, on account of the growth of the cell, the wall is distended, a decrease in the thickness of all its parts was to be expected; the increase in thickness of the ribs must mean therefore that a considerable amount of cellulose has been deposited in them. The possibility that cellulose has been shifted towards the ribs, as well as the cause of the axial orientation of the microfibrils in the latter will be discussed in section 22823; at this place we will confine ourselves to observe that the axial orientation of the microfibrils is often confined to the outer part of the ribs, and that the increase in thickness, therefore, can not be due to secondary thickening, as was originally supposed by MÜHLETHALER (1950b), who is now, however, of a different opinion. The inner part often shows a transverse orientation of the microfibrils, but according to SETTERFIELD and BAYLEY (1958) ribs in which the microfibrils are throughout axially oriented, are more common. These authors call these two types of ribs outer ribs and integral ribs.

In very young cells the primary pit fields are circular in outline and do not differ much from the surrounding part of the wall, whose texture is also very loose, fig. P 44. When the cells begin to widen, the pit fields are drawn out transversely and become at the same time more conspicuous, fig. P 46. At a later stage axially oriented microfibrils begin to advance towards them and to invade their area, and in this way they are more or less compressed and assume once more a rounded form (BÖHMER, 1958), fig. P 47 and P 48. MÜHLETHALER (1950a) too gives excellent pictures of the closure of the pit fields, but his opinion that it is caused by secondary thickening is open to doubt.

In the cells with a conical tip the structure of the wall in the latter is of the same nature as elsewhere. Study of the birefringence has revealed that here too a transverse orientation of the microfibrils predominates; this means that a layer with this kind of orientation must be present underneath the more or less irregularly or axially oriented outer layer shown in fig. P 49.

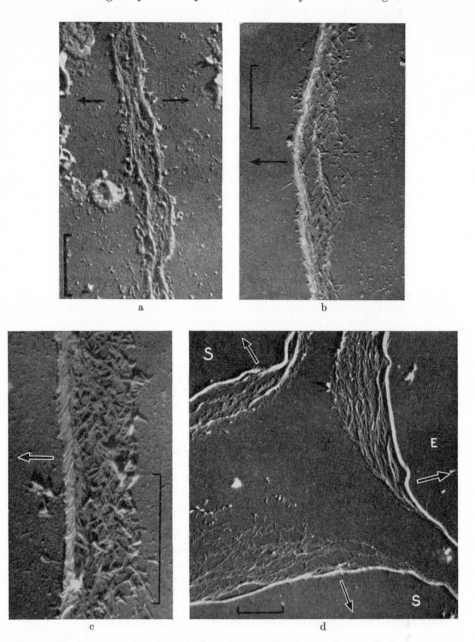

a

b

c

d

Fig. 43. Transverse sections through the primary walls of parenchyma cells from *Avena* coleoptiles. Length of the coleoptile in *a*: 3 mm, in *b* and in *d*: 10 mm, in *c*: 40 mm; in *d*, the wall connects an epidermal cell (E) with two subepidermal cells (S). Arrows point towards the centre of the cell; scales corresponding to 1 μ (from SETTERFIELD and BAYLEY, 1957).

In the middle parts of some old cells, especially in those with a conical tip, helical bands have been observed with a polarization microscope (fig. P 157), as well as in electron micrographs (figs. P 158 and P 159).

They are held by MÜHLETHALER for secondary thickenings, an opinion that is shared by WARDROP and CRONSHAW (1958) and that is confirmed by SETTERFIELD and BAYLEY (1958). We will therefore discuss this structure in section 23451. BÖHMER (1958 and private communication) on the other hand could not find signs of secondary thickening in mature coleoptiles.

The structure of the primary wall of the *parenchyma cells in root tips* has mainly been studied by STECHER (1952) and MÜHLETHALER (1953a) in *Zea mays*, by WARDROP in *Vicia faba* and *Pisum sativum* (1955) and in *Allium cepa* (1956); in the latter it has also been studied by SCOTT et al. (1956) and by SETTERFIELD and BAYLEY (1957, 1958). No essential differences were found with the primary wall of the parenchyma cells in coleoptiles. Fig. P 50 once more shows the transversely elongated primary pit fields on the flat sides and the thickened ribs which mark the angles between the flat sides, and here too the microfibrils in these ribs are axially oriented. According to SETTERFIELD and BAYLEY (1958) there are, just as in *Avena* coleoptiles, "outer ribs" and "integral ribs", the former being more frequent. According to SCOTT et al. the pit fields are at first circular in outline, then, when the cells begin to increase in diameter, they are drawn out transversely, and during the period of longitudinal growth they assume once more a rounded shape; their development, therefore, agrees exactly with that of the pit fields in the walls of the coleoptile parenchyma.

In the walls of the isodiametric apical initials the fibrils form a loose texture and show no definite orientation. Just as in the primary walls of the coleoptile parenchyma, the orientation of the microfibrils becomes, according to SCOTT et al. (l.c.), predominantly transverse when the cells begin to increase in diameter. This orientation can be seen at the inner as well as at the outer side of the wall, fig. 51 a. In fig. P 52 two of the young ribs are shown; the texture of the microfibrils on the flat sides is very loose.

In somewhat older cells that are already growing in length, the wall shows a well-defined inner layer with transversely oriented microfibrils and an outer mass in which the orientation of the microfibrils varies from transverse to axial, fig. 51 b and fig. 53. The orientation of the outermost microfibrils is usually axial, fig. P 52 and fig. P 54. In the period of longitudinal growth the ribs become more voluminous, fig. 51 c.

In still older cells from the root of *Allium cepa*, in which the growth in length presumably was almost completed, SCOTT et al. (1956) noted the presence of crossed fibril bundles, which probably were interwoven. It seems not impossible to us that these already belong to the secondary wall (see section 23451 and figs. P 158 and P 159). These authors also mention a transition from a transverse texture into one consisting of crossed microfibrils. However, the micrograph in which this transition is thought to occur, may very well represent a layer with crossed microfibrils on which a shred of a layer with transversely oriented microfibrils is superposed. Another possibility is that the transition is due to mechanical damage. It seems, at any rate, advisable to await confirmation of this finding.

HOUWINK and ROELOFSEN (1954) studied by means of the electron microscope the primary wall of a special kind of parenchyma cells, viz. the *stellate cells* from the medulla of *Juncus* leaves; to this end young cells were taken from the meristematic zone at the base of leaves of *Juncus effusus*. The growth of these cells and the development of the large intercellular spaces by which the cells are almost entirely enveloped, was described by MAAS GEESTERANUS (1941). So long as the arms of these stellate cells grow in length, the walls in the arms are negatively birefringent, which means that the orientation of the micelles must be predominantly transverse (MAAS GEESTERANUS, l.c.). Fig. P 37 a and P 37 b show that in very short arms the microfibrils in the outer part of the wall are oriented at random, but that in the longer arms they are oriented in the axial direction. However, on the inside of the wall everywhere a

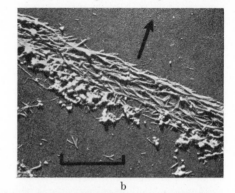

b

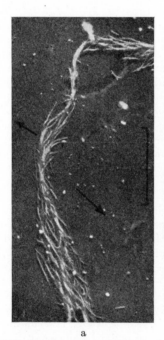

a

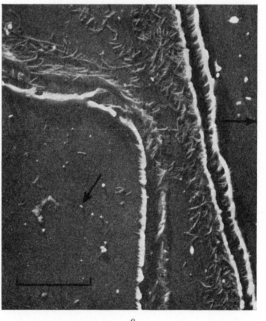

c

Fig. 51. Transverse sections through the walls of parenchyma cells from a root of *Allium cepa*; the distance from the tip is for section *a*: 1 mm, for section *b*: 3 mm, and for section *c*: 5 mm. Arrows point towards cell centres; scales indicate a length of 1 μ (from SETTERFIELD and BAYLEY, 1957).

dense mat of predominantly transverse microfibrils is visible, and it is this mat which is responsible for the negative birefringence mentioned above, fig. P 55. Between the inner and the outer layer the microfibrils seem to be more or less crossed. The fibrillar texture looks very dense, and although it is in the native cell-wall, of course, much less dense, the fact that this mat of microfibrils does extend, still is rather amazing.

The primary walls of isodiametric cells always show an irregular orientation of the microfibrils, at least in the flat sides. This structure is to be seen in fig. P 56; the latter also shows that in the walls of macerated cells the outermost microfibrils are easily set free, and that they may occasionally aggregate into thick bundles, probably during the maceration.

2272. Growing epidermal cells

The epidermal cells that have been studied by the aid of the electron microscope are the hairs on the seeds or on the inside of the pericarp of *Gossypium*, *Ceiba* and *Asclepias*, the cells of the hairs on the stamens of *Tradescantia*, some root hairs, and the epidermal cells of the *Avena* coleoptile and of *Allium* roots. We will confine ourselves here to the cellulose; the structure of the cuticular membrane will be dealt with in section 2362.

The structure of the primary wall in hairs has especially been studied in *cotton hairs* viz. by ROELOFSEN (1951a), KLING and MAHL (1951 and 1952), ROELOFSEN and HOUWINK (1953), HOUWINK and ROELOFSEN (1954), TRIPP et al. (1951, 1954), and O'KELLEY and CARR (1954). The results obtained by the various investigators are in good agreement. At an earlier date young cotton hairs had already been studied with the aid of the electron microscope by BARNES and BURTON (1943), but

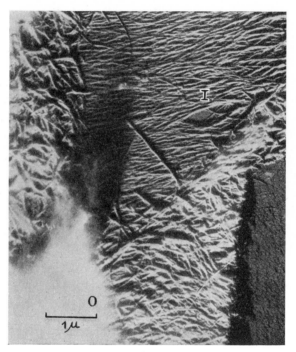

Fig. 53. Outer (O) and inner (I) part of the wall of a parenchyma cell from a root of *Allium cepa*, 2 mm from the tip; the direction of the cell axis is indicated by the edge at right (from WARDROP, 1956).

these investigators did not use the method of shadow-casting, so that the cellulose microfibrils remained invisible. MÜHLETHALER (1949b) too had already made an electron micrograph of a fragment of a young cotton hair, but as the non-cellulose had not been removed, it was not sufficiently clear; it was, moreover, unknown how the fragment was oriented with regard to the axis of the hair, and whether it exposed the inside or the outside.

As so far no transverse sections through growing plant hairs, have been studied electron microscopically, we will have to base our conclusions on surface views of inner and outer parts. Such views are shown in fig. P 57, P 58 and P 60.

On the inner side of the wall a dense mat of microfibrils with a predominantly transverse orientation is noted, fig. P 57. The microfibrils are not straight but wavy, and they form bundles that are interwoven. In some other electron micrographs this crossed texture was even more conspicuous, see fig. P 60 (cf. also ROELOFSEN, 1951, fig. 6 and 8).

On the outer side the fibrillar structure is much less dense, and the fibrils and fibril bundles moreover are axially oriented. The orientation of the microfibrils is, of course, more easily discernable if the shadow-casting has been applied perpendicular to the direction of the fibrils, as in fig. P 58 and P 60, than if it has been applied parallel to the latter, as in fig. P 57.

Owing to the dense texture of the microfibrils in the inner layer, it is impossible to recognize the structure of the outer layer from that side, but as the texture of the outermost layer is comparatively loose and provided with wide meshes, we may study the deeper layers by looking from the outside through these meshes. It then appears that the microfibrils in the layer immediately beneath the meshes are oriented in a more or less oblique direction, fig. P 57, but that in the innermost layers the orientation becomes transverse, fig. P 58. Just as in the parenchyma cells of coleoptiles and roots discussed in the previous section, there is apparently a gradual transition from a more or less axial orientation of the sparse microfibrils on the outer surface via a texture consisting of crossed microfibrils in the central layers, to the rather densely packed, transversely oriented microfibrils of the inner layer.

A cotton hair grows at the top too. The orientation of the microfibrils in the outer layers of the wall has been studied here with the electron microscope by HOUWINK and ROELOFSEN (1954). They noted in the dome-shaped top an irregular network of microfibrils, which passed almost immediately below the latter in a layer with axial orientation. However, from the study

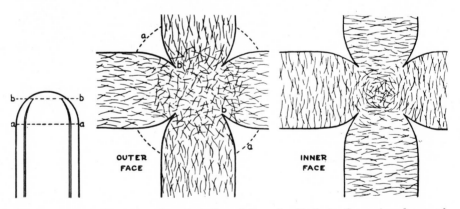

Fig. 59. Schema illustrating the orientation of the microfibrils in the various layers of the wall in the dome-shaped top of a growing cotton hair (from HOUWINK and ROELOFSEN, 1954).

of the birefringence it could be deduced that the orientation in the greater part of the wall of the hemi-spherical top must be transverse; this orientation therefore must be present in the inner layers. This has schematically been indicated in fig. 59. According to O'KELLEY and CARR (1954) the top would have the same structure as the rest of the wall, but their observations do not warrant this conclusion.

The primary wall retains its structure in the subsequent stages of development. That this structure is still present in mature hairs, appeared in the replicas that have been obtained from the latter (KLING and MAHL, 1951 and 1952), but especially from the preparations of TRIPP et al. (1954), which consisted of shreds of the primary wall which had been detached with mechanical means from the full-grown hairs, cf. fig. P 60. The inner side of these shreds shows crossed microfibrils, an orientation therefore that has also been found in some of the growing cotton hairs.

The electron micrographs of the primary wall of *other unicellular hairs*, viz. of young hairs from the inside of the pericarp of *Ceiba pentandra* and of hairs from the seeds of *Asclepias cornuti* reveal the presence of structures which are completely identical with those observed in the primary wall of the cotton hair (ROELOFSEN and HOUWINK, 1953); the wall of the apical part of these hairs has not yet been investigated.

The orientation of the cellulose in the primary wall of the staminal hairs of *Tradescantia virginica* is somewhat different (ROELOFSEN and HOUWINK, 1951). In the cells of very young hairs a transverse orientation of the microfibrils was observed on the inside of the wall, but the orientation of the microfibrils on the outside was not axial but irregular.

The structure of the primary wall has also been investigated in the cells of full-grown hairs, which were taken from withered flowers. These cells were allowed to increase their turgor by the absorption of water; in this way their length increased to about 1.5 times of its original value, and their cuticles were burst. As has already been pointed out at an earlier occasion, the increase in size takes place so rapidly that deposition of new material in the wall must be regarded as excluded, and as the birefringence of the wall remains negative, it is clear that the orientation of the micelles remains predominantly transverse.

Investigation by means of the electron microscope showed that the orientation of the microfibrils in the centripetal layers had remained transverse, but in the outer layers the orientation was sometimes found to be irregular and sometimes axial, fig. P 60 and P 61. However, whether the axial orientation was already present in the period of growth or whether it arose during the osmotic elongation, is unknown. No attempts were made to correlate the oblique extinction that was observed between crossed nicols with the orientation of the microfibrils on the inside of the wall.

Although there appeared to be no fundamental difference in structure between the walls of very young cells and those from full-grown ones, it was plain that the latter were much thicker. However, as the full-grown cells when the cuticle was burst, appeared to be able to increase their size still further, the increase in thickness of the wall can, in our opinion, not be regarded as secondary thickening. That the wall increases in thickness, is in itself of no importance, as this happens also in the earlier stages of cell-growth, and we should bear in mind that the hairs continue to grow till a few hours before the flower withers.

Before entering into a discussion of the structure of the primary wall in *root hairs* as revealed in electron micrographs, we wish to draw attention to the fact that the root hairs, at least in land plants, grow at the tip only, and that the wall is here negatively birefringent or, more rarely, isotropic, whereas already immediately below the tip it appears to be positively birefringent.

Investigations by means of the electron microscope have been carried out mainly by FREY-WYSSLING and MÜHLETHALER (1949) on root hairs of *Zea mays*, by HOUWINK and ROELOFSEN (1954) on the same object and on *Sinapis alba*, and by O'KELLEY and CARR (1954) on the root hairs of *Raphanus sativus*.

An electron micrograph of a root hair of *Sinapis* is also to be seen in a publication of BELFORD et al. (1958).

The first-named authors noted on the outside a predominantly axial structure, though interwoven with some transversely oriented microfibrils. They compared the structure with the warp and weft of textile fabrics. Especially at the tip the structure would be very loose, but this may have been the result of a too drastic cleaning, for HOUWINK and ROELOFSEN (l.c.) found in the same object the structure shown in fig. P 63, in which the texture of the microfibrils at the tip seems to be but slightly less dense than elsewhere.

At the tip as well as elsewhere the outer part of the wall consists of a very thin layer of microfibrils which shows a wide-meshed texture. The orientation of the microfibrils themselves is at the tip predominantly transverse, but immediately below the latter it becomes irregular. Through the meshes in this outer layer we see a more compact texture consisting of axially oriented microfibrils. The latter are more easily discernable if we look at the wall from the inside. This layer too contains fissures, and through the latter we see once more the outer layer with its irregularly oriented microfibrils. The whole wall therefore consists but of two layers, the thin primary wall and the thicker secondary one.

Electron micrographs made by HOUWINK (unpublished) and by BELFORD et al. (1958) of the wall in root hairs of *Sinapis alba* revealed the presence of a fully identical structure. The latter authors stated that the primary wall contained both random and oriented layers, but they evidently overlooked the fact that growth is restricted to the extreme tip, and were not aware that they were studying the mature wall instead of the primary one.

O'KELLEY and CARR (1954) published electron micrographs of the outermost layer of the cell-wall in the root hairs of *Raphanus sativa*. These micrographs show that the greater part of the microfibrils are oriented in an approximatively axial direction. As similar differences in the orientation of the microfibrils have been observed in the outermost layer of the cell-wall in different hairs of the *Tradescantia* stamens, these differences seem to be of subordinate importance. The orientation of the microfibrils in the outermost layer may apparently be axial, but it is not necessarily so.

Electron micrographs of the primary wall in *ordinary epidermal cells* have been published by several authors. Those of MÜHLETHALER (1950b) and of BAYLEY et al. (1957) were obtained from the epidermis of the *Avena* coleoptile, those of SETTERFIELD and BAYLEY (1957) from that of the onion root, and those of SCOTT et al. (1957) from that of the onion leaf. SETTERFIELD (1957) moreover studied the wall of the guard cells of the stomata in the epidermis of the *Avena* coleoptile.

From observations made by means of the polarization microscope and from the configuration shown in the X-ray diagrams it had already been deduced that the microfibrils in the outer wall of the epidermal cells of *Avena* coleoptiles must be axially oriented. This conclusion was fully confirmed by the electron micrographs. It was noted by BAYLEY et al. (l.c.) that these microfibrils form already in 2 mm long coleoptiles a circ. 1 μ thick wall with a very dense texture. In the course of a few days the coleoptile grows out to about 20 times this length, but notwithstanding this rapid extension, it appears that the wall does not become thinner, but that it, on the contrary, shows a considerable increase in thickness; in a 40 mm long coleoptile its thickness amounted to 2—3 μ, figs. 65 and 66.

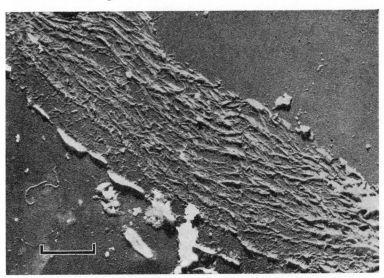

Fig. 65. Transverse section through the outer wall of an epidermal cell from a 2.3 mm long *Avena* coleoptile; the cell was situated circ. 1 mm from the tip; inner side of the wall pointing upwards (from Bayley et al., 1957).

The microfibrils appear to be arranged in several layers, viz. 10—15 in the wall of a young cell and $\pm$ 25 in older ones. The increase in the number of the layers is accompanied by a corresponding increase in the thickness of the wall; the layers themselves do not become thinner on account of the extension to which they are subjected, but seem to increase slightly in thickness. The total wall thickness is in the electron micrographs much more than in the untreated walls; the swelling might be due to the pretreatment with an enzyme preparation and to swelling during the embedding before sectioning.

Where the thin radial wall abuts on the much thicker outer one, the transverse orientation of the microfibrils of the first passes gradually into the axial one in the latter. This transition and the considerable difference in thickness can also be seen in the surface views of macerated epidermal cells photographed by Mühlethaler (l.c.) and reproduced in figs. P 67 and P 68. In the latter figure the tip of an epidermal cell is shown, and here the axial orientation of the outermost microfibrils in the radial wall is clearly seen.

With regard to the structure of the innermost layer of the outer wall there is some difference of opinion. According to Mühlethaler the orientation of the microfibrils in this layer would be transverse, which means that it would be similar to that of the microfibrils in the innermost layer of most thickened ribs of the parenchyma cells. In a few instances this was observed by Bayley et al. (l.c.) too. One of these instances is shown in fig. 65, where it looks indeed as if there is a gradual transition from the axial orientation in the outer layers to an approximatively transverse one in the inner part. As a rule, however, the axial orientation extends throughout the whole thickness of the outer epidermal wall.

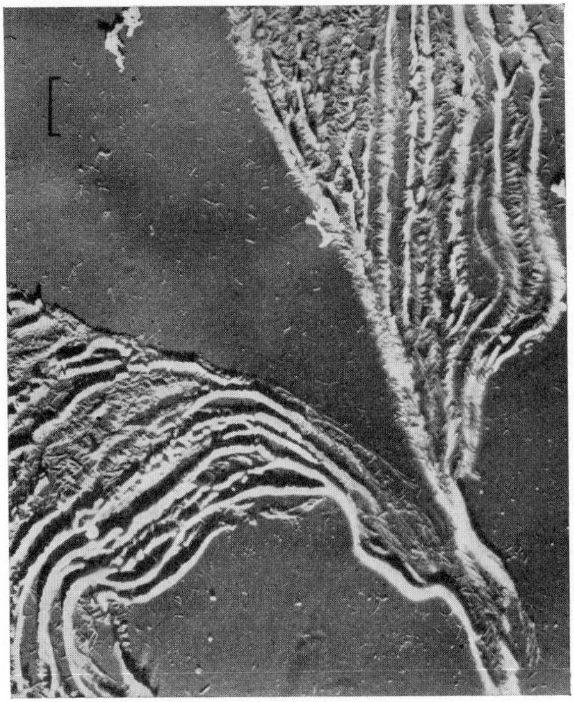

Fig. 66. Transverse section through the outer wall and the radial wall between two epidermal cells from a 20 mm long *Avena* coleoptile; these cells were situated circ. 5 mm from the tip; the radial wall is at the right (from BAYLEY et al., 1957).

Near the tip of the onion root the outer wall of the epidermal cells has a somewhat different structure, for here we find on the inside a thick layer of transversely oriented microfibrils bounded on the outside by an even thicker layer of axially oriented ones, fig. P 69.

From what has been said above, it seems clear that the structure of the outer wall of the epidermal cells need not differ materially from that of the thickened ribs at the corners of the parenchyma cells, although it is considerably thicker, and although the layer with the transverse orientation on the inside is more often absent. In section 228233 we will try to explain the cause of these deviations.

That the building material of the cell-wall consists but for a minor part of cellulose, is a rule that applies also to the epidermal cells of coleoptiles. This is clearly demonstrated by fig. 70. It represents a section through the outer wall in its original condition. The main part consists of a mass with a faint indication of layers, but otherwise without any structure. On the outside an about 0.2 μ thick, likewise structureless cuticular membrane is seen.

In several plants plasmodesmata have been found in the non-cuticular part of the outer wall of epidermal cells from full-grown leaves and perianth parts. They have also been seen in electron micrographs (cf. section 23442). Whether they are already present before these parts have completed their growth, is as yet unknown, but in the objects that have been studied so far, in the outer wall of the growing epidermal cells no plasmodesmata or primary pit fields were observed.

2273. Vascular cambium and not yet full-grown elements derived from it

The behaviour of the cambial initials differs in some respects from that of their derivatives. In the cambial initials the radial walls increase in width, and at each division the cell-plate takes the place of one of the tangential walls. The cell-plate therefore has to grow out, but the increase in surface is not due to distention but to addition of new building material at the ends.

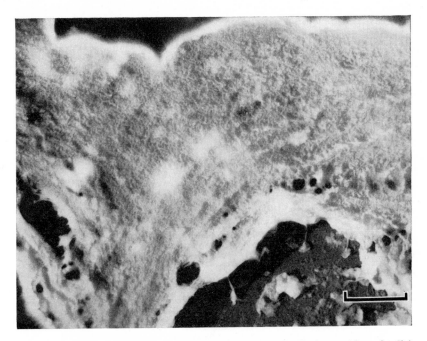

Fig. 70. Transverse section through the non-cleaned outer wall of an epidermal cell from a 20—30 mm long *Avena* coleoptile (from BAYLEY et al., 1957).

The length of the cambial initials, moreover, gradually increases, in *Thuja* e.g. in 3.7 years from 1.6 mm to 4.6 mm (BANNAN, 1950). This growth is strongest at the two ends of the cell, and must obviously be classified as intrusive tip growth, since the zone to which these initials belong, does not grow in length, growth in length being confined to the non-lignified part near the top of the tree. At the upper end of the initials growth is stronger than at the lower one (BANNAN, 1950 and 1956), but the degree in which it decreases in the zones farther away from the tips, and whether there may even be some growth in the middle part of the cell, is unknown. If growth is not restricted to the extreme tips, the expending parts must glide over the walls of adjacent cells, because, as stated above, the zone to which they belong, consists partly of lignified elements and is therefore unable to grow in length.

   If the cell that is split off from the cambial initial develops into a segment of a vessel, it increases in diameter, but if it becomes a tracheid or a fibre, it will grow in length, and as this growth is strongest at the ends, we meet here with another example of intrusive tip growth (SCHOCH-BODMER, 1951 and 1952; WARDROP and DADSWELL, 1952). That regions below the tip or even the central region of the cell may take part in its growth, is not excluded. If this occurs, the intrusive growth will here also, to some extent, be accompanied by sliding growth.

That the study of the cambium by the aid of the electron microscope did as yet not give a clear picture of the structure of the wall in the cambial initials and their derivatives, may perhaps be due to local differences in structure as a result of the local differences in the rate and in the direction of growth mentioned in the two preceding paragraphs. It is, moreover, not improbable that the orientation of the microfibrils in these walls is influenced also by differences in tissue tension and wall tension. To this point we will return in section 22823.

The most important investigations on the structure of the cell-wall in the cambium were carried out by BOSSHARD (1952 and 1956a) and WARDROP (1954a), but we must also mention those of HODGE and WARDROP (1950), PRESTON and RIPLEY (1954) and SVENSSON (1956). The last-named author investigated the primary wall by making replicas of full-grown tracheids. The development of the bordered pits was studied by FREY-WYSSLING, BOSSHARD and MÜHLETHALER (1956).

Before entering into details, it seems worth while to repeat that studies by means of the polarization microscope and of X-ray analysis have already made it clear that the orientation of the micelles in the walls of the cambial cells must be predominantly transverse.

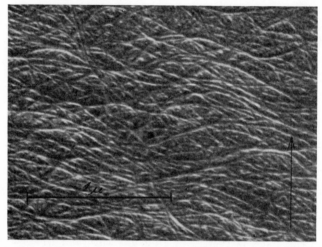

Fig. 71. Outer face of the primary wall of a fully differentiated tracheid of *Picea excelsa* with transverse orientation of the microfibrils; direction of the cell axis indicated by arrow (from SVENSSON, 1956).

In fact in the electron micrographs of the walls of cambial initials a predominantly transverse orientation of the microfibrils was usually found in the outer layer, viz. by BOSSHARD in *Fraxinus*, by WARDROP in *Pinus* and *Eucalyptus*, by PRESTON and RIPLEY in *Pinus, Larix, Pseudotsuga* and *Populus* and by SVENSSON in *Picea*. The orientation sometimes appeared to be almost ideally transverse, as in fig. 71, in other instances there were more or less distinctly crossed microfibrils, as in fig. P 72 and occasionally the orientation of the outermost microfibrils proved to be, at least locally, axial, as in fig. P 73. The inner part of the wall has but rarely been observed, the first time in *Pinus* in a cell in which the membrane of a half-bordered pit in the wall at the opposite side had been destroyed; here the microfibrils in the inner layer appeared to be transversely oriented (WARDROP, 1957a). Afterwards WARDROP has made some more micrographs of the inside, all with

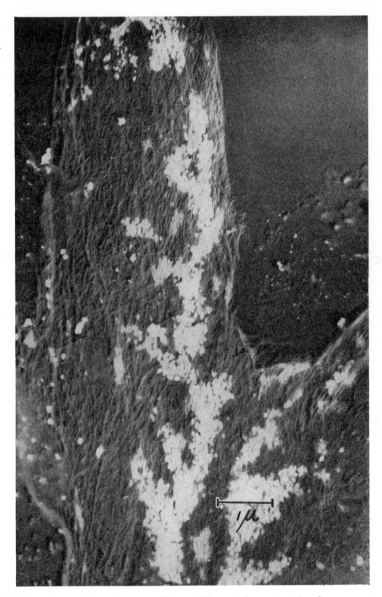

Fig. 75. Outer face of the primary wall near bifurcated growing tip of a young tracheid of *Pinus radiata* (from WARDROP, 1954a).

the same result. Fig. P 74 shows the transverse orientation of the microfibrils in the inner layer as well as the more or less axial orientation on the outside. Just as in parenchyma cells the cell-wall is thickened at the angles, and here too the microfibrils in these thickened ribs are axially oriented, fig. P 72. The primary wall of the full-grown tracheids shows the same structure as the wall of the initials, fig. 71. Especially the thickened ribs are sometimes very conspicuous (WARDROP, 1957 b).

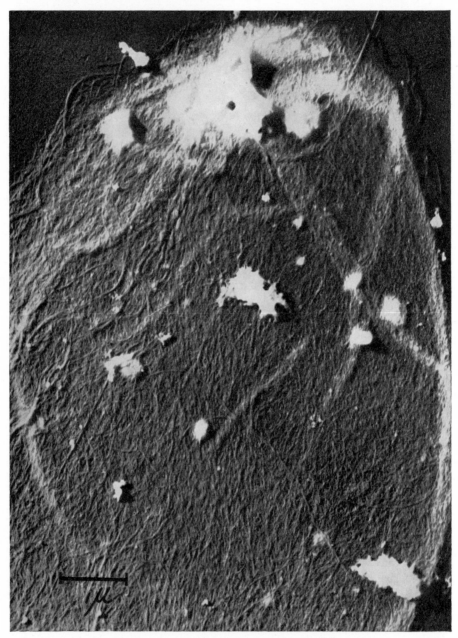

Fig. 76. Outer face of the primary wall in the growing tip of a young wood fibre of *Eucalyptus elaeophora* (from WARDROP, 1954 a).

Micrographs of the growing tips of initials are not available, but in those of fibres and tracheids the orientation of the outermost microfibrils is clearly axial, figs. 75 and 76. The structure at the inner face of the wall of such tips has not yet been observed, but as in the few objects in which it was studied, the wall of the tip proved to be positively birefringent (private communication received in 1958 from WARDROP), it is clear that if there actually is an inner layer with transverse orientation at the tip, it must, at any rate, be very thin.

BOSSHARD (1952) observed in *Fraxinus excelsior* in the primary walls of cambial cells and their derivatives a large number of areas in which the texture of the microfibrils appeared to be rather loose; this situation is shown in some of his micrographs. The areas were supposed to indicate localized surface growth in the sense of the theory of mosaic growth which we will discuss in section 22821. However, as WARDROP (1954a) and PRESTON and RIPLEY (1954) did not find so many areas with a loose texture, but only primary pit fields, we believe that these authors are right in supposing that BOSSHARD's areas with loose texture are artefacts caused by a too rigorous cleaning.

Interesting observations were made by BOSSHARD (l.c.) on the cells that are developing into segments of xylem vessels. These cells undergo an increase in diameter, and during this period of growth he noted in the future pit fields on the inside of the primary wall the development of wavy ridges running in an axial direction; as the cells increased in diameter these ridges were drawn further apart. When the cells had reached their ultimate size, these ridges were connected with each other by the development of other ones running in a transverse direction, and in this way the pit fields obtained their final shape, fig. P 77. He supposes that the connecting ridges put a stop to the growth of the cell, but this has not been proved.

The differentiation of the pit membrane and of the torus of the bordered pits takes place in the primary wall, but only after the tracheid has reached its final length (KERR and BAILEY, 1934). The process was studied by means of the electron microscope by FREY-WYSSLING, BOSSHARD and MÜHLE-THALER (1956) and by STEMSRUD (1956) in *Pinus sylvestris*. In the circular field which will develop into a pit, the microfibrils begin to aggregate in bundles, figs. P 78a and P 78b. Then, in the centre a smaller concentric field is set off from the rest by a ring of microfibrils; this becomes the torus. At the same time the microfibrils in the annular zone outside the future torus are drawn together in radiating bundles, leaving perforations between them, figs. P 78c and P 78d.

Contrary to what happens in *Pinus sylvestris* in the development of the pit membrane of the bordered pits, no bundling of microfibrils takes place in the differentiation of the pit membrane of the half-bordered pits in the walls by which the tracheids are connected with the parenchyma cells of the medullary rays (FREY-WYSSLING et al., l.c.).

2274. Other cell types

The *xylem and phloem elements of the vascular strands* are more or less comparable to the derivatives of the cambium. They differ nevertheless from them not only in their origin from cells belonging to a primary meristem, but also, and this is to us of more importance, by the considerable increase in length as well as in diameter which they undergo in the initial stages of their development. Our knowledge with regard to the structure of the primary wall has almost entirely been derived from the work of MÜHLETHALER (1950b and 1953), who studied the development of these elements in coleoptiles of *Zea* and *Avena* and in roots of *Zea*.

Part of the wall of a very young *sieve-tube cell* from an *Avena* coleoptile is shown in fig. P 79. There appears to be no fundamental difference with the primary wall of parenchyma cells; here too the orientation of the microfibrils is predominantly transverse though some of the outermost ones are axially oriented, and here too we find in the angles between the flat sides thickenings with on the outside an exclusively axial orientation. The whole network of microfibrils, however, is denser. The walls of older cells, such as those shown in figs. P 80 and P 81 are especially conspicuous by the presence of numerous primary pit fields distributed over its whole surface. The microfibrils on the outer face are still axially oriented, fig. P 81. The tips are sometimes rather frail, and it can not be doubted that they are still growing, and so is the rest of the cell (BÖHMER, 1958). Especially at the outside of the wall a great number of axially oriented microfibrils are noted, and in the next layer the orientation is sometimes transverse, sometimes oblique, fig. P 82. In obtuse sieve-tube cells typical sieve-plates may be present.

The primary wall of the *tracheary elements* in the *Avena* and *Zea* coleoptiles and in the *Zea* root shows at first the same structure as that of the young sieve-tube, but shortly afterwards the well-known annular, helical or reticulate thickenings, and occasionally also transitions between them, make their appearance, first of all in the central zone. The cells themselves continue to grow along their whole length (BÖHMER, 1958). Between these thickenings the wall remains thin, and often shows a very clear texture consisting of crossed microfibrils, figs. P 83a and P 84, but this is no rule without exception, for the orientation may also be approximately transverse, fig. P 83b, or more nearly axial, fig. P 85. These differences in the orientation of the fibrils are probably due to differences in growth or in distension.

The orientation of the microfibrils on the outside of the primary wall in the xylem elements of the vascular strands is, just as in the growing tips of the phloem elements and just as in the elements of the secondary wood, predominantly axial. This orientation is particularly clear in fig. P 86, but it is not impossible that it is in this case due to artificial distension. What MÜHLETHALER regarded in this cell as a perforation through which the protoplasm was supposed to protrude and to deposit microfibrils that are oriented axially due to the streaming of the protoplasm, might in our opinion be a damaged tip.

As has already been stated in section 223, the *pollen tube* is a typical example of a cell with tip growth. This was recognized already by NAEGELI in 1846, and has been confirmed since then by several authors, e.g. by SCHOCH-BODMER (1945). It is undoubtedly the most suitable type of growth for the pollen tube, as the latter, at least where no style canal is present, has to force its way through a tissue consisting of full-grown cells; that it succeeds in this task, is partly due to the fact that it first weakens the resistance of the middle lamellae of these cells.

The orientation of the microfibrils was studied by MÜHLETHALER and LINS-KENS (1956) in the wall of pollen tubes grown in artificial culture. They found that the microfibrils in the outermost layer were oriented at random, at the tip of the tube as well as elsewhere, fig. P 87. O'KELLEY and CARR (1954) had observed a similar orientation of the microfibrils. In some of the electron micrographs published by VOGEL (1950), however, a tendency towards an approximately axial orientation may be detected, fig. P 88.

MÜHLETHALER and LINSKENS (l.c.) also studied the wall of pollen tubes that had penetrated into the tissue of the style. Here the texture formed by the microfibrils proved to be more compact. The texture of the microfibrils at the inner side of the wall could be studied in some transverse sections that had been upset, and here too the microfibrils appeared to show no definite orientation. This is in agreement with the usual optical isotropism of the wall indicated by VOGEL. However, the cell-wall part depicted in fig. P 88 shows, as stated above, an approximation to an axial orientation and if the cell-wall as a whole had been optically inactive, this implies that there must have been a predominantly transverse structure on the inner side of the wall.

Electron micrographs have been published of the primary wall of mature *phloem fibres* of *Boehmeria* and *Cannabis* (MÜHLETHALER, 1949b), in which the microfibrils are either crossed or irregularly oriented, but as it is unknown whether the micrographs have reference to the outer or to the inner side of the wall, and in what direction the cell axis may have run, they are of little value to us. Even the possibility that the cell-wall fragments did not belong to the phloem fibre itself, but to a parenchyma cell adhering to the latter, can, in our opinion, not be excluded.

BOSSHARD (1952, and private communication in 1958) observed in the wall of growing phloem fibres of *Fraxinus* a transverse orientation of the microfibrils in the inner layer, and axially oriented bundles of microfibrils in the outermost one, fig. P 89. The predominantly axial orientation of the microfibrils in the outermost layer is also seen in other electron micrographs made by him.

As far as we know, the outer surface of mature phloem fibres has as yet not been studied. In view of the technical importance of some of them, this gap in our knowledge is rather surprising.

The *cortical fibres* from the pericycle of young *Asparagus* shoots were studied by STERLING and SPIT (1957). The outer surface of the wall was studied in replicas made of macerated cells, and the inner surface in replicas of radial sections that had partly been macerated in order to remove the non-cellulose. A drawback of the latter method is that as a result of the maceration the opened cells at the surface of the section may be loosened and washed away, in which case the outer surface of the underlying cell becomes exposed, and may be mistaken for the inner surface of the wall that has been washed away.

The outermost microfibrils of the outer surface shown in fig. P 90, are more or less axially oriented, whereas the next layer consists of transverse or crossed microfibrils. In both micrographs superficial bands of parallel, axially oriented microfibrils, apparently representing angular thickenings, are present. Occasionally a transverse orientation of the microfibrils was noted on the outer surface of the wall, and in the wall of the full-grown cell depicted in fig. P 110a; the orientation of the microfibrils on the outer surface appears to be irregular. The results of these investigations are therefore similar to those obtained in the study of the parenchyma cells, although the variability is greater.

The cell-wall at the tip of the cortical fibres shows at its outer surface a predominantly axial orientation of the microfibrils, fig. P 91, and resembles in this respect, therefore, the wall at the tip of the tracheary elements.

In layers that are regarded by STERLING and SPIT as representing the inner side of the primary wall, the microfibrils were found to be oriented in a crosswise fashion, the crossed microfibrils sometimes occurring in the same layer, as in fig. P 90b, and sometimes in separate layers, as in fig. P 92. Their presence in separate layers has hitherto not been found in other primary walls neither on the inner nor on the outer side. A transverse orientation was never observed by them in what they regard as the inner side of the primary wall.

The more or less random arrangement of the microfibrils in the primary wall of the perivascular fibres of *Agave*, is to be seen in an electron micrograph of a wall fragment published by BALASHOV et al. (1957).

So far *collenchyma cells* were studied electron optically only by BEER and SETTERFIELD (1958). They used mature heads and young plants of celery (*Apium graveolens*) and studied mainly transverse sections of collenchyma cells. These were usually treated with pectinase before embedding and cutting, so that the walls had swollen considerably, and the distances between the different lamellae in them are therefore greatly enlarged.

On the inner side of the wall of young cells often a transverse orientation was found, whereas on the outer side the microfibrils usually showed an orientation, approximately longitudinal, fig. 93 a.

In primary walls of greater thickness, as those depicted in figs. 93 b and 93 c, the thickenings occur mainly in the edges of the cells and are composed of alternate layers of longitudinally oriented microfibrils and non-cellulosic material. These layers arise both outside and inside those layers that are continuous around the entire cell. The original transversely oriented layer in the primary wall appears to have been thinned out or reoriented during elongation. In collenchyma cells of mature celery heads there often is a transversely oriented inner layer (T in fig. 93 b). The authors do not exclude the possibility that this is a part of the elongating primary wall, but it is not of universal occurrence and never occurs in petioles of young plants so that the authors tentatively suggest that it is eventually laid down after cessation of growth.

228. THEORIES ON THE MECHANISM OF THE SURFACE GROWTH OF THE CELL-WALL BASED ON THE LATTER'S STRUCTURE

> „Man sieht also zu welchen Irrthümern es führen kann, wenn man aus dem fertigen Bau einer Zellwand auf die Art und Weise ihres Wachstums Rückschlüsse macht." (KRABBE 1887).

2281. Theories dating from before the advent of electron microscopy

As the growth of the cell-wall is to be regarded as a life-process, the elucidation of its mechanism is primarily a concern of the physiologist. Therefore, we will not enter here into discussion of the ancient but apparently still unsolved problem whether the growth of the cell-wall is caused by an increase in the turgor of the cell or at least by a distension of the wall in which case the deposition of new cell-wall material would merely be an event of secondary importance, or whether it is brought about by "active" intercalation of such material, in which case the distension would be of secondary importance.

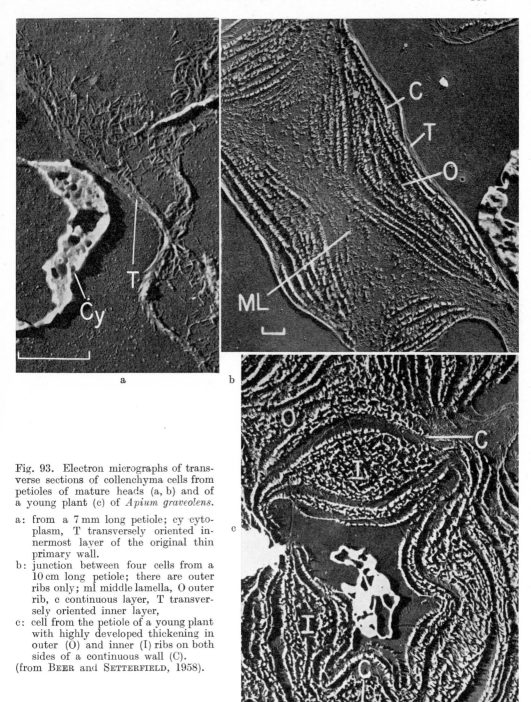

Fig. 93. Electron micrographs of transverse sections of collenchyma cells from petioles of mature heads (a, b) and of a young plant (c) of *Apium graveolens*.

a: from a 7 mm long petiole; cy cytoplasm, T transversely oriented innermost layer of the original thin primary wall.

b: junction between four cells from a 10 cm long petiole; there are outer ribs only; ml middle lamella, O outer rib, c continuous layer, T transversely oriented inner layer,

c: cell from the petiole of a young plant with highly developed thickening in outer (O) and inner (I) ribs on both sides of a continuous wall (C).

(from Beer and Setterfield, 1958).

Since SACHS in 1874 came forward with the view that the distension of the wall is caused by the increase in turgor, and should be regarded as the primary cause, a large number of plant physiologists have given their thoughts to this problem. A new aspect of the latter came to the fore when the activity of growth-substances, and especially the way in which they influence the growth of the cell-wall, became an object of special interest to plant physiologists, but this aspect too will here be left out of consideration.

In this section we will confine our attention to the question what changes the structure of the cell-wall undergoes during the process of growth and how they are to be explained.

The first question that we will try to answer, is whether it has been proved that the ordinary form of cell-wall growth is indeed accompanied by the deposition of new cell-wall material, and that it can therefore not be regarded as merely an irreversible distension. The microscopists of the classical period were already convinced that a deposition of new cell-wall material is involved, for they noted that at least in several cases the thickness of the wall did not undergo a decrease during the period of growth, as it certainly ought to have done when its growth was nothing but a distension.

All doubts with regard to the deposition of new material in the walls of growing cells were removed when the amount of cell-wall material that is present in the successive stages of growth, was accurately determined. These determinations revealed a considerable increase in cell-wall material per cell (see PRESTON and CLARK, 1944; WIRTH, 1946; BAYLEY and SETTERFIELD, 1957). That the cell-wall constituent which interests us most of all, viz. the cellulose, is deposited during the period of growth, was proved, moreover, by the experiments with labelled carbon mentioned in section 223. However, it is noteworthy that the deposition of new material does not always keep pace with the rate of growth; this follows from the fact that in the course of growth the amount of cell-wall material that is present per unit of length sometimes undergoes a slight decrease, GREEN (1958a). That this would be so, was supposed already by OVERBECK (1934) and by DIEHL et al. (1939), who noted, respectively in the setae of *Pellia* and in the hypocotyl of *Helianthus*, a slight decrease in the diameter of the wall during the period of growth; this decrease, however, is in our opinion no proof, for it might also have been caused by loss of water.

We know, however, some instances where cell growth appears to be entirely or almost entirely independent of the deposition of new cell-wall material, but these instances are rare, and may be regarded as exceptional. Three of these exceptions have already been mentioned in section 225, viz. the setae of *Pellia*, the cells of the hairs on the *Tradescantia* stamens and the cells of the filaments in the flowers of the *Gramineae*. In these cases the parts to which these cells belong, grow so rapidly that there seems to be no time for the deposition of more than a negligible fraction of the amount of cell-wall material needed to keep pace with growth. Another instance was given by BONNER (1935), who observed that at low temperatures *Avena* coleoptiles are unable to produce cell-wall material, but that they may nevertheless continue to grow.

The second question to which we want to find an answer, is in what way the new cell-wall material is deposited, whether this takes place by intussusception, i.e. by intercalation of the new particles between those that are already present, or by apposition, i.e. not in, but on the existing wall. The older literature on this question has been discussed i.a. by VAN WISSELINGH (1925), and it will therefore be enough to recollect the following points. Before 1850 it was generally assumed that the cell-wall grew by apposition only, and that, so long as the cell was growing, the increase in thickness of the wall caused by the apposition of new layers was counteracted by a decrease caused by its distension. NAEGELI, however, has already in 1846 expounded the opposite view, viz. that the growth of the cell-wall, in thickness as well as in extent, was due to intussusception, i.e. that it was effected by the inter-calation of new particles, his micelles, between those that were already present; in 1858 he returned once more to this subject to express his view in greater detail.

As to the increase in thickness, the idea that it would be due to intussus-ception, which at one time received the support of such prominent botanists as SACHS and DE VRIES, has now generally been abandoned, although it is not impossible that here too intussusception may sometimes play a part. The opposite view was defended by STRASBURGER who ascribed not only the increase in thickness, but also that in extent, to apposition, although he admitted that there are probably exceptions. Other authors, and among them KLEBS and PFEFFER, were of opinion that the increase in extent may be due to apposition as well as to intussusception or to a combination of the two. To the last-named author we owe the distinction between passive growth due to irreversible distension, and active growth due to intussusception.

Under the influence of results obtained by new methods of investigation, especially with regard to the structure of cellulose, the intussusception theory assumed in the thirties of this century a new form. Studies by the aid of the polarization microscope and of X-ray analysis had shown that the cellulose in the cell-wall must form a more or less cohering network consisting of elongated units separated from each other by interstices. It was also known that the cell-wall of the meristematic cell contains but little cellulose, much non-cellulose and a very large amount of water, but, as the cellulose is the only constituent of which the units form a cohering mass, it seemed clear that it is the latter which, notwithstanding its small amount, is responsible for the firmness of the wall. Now, during the growth of the cell-wall this network of cellulose has to be enlarged, but in such a way that its strength is not impaired. As has been reported in section 225, the study of the birefring-ence of primary walls had at that time revealed that in the wall of tubular cells the majority of the cellulose micelles must be transversely oriented, and that they retain this orientation throughout the period of growth. It was at that time generally assumed that the cellulose micelles had the character of fringe micelles, i.e. that it were rodlet-like bundles of cellulose molecules with a more or less crystalline nucleus and with a fringe consisting of loosened pieces of molecules belonging to the peripheral part and also of molecules protruding at the two ends of the micelle. By means of these fringes the micelles were supposed to be connected with each other, and to these con-nections the tensile strength of the whole network of micelles was ascribed. This hypothetic structure is schematically shown in fig. 94.

A cell-wall provided with such a cohering network is, of course, unable to grow so long as the molecular junctions between the micelles remain intact. BONNER (1935) thought it possible that the junctions would be ruptured by hydrolysis of the cellulose chains, but FREY-WYSSLING (1935 and 1941) suggested that the rodlet-like micelles might be split lengthwise, after which new molecules might be inserted in the correct position, i.e. perpendicular to

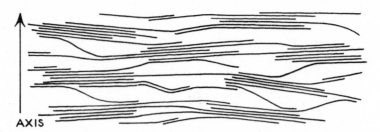

Fig. 94. Schema of the structure of the cellulose in the primary wall of a tubular cell, according to the view that was generally accepted round the year 1935.

the direction of growth. A slightly schematized, but therefore more easily comprehensible exposition of the way in which according to FREY-WYSSLING the growth in extent would take place, is given in fig. 95.

BONNER (1935) noted that in coleoptiles the cellulose units in the wall of the parenchyma cells retained their transverse orientation throughout the period of growth, but that in plasmolysed tissue slices, an artificial extension

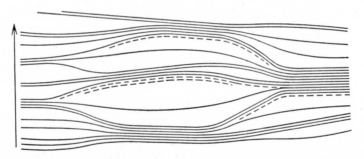

Fig. 95. Schematical representation of the way in which the network of cellulose micelles, according to FREY-WYSSLING, grows in extent, viz. by a splitting of the individual micelles; the arrow indicates the direction of growth, the broken lines the new molecules that are deposited in the space that has arisen by the splitting of a micelle.

of only 10% sufficed to produce a reorientation which led to a predominantly axial arrangement; this was concluded from the fact that the negative birefringence of the wall passed into a positive one. This reorientation was schematized by FREY-WYSSLING as in fig. 96 sub b, whereas the intussusception of the micelles in the wall of a growing cell is represented sub c. BONNER supposed that in normal growth the junction points between the micelles are ruptured, whereas they remain intact when the cell-wall is artificially distended. When this interpretation is correct, it is clear that in case of a reorientation of the micelles the extension in the axial direction must be accompanied by a contraction in the transverse one, so that the diameter of the cell will decrease.

Wall-tension theory

Towards the close of the period with which we have dealt in the preceding paragraphs, a new theory was added to those that had already been proposed in order to explain the relation between cell-wall growth and cell-wall structure. Because of its special importance this theory deserves a separate treatment.

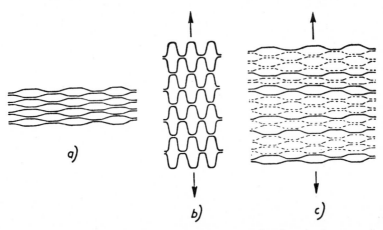

Fig. 96. Diagram of the changes that are supposed to take place in the network of the cellulose molecules and micelles, *b*. as a result of artificial extension, and *c*. as a result of growth (from FREY-WYSSLING, 1945).

It draws the attention towards the influence which the tension in the wall of a turgescent cell exercises on its structure during the period of growth. The importance of this wall tension was recognized simultaneously by CASTLE (1937) and by VAN ITERSON (1937).

The first-named author based his exposition on an at first sight paradoxical fact observed by OORT and ROELOFSEN (1932), viz. that when growing *Phycomyces* sporangiophores are burst by raising the internal pressure, which can be done by squeezing, the slit in the growth zone runs always in the direction of the axis; this involves therefore a rupture of the chitin layer with its transversely oriented micelles in the direction in which it is most resistant, whereas no resistance of this kind would have been met with when the sporangiophore had burst in a transverse direction. That it nevertheless always bursts in the direction of the axis, finds its explanation in a rule which is common knowledge in engineering circles, viz. that when the wall of a tube or of a long hollow prism is exposed to a uniform internal pressure, the tensile stress is in the transverse direction about twice as great as in the axial one. CASTLE as well as VAN ITERSON suggested that the well-known transverse orientation of the cellulose micelles in the walls of growing tubular cells (the so-called tubular texture) depends in some way upon the higher tension in the transverse direction. CASTLE calculated that when the cell has a diameter of 100 μ and when the internal pressure has a value of 8 atm., the transverse tension in a 2 μ thick wall will amount to 208 kg/cm² (2950 lb/sq inch).

In the present author's opinion the axial tension in the *growing* cell-wall will probably be slightly reduced owing to internal friction, and the tension in the transverse direction will therefore be more than twice as large as that in the axial one.

When studying the structure of the wall in the cells of the rapidly elongating hairs that are found on the *Tradescantia* stamens, VAN ITERSON (l.c.) noted that the micelles retained their transverse orientation, and on account of observations made on rubber tubes that were being inflated (see DIEHL et al., 1939), he came to the conclusion that the greater tension in the transverse direction will also be able to maintain the transverse orientation of the micelles when no new material is deposited, and when the lengthening therefore is carried out entirely at the expense of the thickness of the cell-wall. In the latter case the position which the micelles occupy with regard to each other will, of course, undergo a change, but their transverse orientation is retained.

This evidently also explains why the micelles in the wall of other cells in which the growth in length is not accompanied by deposition of wall material, retain their transverse orientation, e.g. in the cell-walls of the rapidly elongating grass filaments (FREY-WYSSLING and SCHOCH-BODMER, 1938) and in those of coleoptiles "growing" at low temperatures (BONNER, 1935, see however, the electron micrographs of such cell-walls made by WARDROP and CRONSHAW, 1958, which are at variance with this observation). The theory also explains why, as BONNER (l.c.) observed, reorientation readily occurs when plasmolysed cells are mechanically stretched, as in that case the tension in the axial direction will exceed that in the transverse one.

VAN ITERSON (DIEHL et al., l.c.) further pointed out that in files of short cells, such as occur in all apical meristems, the tension in the outer walls must be of a similar nature as that in the wall of long tubular cells, even though the diameter of the individual cells may exceed their height. One condition, however, has to be fulfilled, viz. that the resistance to extension in the transverse walls remains low, and does not materially influence the tension in the longitudinal ones.

VAN ITERSON also showed that the predominantly axial orientation of the micelles in the thick outer wall of an epidermal cell is in accordance with the theory. To this end we should realize that this part of the wall is subject to an additional axial tension, as appears when a longitudinal strip of epidermis is torn off, for such a strip rolls up, the original outside becoming concave. This proves that in the intact plant the outer wall must be exposed to a considerable axial tension, and when the latter exceeds the tension in the transverse direction, the micelles in this part of the wall will according to the theory become axially oriented.

The theory that the tension in the wall is the real agent by which the orientation of the micelles is directed, has never been disproved, but it has, in our opinion, not yet received the attention it deserves. This may partly be due to the circumstance that other aspects of the problem of growth are now in the centre of interest. Another reason is, in our opinion, that until recently our knowledge of the structure of cellulose was insufficient to allow a good insight into the mechanism by which an unequal tension in the wall can orient the micelles. However, the merits of the theory will become more apparent when we apply it to the structures that have been revealed in the electron micrographs.

2282. Theories based mainly on the results obtained by means of the electron microscope

During the last ten years our knowledge of the structure of the cellulose and of the cell-wall has undergone an enormous increase. The first electron micrographs made of growing cell-walls and dating from the year 1948, already revealed the presence of the now well-known extremely long, filiform microfibrils, and the way in which they are interwoven, intertwined and bundled. It became clear that the parting of the old microfibrils and the intercalation of new ones in the growing cell-wall was at variance with the concept of fig. 95 and was a less simple process than the schema given in fig. 96 would suggest. Although FREY-WYSSLING himself had emphasized strongly, even too strongly, as we have seen in section 221, the presence of wide gaps between the individual cellulose fibrils, he and his collaborators were opposed to the view that the microfibrils would be able to slide along each other.

They therefore supposed (1950) that the growth of the wall would involve either a rupturing or a dissolution of microfibrils, previous to the expansion of the network, a possibility that had already been suggested by BONNER (l.c.).

22821. "Mosaic Growth"

Soon, however, electron micrographs like those shown in fig. P 52, in which the wall appears to contain numerous small fields with a loosened or at least less dense network of microfibrils, led to another interpretation of the nature of intussusception and the way in which it is effected; for the latter the term "mosaic growth" was chosen (FREY-WYSSLING and STECHER, 1951; STECHER, 1952; BOSSHARD, 1952). It did not assume that the microfibrils as a whole slided past each other, but only definite parts of them, viz. in the many small fields where the texture appeared to be loosened or at least less dense. It was supposed that the microfibrils were here pushed apart either by a transient intrusion of protoplasm or by localized deposition of non-cellulose. This pushing apart would take place simultaneously in a great number of places which were distributed over the wall in a mosaic-like fashion. The extent of these little fields would then be fixed, and their texture would resume its original density by the interweaving of new microfibrils between the old ones. Meanwhile a new mosaic of fields with a more open texture would be created, and so the cycle would move on. Recently this theory was discarded by FREY-WYSSLING (1957) in favour of WARDROP's supposition (1954a) that the regions of active growth are to be found in the primary pit fields, although WARDROP himself had in the meantime (1956) rejected this possibility, (see later). FREY-WYSSLING now (1959: 89) restricts the mosaic growth concept to the single initial formation of a mosaic of areas with open texture. Part of the latter would give rise to the primary pit fields, the others being definitely closed by deposition of new microfibrils. Hence, this is no more a theory of growth.

The theory of mosaic growth has found so far but little appreciation from other sides. MÜHLETHALER (1950b and 1953a) failed to find in coleoptile parenchyma a sufficient number of thin areas with a loosened texture to account for mosaic growth. SCHOCH-BODMER and HUBER (1951) compared the areas with loosened texture to pit fields with plasmodesmata, and concluded from this comparison that the mosaics in adjacent primary walls should coincide, which they thought unlikely. PRESTON and RIPLEY (1954) suggested that the thin areas with loosened texture which they themselves observed in the walls of cambium cells, would be artefacts, and that they would owe their origin to damage inflicted upon them during homogenization, and they remarked that similar artefacts may be found even in secondary walls when the latter have been treated in the same way.

WARDROP (1954a and 1955) remarked that the thin areas seen in the electron micrographs are often as much as 1μ in diameter, which means that they ought to be visible under the light microscope, but under the latter we only see primary pit fields, which, of course, remain always at the same place. At first he was inclined to regard the primary pit fields as the active regions of growth, and he suggested that the fragments of protoplasm with tufts of microfibrils adhering to them which are found e.g. in disintegrated cambium (fig. 12), might have been torn off from the primary pit fields. He further supposed that surface growth which was not accompanied by deposition of new wall material, would be comparable to the first stage in the usual process, viz. a cytoplasmic expansion, not consolidated by the intercalation of new microfibrils. In our opinion, however, VAN ITERSON's explanation mentioned above, is more likely. WARDROP neglects the enormous increase in surface observed in some instances, viz. in grass stamens, and which can not be explained in this way since this would involve the appearance of vast open areas.

Afterwards, when he had found that labelled cellulose was deposited uniformly throughout the whole growing wall, WARDROP (1956) dropped his theory that growth would be confined to stationary regions, in favour of the multinet theory (v. infra) which agreed better with the results of his experiments.

BÖHMER (1958) too rejected the theory of mosaic growth, because he was convinced that the only native regions in which a loosened texture was found, were primary pit fields, and he too expressed himself in favour of the multinet theory, which will be discussed later.

The present author is also of opinion that several of the areas with loosened texture that were depicted by the authors who favoured the theory of mosaic growth, are in reality artefacts, and that those which make a natural impression, are primary pit fields. Moreover, no theory can be regarded as adequate when it is, like that of mosaic growth, unable to account for the possibility of a considerable extension of the wall even if no new building material is deposited.

22822. "Protoplasmic tip Growth"

Further study of the cell-wall structure of growing cells carried out by MÜHLETHALER (1950b) on the cells of *Avena* coleoptiles, revealed that already in the walls of young cells an extensively interwoven texture of microfibrils is present, and like those who advanced the theory of mosaic growth, he considered this texture too intricate to allow a sliding of the microfibrils. He was of opinion that this applies with even greater force to the thickened ribs in the walls of growing parenchyma cells (see section 2271) and to the thick outer wall of growing epidermal cells (see section 2272), where, just as in the secondary walls, a thick mass of axially oriented microfibrils is found.

MÜHLETHALER, however, also noted that in the apical part of some parenchyma cells and in the pointed tips of many xylem and phloem elements a noticeably thinner and less compact texture of microfibrils was found. It looked to him as if these apical parts were sometimes even perforated (figs. P 49 and P 82). This brought MÜHLETHALER (l.c.) and FREY-WYSSLING (e.g. 1953 a) to the idea that these cells are growing only at the top or eventually at the apical and basal tips, and that even here growth does not consist in an intercalation of new material throughout the existing wall, but in the addition of new zones. They assumed that the protoplast protrudes through the perforated tip and penetrates into the softened middle lamella between two cells that are thereby separated, and that this naked protoplast deposits the new cell-wall; the cell-wall therefore grows out behind the advancing protoplast. To distinguish this hypothetical growth-process from the actually observed tip growth, we will call it "protoplasmic tip growth".

As in the primary wall of many tips an axial orientation of the microfibrils was noted, especially in the outermost layer (see e.g. fig. P 82), it was supposed that the orientation of the first microfibrils was brought about by the flow of protoplasm in the advancing tip. These axially oriented microfibrils were supposed to form a kind of warp into and onto which the protoplasm afterwards wove a kind of weft, and that it was to this process that the transversely oriented main part of the growing cell-wall owed its origin. An actual extension of the cell-wall was supposed to be confined to cells growing in diameter, and here "mosaic growth" would be involved.

Since then, however, the measurements made by CASTLE (1955), WARDROP (1955) and SCOTT et al. (1956) by means of the microscope, as well as the autoradiographs made by WARDROP (1955), SETTERFIELD and BAYLEY (1957) and BÖHMER (1958) of walls belonging to cells that had taken up labelled carbon, have shown, as we have already set forth in section 223, that in parenchyma cells of the kind studied by MÜHLETHALER as well as in epidermal cells, growth is not restricted to the tip, but more or less equally distributed over the whole length of the cell, and that not only the ordinary texture of interwoven microfibrils, but the thick bands of microfibrils in the ribs too, actually do grow. This means that the microfibrils must be in a position to slide along each other, which, as CASTLE (1955) pointed out, happens "in spite of impediments suggested by the density and texture of microfibrillar arrangements revealed by electron microscopy".

In connection to the conclusion reached in the preceding paragraph it seems worth while to refer to a fact that was already known to BONNER (1935) viz. that when strips of the epidermis torn from *Avena* coleoptiles and from *Helianthus* hypocotyls, which are in both plants provided with a thick outer wall in which the microfibrils are axially oriented, are stretched mechanically, they may reach one and a half time their original length before they are ruptured.

WARDROP (1955), moreover, has drawn attention to the fact that the majority of the parenchyma cells in coleoptiles are not provided with pointed, but with truncate tips, and that at least part of those which seem to have delicate tips are cells in which in the central part secondary thickening already has set in (WARDROP and CRONSHAW, 1958).

From what has been said in the preceding paragraphs, it will be clear that the idea that tip growth is a normal phenomenon in parenchyma cells, has to be abandoned, and that there is even less evidence of the existence of "protoplasmic tip growth". The concept was not mentioned in FREY-WYSSLING's latest publication (1959) in which the topic of surface-growth was discussed.

22823. *Multinet growth and other wall-tension effects*

In the meantime the author of the present work had come forward with a third theory, for which he proposed the name "multinet growth". This theory is based on the ideas advanced by CASTLE and VAN ITERSON with regard of the effect of cell-wall tension on the orientation of the micelles.

The concept of multinet growth was first brought forward in connection with the changes in the texture of the chitin microfibrils in the growing zone of *Phycomyces* sporangiophores (1950a: 97, 1950b and 1951c; see section 2431) that are revealed in electron micrographs. It appeared afterwards that the changes in the ultra-structure of the cellulose in the wall of the growing hairs on *Tradescantia* stamens (ROELOFSEN and HOUWINK, 1951), of growing *Gossypium*, *Ceiba* and *Asclepias* hairs, and in the protruding parts of the stellate cells in the medulla of *Juncus* leaves (ROELOFSEN, 1951a; ROELOFSEN and HOUWINK, 1953; HOUWINK and ROELOFSEN, 1954) could be explained in the same way.

The principal ground for the formulation of the theory was found in the observation that in all these objects the primary wall shows on the outside, as a rule, a loose network of microfibrils or bundles of microfibrils with a more or less distinctly axial orientation, although their number may be small, and although occasionally the majority may be irregularly oriented, whereas on the inside a denser texture of microfibrils with a predominantly transverse orientation is present. For a detailed description we refer to section 227 (figs. P 37, P 55, P 57, P 58, P 60, P 61 and P 62). At the time the theory was set forth, the *Phycomyces* sporangiophores and the cells of the *Tradescantia* hairs were the only objects in which it was certain that the wall was actually growing or at least increasing in length, but as mentioned in section 223, this was proved afterwards by O'KELLEY for the cotton hairs too.

The theory proceeds from the supposition that at least the major part of the new building materials, cellulose as well as non-cellulose, are deposited against the inner side of the wall. Such a supposition was not new, but it remains as yet a supposition for that it actually takes place in this way, non only in the secondary wall, but in the growing one as well, has to this day been proved only for the cell-walls of *Algae* and the thick outer epidermal walls of *Avena* coleoptiles where cellulose is deposited both on the inner side and within the wall (SETTERFIELD and BAYLEY, 1958a).

In tubular cells the new cellulose microfibrils are always oriented either transversely or in a helix with a very low pitch. In the next phase of growth such a layer of microfibrils will be influenced in three different ways. In the first place, it will be shifted in an outward direction by the new layer which is deposited against it. Secondly, it will be stretched in the axial direction, which will cause a reorientation of the microfibrils, first into an obliquely crossed or a more or less irregular disposition, and then gradually into a more or less axial one. Thirdly, its thickness and the density of its texture will decrease, so that it becomes tenuous with a wide-meshed fibrillar texture.

As a wall constructed according to this principle, may be compared to a set of superposed fishing nets which are successively stretched in the same direction, the type of growth which produces such a structure, was called "multinet" growth. In reality the layers do not exist as distinct units; there is gradual transition in the orientation of the microfibrils and in the width of the meshes from the outside to the inside of the wall. Fig. 97 gives a schema showing the way in which, according to this theory, the structure of the primary wall changes in the succesive layers.

The theory of multinet growth does not only account for the ultrastructure of the primary wall in the particular cells studied by ROELOFSEN and HOUWINK, but also of that in several other kinds of cells studied by later authors, e.g. in the parenchyma cells of roots (figs. 51, 53, P 52, P 54) and coleoptiles (figs. 43, P 44—P 48), in epidermal cells of roots (fig. P 69), in some cambium initials (figs. P 73 and P 74), in vascular elements (figs. P 79, P 81, P 82 and P 85), in fibres (figs. P 89 and P 90), and in collenchyma cells (fig. 93 a).

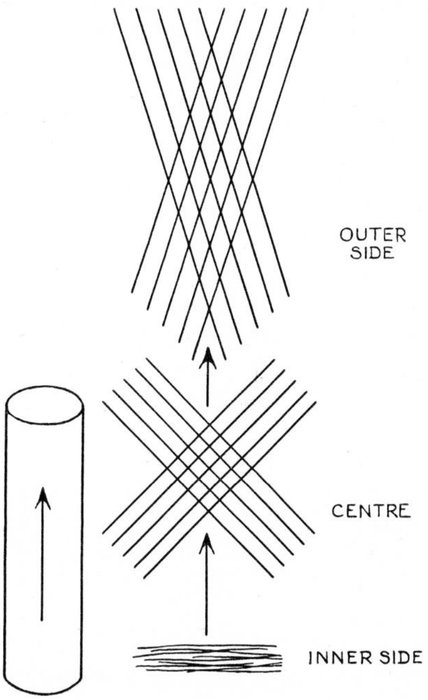

At this moment the theory of multinet growth seems to be generally accepted for the primary wall of the parenchyma cells, but in several other kinds of cells the structure sometimes seems to be at variance with it. However, before entering into a discussion of these not readily accountable structures, it seems appropriate to consider some of the implications of the theory and some of the conditions that have to be fulfilled in order that the theory may be applied.

In the first place, the theory of multinet growth implicates, as is evident from fig. 97, that the meshes can increase in size and that the microfibrils can

OUTER SIDE

CENTRE

INNER SIDE

Fig. 97. Schema of the way in which, according to the theory of multinet growth, the orientation of the microfibrils in the successive layers of the primary wall originates (from ROELOFSEN and HOUWINK, 1953).

slide along each other, as otherwise the fibrillar layer can not increase in length while retaining its original width. That such a sliding, which several authors regarded as impossible, actually may take place, was demonstrated by HOUWINK and ROELOFSEN (1954) in their study of the outermost layer of microfibrils in the apical part of the wall of growing cotton hairs (fig. 59) and in growing cells from the medulla of *Juncus* leaves (fig. P 37). These are cells exposed to intercellular spaces filled with air and the walls studied had to bear the full turgor pressure. The latter will therefore be thicker and denser as compared with wall-areas situated between two cells and probably they will in addition contain more incrustating lipid materials. If, therefore, sliding of microfibrils does occur in the cells mentioned above, there is little reason to doubt that it will, or at least may, also occur in common meristematic cells.

The theory further requires that the difference between the wall tension in the axial direction and that in the transverse direction changes in the successive layers; this aspect of the theory has been discussed more fully in a recent publication of the author (1958). It is assumed that the wall tension in the inner layer with its transversely oriented microfibrils will always be greater in the transverse direction than in the axial one, as otherwise the microfibrils would immediately be reoriented. In layers in wich a reorientation of the microfibrils actually occurs, the wall tension in the axial direction is supposed to be greater than that in the transverse one, as otherwise the original transverse orientation would remain unchanged.

That the difference between the tension in the axial direction and that in the transverse one in the wall as a whole would have an effect of this kind, had already been suggested by CASTLE (1937) and VAN ITERSON (1937) on account of general considerations and of results obtained by experiments with models. At that time, however, our knowledge of the ultrastructure of the cellulose was still insufficient to make it fully comprehensible why the micelles are oriented parallel to the direction of the greatest wall tension.

The present author (l.c.) tried to elucidate the situation by the aid of the schema reproduced in fig. 98. It represents a texture of cellulose (or eventually chitin) microfibrils in the primary wall of an imaginary tubular cell. The microfibrils are predominantly oriented in a transverse direction, but a minor part of them is more or less obliquely oriented, and overcross the transverse microfibrils. Although the cellulose occupies only about 9% of the space inside the wall (cf. section 221), it can not be doubted that it is this substance wich, because of its microfibrillar structure, determines for a large part the character of the cell-wall. Because the latter does not swell beyond a certain measure, and also because of its tensile strength, it is usually taken for granted that the microfibrils must be connected with each other in some way or another. Study by means of the electron microscope has shown that the connections can not consist of true junctions, but that they must be points or regions of adhesion, presumably formed by hydrogen bonds between free OH groups of the molecules situated at the surface of two adjacent microfibrils.

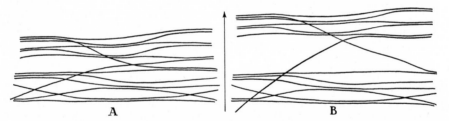

A   B

Fig. 98. Schema of the displacement of the transversely oriented microfibrils in the inner layer of the lengthening tubular cell; a, before lengthening has set in; b, after it has proceeded a little way; cell axis indicated (from ROELOFSEN, 1958).

That such bonds may be present at some points is likely enough as the mean distance between two microfibrils is only four times the diameter of the microfibril (PRESTON and WARDROP, 1949) and as the microfibrils are not fully parallel so that the distance between them may locally disappear; in the inner part of the wall the texture is, moreover, much denser than in the wall as a whole, and the mean distance between the microfibrils therefore much smaller.

The stretches over which the more or less parallel running microfibrils with predominantly transverse orientation, adhere to each other, will be longer than the stretches along which transversely and obliquely oriented microfibrils are in contact with each other. The transversely oriented microfibrils are the building units of annular fibrillar bundles which form a kind of rings around the cell. These bundles are continuously subjected to a tension in the direction of their axis, and on this tension rests the transversal wall tension that counteracts the turgor pressure. The same tension ensures that the fibrillar rings are transversely oriented just as loose rings around a rubber tube will become oriented transversely when the tube is inflated.

For the sake of simplicity we assume that the wall consists of but one layer. In this case the more weakly fixed obliquely oriented microfibrils will have to resist an axial tension which is equal to about half the transverse one. In case of multinet structure there will be a separate layer consisting of more or less axially oriented microfibrils which will bear the axial tension.

For the sake of simplicity, we will also assume that axial lengthening takes place without a simultaneous deposition of new wall material; this simplification is permitted as lengthening may indeed take place in this way, and as it makes not much difference for the point we are discussing whether new material is deposited or not.

Axial extension of fibrillar textures like that of fig. 98a would not take place if the obliquely oriented microfibrils were able to resist the axial tension, and when axial extension does take place, the oblique microfibrils will have to loose some adhesion points, fig. 98b. Meanwhile they will exercise a stress in an oblique direction on the transversely oriented microfibrils with which they are cohering. However, the latter will not as a rule change their position. As they are more strongly attached to the other microfibrils of the annular bundle than to the obliquely oriented microfibrils, they cannot be pulled out of this bundle. Nor is it possible that the transverse orientation of the annular fibrillar bundle as a whole is changed, as this would imply that the wall tension in the axial direction would exceed that in the transverse one, and this is not so. The only possibility that remains, is therefore that the obliquely oriented microfibrils slide along the transverse annular bundles. Eventually a bundle with a not too compact structure might give rise to two thinner ones, a possibility illustrated in fig. 98.

At least in young parenchyma cells of *Avena* coleoptiles and of onion roots the transverse orientation of the microfibrils comes into being, as has already been stated in section 2271, in the period in which the originally isodiametric cells increase in diameter, apparently as a result of the extension of the wall. As this increase in diameter ceases after a time, the microfibrils that are added in the subsequent period seem to be deposited in transverse orientation. Whether the orientation is effected in this case by the microfibrils that are already present or by the protoplasm, and whether the latter would be able to do this because it is itself also transversely stretched (van ITERSON, 1936a) or in some other capacity, remain open questions.

In very thin cell-walls, in which no layers are displaced towards the periphery, the new microfibrils will be intercalated between the old ones, and such a cell-wall therefore grows by intussusception. In thicker cell-walls with multinet structure, growth will be brought about partly by an intercalation of microfibrils, i. e. by intussusception, and partly by apposition of microfibrils.

In the event that no new microfibrils, or not enough of them, are deposited, the increase in surface will take place at the expense of the thickness of the cell-wall. This is what happens in the rapidly elongating hairs on the *Tradescantia* stamen, in the rapidly elongating filaments of the grasses, in coleoptiles that are kept at a low temperature and in the setae of *Pellia*.

The decrease in the degree of birefringence which was observed by FREY-WYSSLING and SCHOCH-BODMER (1938) in the walls of the rapidly elongating grass filaments, is in full agreement with the decrease in thickness of the walls. That the walls in the filaments of one grass (*Anthoxanthum*) become positively birefringent, seems at first sight to be at variance with our experience that no reorientation of the microfibrils takes place in the inner layer so long as the cells remain turgescent. However, just as a positive birefringence finally appears in the cell-walls of *Avena* coleoptiles notwithstanding the minor part of the microfibrils, viz. those at the inner side, retain their transverse orientation (BÖHMER, 1958), so it is conceivable that in the filaments too the orientation of the microfibrils, which originally was predominantly transverse, is changed in the peripheral part of the wall so that it finally becomes predominantly axial. The filaments are finally reduced to a single layer of cells, viz. the epidermis, and it is even not improbable that the microfibrils in the outer wall of the latter were already from the beginning axially oriented. The authors themselves suggested that the change might be due to strain birefringence, but no evidence in support of this opinion was adduced.

If the turgor pressure is removed, the transverse tension in the wall by which the annular bundles of microfibrils are kept in their place, is no longer there, and then a mechanical extension of the wall will immediately cause a reorientation of the microfibrils in the axial direction. BONNER (1935) observed this in plasmolysed coleoptiles, a stretching of 10% already proved to be sufficient to effect the reorientation.

When we apply the preceding considerations to multinet growth, we come to the conclusion that the layers in which, in the course of their displacement towards the periphery, a reorientation of the microfibrils takes place, can not have been exposed during that time to a predominantly transverse tension, but that, on the contrary, the stress exercised on them in the direction of the axis, must have exceeded the transverse one. This apparently implies that some other layers, evidently those that were deposited successively on their inside, must have borne the greater part of the transverse tension.

In cells that retain their diameter the layers that are displaced towards the periphery, the "rings" of microfibrils must first have increased in diameter before they disintegrated and were reoriented, and such an increase in diameter presupposes a sliding of the microfibrils along each other. This involves that the adhesion forces between the microfibrils must have been greatly reduced, and this might have been effected by the intercalation of some unknown material between the adhering microfibrils that constituted the "ring".

WARDROP and CRONSHAW (1958) saw a confirmation of the theory of multinet growth in a change which they observed by means of the electron microscope in the cell-wall structure of parenchyma cells from *Avena* coleoptiles. They had kept these coleoptiles at a temperature which permitted a certain amount of growth, but which was too low to permit the formation of new cell-wall material, and they observed that under these circumstances the transverse structure on the inner side of the wall had been changed into an irregular one, a change which they ascribed to a stretching of the wall. The cell of which they studied the wall structure, may, however, have been an abnormal one, for the observation is at variance with an older one made by BONNER (1935) by means of the polarization microscope; according to the latter the transverse structure is retained under these circumstances. Moreover, according to the multinet growth concept an extension of the wall due to turgor pressure, could not have led to the result observed by WARDROP and CRONSHAW, as in that case the tension would have been greatest in the transverse direction. We presume, therefore, that the cell of which the wall was photographed, had accidentally lost its turgescence, and had been stretched artificially by the growth of the surrounding cells.

In this section we have discussed the conditions upon which the development of a typical multinet structure depends. In the three following sections we will consider what kind of deviations from this structure are to be expected if one or more of these conditions are not fulfilled, and whether structures that at first sight seem to be at variance with the theory, can be accounted for in this way.

228231. Effect of a uniform tension throughout the whole thickness of the wall

In the event that the predominantly transverse tension in the older part of the primary wall of a tubular cell is not taken over by subsequently deposited layers, and if the tension therefore remains the same throughout the whole thickness of the wall, no reorientation of microfibrils will take place, even though the cell may undergo a considerable increase in length.

This will probably occur in cell-walls that remain very thin, i.e. in cell-walls in which the deposition of new material merely compensates the decrease in thickness caused by the extension of the wall. The new material is here probably deposited throughout the whole thickness of the wall, and there is accordingly no question of a differentiation into layers. In such walls the orientation of the microfibrils remains transverse. The thin walls of young parenchyma cells to which "mosaic growth" has been ascribed, show this type of growth, for which the author (l.c.) proposed the name *"thin-wall type of growth"*.

If in the different layers of a thick wall the direction of the predominant wall tension would be the same, such a wall too would evidently exhibit everywhere the same orientation of the microfibrils. This probably applies to the thick walls of *Nitella*, which according to GREEN and CHAPMAN (1955) show a predominantly transverse orientation of the microfibrils throughout their whole thickness, in spite of the fact that new cell-wall material is deposited on the inner side only (GREEN, 1958). The present author supposed that the reason why the direction of predominant wall tension in the outer layers of the walls remains unchanged might be that in this case no reduction is brought about in the adhesion forces between the microfibrils constituting the annular fibril bundles, or only a limited reduction, just sufficient for a small increase in circumference of the rings, which therefore will continue to bear their part of the transverse tension.

228232. Structure of the primary wall in the absence of growth

Reorientation of the microfibrils in the layers that are displaced outwards, and in which the transverse tension is smaller than in the innermost layer, depends on the presence of an axial tension which is stronger than the transverse one. It will therefore be impossible in the event that there is little or no elongation. For this reason tubular cells in which growth is confined to the tips, may show in the rest of the cell a transverse orientation of the microfibrils on the outer as well as on the inner side of the wall, although the wall tension might be very different in the various layers.

It is as yet not certain whether cambial initials and cambial derivatives grow at their tips only. If there is in the rest of the cells no growth in length, a predominantly transverse orientation of the fibrils may be expected throughout the whole thickness of the wall, and this orientation will become even more pronounced in the radial walls because the latter grow in a radial direction, i.e. in the direction in which the microfibrils are already predominantly oriented. However, it seems that cambial cells of different origin behave differently. The uniform structure of the wall depicted in fig.71 suggests absence of longitudinal growth, but the wall fragments shown in figs. P 73 and P 74 have a multinet structure, and this would indicate that the areas from which they were taken, were actually growing in length.

Other cells that do not grow in length, are the segments of future xylem vessels and the wide and short cells of some hairs. These cells are about as long as they are wide, and there is therefore no reason to expect that the tension in the axial direction will differ from that in the transverse one. If in this case the microfibrils in the primary wall would prove to be transversely oriented, this could not be due to a greater tension in the transverse direction, but it might perhaps be due to a stronger growth in that direction.

An entirely different situation is found in more or less disk-shaped (tabular) cells, e.g. in flat epidermal cells. According to the laws of hydrostatics, the tension in the anticlinal walls of these cells will be strongest in the anticlinal direction, i.e. parallel to the axis of the disk (DIEHL et al., 1939: 781), and in complete agreement with this, the cellulose microfibrils in these walls prove to be anticlinally oriented. As epidermal cells mainly grow in surface, in this case therefore perpendicular to the axis of the disk, the orientation of the microfibrils in the anticlinal walls is perpendicular to the direction of main growth, and not, as in the walls of the cells discussed in the preceding paragraph, parallel to this direction.

The effect of an inhibition of growth on the orientation of the microfibrils in the primary wall of a tubular cell has been studied experimentally by WARDROP (1956) in onion roots. The growth of these roots was inhibited by the use of colchicin. As was to be expected, the transverse orientation of the microfibrils was in this case retained throughout the whole thickness of the wall.

228233. Effect of additional wall tension

Another type of wall structure that was considered to be at variance with the theory of multinet growth, is the one that is found in the outer wall of the epidermis of *Avena* coleoptiles. As pointed out in section 2272 and shown in the figs. 65—P 68, the microfibrils in these outer walls are throughout or nearly throughout the whole thickness of the wall axially oriented. That the orientation of the microfibrils in the walls of most epidermis cells must be predominantly axial, had been found out already by the aid of the polarization microscope and by X-ray analysis (sections 225 and 226), and, as we have mentioned before, this was ascribed by VAN ITERSON (cf. DIEHL et al., 1939) to the prevalence of an axial tension in the walls of these cells.

The principle adopted by VAN ITERSON is the same as that on which the theory of multinet growth was based (cf. ROELOFSEN, 1958). If an axial tension prevails throughout the whole thickness of the wall, the orientation of the microfibrils will everywhere be axial. In the innermost layer the microfibrils would even be reoriented if they were deposited by the protoplasm in a transverse position. If an axial tension would prevail in the outer part of the wall and a transverse tension in the inner part, the development of a typical multinet structure could be expected. This was found in the outer epidermal wall of the onion root, fig. P 69.

More or less comparable to the thick outer wall of the epidermal cells in the aerial parts, are the thickened ribs which are met with e.g. in parenchyma cells (figs. P 44, P 46, P 47, P 50 and P 52), cambial cells (figs. P 72 and P 73), cortical fibres (fig. P 90), phloem vessels (figs. P 79 and P 82) and collenchyma cells (fig. 93).

VAN ITERSON (l.c.), in discussing the situation in the well-known angular thickenings of the collenchyma cells, already pointed out that the axial tension in the wall caused by turgor pressure, is probably borne for the greater part by these thickened ribs, so that in the latter the tension in the axial direction may exceed that in the transverse one, and that, if the ribs are not all equally thick, the tension will be higher in the thicker ones. In that case the cell will, when it is separated in turgescent condition from the adjacent ones, curve towards the side with the thicker ribs. An isolated epidermal cell will, for the same reason, curve in the direction of the outer wall.

Just as in the thick outer wall of most epidermal cells of *Avena* coleoptiles, the axial tension may in the thickened ribs prevail over the transverse one throughout the whole packet of layers, but it is also conceivable that just as in the outer epidermal wall of the onion root, the transverse tension will retain the upper hand in the innermost layers, and that here therefore the microfibrils will be oriented transversely. Hence two types of ribs may be expected, those with an axial structure throughout and those with an internal layer with transverse structure.

As a matter of fact, both types were found in parenchyma cells of *Avena* coleoptiles and of onion roots by SETTERFIELD and BAYLEY (1958). They speak of outer ribs and integral ribs and observed the former type more frequently in onion roots than in *Avena* coleoptiles, in which the integral ribs are said to prevail. However, in our opinion, it is probable that the frequency of the two types of ribs will also depend on the age of the objects studied and on the environmental conditions.

As the cell-walls in growing parts are not only exposed to the tension that is caused by the turgor pressure of the cell to which they belong, but because of the unequal extension of the various elements of which the part consists, also to tissue tension, various kinds of deviations from the ideal multinet structure may be expected. The author (1958) supposed that the wall of collenchyma cells which, like those of *Heracleum* and *Apium* show a predominantly axial orientation of the microfibrils (cf. section 225), are throughout the period of growth exposed to an additional axial tension (see also MAJUMDAR and PRESTON, 1941), and he is of opinion that the presence of "anomalous" tensions seems likely in the walls of cambial cells and in tips of cells showing intrusive growth.

How is it to be explained that the transversely oriented microfibrils in the inner layer of the wall of a tubular cell do not give way to the tension by sliding along each other, whereas we must assume that in the thick outer wall of the epidermal cells and in the thickened ribs of other cells the axially oriented microfibrils, which nevertheless seem to occupy a similar position with regard to each other, do give way to it, as otherwise an increase in length would be impossible? It might be that this is due to the presence of a larger amount of non-cellulose in the last-named structures, as in that case the individual microfibrils may be enveloped by these substances so that there would be less adhesion between them. A similar reduction of the adhesion forces between the microfibrils was assumed by us to explain the reorientation of the microfibrils observed in wall layers that in walls with multinet structure are displaced towards the periphery (section 22823).

The exposition given in the preceding pages, will have made it clear that it can certainly not be regarded as a rule that the microfibrils are in all circumstances oriented perpendicular to the direction of main growth. If we wish to arrive at a definite rule, we should restrict our attention for the time being to cell-walls and wall layers in which the tension is due entirely to turgor pressure. In that case the tension may be equal in all directions or unequal. It is usually unequal, and then the orientation of the microfibrils proves to be parallel to the direction in which the tension reaches its highest value, no matter what the direction of growth may be. However, in the event that the tension is equal in all directions, the microfibrils appear to be oriented parallel to the direction in which the cell shows its strongest growth.

22824. *Displacement of cell-wall material due to turgor pressure*

It can not be denied that the turgescent protoplast exercises a pressure on the cell-wall. One of the facts which prove this, is that the water content of the cell-wall, as was found in several instances, undergoes an increase when the turgor pressure is eliminated. In certain Algae the wall shows under these circumstances a strong swelling (cf. KÜSTER, 1956: 722; KINZEL, 1956).

According to the author (1958) there are in the ultra-structure of the wall of growing parenchymatic and epidermal cells indications of a displacement of the loose outermost microfibrils within the plane of the wall, and he is inclined to ascribe these displacements to the pressure exercised by the turgescent protoplast on the plastic matrix in which the cellulose is embedded.

As pointed out in section 221, this matrix occupies in the primary wall as a whole about 92% of the space, and includes about 72% water. As the inner layer of the wall contains more cellulose than the other ones, the latter will contain even more non-cellulose, the middle lamella even up to 100%. As the pressure which the turgescent protoplast exercises on the wall, must be higher on the flat sides than in the edges of the cells, there must be a surplus pressure in the flat sides which tends to squeeze all movable cell-wall material towards the edges. A similar phenomenon is observed in foams, where the liquid in the envelopes of the air bubbles is squeezed towards the edges in which the latter meet, and runs off through them. If we suppose that the non-cellulose part of primary walls is of a plastic nature, then this material will accumulate in the edges, with the result that the edges become ribs and that the inner face of the wall is gradually rounded off. This hypothesis is illustrated by fig. 99.

This flow of non-cellulose is supposed to draw along the loosely fixed, more or less axially oriented microfibrils and fibril bundles occurring in the outermost layers of the primary wall. The well-fixed microfibrils in the inner layer, however, will not be dislodged.

It is not impossible that part of the non-cellulose synthesized by the protoplasm is squeezed through the meshes that are present in the texture of microfibrils, in a direction perpendicular to the plane of the wall, i.e. towards the middle lamella. This would ensure a constant flow of non-cellulose from the protoplasm via the middle lamella towards the cell edges, a process that might continue as long as there is growth.

The rate of flow will evidently depend upon the pressure gradient, and the latter will increase considerably when the cells come into contact with air, i.e. as soon as intercellular spaces are formed, but so long as the cells are growing, this will happen but rarely. In epidermal cells, however, the radial walls are from the beginning at one end in contact with the air, and here therefore there is always a high pressure gradient. The loose microfibrils from the greater part of the surface of the radial walls, or perhaps even from the whole surface, will therefore be shifted towards the periphery, and as this process goes on from the beginning, it is tempting to suppose that the high pressure-gradient is partly responsible for the considerable thickness of the outer wall. That the thickness of the subcuticular cellulose layers in this wall remains more or less constant notwithstanding the wall is all the time growing (BAYLEY et al., 1957), could also be accounted for along these lines.

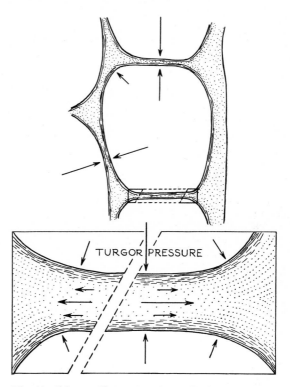

Fig. 99. Schema illustrating the author's concept of a displacement of cell-wall material from the flat sides to the edges and to the outer wall of a tubular epidermal cell under the influence of the turgor pressure (ROELOFSEN, 1958). Lines represent transversely oriented microfibrils, points axially oriented ones.

For another part, however, the greater thickness of the outer epidermal wall might very well be due to the deposition of a greater amount of material on its inner side, and finally this thickness as well as the maintenance of a constant thickness in the extending subcuticular cellulose layers might be the result of deposition of new wall material between the material that is already present, a process which was detected by SETTERFIELD and BAYLEY (1958a).

It was also pointed out (ROELOFSEN, l.c.) that the supposed shifting of the axially oriented outermost microfibrils towards the edges would keep the rest of the wall thin, and that this would obscure the presence of multinet growth. This might explain why the multinet structure sometimes is absent, although the circumstances for its development look favourable.

In several electron micrographs fibrillar structures are to be seen which, as a matter of fact, suggest that at least in some instances, displacement of loose microfibrils does occur. A great many micrographs, e.g. those reproduced in the figs. P 44, P 54, P 56, P 73, P 78, P 80, P 82 and P 90 seem to indicate that the microfibrils occurring on the outer surface of primary walls are not fixed, but lie more or less loosely on the dense mat of microfibrils underneath. As they are wavy, they are obviously not exposed to any stress. At the edges of the ribs, microfibrils can be seen to change their direction from longitudinal in the rib to irregular or transverse in the region between the ribs. There are, moreover, several micrographs of primary pit fields, like those shown in figs. P 46 and P 47, which suggest that the axially oriented microfibrils are being pulled around them. According to BÖHMER (1958) and WARDROP and CRON-SHAW (1958) these outermost microfibrils would "encroach upon" the primary pit fields, and according to the first-named author they may in the end cover them up, fig. P 48. As the authors who described these microfibril displace-ments, were not yet acquainted with the present author's hypothesis of dis-placement by turgor pressure, their observations may be regarded as an unbiassed support of his hypothesis that the outermost microfibrils in the flat parts of the wall are dragged along by the flow of non-cellulosic material towards the ribs, where they are attached once more to oriented microfibrils and are, as a result of the extension of the rib in the axial direction, stretched and axially oriented.

This hypothesis is quite compatible with the possibility that the accumulation of cellulose in the ribs of polyhedral cells and in the outer wall of epidermal cells is partly effected by other processes already mentioned, viz. by a locally increased deposition of new microfibrils either on the inner wall surface or within the wall or in both places. That the synthesis of cellulose on or in the outer wall of epidermal cells is especially intensive is evident from the auto-radiographs produced by WARDROP (1956), GORHAM and COLVIN (1957), SETTERFIELD and BAYLEY (1957, 1958a) and BÖHMER (1958).

22825. *Other attempts to explain the mechanism of cell-wall growth*

In the last few years several authors have expressed doubt as to the validity of the theoretical considerations of CASTLE, VAN ITERSON and the present author, which have been discussed in the preceding pages. They believe that the protoplasm does not confine its activity to the production of cellulose microfibrils, but that it also determines in some unknown but in any case direct and deliberate way the position in which the latter are deposited as well as any changes in orientation that afterwards may occur. That phy-sical forces would play a part in their orientation, is denied or at least con-sidered of minor importance. This leads to what in contrast to the "mecha-nistic" theories may be called "protoplasmic" theories.

Typical "protoplasmic" concepts are those of mosaic growth, of growth confined to the primary pit fields and of protoplasmic tip growth, by the aid of which FREY-WYSSLING and his collaborators tried to explain the growth of the cell-wall. These concepts have been discussed in the sections 22821 and 22822. We will now discuss some other concepts which fall in this category.

GREEN and CHAPMAN (1955) found in the cell-wall of *Nitella* no difference between the orientation of the microfibrils in the outer layers and in the inner ones, and thought that this meant that the microfibrils could not have been deposited on the inner face of the wall only. They assumed therefore a kind of three-dimensional mosaic growth which would extend throughout the whole thickness of the wall.

However, some physical objections may be raised against this concept. The intercalation of new microfibrils throughout the thickness of the wall is in itself not sufficient to warrant the maintenance of the transverse orientation. Since the wall extends and the already present microfibrils are supposed to retain their original orientation, their connections with other microfibrils will have to be severed. Moreover, the intercalation of new microfibrils and of non-cellulose material should exactly keep pace with the decrease in thickness which the wall layer would undergo because of the extension.

As we have pointed out in section 228231 our "mechanistic" theory can readily explain the maintenance of the transverse orientation of the micro-fibrils after their deposition on the inner face of the wall. When the layer is displaced towards the outside, their orientation will undergo no change if the transverse tension predominates over the axial one throughout the whole thickness of the wall. Therefore, unless there is reason to believe that this does not occur, the hypothesis of these authors seems to be unnecessary, although of course not disproved.

GREEN himself (1958) recently observed the deposition of new cell-wall material on the inner side of the wall, and abandoned for this reason his original hypothesis.

In growing cortical fibres of *Asparagus* STERLING and SPIT (1957) observed microfibril orientations that were partly in agreement with multinet growth (figs. P 90 and P 91), and partly at variance with it. Especially the circumstance that the microfibrils in two successive layers might be crossed (fig. P 92), suggested to them a directing influence of the protoplasm.

This orientation, however, as the present author (1958) has pointed out, does not actually disprove multinet growth, as the walls of these cells may be exposed to an additional tension in the axial direction, which would tend to disturb the transverse orientation. As a rule, the reorientation of a transverse fibrillar texture leads to the development of a network of crossed microfibrils, but it does not seem unlikely that occasionally the reorientation in two suc-cessive layers will take place in such a way that the microfibrils in each of them retain their parallel arrangement, but that they are forced in the one in an S-helix and in the other in a Z-helix. At any rate, more evidence should be awaited before this crossed orientation of the microfibrils in the successive layers is accepted as proof of a direct influence exercised by the protoplasm on the orientation of the microfibrils.

That further evidence should be awaited, applies also to the suppositions of these authors that during growth cell-wall material is deposited throughout the whole thickness of the primary wall, and that the firmness of this wall would not be caused by the presence of connections between the cellulose microfibrils, but that it would rest for a considerable part on the non-cellulose. Regarding the latter hypothesis, we wish to draw the attention to the fact that rejection of the idea that the cellulose microfibrils are connected with each other, would raise a great many problems, not only with regard to the explanation of the firmness of the primary wall, but also with regard to the fact that its tensile strength, its extensibility, its mode of swelling and shrink-ing, and its tear resistence appear to differ in various directions; it would therefore lead to difficulties of a similar kind as those that led to the discarding of NAEGELI's original hypothesis of independent micelles.

Regarding the former hypothesis, it must be admitted that although a transport of microfibrils from the place where they are produced by the protoplasm, to the outer layers of the wall must be regarded as excluded, a synthesis inside the wall is quite conceivable. The primary wall contains a certain amount of protein, and although it is not certain that this is enzyme protein, this is certainly not impossible.

However, the results of STERLING and SPIT do not in our view necessitate this assumption and even fail to make it probable.

The ground on which BAYLEY et al. (1957) came to the same supposition, is however, more convincing. They observed that the individual layers in the outer wall of growing epidermal cells of *Avena* coleoptiles (see figs. 65 and 66) do not become thinner as a result of the extension they undergo during growth, but that they retain their thickness. Recently SETTERFIELD and BAYLEY (1958a) made autoradiographs from sections of *Avena* coleoptiles that had been kept in a solution of tritium-labelled sucrose for 9 and 21 hrs. and that had been treated with acid and alkali in order to remove non-cellulose materials. The outer epidermal wall showed the presence of the isotope on the inner surface and throughout its thickness, which proved that cellulose had been deposited in these locations.

As was discussed in section 2272 the orientation of the microfibrils usually is axial throughout the thickness of these walls. However, in some cases a transverse orientation was observed on the inner surface, a structure which is intermediary to the typical multinet structure that is found in the outer epidermal wall of onion roots. It is unlikely that entirely different mechanisms of growth are operating in these walls and it is very likely, that the differences in structure are the result of quantitative differences only. We suppose that in the case of the onion root the major part of the total synthesis of cellulose in the outer epidermal wall is localized near the inner surface, whereas in the corresponding wall of the *Avena* coleoptile the major part of the synthesis is localized within the wall.

Although SETTERFIELD and BAYLEY (1957) believe that the multinet growth mechanism does apply in several cases, they express as their conviction that physical explanations of the orientation of the microfibrils, like that given by the theory of multinet growth are inadequate and that the high degree of specific order in the walls of different growing cells can only be explained by assuming that the final orientation of the microfibrils is determined in some, as yet unknown, way by the protoplasm. In this connection they point out that in the secondary wall no other agent but the protoplasm can be held responsible for the orientation of the microfibrils.

The present author admits that the protoplasm may very well determine the orientation of the microfibrils at the moment they are deposited, but with primary walls it is, in his opinion, difficult to believe that this is the final orientation, since this means that it would remain unchanged when the network of microfibrils is subjected to extensions that differ in various directions.

FREY-WYSSLING's views have been discussed already in previous sections. At this place we may confine our attention, therefore, to an argument that was recently advanced by him (1957) in support of his well-known view that the structure in the primary wall is entirely determined by the morphogenetic activity of the protoplasm. He rightly remarks that the hemispherical shape shown by the top of the cotton hair, involves that the tension in the wall must be the same in every direction (tension isotropism) and argues that the difference observed in the orientation of the microfibrils, transverse on the inner side and irregular on the outer side (cf. fig. 59), must therefore be due to the morphogenetic activity of the protoplasm. This conclusion, however, is in our opinion not justified, for the hemispherical shape of the top merely involves that there is tension isotropism in the wall *as a whole*, not that this also applies to the inner and the outer layers of the wall. If we assume that the tension in the inner layer is predominantly transverse and that in the outer layer predominantly axial, there might still be tension isotropism in the wall as a whole. In this case the structure would be in agreement with our theory, and it would not be necessary to invoke the aid of such a vague concept as the "morphogenetic activity of the protoplasm".

It goes without saying that the protoplast will determine the place and the rate of cell-wall growth, and consequently the form of the cell, of the tissue and of the whole plant. It evidently also determines the orientation of the microfibrils in the secondary wall, and probably also the initial orientation of the microfibrils in the primary wall. However, so far as the author can see, there is not a single authentic case of a primary wall in which the orientation which the microfibrils acquire during growth, must be ascribed to a directing agency of the protoplast. In most cases the final orientation of the microfibrils can be correlated to differences in wall tension in the transverse and the axial direction or, where such a difference is absent, to the direction of main growth. However, it must be realized that the differences in wall tension as well as the direction of main growth are in the end in fact determined by the specific nature of the plant, which is unbreakably bound to the specific nature of the protoplasm.

In the field of morphogenesis physical explanations are, on the whole, not well-received by botanists. The latter are inclined to regard them as too artificial and too little "biological". The statement that the orientation of the microfibrils in growing cell-walls is determined by the protoplasm, is usually accepted as sound biology, although it is actually no more than an admission that we do not know in what way the orientation is effected, and that we see no possibility to find this out. A direct regulatory activity of the protoplasm can neither be proved nor disproved, as it is not open to any tests.

22826. *Tip growth*

It is, as stated in section 223, no uncommon phenomenon that a cell does not grow equally strong in all its parts, and it may even be that its growth is confined to a definite part, very often to the tip. A cell may grow more or less rapidly at the tip while the rest of it grows at a slower rate, as in the cotton hair, or while its growth gradually decreases and disappears in the adjoining zone, as in the young sporangiophore of *Phycomyces*, or its growth may be confined almost entirely to the, rather short, tip, as in the root hairs of land plants. With regard to the length of the growing zone at the tip of xylem and phloem fibres, of tracheids and of some tubular parenchyma cells, nothing seems to be known with certainty.

As far as we know, it is now generally assumed that there is no essential difference between the mechanism of cell-wall extension in the growing tip and that found in a more or less cylindrical cell-wall zone. The tip growth would merely be an example of a strongly localized surface growth. At one time it was believed that the tip was perforated, and that the wall grew by the aid of cell-wall material that was deposited by the protruding protoplast, but as we have already pointed out, this hypothesis of protoplasmic tip growth has now been discarded.

Up to now the orientation of the microfibrils in the growing tips was always found to be in agreement with the assumption that here the same factors are at work which in the wall of the growing tubular cell lead to the development of a multinet structure. In the dome-shaped tip of the cotton hair HOUWINK and ROELOFSEN (1954) noted a reorientation of the microfibrils that is schematically reproduced in fig. 59. The reorientation that we observe here at the surface of the cell-wall, is identical with that which we observe elsewhere when a layer is displaced towards the periphery; in both cases it leads to a multinet structure.

In the tips of vascular elements in the course of differentiation (figs. P 79, P 82 and P 86), of parenchyma cells (fig. P 49) and of epidermal cells (fig. P 68), the structure seems to be of the multinet type, and that at the outside of the tips of wood fibres (figs. 75 and 76), and cortical fibres (fig. P 91), is at least not at variance with the theory. The cell-wall structure at the tip of pollen tubes is not known. In the tips of the root hairs of *Zea* and *Sinapis* the microfibrils are irregularly oriented (fig. P 63).

In the case of intrusive growth, it is certainly possible, as we have pointed out in section 228233, that in addition to the normal wall tension caused by the pressure of the turgescent protoplast, an additional tension may be present. The presence of an anomalous wall structure, which however has not yet been observed, should therefore not disturb us. Differing structures may be expected also in the tip of cells that are not surrounded by other ones, e.g. in cotton hairs and in root hairs, as has been expounded by HOUWINK and ROELOFSEN (l.c.) and, in a mathematical formulation, also by DE WOLFF and HOUWINK (1954; the figs. 16a, b and c are called in the text 5 I, II and III). The extend to which in the tip the outermost microfibrils will be reoriented, depends on the amount of cell-wall material that is deposited in different parts of the wall. Under certain conditions the original orientation of the microfibrils, no matter whether it is irregular or transverse, will remain unchanged, as e.g. in the growing tip of the *Zea* root hair, whereas under different conditions a reorientation will take place, e.g. in the growing tip of the cotton hair.

22827. *Spiral growth*

In zoology as well as in botany we find numerous examples of parts which show a spiral, or better a helical, structure. Spiral growth, which finds its expression in a torsion of the cell as well as in a rotation of the latter's free end, has but rarely been studied in detail, and such studies, moreover, were usually confined to free growing cells. We will restrict our discussion here to those objects in which the structure of the cell-wall has been investigated, with the exclusion of the cotton hair, since here spiral growth has not been shown, but merely suggested (section 23441).

Phycomyces

The object that has been studied more often than any other, is the sporangiophore of *Phycomyces blakesleeanus*. Its spiral growth was discovered by BURGEFF (1915), and has been studied in more detail by OORT, CASTLE and ROELOFSEN. The extensive literature on the subject has been brought together and discussed by ROELOFSEN (1950a) and by CASTLE (1953). For theories proposed before the year 1949 we refer to these papers.

The structure of the cell-wall in the zone of growth, which in young sporangiophores is situated at the tip, and in older ones immediately below the sporangium, will be discussed in section 2431. The differences between the inner and the outer part of the wall indicate multinet growth, but the fact that the tip in the period of growth is rotating round its axis, suggested that the microfibrils at the inner side of the wall would not be oriented transversely, but in a spiral with a low pitch (OORT and ROELOFSEN, 1932; ROELOFSEN, 1950a and b, 1951c; ROELOFSEN and HOUWINK, 1953). In that case the reorientation of the microfibrils according to the principle of multinet growth, by which the spiral with a low pitch on the inside of the wall would gradually be changed into the irregular orientation that is found on the outside, and also the intercalation of new cell-wall material (intussusception) in the spiral on the inside, will cause, as fig. 100 illustrates, a torsion of the growing part of the cell.

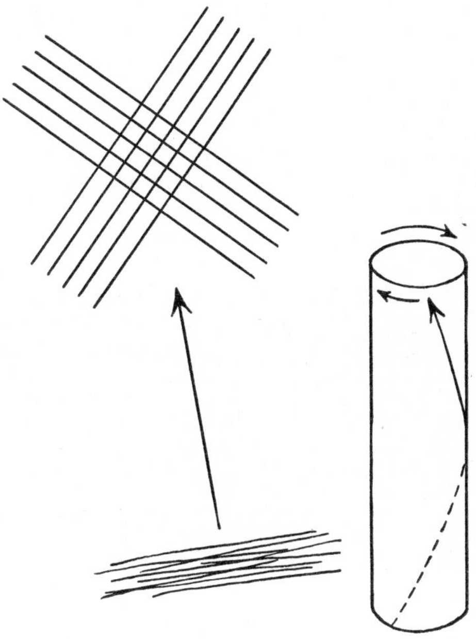

That a flat spiral structure when extending will, in accordance with fig. 100, cause rotation, was demonstrated by the aid of a model consisting of a cellophane tube; this tube could be subjected to an increasing internal pressure. In the *Phycomyces* sporangiophores too, rotation could be effected by increasing the internal pressure, viz. by squeezing (1950a).

Fig. 100. Schema of the mechanism of spiral growth, based on the assumption that it is due to the extension, in accordance with the theory of multinet growth, of a flat spiral structure; note that the direction of the flat spiral and that of growth stand perpendicular to each other (from ROELOFSEN and HOUWINK, 1953).

However, as will become apparent in section 2431, although the wall in some of the sporangiophores showed the required prevalence of Z-spiral orientation of the microfibrils, in most cases a transverse orientation was found. Even if the orientation would not actually be transverse but according to a Z-spiral with a pitch so low that it was not detected, the facts would be at variance with the theory, since the direction of the Z-spiral would not be perpendicular to the direction of growth as the theory requires (see fig. 100).

Still, the rotation produced by squeezing proves that the wall must possess a helical structure of some kind, although the latter is, as a rule, not noticeable. This has induced the author (1958) to discard his original schema, the one illustrated in fig. 100, which involves an orientation of the microfibrils in a flat spiral, whose direction is perpendicular to the direction of the spiral growth. We realized that spiral growth may also be affected by physical forces occurring in a wall in which the major part of the microfibrils are oriented transversely. They may form annular fibril bundles as described at an earlier occasion, and as shown in fig. 98. If this figure is carefully studied, it becomes clear that to cause the rotation during growth or when squeezing the cell, it must be sufficient if among the small number of microfibrils that are not oriented transversely, but overcross the "rings" of the transversely oriented ones, a somewhat larger part is oriented in a Z-spiral direction than in an S-spiral one. In that case on axial extension of the wall every "ring" will slide a little along the preceding lower one in a clockwise direction (as seen from above). The summation of a huge number of such minute but similarly directed movements may well result in an appreciable rotation, like the one observed during spiral growth, or like that produced by squeezing. This might happen even if the mean orientation of the microfibrils would deviate so slightly from the transverse one, that the deviation could be detected neither optically nor electron optically.

An entirely different explanation of the spiral growth of the *Phycomyces* sporangiophore was given by PRESTON, and has aptly been summarized in his book (1952). He compares the spirally wound chitin microfibrils with spiral springs, and believes that the elastic extension of the microfibrils caused by the growth of the cell, would produce the rotation. However, several objections have been raised against this theory (ROELOFSEN, 1949, 1950b; CASTLE, 1953). The alleged arrangement of the microfibrils in an S-helix, which the theory requires, is open to doubt (see section 2431).

FREY-WYSSLING (1950, 1952 and 1953) does not see the explanation of the spiral growth of the *Phycomyces* sporangiophore in the orientation of the microfibrils, but ascribes it to the specific nature of the protoplasm. He believes that it is due to a circular wandering of a growing region in the growth zone. No experimental evidence was advanced in support of this assumption, except an apparently exceptional behaviour observed by OORT and ROE-LOFSEN (l.c.) in the variety *piloboloides* (cf. section 2431). ROELOFSEN's objection (1951a) that a circular movement of a region of maximum growth round the cell would not produce spiral growth, but only circumnutation, was apparently overlooked. In addition, CASTLE (1953) pointed out that the explanation is at variance with what is known of the distribution of growth in the growth zone. It can, moreover, not explain the rotation caused by an increase of the internal pressure. FREY-WYSSLING (1959: 99) has attempted lately to defend his hypothesis by remarking that CASTLE (l. c.) determined the distribution of growth by means of markers adhering to the outer surface of the cells and that this passively stretched layer needs not show the same dimensional changes as the actively growing inner layer of the wall that was supposed to cause the spiral growth. This objection seems untenable to us since it would involve that the two layers in question would slide along each other, at least locally.

The hairs on the stamens of *Tradescantia*

Although it is not known with certainty whether spiral growth and the concomittant torsion occur in the hairs that are found on the stamens of *Tradescantia*, and although no torsions have been observed in the cells of these hairs when they underwent an osmotic distension or when the internal pressure was increased, it does not look improbable that spiral growth actually will be present, at least in the major part of the cells. In support of this opinion we refer to the well-known helical course of the cuticular striations and of the ectoplasm threads which occur in most of the cells (see MARTENS, 1934).

As we have mentioned already in section 225, a spiral unwinding of wall strips as well as, in single walls, an oblique extinction between crossed nicols, have been observed in some of the cells of these hairs (ROELOFSEN and HOUWINK, 1951). In part of the cells the micelles in the primary wall are oriented in a Z-spiral, in other ones in an S-spiral, but there are also cells in which they are not helically oriented. This is in line with the variability of the cuticular striation. ROELOFSEN and HOUWINK (l.c.) regarded the structure of the wall as comparable to that of the *Phycomyces* sporangiophores, and supposed that spiral growth or spiral extension would have a similar cause. The modified explanation subsequently proposed by the author (1958) for the structure of the *Phycomyces* sporangiophore and discussed in the preceding section can be applied in the case of these cell-walls too.

If we may base our conclusion on the presence of spiral striations either in the wall as a whole or in the cuticle, spiral growth must be present in quite a number of hairs. In the hairs on the stamens of *Tinantia*, which superficially resemble those of the related genus *Tradescantia*, the direction of the spiral is sometimes reversed in the same cell.

Nitella

Another classical example of a cell whose protoplasm rotates in helical tracks, is that of *Nitella axillaris*. The spiral growth of these cells has been studied by GREEN (1954), and the structure of the wall by GREEN and CHAPMAN (1955). During the period of growth the cells increase also in diameter, and they become at the same time twisted in a steep Z-spiral. Whether the torsion increases with an artificial increase in the internal pressure, is unknown. This steep Z-spiral suggests that the microfibrils in the wall will be oriented in a flat S-spiral. It is noteworthy, however, that single walls never show oblique extinction between crossed nicols (see section 3413). Since this indicates a complete absence of spiral structure, GREEN and CHAPMAN believe that the torsion is due to some unknown special way in which the protoplasm deposits new transversely oriented microfibrils between the old ones. This process was originally supposed to take place throughout the whole thickness of the wall (see section 22825).

That the direction of growth needs not coincide either with the major or with the minor axis of the elements of which the wall is built up, was already pointed out by OORT (1931), and at one time the present author (1950a) believed that this kind of "active intussusception", as it was called, would be responsible also for a part of the torsion shown by growing sporangiophores of *Phycomyces*. OORT compared the growth of the cell-wall to the construction of a pavement out of blocks arranged e.g. in oblique rows or in a herring-bone pattern. The direction in which such a pavement is laid out, may be entirely independent of the direction in which the blocks are pointing.

However, the present author finds it difficult to imagine how in a mass of interwoven microfibrils the insertion of new microfibrils could effect a shifting. Admittedly a pavement may easily be laid out in any direction, but it seems difficult to do this by inserting new blocks between the old ones.

The author (1958) has suggested that the spiral growth of *Nitella* may be explained along similar lines as that of *Phycomyces* and *Tradescantia* (see preceding sections). He assumes that there is among the obliquely oriented microfibrils a slight preference for one direction, and that this suffices to cause the torsion. The preference may be so slight that it does not change the direction of the extinction between crossed nicols in an appreciable way, and that it can not be detected in the electron micrographs either. The fibrillar texture at the inner surface of the growing wall (see section 2413) is not at variance with this concept.

Our supposition that there actually is in a way a spiral structure in the growing walls of *Nitella axillaris*, although it can not be detected, seems to be supported by the demonstration of a pronounced spiral structure in *Nitella opaca* by PROBINE and PRESTON (1958). It is unlikely that the mechanism of spiral growth in the two species would be different. Studying the single walls of *N. opaca* between crossed nicols, these authors found a major extinction direction that followed as a rule an S-helix with a pitch of 5⁰ on the average. The direction of growth and that of the streaming protoplasm was as in *N. axillaris*, that of a steep Z-helix. There is in so far an analogy with the situation in *Phycomyces* sporangiophores, that here too a spiral growth always occurs, although the corresponding spiral structure in the wall is detectable only in some cases.

In the preceding pages we have discussed the way in which spiral growth might find its origin in some kind of helical structure of the wall. We will now shortly consider the way in which this helical structure itself may come into being. For a discussion of the various hypotheses that have been proposed to account for the origin of such a structure, we refer to ROELOFSEN (1950a) and to CASTLE (1953). The most recent hypothesis has apparently been advanced by the author. It starts from the idea that new microfibrils are deposited parallel to the old ones, and supposes that the oblique orientation of the microfibrils that overcross the annular bundles formed by the transversely oriented microfibrils (fig. 98) is caused by an axially directed force by which microfibrils that are fastened at one end only, are swung into an oblique orientation. This axial force would be the flow of protoplasm that is directed towards the tip of the cell.

Proceeding from his supposition that the microfibrils grow at the "reducing" end only (section 114), the author ventured to suggest (1958) that if there was some preference for the kind of growth that, seen from the tip of a tubular cell, would have to be called anticlockwise, the microfibrils that are only partly fixed would have a greater chance to become oriented in a Z-spiral, an orientation that in its turn would cause a torsion in the growth according to an S-spiral and a rotation of the tip that, seen from above, would be clockwise. This is obviously as yet pure hypothesis, but the idea might perhaps prove to be of some value in future attempts to test the validity of theories on the origin of spiral structures.

23. The Structure of the Secondary Wall in the Anthophytes.

231. DEFINITIONS

The term *"secondary wall"* is now generally used for that part of the compound wall that is formed after the latter has ceased to grow in surface. This moment need not be the same for all parts of the cell; it often happens that secondary wall thickening has set in at one place, whereas at another place the cell is still extending, so e. g. in long phloem fibres.

The secondary walls of two adjacent cells are separated from each other by two primary walls and a middle lamella. This arrangement and the use of the terms that were proposed for the different layers by KERR and BAILEY (1934), and which are now generally accepted, are shown in the schema given in fig. 101. This terminology appears to be logically justified, and its introduction put an end to the confusion caused by the use of a different terminology by some authors. The latter called KERR and BAILEY's "middle lamella" the "intercellular substance", the three-layered wall of the growing cell the "middle lamella", the oldest layer of the secondary wall the "primary wall", the next one the "secondary wall" and the youngest one the "tertiary wall".

VAN ITERSON (1927) called the complex formed by the middle lamella and the primary walls on each side of it, the "compound middle lamella", while KERR and BAILEY call it the "cambial wall". In this work we will use for this complex the term *"meristematic wall"*, in order to contrast it with the *"mature wall"*, which comprises five or more layers, i. e. in addition to the three layers of the meristematic wall, on each side at least one secondary layer.

As a rule the secondary wall of tracheids and fibres consists, as is shown in the schema given by KERR and BAILEY, of three layers that may vary in thickness, and that can be distinguished under the microscope as they differ in chemical composition and in the orientation of the cellulose microfibrils. In conformity with KERR and BAILEY we will use for these layers the indications S_1, S_2 and S_3, but with the proviso that we will restrict their use to those cases where there is a difference in the orientation of the microfibrils. In this sense they were apparently also used by KERR and BAILEY themselves.

The microfibrils are always spirally oriented, but the steepness and as a rule also the direction of the spiral differs

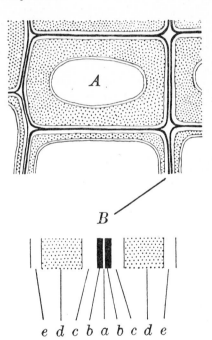

Fig. 101. Diagram illustrating the commonly accepted terminology of the cellwall layers proposed by KERR and BAILEY (1934); a: middle lamella; b: primary wall; c: outer layer of the secondary wall (S_1 layer); d: central layer of the secondary wall (S_2 layer); e: inner layer of the secondary wall (S_3 layer).

in subsequent layers, and occasionally one of the layers may show a crossed fibrillar structure. The steepness of the spiral, or better of the helix, will be indicated by means of the angle which its direction makes with the cell axis. To indicate the direction or sense of the helix the S and Z terminology defined in section 211 will be used.

It should be noted however, that there are not rarely but two layers differing in orientation, or that there is no differentiation at all, and it may also happen that there are more than three differently oriented layers. BAILEY himself (1957) has rightly pointed out that the presence of three layers with a different orientation of the microfibrils has been unduly generalized.

It is worth while to draw the attention to the fact that the S_2 layer consists nearly always, and the S_1 layer rather often, of thinner layers with identical or only slightly different orientation. For the latter we will use the term "lamellae", which was introduced by STRASBURGER (1882), who called the layers themselves "Schichte". So long as the wall is not treated with swelling agents, these lamellae remain invisible under the microscope. The differences in chemical composition or in physical properties are often but slight. Due to lack of detailed information the distinction between layers and lamellae is sometimes arbitrary or even impossible.

Recently several authors, e. g. BUCHER (1957a) and MEIER (1957) have returned to the use of terms like tertiary lamella, tertiary layer and tertiary wall instead of S_3 layer, at least when dealing with the cell-wall of tracheids and wood fibres. They use, moreover, a different criterion for distinguishing this layer from the S_2, viz. the different way in which it reacts to stains and swelling agents, a difference to which HARTIG and VON MOHL already had drawn our attention, and so they apply the name tertiary layer also to layers which do not differ from the next older one in the orientation of the microfibrils. They are of opinion that the difference in chemical composition is of more importance, as it would point to a special physiological function. Another important argument for the exceptional character of this layer is found in the circumstance that it is in the bordered pits in direct contact with the first formed layer of the secondary wall and with the primary wall (BUCHER, 1957 a).

FREY-WYSSLING (1959: 33) argues that the innermost layer with dissimilar chemical constitution might be present in addition to the S_3 layer and should therefore be called tertiary layer or better: terminal layer (Abschlußlamelle). He supposes that it is a remnant of a membranogenic layer (Bildungshaut).

BUCHER and MEIER and also some other authors, use for the S_1 layer too another term, viz. "transition layer" or "transition lamella" (Uebergangslamelle). In cotton hairs it is sometimes called "winding layer" or "inner sheath of the primary wall" and even, though probably more or less inadvertently, "primary wall". The name "transition" layer has been chosen because it forms, in the orientation of the microfibrils as well as in chemical composition, a transition between the primary wall and the S_2 layer.

From various sides objections have been raised against these new terms (e. g. by WARDROP and DADSWELL, 1957, and by EMERTON, 1957a, b). The present author agrees with them. It is impossible to know whether the chemical differences on which in a dead cell the aberrant behaviour of the S_3 layer with regard to swelling agents and stains rests, were already present in the living cell. Moreover, so long as we have no reliable and universally accepted reaction by which the extent of the chemical differences can be judged, it is not to be expected that the latter will be appreciated by various authors in the same way. Further-more, in several instances no chemical difference could be detected so far, which indicates that the significance of the chemical differences observed in other cases is not of fundamental importance. Such a difference can, therefore, hardly be regarded as of the same value as the difference between the primary and the secondary wall, and there is accordingly no sufficient reason to call the S_3 layer a tertiary wall. A different orientation of the microfibrils can not have arisen after the death of the cell, and this is therefore a more trustworthy cri-terion. If no difference can be seen by means of the polarization microscope, this does not prove that the S_3 is absent, for this may be due to the extreme thinness of this layer or to the circumstance that the difference in orientation is very small. In that case the results of an investigation by means of the elec-tron microscope will have to be awaited.

There is no difference of opinion with regard to the distinct nature of the gelatinous layer, indicated by the letter G, which is found in tension wood of *Angiosperms* on the inside of the other ones. As it is an anomalous layer, the indication S_3 should not be applied to it.

The objections against the use of the term "transition layer" for the S_1 layer are of a less serious nature; as there is no difference of opinion with regard to the definition of this layer, but only a difference in the choice of a name. Neverthe-less the use of the term S_1 layer seems to deserve preference since there may be other layers which are also transitional in structure. In the primary wall e. g., a lamella may be present that is intermediary in structure between the inner and the outer one, and no objection could be raised if someone would call this a "transitional lamella". Moreover, it is by no means certain that the S_1 layer is always, as in the tracheids, intermediary in structure between the primary wall and the S_2 layer. Its structure in other kinds of cells, e. g. in collenchyma cells, vessels and isodiametric cells, is very imperfectly known; it might even be absent in some of them. For the moment it seems dangerous to generalize. The term "winding layer", which is often used for the S_1 of the cotton hair, should obviously be rejected, since, even in the wall of the cotton hair, all layers show a "winding" orientation of the microfibrils.

A serious disadvantage of the use of the S_1, S_2, S_3 terminology, which, as we have seen, is based on differences in the orientation of the microfibrils, is that in some secondary walls more than three layers with different orientation of the microfibrils are present. In such cases the third layer is not comparable with the normal S_3, and then it might be recommendable to introduce the indica-tions S.externa, S.mediana and S. interna,or, abbreviated, S. e., S. m. and S. i., and where these main layers prove to be of a compound nature, to indicate the component parts with a number, e. g. S. m. 1, S. m. 2, etc. However, this is as yet merely a suggestion, and for the time being we will stick to the S_1, S_2, and S_3 terminology.

Although the difference between the primary wall and the secondary one seems at first sight to be well defined, it appears that there are nevertheless circumstances under which it is by no means easy to decide whether a definite part of the cell-wall should be referred to the first or to the second.

It may in the first place be difficult to decide whether a wall is still growing in surface. If, under such circumstances, a thickening of the wall is observed, the observer will be inclined to suppose that there is no growth and that the thickening therefore is to be regarded as part of the secondary wall. A characteristic example of such a misinterpretation are the thickenings in the edges of meristematic parenchyma cells (cf. section 2271). These thickenings were originally regarded as parts of the secondary wall, because it seemed improbable that such thickened walls could undergo extension. Afterwards, however, it appeared that these cells are by no means fullgrown (section 223), and then these walls were classified as "thickened primary walls". A similar change of appreciation took place in the case of the strongly thickened outer walls of epidermal cells, like those of the *Avena* coleoptile (figs. 65–P 68), of which it originally looked even more improbable that they could undergo an extension, but now these walls too are included in the category of thickened primary walls. Especially the last-quoted instance makes it clear that it is not in the first place the thickness nor, we may add, the orientation of the microfibrils, which determines whether a wall will be able to undergo a further increase in surface or, more precisely, whether it may ,under the influence of the turgor pressure, undergo an irreversible extension. It is much more probable that this depends on the degree of adhesion between the microfibrils, i. e. on the greater or lesser facility with which the latter can slide along each other.

The term "thickened primary wall" was first applied to collenchyma cells (MAJUMDAR and PRESTON, 1941). Although these cells continue to grow, their walls become thicker and thicker. It should be noted, however, that in this case the localization of the cell growth was not studied, and it might be, therefore, although this does not look very probable, that the growth of these cells is in this stage confined to a special part, e. g. to the top, and in that case the thickening might take place in the full-grown parts.

Strictly speaking, most primary walls belong to the category of the "thickened primary walls", for all primary walls that so far have been studied by means of the electron microscope, appeared to be thicker in older, but still growing cells than they are in the younger stages of development. This is not only directly visible in the electron micrographs (cf. e. g. fig. 43 and fig. 51), but it appears also from the development of the multinet structure with which we have dealt in a previous part of this work, and which seems to be of fairly universal occurrence (cf. section 22823).

In the examples that we have quoted so far, the uncertainty was not due to shortcomings in the definition of the two parts of the wall, but to insufficient information with regard to the surface growth of the particular walls to which the definition had to be applied. However, there are also instances in which the definition itself leads to difficulties.

Cells may be full-grown at one place, and continue to grow at another. Layers that are deposited on the wall of the full-grown part, are in such cases sometimes classified as parts of the secondary wall and sometimes as parts of the primary wall. In fibres with apical growth, the thickening of the wall that at the same time takes place in the basal and central parts, is usually reckoned to be part of the secondary wall, but in the transverse septs of phloem vessels and of growing tubiform parenchyma cells the thickening is regarded as a further development of the primary wall, although the septs do not grow. Thickenings deposited on parts of the wall that are still growing, are, on the other hand, sometimes classified as secondary thickenings. Typical examples are the annular and spiral thickenings on the wall of protoxylem vessels and tracheids, that are shown in figs. P83, P84 and P85. These thickenings themselves undergo no further extension, but during the period of expansion they are separated from each other by ever increasing spaces of primary wall.

It should also be realized that it is nowhere known with certainty whether the growth in surface has actually come to a stop before the S_1 layer is deposited. This layer sometimes shows features that seem to be the result of extension, and it has been argued that the loss of the faculty of the cell to undergo a further extension might be due to the increasing resistance to extension in this layer. The supposition rests on the fact that study with the electron microscope has revealed in the S_1 layer the presence of the same kind of crossed fibrillar structures, either interwoven or in alternating layers, that have been observed in walls that are undoubtedly primary ones. Such structures seem to indicate a reorientation of the microfibrils due to extension. See e. g. the primary walls in the figs. P58, P60, P72, P83, P84, P90 b, P92 and the S_1 layers in the figs. P116—P122.

If the explanation given in the preceding paragraph should prove to be right, in other words if it would appear that this layer actually was deposited before the moment at which growth came to a stop, it seems to us that there is still good reason to regard it as part of the secondary wall.

When plant anatomists are fixing the place of the boundary line between the primary and the secondary wall, they do this, as a rule, by means of criteria that are totally different from those that are mentioned in the definitions given above. In the first place they are of opinion that the primary wall must always be very thin and then they expect in the secondary wall a different orientation of the microfibrils, a much higher cellulose content, which becomes apparent when the wall is treated with staining reagents and eventually the absence of the faculty to be stained with so-called pectin reagents, etc., and they tacitly assume that growth was stopped at the moment the deposition of this layer started. For most objects this will be approximatively correct, but there are doubtless exceptions. The outer wall of the epidermal cell may be cited as a case in point. Even in the electron micrographs no abrupt change is recognizable; this becomes clear when we compare the mature wall shown in fig. P153 with the primary wall shown in figs. 65 and 66.

The primary as well as the secondary wall may undergo secondary changes, which may or may not be accompanied by a thickening. The most striking example of such a secondary change is the lignification, which is, as a rule, most prominent in the primary wall. Simultaneous with the lignification there is an increase in thickness (ALEXANDROV and DJAPARIDZE, 1927; PRESTON, 1941; PRESTON and MIDDLEBROOK, 1949), but the latter is, of course, of another kind than the ordinary secondary thickening. As was pointed out in section 16, it seems probable that precursors of lignin diffuse into the wall, where they are polymerized to lignin, and that by this process the cellulose microfibrils are pressed apart; this is therefore a case of growth in thickness by intussusception. A somewhat similar secondary change is brought about by the intercalation of wax and of cutin in the cuticular layer of epidermal cells. With regard to the thick walls which contain reserve cellulose, it is as yet unknown whether the latter is likewise deposited by intussusception in layers that are already present and which in this way increase in thickness, or whether it is deposited by apposition at the same time as the other constituents of these layers.

232. APPOSITION AND INTUSSUSCEPTION

It has often been said that the primary wall is formed by intussusception, i. e. by the deposition of new material between material that is already present, and that the secondary wall grows by apposition, i. e. by the deposition of new layers against the existing ones. However, as has been pointed out in section 228, the way in which the primary walls are formed, shows, at least in many instances, a greater resemblance to apposition than to intussusception, at least in so far as the cellullose fraction is concerned, although it must be admitted that intussusception of part of it is likely (see section 22825). With regard to the way in which the non-cellulose is deposited in primary as well as in secondary walls, unfortunately nothing is known.

The development of the secondary wall has already since the beginning of the nineteenth century been ascribed to apposition. NAEGELI was one of the few who were of opinion that intussusception was not only responsible for growth in surface, but also for the increase in thickness. Since his time, however, in a large number of objects, although mostly belonging to the *Algae*, apposition could be demonstrated irrefutably. In this connection we may refer to the investigations of DIPPEL (1878), SCHMITZ (1880), STRASBURGER (1882), KRABBE (1887) and NOLL (1887); a summary of their work has been given by KÜSTER (1956). From the more recent literature dealing with higher plants we may quote the very convincing proof that is to be seen in the daily growth-rings found in transverse sections of the S_2 layer of the cotton hair (section 23441), the increase in the number of the lamellae in maturing hairs of *Humulus lupulus* and *Echium vulgare* (section 23442), and the telescoping lamellae in the wall of young phloem fibres (section 2341). Among *Algae*, apposition has been studied in recent times especially in *Valonia* (section 2411).

In higher plants, up to the present day, not a single instance has been found of a cell-wall whose secondary thickening, at least in so far as the cellulose fraction is concerned, is not due to apposition. As the amount of protein in the secondary wall is, as a rule, but small, it is in fact in our opinion hardly conceivable that intussusception will play an important part in the thickening of this part of the wall of those cells, in which the process of secondary thickening has not yet been studied.

In lower plants too, cellulose is, as a rule, deposited against the already existing layers, so that here too the walls increase in thickness in a centripetal direction. With *Acetobacter xylinum*, however, (section 114), and presumably also with *Dictyostelium* (GEZELIUS and RÅNBY, 1957), the cellulose is deposited outside the cell-wall proper. New microfibrils apparently appear between cellulose that already is present, and this could therefore be taken as an example of intussusception.

More numerous are the instances of an increase in thickness by the intussusception of other carbohydrates. CORRENS (1893) discussed the observations made by NAEGELI on the *Cyanophycea Gloeocapsa* and the *Chlorophycea Apiocystis*, and repeated some of them. The outer part of the wall undergoes in these organisms a considerable increase in thickness, and as this part is not in direct contact with the protoplasm, this can not be due to apposition, nor can it, in his opinion, be due to swelling, as had been supposed by STRASBURGER. CRAMER (1890, 1891) describes similar phenomena in *Rhodophyceae*, and the well-known production of a capsule in many kinds of bacteria is essentially the same thing.

An increase in thickness by intussusception of non-cellulose is not uncommon in the higher plants. We have mentioned already the deposition of lignin between the already present constituents of the cell-wall, and that of cutin and wax which in the cuticular layer undoubtedly is effected in a similar way. The lipid materials in the membranes of pollen grains and spores are also deposited in parts of the wall that are no longer in contact with the protoplasm. In these cases the deposition of the non-cellulose constituents is sometimes called incrustation. SITTE (1955) speaks of adcrustation when the deposits form a new layer in or against the wall. This applies e. g. to the cuticle proper and to the suberin lamella in the wall of cork cells.

The use of the terms apposition and intussusception presupposes that a wall is already present. However, cell-wall material may also be deposited without contact with a wall, viz. in the protoplasm itself. This happens e. g. when a cell-plate is formed, a process dealt with in section 222. Most curious is the development of the several cm long and 1μ thick cellulose threads in the vesicular epidermal cells of the seed-coat of *Cobaea scandens* (AMBRONN, 1925), which are formed in the protoplasm and free from the cell-wall. The thickenings in the elaters of liverworts and the strange tubiform bodies that are found in the epidermal cells of the seed-coat in *Cuphea* and some other *Lythraceae* are also formed partly or entirely in the protoplasm.

The deposition of substances in the wall of dead cells is a process of an entirely different kind as the intussusception described above; we will call it impregnation. The substances themselves are the so-called extractive materials, which are not included in the group of the cell-wall constituents proper (section 182).

233. CHEMICAL COMPOSITION OF THE SECONDARY WALL

The chemical composition of the secondary wall shows a much wider range of variability than that of the primary wall. In table I we have already given some figures, and in our discussion of the various cell-wall constituents too we have entered into some detail. It appears that the cellulose content of the secondary wall may vary between 0 and 97 %, the lignin content between 0 and 30 %, the hemicellulose content between 1 and 50 %, the pectin content between 0.5 and 45 %; the amount of soluble polysaccharides varies between 0 and 50 %, the mannan content between 0 and 60 %, xylan between 0 and 40 %, substances with lipid character between 1 and 60 %, etc. It is therefore hardly possible to describe the chemical constitution of the secondary wall in a general way, and it does not look profitable either to adduce more examples of analyses than there are given in table I.

234. STRUCTURE OF THE CELLULOSE IN SOME OF THE BEST-KNOWN SECONDARY CELL-WALLS

As the chemical composition of the secondary wall shows such a wide range of variability, it is certainly no wonder that the submicroscopical structure too differs considerably. An attempt to arrive at a complete enumeration of all the differences that have come to light, would be an enormous task, and it would, in our opinion, be hardly worth the trouble. It seems sufficient to give an impression of the kind of differences that have been found, and the best way to do this, seems to be to enter into some detail with regard to those kinds of cell-walls that have been studied most extensively.

The structure that has been observed in the cell-wall of fossil material, will be left out of consideration; we refer the reader to the summary given by SEN (1956).

2341. Phloem fibres

Especially in the older literature a considerable number of communications is met with, dealing with helical striations that had been observed under the microscope either in untreated or in swollen phloem fibres; sometimes the latter had to this end been isolated and sometimes they were studied in tissue sections. These striations are caused by the presence of bundles of microfibrils that are separated from each other by fissures. They were described already in 1835 by MIRBEL in the phloem fibres of *Nerium oleander*, and in 1854 by CRÜGER in the phloem fibres of several other plants. NAEGELI (1864a) discovered in the phloem fibres of some plants, e. g. in those of *Cinchona* and *Vinca*, that there were two sets of striations in the same wall, the one much less steep than the other and running in the opposite direction. At first the threads causing the striae were supposed to be interwoven, like the threads in textile fabrics, but DIPPEL, STRASBURGER and KRABBE (1887) found out that they form distinct layers, and that the pitch of the spiral in the outer layer is always less steep than that of the spiral in the inner one. DIPPEL (1898 : 154) noted that in young phloem fibres of *Vincetoxicum* first a layer with S-striation is formed, and at a somewhat later stage a layer with Z-striation. NAEGELI (l. c.) published a drawing of the helical slit-like pits found in the walls of phloem fibres of *Cinchona*, and stated that the direction of the slit runs parallel to that of the striation in the layer it passes. In the two layers of a wall the striations were of opposite helical sign, so that the slit-like pore-canal itself looked like a piece of a corkscrew.

KRABBE (1887) *recognized the spiral structure also in transverse sections;* the latter show radially oriented striae corresponding to the striations that are seen in the surface view and which probably mark the boundary lines between bundles of microfibrils, fig. 102. He noted that when the microscope is focussed on successively deeper levels, these radial striae move like the clock hands when the layer shows a Z-striation in surface view, and in the opposite direction when the layer has an S-striation in surface view. During the focussing the two wall-layers look in the transverse section of a cell like two wheels turning in the opposite direction. The rate at which they moved, enabled him to arrive at an estimate of the steepness of the spirals.

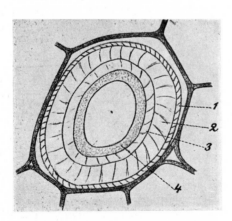

Fig. 102. The so-called turning wheels seen in the transverse section of a phloem fibre of *Nerium oleander*. The outermost layer with a Z-spiral, the subsequent ones respectively with an S- and a Z-spiral and with the spiral still undifferentiated (from KRABBE, 1887).

A study of the phloem fibres of various *Apocynaceae, Asclepiadaceae, Linum, Urtica,* etc. led KRABBE to the conclusion that the wall always consists of two and sometimes of three layers with an alternating helical orientation of the cellulose, fig. 102. The outer layer may show an S- or a Z-striation, and he is of opinion that this may vary even with the same species, but in the light of more recent findings this seems improbable; we suppose that he will occasionally have overlooked the presence of the outer layer when the latter happened to be very thin. Furthermore KRABBE noted that the second layer is often rather thick, and that it consists in that case of several thinner layers which he calls lamellae, because the spirals are oriented in the same direction, although not rarely with a different pitch. In several of his drawings the innermost layer is still incompletely developed and shows as yet no striation.

KRABBE's "turning wheels" have been observed by other authors too, but they have received insufficient attention, especially in later years, and they have not been used for establishing the correct sequence of the spiral structures. The *latter was usually determined by means of the striations* which were studied in isolated cells seen in surface view, but this method is less reliable. With flattened cells there is always a chance that a layer of the lower cell-wall is mistaken for a part of the upper cell-wall that we are studying. Furthermore, the sometimes very vague striation of the outermost layer may easily be overlooked. The striation of deeper layers is, moreover, very often invisible, so that this method allows us but rarely to observe the striations in more than two layers, although there are very often three layers with different striation.

We will confine ourselves here to the phloem fibres that have most often been studied. The results obtained by the various authors have been summarized in Table VII. They appear to vary considerably, and in connection with these discrepancies it is worth noting that two of the earlier authors have revoked part of their former conclusions. In view of the observations made by KRABBE (1887) and of the fact that the present author (1951 b) found three layers in

Table VII. Direction of the striations occurring in the various layers of the wall of flax, ramie and hemp fibres, as recorded by different observers.

Author		Linum		Boehmeria		Cannabis	
		Outer	Inner	Outer	Inner	Outer	Inner
SONNTAG	(1909)	S	Z	S	Z	S	Z
SONNTAG	(1911)	S	Z	S	Z	Z	S
REIMERS	(1921)	S	Z	S	Z	Z	Z
REIMERS	(1922)	S	Z	S	S (steeper)	Z	Z (steeper)
NODDER	(1922)	S	Z	S		Z	
HERZOG	(1926)	S	Z			Z	S
ANDERSON	(1927b)	alternating					
HOCK	(1942)	Z	S	Z	S	Z	axial
ROLLINS	(1945)			Z	S		
ROELOFSEN	(1951b)	Z	S Z	Z	S and?	Z	S Z

flax fibres (fig. P28) and in hemp, it is not improbable that the explanation of the discrepancies is to be found in the fact that the outer Z-layer in flax and ramie may be very thin, and that it is in the technical product often entirely absent. The innermost layer, moreover, may have varied in thickness, and in parts of the cells that were not yet fully mature, this layer even may have been absent. It is a well-known fact that in the apical part of these fibres the thickening begins at a much later stage than at the base.

In fig. 103 a schema is given of the most probable structure of mature flax and hemp fibres. They differ in the S_1 and S_3 layers. The S_1 layer is in hemp always present and well-developed, whereas it is in flax either very thin or, at least in retted flax, completely absent. The S_3 on the other hand, is in flax well-developed, whereas it may apparently sometimes be lacking in hemp.

That isolated flax and hemp fibres may be *distinguished by means of their optical behaviour,* has been known for a long time. Ramie shows similar optical properties as flax; from the two other fibres it differs distinctly in its greater thickness. Between crossed nicols with the red I platelet inserted, flax and ramie

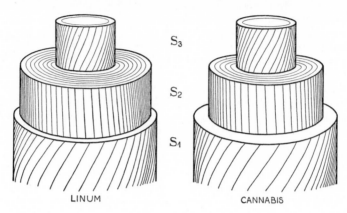

Fig. 103. Schema of the structure shown by the secondary wall in flax and hemp fibres based on observations made by means of the light microscope (ROELOFSEN, 1951*b*).

fibres show addition colours in the E–W position, whereas hemp fibres do this in the N–S position (parallel to the vibration plane of the polarizer). If there was but one layer with a spiral structure, this would mean that this layer had in flax and ramie an S-structure, in hemp a Z-structure. As there are in all these fibres more than one layer with a spiral structure, and as the spirals differ in direction, the result has generally been ascribed to a greater thickness of the layer in which the orientation of the microfibrils corresponds with the direction indicated by the optical behaviour.

As we are not convinced that this conclusion is fully justified, we wish to draw the attention to another possibility. As we have pointed out in section 212, the explanation given above can be accepted only if the other layers are so thin that their birefringence may be neglected. This seems to apply to the outermost Z-layer in the flax and ramie fibres, which is so thin that it is difficult to see, and which may even be absent. In such cases the optical behaviour of the fibre will be determined entirely by the S-spiral in the S_2 layer and it will show addition colours in the E–W position. If the S_3 layer too is sufficiently birefringent, we will in each fibre have to reckon with four birefringent layers, two forming part of the S_2 layer with the S-spiral, and two belonging to the S_3 layer with the Z-spiral. This combination of four layers, viz. S–Z//Z–S, would however, also show addition colours in the E–W position.

In the hemp fibre the outermost S_1 layer with Z-structure, is always well-developed, as well as the S_2 layer with S-structure, so that there are always four layers (S_3 may presumably be left out of consideration). These four layers are part of a double cylinder with Z-structure on the outside and S-structure on the inside, and these two cylinders would optically behave like a single cylinder with Z-structure, i. e. show addition colours in the N–S position.

The *direction in which these fibres twist* under the influence of swelling and shrinking agents, is in agreement with their structure. The reason why the twist of a hemp fibre differs from that of flax and ramie fibres, is apparently to be seen in the circumstance that the S_1 layer is in the hemp fibre mechanically of far greater importance. It is true that the S_2 layers are very thick, but their microfibrils are oriented in such a steep spiral that the torsional force of this layer can be but very slight.

The direction of the twist is for each species, and apparently even for each family, constant. This appears from the investigations of REIMERS (1922) and of NEWMAN and RIDDELL (1954) who studied this phenomenon in a large number of plants. Their results are summarized in Table VIII.

Table VIII. Predominant structure of the phloem fibres in various families, as revealed by the twist test (the Z-helix is recognized by the anticlockwise movement which is observed when looking down on a drying fibre when the top of the latter points upwards). The numbers behind the families indicate the number of genera of which species were tested. 1: as determined by REIMERS (1922); 2: as determined by NEWMAN and RIDDELL (1954).

Predominant structure

Z-helical		S-helical	
1) *Ulmaceae*	1		
1) *Cupuliferae*	1		
2) *Malvaceae*	9	1) + 2) *Apocynaceae*	2
2) *Araliaceae*	1	1) + 2) *Asclepiadaceae*	2
1) + 2) *Leguminosae*	13	1) + 2) *Linaceae*	1
1) + 2) *Moraceae*	5	1) + 2) *Urticaceae*	5
2) *Tiliaceae*	3		
1) *Salicaceae*	1		

DIPPEL (1898: 270) reported that the walls of phloem fibres when *studied in transverse section and between crossed nicols*, are seen to light up over their whole thickness. With reference to the fibres of flax, ramie and hemp, this at first sight seems puzzling, for in these fibres the spiral of the S_2 layer is so steep that in perfectly transverse sections which are oriented perfectly perpendicular to the beam of light, the wall should light up but slightly or not at all. That a large part of the sections nevertheless do light up, is obviously due to the circumstance that the two conditions mentioned in the preceding sentence, are but rarely fulfilled. Only by using hard embedding media and a very sharp microtome knife, and by choosing a thickness not exceeding 5μ, sections may be obtained that give reliable results.

The difficulty to obtain suitable sections and to adjust them in the right way, explains why, so far as is known to us, but a single microphotograph of a transverse section between crossed nicols has been published; it is that of a hemp fibre, and it was made by KUNDU and PRESTON (1940). It shows the presence of a thin peripheral layer which lights up more strongly than the rest of the wall; it presumably represents the S_1 layer together with the primary wall. An S_3 layer is, according to these authors, only very occasionally observable. This agrees with our own experience.

In transverse sections of ramie fibres we regularly observed both the S_1 and the S_3 layer, although they were much less clear than the S_1 layer in the hemp fibre, see fig. P104. The best embedding medium for the fibres is, according to our experience, methacrylate. From fibres that are embedded in this substance, with a good microtome knife sections with a thickness of circ. 4μ can be cut; in order to flatten them, they have to be treated with 30 % aceton, after which they can be studied in glycerol. Even then it appears that only part of the sections are really horizontal and flat.

These observations indicate that the spiral structure of the S_1 layer is always less steep than that of the S_2 layer, and that this applies probably also to the S_3 layer, which is often difficult to discern. In swollen fibres this difference in steepness can be recognized also by looking at the striations, but in this condition the speed of the spirals has undergone a considerable decrease.

By glueing isolated hemp fibres to a microscope slide and by scraping off the cell-wall on the upper side of the fibres, KUNDU and PRESTON (1940) have tried to estimate the spiral angle in the main layer of the remaining cell-wall by observing the striations as well as the direction of the extinction. In both ways they found in hemp fibres S- as well as Z-spirals with a mean angle of circ. 3°. However, the circumstance that S- as well as Z-spirals were found, is in our opinion an indication that something is wrong, for we have seen that the sense of the helical structure of the fibres is for each species constant. It may be that the fibres had been twisted locally either when they were glued to the slide or when they were drying on the slide, so that the authors did not measure the original orientation of the spiral, but the one that appeared after the fibre had been twisted to some extent. PRESTON (1941) used the same method in studying the spiral structure of jute fibres. He found a spiral angle of 8°; here the direction was nearly always that of a Z-spiral, and this therefore looks more plausible.

The classic *X-ray studies* of cellulose discussed in detail in section 113, were carried out on phloem fibres, especially on those of ramie, flax and hemp. The spot diagrams which are obtained if the fibres are well aligned, indicate that the mean deviation of the microfibrils from the longitudinal axis is in the ramie fibre practically nil, and that it amounts at the most to a few degrees in the two other kinds of fibres.

The circumstance that the X-ray diagrams reveal, as a rule, no trace of the S_1 and S_3 layers, whose orientation is less steep, induced PRESTON to look for another explanation of the birefringence which these layers show in transverse sections. He suggested that the microfibrils might actually be oriented in the same steep spiral as those of the S_2 layer, but that their mean angular dispersion from this direction would be higher. This explanation is obviously inconsistent with the earlier microscopical observations on the presence in the S_1 layer of a spiral running in the opposite direction and exhibiting moreover a lesser speed, but PRESTON was presumably acquainted only with observations that had been made on swollen fibres, and these observations were in his opinion of no value. Especially for the tracheids of the conifers the presence of but a single spiral structure in the cell-wall was defended by him, but in 1947 he changed his view. Although he did not mention the cell-wall structure of the phloem fibres at that occasion, it is clear that the arguments which forced him to change his attitude, are applicable to the latter also. This was one of the not very rare occasions at which a too implicit faith in the sensitivity of the X-ray method has led to a misinterpretation.

It has since long been known that the *S_2 layer consists of several lamellae.* NAEGELI (1864a) in studying hemp fibres which showed ballooning, observed and drew several lamellae in the cell-wall (fig. 26), and DIPPEL (1898: 270) states that the walls of many kinds of phloem fibres when studied in transverse section and between crossed nicols, show concentric rings of different light intensity, and supposes that this is due to differences in density. The three kinds of fibres that are mainly dealt with in this section, were not mentioned by him; it is therefore worth while to state that as a matter of fact in the walls of these fibres no lamellae can be seen between crossed nicols.

KRABBE (1887) gives many drawings of sections through various kinds of phloem fibres, including flax, in which 2–7 lamellae with the same spiral orientation are shown. More recently these lamellae, which become more easily recognizable after staining with congo-red or with chlor-zinc-iodine, in flax also with ruthenium red, are mentioned by several authors. If the fibres are treated with a swelling agent, a much larger number of lamellae becomes visible, and the majority of the latter, although not necessarily all of them, prove to belong to the S_2 layer. Fig. P105 shows transverse sections through a flax fibre before and after the swelling; the first with more than 10, the second with circa 35 lamellae. In the original condition the latter must have had a thickness of 0.1 -0.2μ. Whether these are day growth-rings, is unknown. A concentric lamellar structure is also indicated in electron micrographs of transverse sections, cf. fig. 108.

HOCK (1942) stated that such a set of lamellae becomes also recognizable in the cell-wall of the flax fibre after removal of the cellulose and staining with ruthenium red. This proves that at least in the wall of this fibre the lamellar structure can not be due entirely to differences in the density of the cellulose, but that differences in the content of pectin, or at least of non-cellulosic substances that stain with ruthenium red, also play a part. Whether there are still other differences, e. g. in the orientation of the cellulose, is unknown, but such differences can not be great, as otherwise they would reveal themselves when transverse sections are studied between crossed nicols.

HOCK (l. c.) also noted that the number of lamellae in sections that had been treated in the way indicated in fig. P105b, increased with the distance from the growing tip, and reached a maximum of circa 35 at about 50 cm from the latter. TAMMES (1908) had already found that the secondary thickening of the cell-wall in the flax fibre proceeds but slowly, and that it begins in the lower part of the fibres at a time that they are still growing at the apex, which is at a considerable distance, since the final length is 1–10 cm. This was confirmed by ANDERSON (1927b) and by ALDABA (1927), who studied the fibres of *Boehmeria* too; A. D. J. MEEUSE (1941) finally found the same behaviour in a considerable number of other phloem fibres which reach a great length. The successively younger lamellae look like progressively thinner and shorter tubes telescoped one into the other with their mouths directed towards the apex of the fibre, which lengthens by intrusive growth (cf. ESAU, 1953: 210).

In various kinds of fibres the inner layer of the wall seems to have another chemical composition than the rest of the wall. In our discussion of the xylem elements we will return to this question. In phloem fibres this condition was found in *Asclepias syriaca* (ROLLINS, 1947).

Other fibres are lignified, e. g. the jute fibers (*Corchorus capsularis*), which contain 11 % lignin. PRESTON (1941) stated that by far the greater part of the lignin is deposited in the external layer, and that the thickness of the latter, whose lignin content therefore is far higher than 11 %, increases as a result of this deposition to about twice the original value.

In all phloem fibres with little or no lignification many nearly *transverse markings* are present; these are the so-called dislocations or slip planes. They include an angle of 60–70° with the longitudinal axis, and occasionally two of them approach each other or overlap, so that V- or X-shaped figures are formed (fig. 106). They are visible already in ordinary light, but become more conspicuous if the fibres are studied in orthogonal position between crossed nicols. In that case the dislocations light up because here the microfibrils are not oriented orthogonally. Reagents penetrate at these locations more rapidly than elsewhere, e. g. sulphuric acid (fig. 106) and chlor-zinc-iodine. In the slightly lignified jute fibres only ordinary markings are found, not the V- or X-shaped ones. In more strongly lignified fibres, e. g. in the sclerenchyma fibres of the Monocotyledones and in wood fibres, they may appear after the lignin content has been reduced to less than 8%, but before this treatment they rarely or never occur. In cotton hairs they are also present, but here they are less conspicuous.

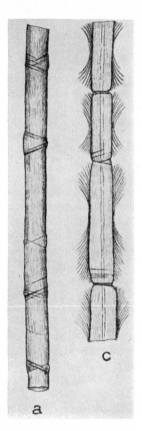

Although some recent investigators (WIELER, 1943) agree with VON HÖHNEL, by whom the markings were detected, that the latter are native, the opposite view that was first brought forward by SCHWENDENER, viz. that they are artefacts produced either by rough handling of the stems, by the mechanical isolation of the fibres from retted stems, or by the sectioning of the fibres, is now more generally accepted.

AMBRONN (1925) described this kind of markings also from the thin solid cellulose threads that are found in the testa cells of *Cobaea scandens*, and stated that the angle with the axis always had a value of 62°. He thought that it were crystalline slip planes. FREY-WYSSLING (1934) confirmed his observations, but made it clear that AMBRONN's explanation must be wrong. It are dislocations, but the microfibrils and molecules are not fractured but merely bent, as is shown in fig. P147. This was essentially the same explanation as that which NAEGELI (1864a) already had suggested. It explains why the dislocations are so very conspicuous between crossed nicols, and why stains and other reagents penetrate here so easily; the interfibrillar space has become wider, and the microfibrils themselves perhaps become more amorphous at these places. If the interfibrillar spaces have already been filled with a more or less tough substance like lignin, then there are no dislocations at all.

Fig. 106. Dislocations in phloem fibres as drawn by NAEGELI (1864a); a: normal fibre; b: fibre that is dissolving in conc. sulphuric acid. See also figs. P147 and 148

Another kind of transverse striation has already been described by various investigators (e. g. KRABBE, 1887; STRASBURGER, 1892; CORRENS, 1893) in the preceding century. These striations are more frequent and much less conspicuous than those resulting from dislocations. WIESNER (1892) thought that it was identical with the striations that he had obtained by treatment with hot acid, and which ultimately lead to the disintegration of the fibre wall into small disks and granules, a phenomenon which brought him to the formulation of his theory of the "dermatosomes". Without knowing of WIESNER'S work, SEARLE (1924) and KELANEY and SEARLE (1930) have in more recent times investigated this phenomenon, which they call "chemical sectioning". It is since long the basis of a technical procedure by means of which worn woollen fabrics may be freed from cellulose fibres. KUNDU and PRESTON (1940) too were of opinion that there was a marked resemblance between the transverse striations that are observed in the native fibres and the striations which appear as a result of a treatment with chromic acid and with alkali. Apparently there are along the fibre a large number of thin transverse zones where the wall is more easily attacked by chemicals, although not in the same measure as in the comparatively sparse dislocations.

WIESNER'S theory has been abandoned in the original form, but since 1925 it has been revived in somewhat modified versions by K. HESS, SCHRAMEK, LÜDTKE, FARR, DOLMETSCH (1955) and others; however, these attempts met with little response .We refer to TREIBER (1957: 192) and to FREY–WYSSLING (1959). The most recent development in this field is the demonstration, by means of the electron microscope, of alternating transverse zones which differ in their behaviour towards iodine; this is supposed to indicate alternating differences in crystallinity (K. HESS et al., 1957). So far only observations made on artificial fibres and on mercerized native ones consisting of cellulose II, have been published, but according to a private communication received from HESS, the same structure would have been found in native cotton fibres. Without treatment with iodine no periodic structures are visible.

In view of the fact that phloem fibres are technically of the utmost importance, it is rather remarkable that they have been studied so rarely by means of the *electron microscope,* and then almost exclusively after disintegration. Fig. P 107 shows cellulose fragments obtained by disintegrating ramie fibres. The perfectly parallel orientation, the very dense structure, and the arrangement of the microfibrils in bundles, are characteristic features of the cellulose in the secondary wall not only of the phloem fibres but of all kinds of fibres as well.

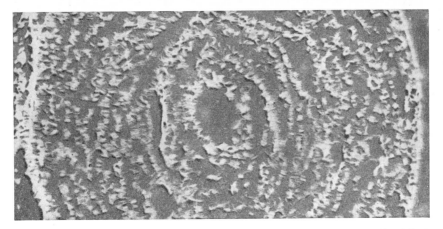

Fig. 108. Part of a transverse section of a flax fibre swollen in hot ethylene glycol and during the embedding in methacrylate, as seen with the electron microscope. (Made by TRIPP and MOORE, official U.S.D.A. photograph).

The only electron micrographs of transverse sections that so far have been published, are apparently those found in the papers by MAERTENS et al. (1956) and TRIPP and MOORE, cf. fig. 108. They show a lamellar structure, but the fibres were not studied in the original condition, and the figures, moreover, give no new information.

There are many points on which we should like to be informed, e. g. whether there are differences in orientation in the various lamellae of the S_2 layer, how the orientation is in the S_3 layer, and whether the S_1 layer shows a similar crossed fibrillar structure as is seen in the corresponding layer of the wood fibres, or merely, as the study with the ordinary microscope suggests, an orientation in one direction.

2342. Fibres of Monocotyledones

In the Monocotyledones the majority of the fibres are found in the cortex at varying distances from the surface as well as in the sheaths which envelop the vascular bundles. We will distinguish these two groups as cortical and perivascular fibres (ESAU, 1953: 201). They are most often met with in stems and in the thicker leaves, but may occur also in carpels, e. g. in those of the coconut. The well-known hard fibres belong to this group; as the name already discloses, they are usually lignified; the least lignified ones are found in the *Bromeliaceae*.

The greater part of our knowledge with regard to *the helical structure and the stratification of these fibres* as revealed by the aid of the ordinary microscope, is due to SONNTAG (1909). Just as the microscopists of the classic period, he studied by preference the plane of rupture in fibre bundles that had been pulled in two by longitudinal stress, as under these circumstances not only the individual fibres but the various layers of the secondary wall too are often severed from each other, and as the latter may even be drawn out into shreds which may be studied separately. In the S_1 and S_2 layers a striation was often observable, and it appeared that the orientation of the slit-like pits agreed with that of the striation in the S_2 layer, which is here, just as in the phloem fibres, the dominant one. Corkscrew-shaped pit-canals as seen in phloem fibres, have not been described. Some of SONNTAG's data are reproduced in table IX; they reveal that the S_1 layer always has an S-helix, and the S_2 layer a Z-helix, and that the speed of the first is always lower than that of the second. This is in full agreement with the fact that in transverse sections the outer layer, as SONNTAG's observations show, is always more strongly birefringent than the rest of the wall.

Table IX. Helical structures in the wall of perivascular fibres from leaves of Monocotyledones, as recorded by SONNTAG (1909); S = S-spiral; Z = Z-spiral.

	Angle with axis in	
	S_1 layer	S_2 layer
Caryota urens	40—52 S	37—44 Z
Cocos nucifera (carpel)	52—54 S	30—53 Z
Arenga saccharifera	42—62 S	36—50 Z
Agave americana	25—38 S	25—40 Z
Fourcroya gigantea	41—55 S	10—32 Z
Phormium tenax	50—90 S	13—35 Z
Chamaerops humilis	64—78 S	22—27 Z

In some fibres, e. g. in part of those found in the carpels of *Cocos nucifera*, the main helix includes an angle of more than 45° with the longitudinal axis, and the whole fibre therefore shows negative birefringence. The same macerate contains in this case positively as well as negatively birefringent fibres.

A painstaking study by PRESTON and MIDDLEBROOK (1949) has confirmed the conclusions of SONNTAG for the fibres of sisal (presumably *Agave sisalana*). These investigators determined the orientation of the cellulose in the S_1 layer of young fibres obtained from the basal part of the leaves. They used to this end three criteria, viz. the orientation of the slit-like pits, the length of the sickle-shaped X-ray interferences, and the major extinction position in the single wall. By the aid of the two last-named methods mature fibres too were investigated. In the S_1 layer the spiral angle appeared to be 40°, whereas it will have amounted to circ. 20° in the S_2 layer (the directions of the spirals are not indicated but are presumably S and Z respectively). The deviations of the micelles from the average direction proved to be much larger in the S_1 layer than in the S_2 layer. They suppose that this less regular arrangement was favoured by the distension caused by the lignification and this is not improbable, as the opposite effect, viz. a more regular orientation, was found to arise in coconut fibres as a result of delignification (PRESTON and ALLSOPP, 1939).

Recently STERN (1957) has studied the birefringence of oblique sections of coconut fibres, and in this way he too confirmed that there are two layers with opposite helical structure.

Neither SONNTAG nor STERN mention the presence of an S_3 layer, but PRESTON and MIDDLEBROOK indicate its birefringence in transverse sections of mature sisal fibres.

As far as we know, no good pictures of transverse sections as seen between crossed nicols, have as yet been published. Suitable sections must be very thin and exactly transverse, and they are therefore difficult to obtain. The S_1 layer and the primary wall prove to be strongly birefringent, and if the spiral of the S_2 layer is sufficiently steep, it is sometimes possible to distinguish a thin S_3 layer with a somewhat stronger birefringence, cf. fig. P109.

When seen in surface view between crossed nicols with the red I plate, all monocotyledonous fibres that so far have been investigated, show an addition colour in the N–S position. If the S_1 layer, which has an S-spiral structure, were sufficiently thick to be clearly birefringent in surface view, this would be impossible (see section 212), and we must assume therefore that the effect is entirely due to the S_2 layer with its Z-spiral, the S_3 layer being evidently too thin to exercise effect.

The twist-test too indicates a predominant Z-structure. NEWMAN and RIDDELL (1954) studied by the aid of this method 14 genera of *Palmae*, 6 of *Liliaceae*, 4 of *Bromeliaceae*, 3 of *Gramineae*, 2 of *Amaryllidaceae*, and one genus of each of the families *Cyperaceae*, *Musaceae* and *Typhaceae*.

The helical structure has also been confirmed electron optically by STERLING (1957 a) and STERLING and SPIT (1957) who have not only studied the primary wall of the cortical fibres in *Asparagus* shoots, but the secondary wall as well. The first quoted paper shows, by the aid of the polarization microscope as well as by X-ray analysis, that the cellulose micelles in the secondary wall are deposited in a spiral with a mean angle of 50°. Electron micrographs obtained by the aid of the replica method, are in agreement with this conclusion. Fig. P110a shows a steep spiral, but in most of the fibres the expected flat spiral is seen.

A. D. J. MEEUSE (1938) thought that the perivascular fibres of *Sanseviera* showed a *correlation between length and spiral speed* and that such a correlation really exists, was proved by PRESTON and SINGH (1950) for bamboo fibres, and, though with less precision, by PRESTON and MIDDLEBROOK (1949) for those of sisal. It appears that the correlation is not confined to fibres of the same species, but that it applies also, at least approximatively, when fibres of different species are compared. This appears clearly from a study by HEYN (1949), who, by the aid of the small angle scattering method, determined the average speed of the spiral structure in a number of fibres derived from different Monocotyledones and Dicotyledones, cf. fig. 111. The spirals of the short coconut and sisal fibres appear to have a very low speed, whereas the spirals of the longer fibres of the ananas and the banana are steeper.

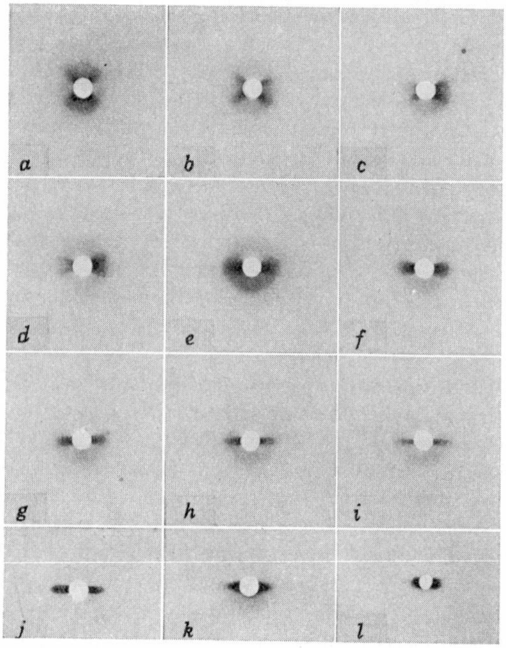

According to BALASHOV et al. (1957) and STERN (1957), X-ray diagrams of stretched and non-stretched bundles of fibres of sisal and coconut indicate that the spiral structure steepens in the same way as a spiral spring, as a result of stretch. In our opinion however, the difference observed by them will at least partly be due to a more perfect alignment of the elementary cells which constitute the compound fibres (vascular bundles) and of these compound fibres themselves. In the former publication electron micrographs of fragments of the primary wall and of the secondary wall of the sisal fibre are given.

Fig. 111. Small-angle-scattering X-ray diagrams obtained from the fibres of six Monocotyledones and of three Dicotyledones; a: *Cocos nucifera;* b, c, d and f: *Agave spp.;* e: *Sanseviera guineensis;* g: *Yucca;* h: *Musa (Ensete) textilis;* i: *Ananas comosus;* j: *Corchorus capsularis;* k: *Boehmeria nivea;* l: *Gossypium hirsutum* (from HEYN, 1949).

In various other Monocotyledones than those mentioned earlier *the fibres appear to have a more complex structure,* as there are more than three layers with a different orientation. This applies presumably to the various palm fibres that were studied by DIPPEL (1898), viz. those of *Caryota, Metroxylon* and *Corypha,* and also to those of a *Musaceae (Urania guyanensis).* His figure of a transverse section through a palm fibre seen between crossed nicols, agrees completely with that of a transverse section through fibres of *Pandanus odoratissimus* which more recently was published by BAILEY and KERR, cf. fig. 112a. In diluted cuprammonium these fibres too showed the peculiar double ballooning discussed in a previous section, cf. fig. 112b.

The last-named authors suppose that the stratification in the *Pandanus* fibres is due to the presence or absence of cellulose in the successive deposits, but this has not been proved. In view of the circumstance that a similar explanation has been proposed by these authors for the structure of the ramie fibre, where it is certainly unacceptable, another interpretation would seem to deserve preference, viz. that the lamellar structure is due to successive changes in the orientation of the cellulose. Without revoking his earlier explanation such

a

Fig. 112. Fibres of *Pandanus odoratissimus;* a: transverse section seen between crossed nicols; b: delignified fibre in diluted cuprammonium; the various layers appear to be capable of ballooning (from BAILEY and KERR, 1935).

b

an interpretation has also been suggested by BAILEY himself (1954, figs. 17 and 18) at a later date.

A similar situation was found in the fibres of various kinds of bamboo by PRESTON and SINGH (1950). By applying a special optical method these authors could show that the outermost layer of the secondary wall has a mean orientation of 35° to the fibre axis, and that the spiral in the other lamellae, which in transverse section light up between crossed nicols, becomes steeper in the direction of the lumen; in the middle of the wall it amounts to 20°, in the innermost layer to 11°. Between these lamellae other, thicker ones occur in which the spiral is much steeper, making an angle of 5 to 6° with the cell axis. Here too the average speed of the spiral increases with the value of the ratio fibre length to fibre width (PRESTON and SINGH, 1952).

The fibres of *Saccharum officinarum* showed a smaller number of layers, but a similar variation in the speed of the Z-spiral (VAN DER HOUVEN VAN OORDT-HULSHOF, 1957). The telescoping of these fibres in swelling media has been mentioned in section 211. In electron micrographs of transverse sections the facility with which the various layers come apart, is a rather striking feature. In this publication literature is cited where similar structures have been described.

2343. Xylem fibres and tracheids

23431. Stratification of the wall

In the preceding century a large number of observations on the secondary wall of wood elements have been made by the aid of the ordinary microscope and the polarization microscope. At that time the interest was centred almost entirely on the location of the various components of the cell-wall, a point that we will leave out of consideration in this section, and further on the orientation of the cellulose, and this is the aspect that we will discuss here in some detail. The orientation was originally determined by the aid of three criteria, in the first place by the orientation of the striations which may be seen in the various layers of a fibre that is studied in surface view; in the second place by the position of the slit-like pits, which is determined by the structure of the principal layer of the cell-wall, and thirdly by differences in optical properties like the birefringence shown by the various layers in transverse and longitudinal sections, the dichroism produced by the use of certain stains, addition and substraction colours appearing in the orthogonal position, etc.

The observations made by men like VON MOHL, HARTIG, NAEGELI, DIPPEL, CORRENS and STRASBURGER (cf. KÜSTER, 1956) by the aid of the ordinary microscope, and those of NAEGELI, SCHWENDENER, DIPPEL and N. J. C. MÜLLER (cf. DIPPEL, 1898) by means of the polarization microscope, had already led to the view that there are, as a rule, three layers with alternating helical orientation, a view which since then has been confirmed by the use of new methods of investigation. The outermost as well as the innermost layer possess a helical structure with usually a lower speed than the thick central layer and with a different sign. DIPPEL proved that the three layers appear in succession during the process of secondary wall thickening, and in conformity with these classic observations on wood, as well as on account of their own findings, KERR and BAILEY introduced the S_1, S_2 and S_3 terminology (cf. section 231), which will be applied in this work too.

Turning our attention to the principal investigations that have been carried out since the beginning of this century, we will begin with *those in which the striations were used as the main criterion for studying the stratification* of the wall. Occasionally the striations had to be accentuated by the use of swelling agents, and sometimes this treatment was preceded by delignification and by maceration of the wood, but in many instances this proved unnecessary, as the striations of one or two of the layers are, at least if fresh wood is used and if the elements are embedded in media with a low refractive index, usually easily distinguishable. In compression wood and along the margin of fractures they are very conspicuous.

KRIEG (1907) confined his attention to the conspicuous striation in the S_2 layer; the orientation of this striation agrees with that of the slit-like bordered pits. In the tracheids of compression wood obtained from five different kinds of Conifers the angle of this striation with the cell-axis varied between 25 and 40°; in the tracheids of *Larix* it was circ. 17°. In compression wood the spirals are always less steep than in normal wood. The helices were always directed in the same sense, but the author does not tell us in what sense he uses the terms left and right.

SONNTAG (1909) reports, in conformity with the older literature, for the tracheids of *Pinus sylvestris* and *Abies pectinata* in the S_1 layer the presence of striations in the direction of an S-helix with an angle of 49 to 63°, and in the S_2 layer slit-like pits and striations in the direction of a Z-helix with an angle of circ. 20°. In the fibres of various deciduous trees he notes in the S_1 layer S-striations with an angle of 10° and in the S_2 layer an almost axial orientation.

The observations of SCARTH et al. (1929) with regard to the spiral structures do not look convincing .In *Picea excelsa* there would be an S_1 layer with transverse orientation, and below the latter several layers with steep, though varying spirals.

BAILEY and VESTAL (1937a, b) based their conclusions not only on the striations but also on the orientation of iodine crystals that had been deposited in the wall, and that of corrosion figures caused by soft rot, cf. section 211. They measured in the S_1 layer angles between 50 and 90°, and in the S_2 layer angles of 0 to 45°, and although the direction of the helices is not recorded, their photographs seem to indicate that in *Pinus, Larix* and *Sequoia* the S_1 layer has an S-helix, the S_2 layer a Z-helix, which would be in agreement with the findings of SONNTAG. BAILEY and VESTAL emphasize the high degree of variability that is found not only in different species but also in various specimens of the same species and even in the same trunk. In their opinion the variation within a single species is already so considerable that it is apparently of no use to look for differences between the different species, but in the light of the results obtained by subsequent studies this view seems hardly acceptable.

In a series of papers that have appeared since 1934 (cf. 1952: 152) PRESTON has shown that there is in the tracheids of the Conifers (just as in the bamboo fibres cf. section 2342), a strong correlation between the ratio length to width and the speed of the spiral in the S_1 layer as well as in the S_2 layer. The speed however, should be measured in the various fibres in corresponding situations, i. e. either all of them in the tangential wall, or all of them in the radial one (in the tangential wall the speed of the spiral is always higher). Since in the annual rings formed in older trees, the length of the tracheids increases, the spirals become in every trunk steeper the further they are away from the centre. In summer wood the spiral proves to be steeper than in spring wood.

WARDROP and PRESTON (1950), also noted a correlation between the speed of the spiral and the rate of growth of the cambial initials, the speed being highest in the tracheids that originated from initials that took the longest time to reach their final length. In deciduous trees the spirals were found to be less steep in compression wood than they are in tension wood.

PRESTON (1947) also studied the striations in the tracheids of *Pinus insignis*, and estimated the major extinction in the S_1 layer (which he mistook for the primary wall) and in the S_2 layer. The character of the S_1 layer proved to be determined by an S-spiral with an average angle of 79°, and that of the S_2 layer by a Z-spiral with an average angle of 19°.

In longer cells the spiral thickenings are steeper than in the shorter ones, but not in proportion to the length of the cell; at any rate in the longer cells the number of turns is larger (WARDROP and DADSWELL, 1951).

If we turn our attention now to *the polarization optical properties* that have been adduced as arguments in favour of the view that the secondary wall of wood fibres and tracheids consists of three layers, it appears that DIPPEL was the first who, on the ground of arguments of this nature, arrived at his conclusion; this was in 1878 (cf. 1898). Up to 1934 but little has been added to his observations and to those of the other investigators whose names have been men-

tioned above. It appears to be an almost general rule that the S_1 and S_3 layers
are thinner than the S_2 layer, and that in transverse sections they light up between crossed nicols, whereas the S_2 layer does not light up at all or only slightly;
this layer, on the contrary, lights up in longitudinal sections. The photographs
taken by KERR and BAILEY show this with particular clearness, because they
were made from exactly transverse and very thin sections (cf. fig. 113). The
primary wall was nevertheless but very rarely visible, because, as a rule, it was
too thin and did not light up sufficiently to be distinguishable from the S_1 layer.

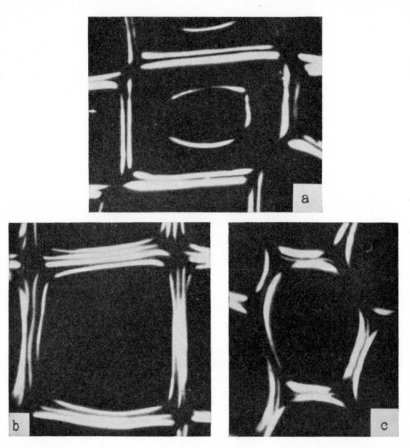

Fig. 113. Transverse sections seen between crossed nicols, of a: a summer-wood tracheid,
and b: a spring-wood tracheid of *Trochodendron aralioides;* c: fibre tracheid of *Myodocarpus
simplicifolius.* They all show bright S_1 and S_3 layers, whereas the S_2 layer and the middle
lamella are isotropic. In c, traces of the faintly birefringent primary wall can be seen (from
KERR and BAILEY, 1934).

PRESTON (1934), and other authors too, rightly argued that this optical behaviour does not really prove the classical conception of a wall consisting of
three layers, two with a gently sloping spiral and one with a steep spiral, and
that it tells us nothing at all with regard to the sign of the spirals. He points
out that if the angular dispersion normal to the plane of the wall was greater
among the micelles of the S_2 layer than among those of the two other layers, the

optical behaviour of the wall would be as is actually found, even if the speed of the spiral in the three layers did not differ at all. This possibility was more attractive to him, because of his supposition that the greater steepness of the structure in the longer fibres was the result of a stronger extension of a spiral whose speed in the beginning did not differ from that in the shorter fibres. This hypothesis, obviously is irreconcilable with the presence of spirals with different speed and with different sign in the same wall. As we have already pointed out in our discussion of the structure of the phloem fibres, the observations of the older microscopists on the occurrence of such spirals, were not sufficiently taken into consideration. In a later publication PRESTON (1947) recognized that his hypothesis was untenable.

The investigations of PRESTON and his collaborators on wood elements have nevertheless exercized a beneficial influence, as they have provided us with a number of exact data; these authors, moreover, have developed some useful methods of investigation.

It was, for instance, PRESTON (1934) who introduced a method by the aid of which in isolated fibres single walls could be studied. To this end he glued the fibres to a glass slide, and scraped the upper wall away by means of a microtome knife; in this way it was possible to estimate the direction of the extinction in the remaining wall, and so the orientation of the cellulose micelles in the predominating S_2 layer could be determined. However, as we have pointed out in our discussion of the wall structure of the phloem fibres, it seems to occur that, at least with long flexible fibres, an unintended twist of the cells spoils the results. In the tracheids of *Pinus* it is not necessary to scrape the upper wall away, as the opposite one can here be observed through one of the large half-bordered pits, but in many instances PRESTON'S method has proved its usefulness.

Other valuable additions to our methodology are his demonstration of the successive deposition of cell-wall layers by comparing the values found for the birefringence in the walls of fibres in successive stages of development, and especially the calculation of the mean angular dispersion by means of the values obtained for the birefringence in transverse and longitudinal sections (carried out for bamboo fibres by PRESTON and SINGH, 1950, and for wood parenchyma by WARDROP and DADSWELL, 1952a).

WARDROP has further introduced a most elegant method for estimating the direction and the angle of the spiral in the successive layers of the wall by measuring the birefringence in a series of oblique sections (WARDROP and PRESTON, 1947 and 1951). In this way in the tracheids of *Picea excelsa* for the S_1 and S_2 layers, angles of 50° and 18° were found, and in the tracheids of *Nothofagus cunninghami* angles of 60—90° and 10°. Although these results were a confirmation of a part of the classical interpretation of the wall structure, they apparently still did not accept the other part, viz. the alternation of an S- and a Z-spiral.

In X-ray diagrams of wood the orientation of the cellulose crystallites in the S_2-layer is clearly shown, but their orientation in the S_1 and S_3 layers is shown not at all or only indistinctly. This was the reason why PRESTON (1934) thought that the orientation in the last-named layers would be the same as in S_2. BAILEY and BERKLEY (1942), however, did observe meridional interferences which they ascribed to the S_1 and S_3 layers, and this conclusion, although rejected by PRESTON (1946), was reaffirmed by BERKLEY and WOODYARD (1948). The controversy was settled by WARDROP (1952a, 1954b), who stated that normal wide-angle X-ray diagrams usually do not give unmistakable evidence of the presence or absence of these layers, but that their presence can be demonstrated with more certainty by the aid of the small-angle scattering method.

The ordinary procedure of X-ray analysis proved to be very useful for estimating the average steepness of the spirals in various kinds of wood and in successive annual rings. With this method it could be proved that as already mentioned, the steepness increases towards the periphery of the stem, that the tangential walls have a steeper structure than the radial ones, and that compression wood shows more gently sloping spirals and tension wood steeper ones.

The three-ply structure with alternating orientation of the micelles in the successive layers has been fully confirmed in recent years by *the study of these walls by means of the electron microscope* and by supplementary observations by the aid of older methods to which we will return in our discussion of the finer structure of the S_1, S_2 and S_3 layers. Very thin sections in which the three layers can be recognized by means of the electron microscope, have been made by RIBI (1953) through fibres of *Ochroma* and *Populus*, by WARDROP and DADS-

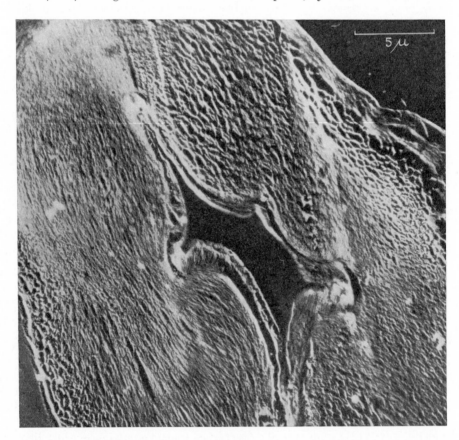

Fig. 114. Oblique section of a partly delignified tracheid of *Pinus radiata*, showing the three-ply structure of the wall and the helical orientation of the S_2 layer (from FREI et al., 1957).

WELL (1957) through fibres of *Eucalyptus,* and by the last-named investigators
as well as by FREI et al. (1957) through tracheids of *Pinus.* Fig. 114 shows a
section through the last-named object in an oblique direction, in which the S_1
and S_3 are recognizable as separate layers, and in which the pieces cut off from
the microfibrils in the S_2 layer appear to be longer on the left than on the right,
which proves that the microfibrils are arranged in a spiral.

In fig. 115 a schematical drawing is given of the three-layered structure that
has been found in the tracheids of by far the greater part of the *Conifereae,* and
very often also in the secondary wall of the wood fibres of deciduous trees. The
crossed structure of the S_1 layer will be discussed further on, and then we will
mention also various exceptions, e. g. the presence of strata with different orientation in the S_2 layer, the occasional absence of the S_3 layer, and the fact that
reaction wood falls outside this pattern. In tracheids the S-Z-S-helical structure
is regarded by various authors as the normal one (cf. e. g. NAEGELI, 1864; DIP-
PEL and SONNTAG as to the S_2 layer; and to quote more recent publications:
PRESTON, 1947; BUCHER, 1957b; MEIER, 1957; EMERTON and GOLDSMITH,
1956). However, already in the older literature the occasional occurrence of
tracheids with different helical structures among those with the ordinary
structure has been mentioned, and this has recently been confirmed by BU-
CHER (l. c.). A reversal of the sequence, i. e. a Z-S-Z helical structure seems to
be a normal condition in *Pinus radiata* (WARDROP and DADSWELL, 1957; WAR-
DROP, 1957a, FREI et al., 1957).

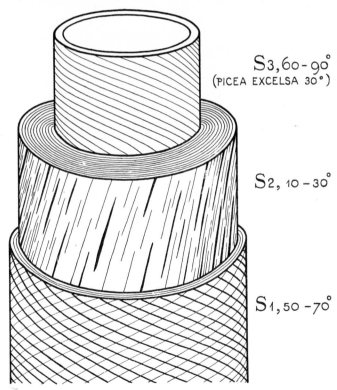

S3, 60-90°
(PICEA EXCELSA 30°)

S2, 10-30°

S1, 50-70°

Fig. 115. Schema of the orientation of the cellulose microfibrils in the normal three-ply
structure of fibres and tracheids.

When *Pinus* tracheids were subjected by EMERTON (1955) to the twist-test, the result indicated the presence of a predominating Z-structure.

Our own observations on the behaviour in polarized light too seem to confirm the view of the presence of a predominating Z-structure for the tracheids of *Pinus* and *Picea* and for the wood fibres of *Populus*. However, as pointed out in section 212, this conclusion is invalid in case there are more than one wall layers with a sufficiently strong double refringence. The same optical behaviour is found e. g. in the wall of the cotton hair in parts in which the S_2 layer shows an S-spiral. This is due to the fact that the S_1 layer with its Z-spiral is so thick that it acts as a separate birefringent film. The S_1 layer of the hemp fibre acts presumably in the same way. In tracheids and wood fibres the S_1 layer, however, is thinner, has a crossed structure, and is much more transversely oriented, whereas the spiral of the S_2 is steeper than that in the wall of the cotton hair. It is therefore not probable that the S_1 of these elements will act as a separate birefringent layer; in the fibres of the Monocotyledones it does not act in this way either.

23432. The S_1 layer

As was mentioned already in our discussion of the wall structure of the phloem fibres, it was originally thought that the different striations that are normally observed under the microscope, were situated in the same layer. Already round the year 1880, however, it was found out that these striations belonged to the S_1 and the S_2 layers. More recently, however, it appeared that actually two different striations may be present in the S_1 layer, although it seems undeniable that only one of these two striations, viz. the predominating one, can have been seen by the microscopists and that therefore the view of those who maintained that the different striations that actually were observed belonged to different layers, was correct. We will discuss the publications regarding the detailed structure of the S_1 layer in chronological sequence.

The first indications of a crossed structure of the S_1 were found in the electron-micrographs of HODGE and WARDROP (1950) which showed fragments of disintegrated and delignified tracheids of *Pseudotsuga taxifolia*. They agreed more or less with the picture shown in fig. P 116, the two directions in which the microfibrils are oriented, forming an angle of circ. 110°. The authors were not quite certain whether these microfibrils belonged to the S_1 layer or perhaps to a combination either of this layer or of the S_3 with part of the S_2. BOSSHARD (1952) too saw fragments with such a structure, viz. in fibres of *Fraxinus excelsior*, cf. fig. P 116, but he too could not make out to what part of the wall these fragments belonged. He saw so many of them that he was inclined to think that the whole S_2 layer consists of such layers with alternating orientation, a supposition which, in our opinion, is irreconcilable with the optical isotropism which is seen in transverse sections of this layer.

In subsequent studies carried out by WARDROP (1954 d; see also WARDROP and DADSWELL, 1955) it was proved that the fragments were part of the S_1 layer, for it appeared that similar fragments could be obtained also from the wall of young fibres in which the other layers were not yet developed.

Crossed structures were found in the wall of young tracheids of *Alstonia spathulata* too, but in this case they formed broad flat bundles recurring at regular intervals (fig. P117).

MEIER (1955) studied wood fibres of *Betula verrucosa* that had been exposed for some months to the attacks of fungi, and noticed that the S_1 and the S_3

layers were better preserved than the S_2 layer, and that the S_1 layer showed a conspicuous crossed structure. It appeared moreover that one of the two directions often prevailed; both included an angle of 40–55° with the longitudinal axis; the thickness of the whole layer amounted to 0.1–0.2μ.

In the tracheids of *Picea excelsa* too the S_1 layer proved to be more resistant than the S_2 layer, and showed another orientation of the microfibrils, but the number of observations was too small to allow a definite conclusion. SVENSSON (1956) found in replicas made from the wall of these tracheids obliquely oriented microfibrils (arranged in a Z-spiral with an angle of 50–80°), but he saw no crossed structure.

Shortly after these electron microscopical observations had been published, it appeared that the crossed structure of the S_1 layer can under definite circumstances also be seen by the aid of the light microscope (EMERTON and GOLDSMITH, 1956; EMERTON, 1957a, 1957b; WARDROP, 1957b).

EMERTON studied tracheids of two *Pinus* species. These tracheids had been isolated by means of a sulphate pulping process, and they were subsequently beaten for a short time with the result that the outer layers of the cell-wall were partly detached, although they often still adhered to the rest of the wall. The primary wall could easily be distinguished, and it showed, like the S_1 layer, a tendency to separate itself cleanly from the rest of the wall. After these detached fragments of the outer layers had been dried, they were metal shadowed obliquely, and studied by means of a reflecting microscope (illumination from above). By the aid of this technique inegalities of the surface are strongly accentuated, and in this case the crossed structure of the S_1 layer became clearly recognizable, cf. fig. P 118. The angle between the two spirals was on the average 126°, which is somewhat more than the value that had been measured by other investigators in hardwood tracheids. The angle itself proved to be bisected by the cell axis. The whole layer had a mean thickness of 0.15μ (in dry and delignified condition), and one of the striations proved to be more conspicuous than the other one; there were also indications that they occurred in separate lamellae.

When dry, the detached fragments often exhibited conspicuous markings in the axial direction, and originally (1957a) the latter were regarded as axially oriented bundles of microfibrils, such as often occur at the cell edges, but later EMERTON (1957b) admitted that they might be folds, and ascribed their origin to the shrinking the wall had undergone when it was dried. In our opinion it is indeed likely that the folds arise at the cell edges, for if a prismatic tube is cut open and flattened, the deformation of the cell-wall proves to be strongest at the cell edges. Another striking feature of the fragments are the dentate margins, the sides of the teeth running parallel to the direction of the two sets of microfibrils. Fragments of the primary wall and of the S_2 layer showed an entirely different margin.

WARDROP (1957b) too could see the crossed structure of the S_1 layer quite well under the microscope, viz. if the fragment had been stained with congo-red and if it was then studied in polarized light or between crossed nicols, fig. P 119.

A more extensive study of the fragments by means of the electron microscope has led WARDROP to the conclusion that the S_1 layer does not consist simply of an interwoven structure of crossed microfibrils or bands of microfibrils, but that it is composed of four layers arranged in two pairs differing in the thickness of the fibrillar bundles. This structure is schematically shown in fig. 120.

In the thinner fragments, which were probably split off from the thicker ones by the mechanical treatment, a fine grid of microfibril bundles, each about 600 Å in width is shown; the bundles in this lamella, which presumably was deposited immediately after the primary wall, intersect at an angle of circ. 80° (and 100°), each set including with the cell axis an angle of circ. 50°, cf. fig. P121a. In thicker wall fragments this fine grid proved to be overlain by a

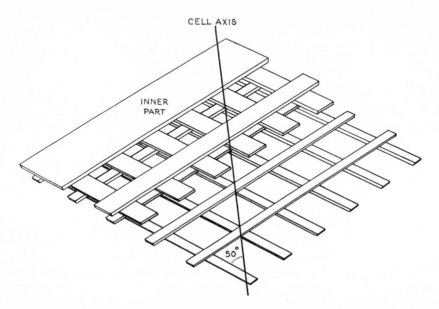

Fig. 120. Model of the S_1 layer from the wall of a tracheid of *Pinus radiata*, showing four lamellae arranged in two parallel grids, the lower one, which consists of the finer bundles, lying on the outside. The upper grid, which therefore lies on the inside, consists of thicker bundles, and of this grid the uppermost stratum may form a complete lamella. The cell axis bisects the angle of circ. 100° at which the two spirals cross each other (adapted from WARDROP 1957b).

coarser one, consisting of bundles with a diameter of 2000–3000 Å arranged parallel to the bundles of the finer grid. Sometimes only one of the systems of coarse bundles was present, cf. fig. P121b, and sometimes the innermost system of bundles formed a well-defined lamella; such a lamella is shown in the upper part of the model reproduced in fig. 120.

The bundles with a diameter of 600 Å are in contrast to those with a diameter of 2000 Å not distinguishable by the aid of the ordinary microscope. The crossed structure visible in figs. P118 and P119 must be due to the latter. The fact that one of the spirals usually predominates, explains why the older microscopists saw but one of them.

That the bundles of microfibrils with different orientation are actually forming separate lamellae, was confirmed by electron micrographs of very thin tangential sections through the same tracheids, which we owe to FREI et al. (1957), cf. fig. P122. At A and C the various orientations in the S_1 layer are recognizable, whereas at B the S_2 layer is shown. In this case the cell axis includes an angle of circ. 65° with each of the spirals in the S_1 layer.

The structure of the S_1 layer that was found in the instances mentioned in the preceding paragraphs, probably returns in its main features in the tracheids of other Conifers and in the wood fibres of other Dicotyledones.

Noteworthy is the behaviour observed by WARDROP (1957b) in shrinking or expanding fragments of the S_1 layer. If such fragments are allowed to dry out, the shrinking appears to be confined to the axial direction; in the transverse direction there is, curiously enough, a dilatation. If water was added, these changes were reversed. This behaviour, which never before had been observed in cell-walls, reminds one of the change that is observed in the shape of a true grid or of a piece of wicker work when these are subjected to a deformation in one direction. It indicates that the crossing points of the bundles act more or less as hinges, and that the bundles themselves possess a certain rigidity. That the crossing points would act as hinges, might have been expected, and needs no further comment, but with regard to the rigidity of the bundles the question may be raised whether the latter may be ascribed to the cellulose itself or whether it is due to the presence of lignin remnants.

As was discussed in section 211 the phenomenon of the *ballooning of fibres* that are swollen in suitable agents may be taken as an indication that there is an outer layer with a predominantly transverse orientation. Often this is the primary wall. Tracheids and wood fibres show the phenomenon provided they are delignified to a lignin content of less than 8 %.

Regarding the ballooning of Conifer tracheids, however, already BAILEY & KERR (1935) supposed that it is not the primary wall but the S_1 layer which is responsible for the constrictions that cause the ballooning. This supposition was confirmed by WARDROP and DADSWELL (1950), EMERTON (1957) and BUCHER (1955, 1957a). In tracheids that had been treated with a metachromatic stain which gives the primary wall and the S_3 layer a blue colour and the S_1 and S_2 layers a red one, BUCHER noted that the primary wall is, as a rule, split length-wise and thrown off. The S_1 layer is broken up in cylinders which subsequently are rolled back into the rings that are responsible for the constrictions between the beads formed by the swollen S_2 layer, cf. fig. P123. In the first of BUCHER'S two papers, fine coloured photographs of the phenomenon are given. The displacement of the S_1 layer towards the rings indicates in our opinion that the connection between the S_1 and S_2 is not strong.

With regard to the location of the balloons along the tracheids STEENBERG (1947) observed that they usually develop at places where a dislocation has taken place.

The structure of the S_1 layer evidently shows a greater resemblance to that of the primary wall, which may also consist of lamellae and in which more or less similar crossed structures have been observed (figs. P58, P60, P72, P83, P84, P90b, P92; cf. also SCOTT et al., 1956), than to the S_2 layer in which such structures have never been found. Its chemical constitution is probably also transitional, since the amounts of lignin and of hemicellulose are known to decrease progressively from the primary wall to the S_2 layer, whereas the amount of cellulose at the same time increases.

As mentioned in section 231, these considerations induced MEIER (1955) to propose for the S_1 layer the term "transition lamella" (Übergangslamelle). WARDROP (1957a), although he has objections against the use of the term "transition lamella", has suggested that the S_1 layer may be intermediary between the primary wall and the S_2 also in another respect; in his opinion the crossed structure might be due to the persistence of some surface growth after the deposition of the layers.

23433. The S_2 layer

The most conspicuous difference in the structure of the S_2 layer on the one hand and that of the primary wall and the S_1 layer on the other, is found in the greater compactness of the cellulose and in the far more perfectly parallel orientation of the microfibrils. This explains why with the aid of the electron microscope only detached fragments of this layer and replicas can be studied; the rare microfibrils that in the electron micrographs appear to be non-oriented, have doubtless been detached during the treatment with mechanical and chemical agents (fig. 22).

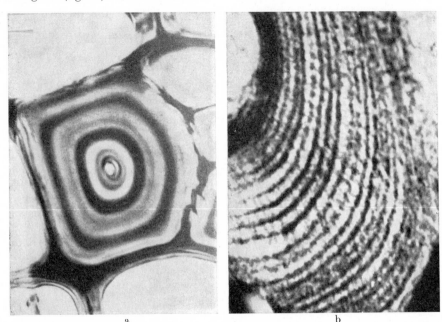

a   b

Fig. 124. Transverse sections through fibre tracheids of *Siparuna bifida* stained with haematoxylin showing lamellae in the S_2 layer; a: with the carbohydrates still present, and b: after the latter had been removed with 72% sulphuric acid (from BAILEY and KERR, 1935).

The fact that the S_2 layer of tracheids and wood fibres consists, just as in the phloem fibres and in the perivascular fibres, of several lamellae, was discovered already long ago by the microscopists (cf. e. g. STRASBURGER, 1882). The most striking pictures of this lamellar structure are nevertheless those published by BAILEY and KERR (1935, 1937). It looks as if this structure is due to alternating changes in the lignin content, and therefore also in the cellulose content, as the lamellae become more numerous and more clearly distinguishable if, after removal of the cellulose, the lignin is stained, or if, after the lignin has been removed, the cellulose is allowed to swell and then stained, figs. 124 and 125. If by the aid of fig. 125, the original thickness of the lamellae is calculated, we arrive at a value of circ. 600 Å, which makes it clear that the lamellae observed before the swelling must have consisted of a considerable number of thinner lamellae.

TRAYNARD et al. (1952, 1954) observed that in transverse sections of wood of *Populus, Picea excelsa* and several other species that are delignified and then swollen slightly, a number of separate lamellae are formed in what presumably is the S_2 layer. There are usually three lamellae, but in the thick walls of the summer wood of some species there may be more of them. They believe that prior to the delignification these layers were separated by lamellae, that con-

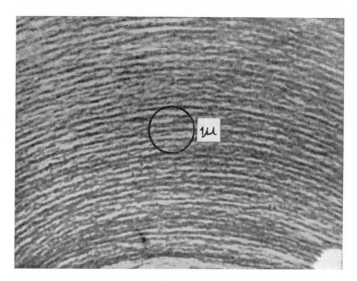

Fig. 125. Transverse section through a delignified tracheid of *Pinus*, swollen with cuprammonium and stained with congo-red; the encircled part had in the original cell-wall a thickness of 1μ (from BAILEY, 1938).

sisted mainly of lignin, but this in our view is not proved by their observations; the separate lamellae might also have arisen as a result either of lamellar differences in structure of the cellulose or of the degree of coherence between chemically and structurally identical lamellae.

There might of course be very thin lignin-rich and cellulose-poor lamellae, such as those visible in fig. 125, but the lignin-rich lamellae, postulated by TRAYNARD et al., should have been detectable in the sections before delignification, like the ones depicted in fig. 124. This, they obviously are not.

Although concentric structures are the rule in tracheids and wood fibres, radial ones are also met with, even in objects that usually show a concentric structure, cf. fig. 126. In the older literature too radial structures have repeatedly been mentioned.

That the successive S_2 lamellae alternately light up and remain dark between crossed nicols, is but rarely observed in transverse sections of tracheids or wood fibres. BAILEY and KERR (1935) report that they have seen it in the wood fibres of *Flacourtiaceae*, where they ascribe it to an alternation of layers consisting of cellulose and of non-cellulose, whereas in other instances, e. g. in the fibre tracheids of *Myodocarpus* (fig. 127), it would be due to differences in the orientation of the cellulose, but neither for this view nor for the other one proofs are produced. Thinner (perhaps younger) walls of *Myodocarpus* seem to be of a more simple structure, cf. fig. 113c.

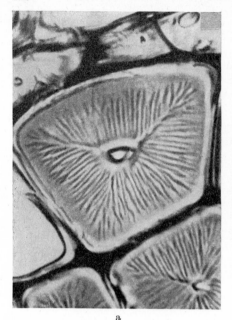
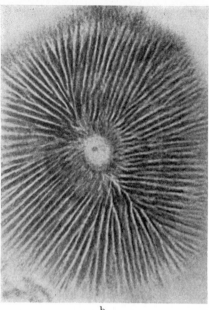

a   b

Fig. 126. Transverse sections through fibre tracheids of *Siparuna bifida;* a: stained with haematoxylin; b: delignified, swollen and stained with congo-red (from BAILEY and KERR, 1935).

RIBI (1953) saw no lamellar structure in electron micrographs of sections through wood fibres of *Ochroma lagopus* and of *Populus tremuloides,* but WAR-DROP and DADSWELL (1957) were more successful with wood fibres of *Eucalyptus,* and the lamellae are very conspicuous in the electron micrographs of transverse sections through tracheids of *Pinus radiata* published by FREI et al. (1957), cf. fig. 128, and of *Pinus rigida* by LIESE (1958), cf. fig. 129.

In fig. 128 it looks as if the microfibrils in the successive lamellae differ in orientation, but the authors rightly remark that this may be due to an upsetting of the microfibrils after the removal of the methacrylate used for embedding the specimen prior to cutting the sections. The impression that there was originally an alternation of lamellae with cellulose and other ones without cellulose, need not be correct, as the lamellar structure might be due to a swelling of the wall in the methracrylate, a phenomenon which is often met with.

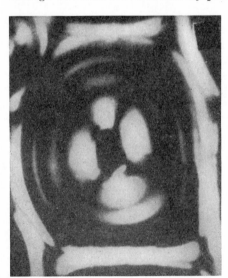

Fig. 127. Transverse section through a fibre tracheid of *Myodocarpus simplicifolius* seen between crossed nicols; the lamellar structure is said to be due to differences in the orientation of the cellulose (from BAILEY and KERR, 1935).

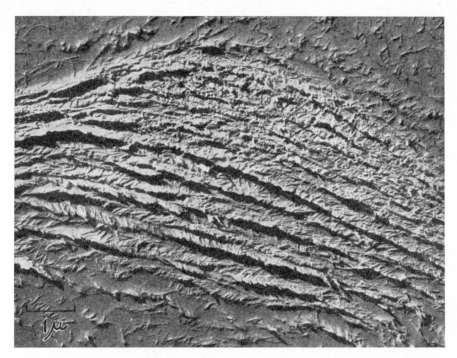

Fig. 128. Transverse section through the S_2 layer of a delignified tracheid of *Pinus radiata*, showing lamellar structure (from FREI et al., 1957).

The lamellar structure of the S_2 layer is especially well shown in fig.129. Some of the lamellae appear to have a thickness of only 300 Å, and as only part of the whole set of lamellae is shown, this proves that the number of the latter must be very considerable. The lamellae and the interlamellar layers obviously differ in chemical constitution. Although of the nature of these differences nothing is known, it seems likely that layers containing much cellulose and little hemicellulose and lignin, alternate with layers containing little cellulose and much hemicellulose and lignin.

According to LIESE (1. c.) the replicas obtained from tangential sections of the S_2 layer show quite clearly that the microfibrils in different lamellae may differ in orientation.

Various investigators (SVENSSON, 1956; WARDROP and DADSWELL, 1957) noted in the replicas made from the surface of delignified tracheids and wood fibres rather conspicuous wrinkles or folds. According to the last-named authors they run more or less in the longitudinal direction, which means that they run parallel to the microfibrils in the S_2 layer. Similar wrinkles were observed in the wall of cotton hairs, and here they were studied in more detail. It appeared that the latter arise as a result of the shrinkage during the desiccation to which the hairs were subjected, and that they do not run parallel to the cellulose microfibrils in the S_2 layer, but to those in the S_1. On account of the delignification the shrinkage in the wall of the tracheids will be stronger than in that of the cotton hairs.

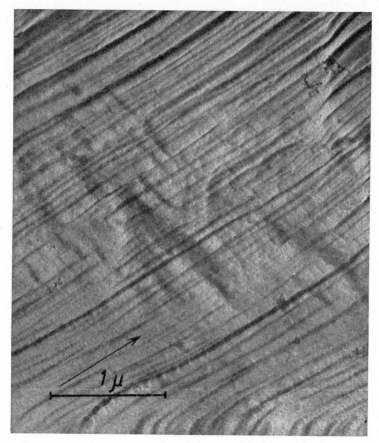

Fig. 129. Electron micrograph of a replica made of a longitudinal section through the wall of a tracheid from *Pinus rigida* (obtained from Liese, 1958).

23434. The S_3 layer

Already more than a century ago it was known to Hartig and to von Mohl that the innermost layer of the cell-wall showed, e. g. in certain wood elements, a chemical behaviour which differed from that observed in the rest of the cell-wall, and that it possessed a spiral structure with a different direction. Hartig thought that this layer acted as the matrix of the cell-wall, but since Stras-burger pointed out that this function appertains to the ectoplasm, this hypothesis has found no further support.

That Dippel studied the birefringence of this layer in transverse sections of tracheids and fibres, and confirmed along this way the view that it possesses a spiral structure with a rather low speed, has already been reported in section 23431. It has since Dippel's time been observed by several other authors, and although for a time the birefringence was explained in a different way, it can now no longer be doubted that normal tracheids and wood fibres possess, with some rare exceptions, an S_3 layer with a rather flat spiral structure and with a different chemical composition.

In recent years the microscopical study of the S_3 layer showed a revival. This was due to the accurate observations and the especially beautiful micrographs obtained by BUCHER (1953, 1955, 1957a, 1957b) by the aid of the phase-contrast microscope. This author (1953) also gives a critical survey of the older literature on the S_3 layer. He studied in the main, tracheids of *Coniferae*, which he delignified, after which he applied a special stain which at the same time enhanced the resistance of the cellulose to some extent; finally he treated them with diluted cupric-ethylene-diamine, in which the S_2 layer was for the greater part dissolved; as the dissolution was preceded by a swelling ,this temporarily led to the well-known ballooning. The S_3 layer too loses part of its cellulose, and as it has to follow the movement of the contracting tracheid, it is laid in undulating folds. However, according to BUCHER it does not decrease in length, and the speed of the spiral structure, which owing to the staining stands out very clearly, can therefore still be measured, fig. 130. In different tracheids and in different species the spiral differs very considerably in its nature and in steepness; there are open spirals, coiled spirals and complex systems.

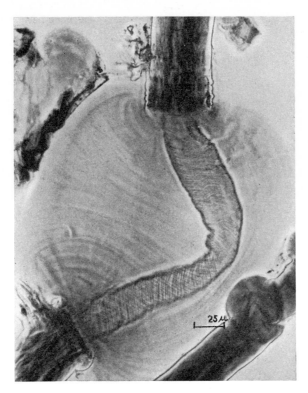

Fig. 130. Flat S-spiral structure in the S_3 layer of a tracheid of *Picea excelsa* (from BUCHER, 1957*b*).

Especially in dark-coloured, resiniferous woods such as those of *Pinus* and *Larix*, he noted the presence of another kind of S_3 layer, viz. a structure less hyaline tube which reminds one of the gelatinous layer that is found in the fibres of the anomalous tension wood of the *Angiospermae*. However, as such gelatinous layers are found neither in the ordinary wood nor in the reaction wood of the *Coniferae*, these two types of layers are probably not directly comparable, cf. fig. 131.

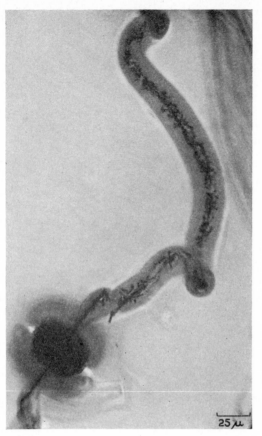

25 μ

Fig. 131. Structure less S₃ layer in a tracheid of *Pinus insignis* (from BUCHER, 1957a).

The value found for the spiral angle, which on account of the swelling may have been on the high side, varied in *Pseudotsuga, Abies, Pinus, Larix* and *Picea canadensis* between 60° and 89°. In the wider tracheids of *Picea excelsa* the same value was found, but in the narrower ones the angle measured only circ. 30°, and as in transverse sections the innermost part of the wall would not show birefringence, it has sometimes been assumed that in this species the S₃ layer is absent (WARDROP and DADSWELL, 1957). In most cases the S₃ layer possesses, as a rule, an S-spiral, although Z-spirals too have occasionally been observed.

One other observation made by BUCHER (1953, 1957a), deserves special attention, viz. that the S₃ layer extends in the bordered pits over the inside of the overhanging margin, where it is therefore in contact with the primary wall, fig. 132. Although it is, in our opinion, not quite excluded that the resemblance between the layer covering the inside of the overhanging margin and the S₃ is due to postmortal etching of this part of the wall, this does not look very probable.

That the spiral structure of the S₃ is less steep than that of the S₂ has been confirmed by means of the electron microscope for the tracheids of *Pinus radiata*, viz. by FREI et al., (1957), fig. 133.

Judging from the birefringence observed in transverse sections, in the wood fibres of deciduous trees too an S₃ layer is regularly present, although the flat spiral structure of this layer has but rarely been observed (e. g. by RUNKEL, 1942). Its presence has usually been deduced from the birefringence observed at this place in transverse sections. This layer too may sometimes be structureless (BUCHER, 1953).

In *Betula*, according to MEIER (1955), the S₃ layer would possess a nearly axial structure, but as it dissolves more slowly in cellulose solvents and as it shows a greater resistence against the attacks of fungi (cf. fig. 21) it nevertheless would have to be regarded as a distinct layer, for which he used the term "tertiary wall". As pointed out in one of the preceding sections, we agree with WARDROP and DADSWELL (1957) that it is not allowed to regard such a layer as homologous with the S₃, as it is quite possible that it belongs to the S₂, and owes its aberrant chemical character to postmortal changes in the part of the S_2 layer which is contiguous to the cell-lumen.

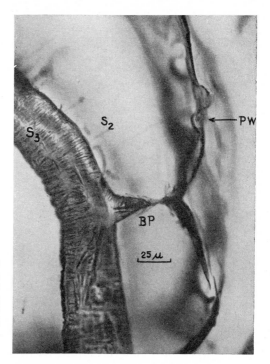

Fig. 132. S_3 layer in the wall of a tracheid from a Conifer; it shows a flat spiral structure, and extends over the inner face of the overhanging margin of a bordered pit (BP), where it is in contact with the primary wall (PW); S_2 layer swollen, (BUCHER, 1953).

WARDROP and DADSWELL (l. c.) further warn against the danger of relying on the reaction to stains and on the chemical resistance ,because with these criteria cytoplasm rests too may be mistaken for an S_3 layer.

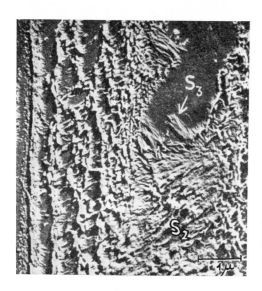

Fig. 133. Oblique section through a partly delignified tracheid of *Pinus radiata*, showing that the orientation in the S_3 is different from that in the S_2 (from FREI et al., 1957).

Various investigators have made replicas from the entirely *untreated surface of the S_3 layer*. Everywhere where microfibrils were visible, the flat spiral structure was confirmed. The clearest micrographs are those that were published by LIESE and his collaborators (1953, 1954, 1957a). These papers also contain a survey of the other literature. In some species the surface appears to be smooth with traces of microfibrils bending round the bordered pits, fig. P134.

This surface is sometimes covered by a thin film which does not contain microfibrils and which is easily detached; in various species it shows a varying pattern consisting of larger and smaller lumps, figs. P135 and 136.

This "warty" structure seems to be characteristic for distinct species, and occurs among the *Coniferae* as well as among the *Dicotyledones* (LIESE, 1957b). The warts themselves are visible under the ordinary microscope too. The chemical constitution of this layer is still unknown; so far, we know only that it does not dissolve in hot water and in aceton. It is not excluded that it is a post-mortal deposit from the cell contents or from the water that is transported through these elements.

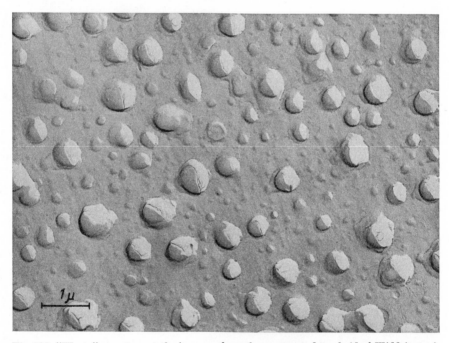

Fig. 136. "Warty" structure at the inner surface of an untreated tracheid of *Widdringtonia dracomontana* (LIESE, 1957a).

That in certain species the "warty" structure was found to extend over the inner side of the overhanging margin of the bordered pits, as is shown in fig. P137, is in agreement with the observations of BUCHER (1953, 1957a) according to which the whole S_3 layer too extends over the inner side of the margin, fig. 132.

Fig. P137 also shows that the overhanging margin of the bordered pit possesses on the inside a circular structure. As it does not possess such a structure on the outside (figs. P134 and P135), and as optically the circular structure clearly predominates, the layer with the circular structure on the inner side of the margin must be much thicker than the layer on its outside. As was found out already long ago, the whole overhanging margin is part of the secondary wall.

It further appears that the *pit membrane* is provided with large radially oriented perforations which are separated from each other by bundles of micro-fibrils; by means of these bundles the torus is suspended in the middle of the membrane, (LIESE l. c.; HARADA et al., 1958; CÔTÉ, 1958). This structure had already been suggested by BAILEY in 1913. Other investigators thought that their electron micrographs proved that no perforations were present, but this conclusion has since then been withdrawn (BOSSHARD, 1956a). Only in young tracheids the pit membrane is as yet unperforated, cf. section 2273. The membranes of full-grown half-bordered pits of Conifers and of simple and bordered pits of hardwoods likewise appear to be imperforate (HARADA et al., 1958; CÔTÉ, 1958).

Fig. P137 shows not only in the overhanging margin but also in the torus a circular structure. In the latter it is already present before the cell has completed its growth, fig P78, and the deposition of microfibrils continues during the development of the secondary wall; in that phase of its development the edge undergoes a thickening, fig. P138.

The idea that the S_3 layer would be deposited in another way than the S_2 layer, has from the beginning found advocates and opponents; the latest hypothesis as to its origin is that of MEIER (cf. TREIBER, 1957: 215).

23435. Reaction wood

As reaction wood is an anomalous kind of wood, we will confine our exposition of its peculiarities to a few notes.

In *Gymnosperms* it is compression wood, so called because it occurs mainly on the lower side of branches and bent stems. It is here also known as red wood (Rotholz), as it has a darker colour. In *Angiosperms* it is called tension wood, as it occurs especially on the upper side of bent stems. There is an extensive literature dealing with the development and with the special properties of this kind of wood.

In compression wood the secondary wall has no S_3 layer, the spiral structure is very flat, and striations are, as a rule, very pronounced and have already been depicted in the oldest literature on wood microscopy. It contains more lignin and less cellulose than ordinary wood does.

Tension wood has in recent times especially been studied by WARDROP and DADSWELL (1955). Here the layers S_1, S_2 and S_3 may all three be present, but S_3 and even both S_3 and S_2 may also be absent. On the inside we find almost always a remarkably thick layer of an aberrant character. This is the so-called gelatinous layer. It is not lignified and contains little hemicellulose; the cellulose is always axially oriented, and seems to have an unusually high degree of crystallinity and a relatively low degree of polymerization. As this layer stains with chlor-zinc-iodine and with other cellulose reagents, and as it has, on account of the high cellulose content, a high refractive index, it is a suitable means for recognizing tension wood.

2344. Epidermal cells

23441. The cotton hair

Among the epidermal cells as well as among the industrial "fibres", there is not one whose cell-wall structure is so well known as that of the cotton hair. It

should be realized, however, that the latter has a very peculiar structure which
so far has been seen nowhere else, so that it can certainly not be regarded as a
characteristic example of a plant hair. The literature dealing with this object has
extensively been surveyed, but in our opinion not very critically, by FLINT
(1950). We will discuss the literature under the various headings in chronological sequence.

Microscopy

Already in 1864 NAEGELI had noted that the wall of cotton hairs, if it had
been swollen by a treatment with sulphuric acid, shows the well-known ballooning, cf. fig. 26, and that in the swollen parts two sets of crossing striations may
be detected. The striations belonging to the outer set, which were already
distinguishable before the swelling, were said to include a larger angle with the
cell axis than those of the inner set. The latter would make an angle of 25°
with the axis, a value which agrees remarkably well with recent estimations.
The two sets of striations were usually arranged in spirals with an opposite direction. NAEGELI also noted that the sets of spirals can be followed over some
distance and that both of them then undergo at the same time a reversal, a
procedure that is repeated at irregular intervals. He gave a drawing of such a
reversal, which shows that at this place the striations are over a small distance
axially oriented. He also mentioned the fact that the dry cotton hairs are flat
and twisted, and that the direction in which they are twisted, changes at the
places where the direction of the spirals is reversed, although his remark that
the direction of the twist is always opposite to the direction of the predominating striation spirals, fig. 139a, is a mistake; in reality it agrees with the latter
(BALLS, 1923; DENHAM, 1923), fig. 139b. The lamellar structure of the secondary
wall too was known to NAEGELI.

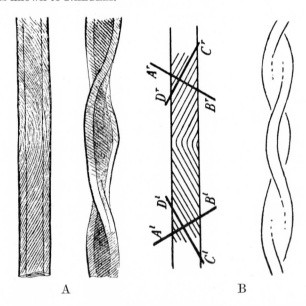

A   B

Fig. 139. Relation between the reversal of the twist and that of the predominating striation
spiral (S₁ layer), a: as indicated (erroneously, see text) by NAEGELI, and b: according to
BALLS (1923).

The twist, or convolution as it is often called, as well as the reversals in the direction of the twist, of which there may be 4–7 per mm in some varieties, are so far known from cotton hairs only. The flattening and the twist arise when the originally cylindrical hairs are dried, but they do not disappear when the dry hairs are afterwards immersed in water. Plasmolysis of living cotton hairs produces no convolution, neither did an immersion in alcohol (presumably 96%).

Our knowledge of the cell-wall structure of the cotton hair rested up to 1919 mainly on the observations made by the microscopists of the preceding century. In that year BALLS showed that the lamellae of the secondary wall are probably daily growth-rings. The first layer, which we will call the S_1 layer, is deposited as soon as the hair has completed its longitudinal growth, i. e. circ. 20 days after flowering. After that for 25 days every day a lamella with a thickness of circ. 0.4μ is deposited.

BALLS and HANCOCK (1922) and BALLS (1923) showed in contrast to NAEGELI's observation, which, however, was unknown to them, that the convolution of the hair and the reversals in the direction of the convolution are determined by the pattern of the outermost and most conspicuous spiral, viz. by the latter's direction and pitch. Their other views on the cell-wall structure, however, have been proved to be wrong. They called the outermost spiral the "pit spiral", since they believed that the striations were slit-like pits. Its angle with the cell axis varied, if the parts in which the direction is reversed are left out of consideration, from 20° to 30°, with an average of 27°. Although they gave pictures of the striations in flattened swollen hairs, they curiously enough, failed to notice that this „pit spiral" differs in direction from the spirals in the other layers of the secondary wall, which under these conditions usually are clearly visible. They stated, on the contrary, that all layers of the secondary wall follow the same pattern. As they moreover erroneously (cf. section 225) thought that they had seen in the primary wall two very flat spirals (making an angle of 70° with the cell-axis) running in opposite directions, and as they saw in the secondary wall locally similar oblique striations (so-called "slow spirals", recognized by DENHAM (1923) as dislocation markings), they assumed that one of the two flat spiral structures from the primary wall was also present, side by side with the "pit spiral", throughout the whole secondary wall! The directions of these two spirals, viz. one with very low speed and one with high speed, was invariably opposed, which is in agreement with the fact that the former is in reality a dislocation spiral.

At a later date BALLS and HANCOCK (1926) have published a detailed investigation on the steepness of the convolutions and on the number of reversals in connection with the size and with the origin of the hairs. They confirmed in this paper once more that in the same part of the wall the direction of the twist and that of the "pit spiral" always correspond. As new facts they mentioned e.g. that the torsion at the base of the hair is almost always an S-spiral, and that with a certain cotton variety always the same spiral structures and the same number of reversals are found no matter whether the plants are grown at a constant temperature and illumination or in the open. The average distance between the reversals appeared to be 0.4–0.5 mm according to the variety from which the hairs were taken.

The extensive investigation of BALLS and HANCOCK did not furnish any proof regarding the true cause of the reversals; the authors could only advance a possible one. The tips of the hairs growing in the boll are supposed to rotate owing to spiral growth and the direction of spiral growth would in some unknown way determine the orientation of the cellulose in the secondary wall that is deposited after growth has ceased. If in the writhing mass of growing hairs the rotation of a tip would be hindered by contact with a neighbouring hair, the direction of rotation would be reversed and this would later become the spot of a reversal in the secondary wall. Probably not acquainted with the work of BALLS and HANCOCK, FREY-WYSSLING (1959: 19) has supposed that the reversals result from daily periodicity in growth of the young hairs, but this hypothesis is inconsistent with the data of the first-named authors. The mean number of reversals in a hair is much greater than the number of days of growth in length and moreover the variation in distance between reversals seems too great, viz. between 0,01 and 12,7 mm.

In contrast to BALLS and HANCOCK, DENHAM (1922, 1923) observed, just as NAEGELI had done, but of this he was unaware, that the conspicuous outermost striations are not necessarily parallel to the similar though less conspicuous striations in the other layers of the secondary wall. He believed that in these layers the spirals might show different degrees of obliquity, and that their direction might in successive layers be reversed independently, but these observations were afterwards denied by other investigators. The "pit spirals" of BALLS and HANCOCK, which undoubtedly belong to the S_1 layer, are called by DENHAM "spirals of the primary wall", a striking example of the confusion that may be caused by the use of two different sets of terms for the various layers of the cell-wall. That the direction of the striations in this layer agrees with the direction of the torsion, even at the places where the latter undergoes a reversal, was, at any rate, confirmed by DENHAM.

That the originally cylindrical hairs in drying collapse and assume the well-known twisted ribbon-like shape, is due, according to DENHAM, to the presence of two preformed spiral lines of weakness that run parallel to the striations in what he calls the primary wall (the S_1 layer), and that are diametrically opposed, cf. fig. 140. As in these lines the secondary wall is thinner than at other places, they act as hinges. The twist of the flattened hair is due therefore to the spiral course of these lines of weakness, and it is clear that its direction must coincide with that of the striations in the S_1 layer.

As DENHAM in studying living young hairs had observed that the protoplasm was streaming in an oblique direction, he assumed that in these hairs, just as in the cells of *Nitella*, a stream of protoplasm half as wide as their circumference would move in an oblique direction towards the top, to return at the opposite side to the base, and that the lines of weakness would develop along the dividing lines between these two streams. However, although this is doubtless an inspiring thought, it is no more than a possibility. In the rest of the literature, remarkable enough, neither the spiral protoplasmic streaming nor the lines of weakness have been described again; in transverse sections the latter are at any rate hardly recognizable.

VAN ITERSON (1927) pointed out that the explanation of the torsion given by DENHAM is not the only one that deserves our attention. Another possibility should also be taken into consideration, viz. that it is due to the circumstance that there are two or more of the layers of the cell-wall which differ in the orientation of the cellulose micelles and therefore also in the degree of shrinkage in various directions. STEINBRINCK (1906) ascribed the torsion shown by the dehiscing valves of some capsules to such a difference in orientation, and demonstrated the action of this principle by means of a model using strips of writing paper.

In paper the fibres are not oriented at random, but have a preferential direction parallel to the movement of the wire gauze of the paper machine. This is parallel to either the long or the short edge of the writing paper. Two strips of paper are cut out parallel to the diagonal from the same sheet of paper and are moistened thoroughly. They are then glued together in such a way that the preferential fibre directions in the strips form an angle that is bisected by a line running parallel to the longer side of the double strip of paper. When the latter is dried, it proves to develop a twist, and if strips are superposed in such a way that the fibres in the lower one ascend from left bottom to right top, and in the upper one from right bottom to left top (S-overcrossing), an S-twist will be formed; in the opposite case a Z-twist arises.

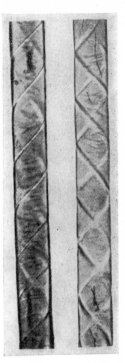

It might be objected that the two opposite walls of the cotton hair are not glued together, but this is apparently no essential condition, for the torsion can also be obtained by drying a moist paper cylinder which has an oblique fibre direction, provided the latter has previously been flattened.

Another possible objection, however, appears to be of real importance. As stated above, the twist in a cotton fibre turns always parallel to the spiral of the S_1, and we would therefore have to assume that the S_1 layer, which is merely the first of the more than 20 day-growth-rings, exercises a greater influence than the rest of these day-growth-rings together, and this notwithstanding the fact that the micelles in these layers are oriented at an angle with the axis which is but slightly smaller than that at which the micelles of the S_1 layer are oriented. This is inconceivable, and it must therefore be admitted that the direction of the torsion can not be determined exclusively by the S_1 layer.

Fig. 140. The two spiral lines of weakness in the wall of not yet collapsed cotton hairs, as observed by DENHAM (1923).

In our opinion the explanation obviously is that in each of the two opposite walls of the fibre the combination of the layers S_1 and S_2 acts in the same way as STEINBRINCK's double strip of paper. If the S_1 layer has an S-spiral, the sets in the opposite walls will both act as S-overcrossings, and hence the two opposite walls will co-operate in producing an S-twist in the fibre. If a cylinder is made of a double strip of paper prepared in the way described above, and if this cylinder then is flattened and dried, we indeed see that under these conditions the expected twist arises.

A twist does not arise if the cylinder has not previously been flattened. It seems therefore necessary that the cotton hairs too collapse, in order to twist. In fact no twist or but a slight one is to be noted in thick-walled hairs, which are circular or oval in transverse section.

That the plane in which the hair collapses, is already from the beginning spirally twisted (since the flattening is due to the spiral lines of weakness) proves not to be an essential condition. Even if this plane would at first be completely flat, the drying hair would become twisted. This follows from the behaviour of the dried paper cylinders mentioned above.

If the explanation that has been given is correct the two opposite walls would become twisted also if they were separated from each other, but this has not yet been verified. We further refer to what hereafter will be said with regard to the optical behaviour of the wall of the cotton hair.

DENHAM (1923) further describes the presence of dislocations in the wall of the cotton hair, a phenomenon that has often been observed in phloem fibres, but which in the cotton hair is far less conspicuous. They may already be present in fresh hairs, and would owe their origin to stresses arising during growth inside the boll. The number increases considerably when dried hairs are strongly twisted. They often show a spiral shape, more or less like the blade of a screw-propeller. The beaded pits which were observed by MOSENTHAL at an earlier occasion, are according to DENHAM, a special kind of dislocations. In fig. P 147 a fragment of the wall is seen, in which the microfibrils show a change in direction which MÜHLETHALER (1949b) ascribes to a dislocation in the fibre, but which might in our view as well be a dislocation in the fragment only. At the surface of the wall dislocations appear in the form of grooves and ribs, fig. 148.

By studying cotton hairs in oblique light falling in from above, DENHAM has probably also seen the wrinkling of the surface that was afterwards observed with greater precision in electron micrographs, cf. figs. 148, 149, 150.

SAKOSTSCHNIKOFF and KORSCHENIOVSKY (1932) were not convinced that BALLS' theory of the day-growth-rings was justified, but KERR (1937) adduced fully convincing evidence for the latter. He used very thin sections which were first swollen and then stained with congo-red, and could show that each of the circ. 25 growth-rings of BALLS, consists of two lamellae, a denser one which stains more strongly, and a less dense one which does not stain so strongly; he supposes that the first is deposited in daytime, and that the second is formed during the night. Together they are circ. 0.35μ thick, cf. fig. 27. In cotton that is grown in a glass house, the hairs take a longer time to reach full maturity, and these hairs prove to possess a larger number of rings, which, however, are thinner.

ANDERSON and MOORE (1937) and ANDERSON and KERR (1938) have shown that the growth-rings in the wall of the cotton hairs, unlike the lamellae in the wall of the collenchyma cells of this plant, fail to develop if the illumination and the temperature are kept constant, and that differences in temperature induce more conspicuous rings than differences in light intensity do. Like BALLS and HANCOCK they found that differences of this kind do not influence the spiral structure and the reversals, nor the strength of the wall, at least if a correction is made for the fact that the hairs of the glass-house plants are thinner. BARROWS (1940) found that there were no differences in the X-ray diagrams either.

Although NAEGELI (1864a) had already described two different sets of striations, and although DENHAM (1923) indicated the presence of a well-marked difference between the conspicuous striations in the outermost layer (for which he unfortunately used the term "primary wall") and those in the rest of the wall, it were ANDERSON and KERR who showed that the outermost set of striations is confined to the first day-growth-ring. They confirmed DENHAM's observation according to which the hand of the spiral in this lamella, which we call the S_1 layer, does usually but not invariably differ from that in the rest of the wall. The angle with the longitudinal axis is, as a rule, 20–30°, but may, as their figures show, increase to 45°; at the reversals it decreases, of course, to 0°.

HOCK et al. (1941) on the other hand emphasized the fact that an S-spiral in the S_1 layer is always accompanied by a Z-spiral in the next lamella, i. e.

in the outermost lamella of the S_2 layer and presumably also in all the following ones. The S_1 layer, moreover, has a coarser fibrillar structure, and the
spiral has, as a rule, a somewhat lower pitch. They called this layer the "winding layer", because of its conspicuous spiral striation. This term has since then
often been used in the American literature, but although to some extent a
telling expression, its use should not be encouraged. Unlike BARROWS (1940)
they confirmed the presence of growth-rings, and like KERR they found that
each day-growth-ring consists of two lamellae; the thickness of each pair was
estimated by them at $0.2-0.4\mu$. They further showed that the later rings are
thinner than the earlier ones, and that some of the hairs take a smaller number
of days to reach full maturity than others, so that the number of day-growth-
rings may vary between 20 and 40.

The coarse helical structure of the S_1 layer could be demonstrated very conspicuously by ROLLINS (1945) in hairs that were treated with nitrogen dioxide.
The wall of such hairs never shows
balloning, but the outermost layer is
ruptured in the form of a spiral. It appears, moreover that a sheath consisting
of the primary wall and the S_1 layer is
easily detached from the remainder of
the wall. For this reason she wished to
regard the S_1 layer as the inner part of
the primary wall. Although this is not
acceptable to us, we will see that it behaves indeed in some respects as a transitional layer.

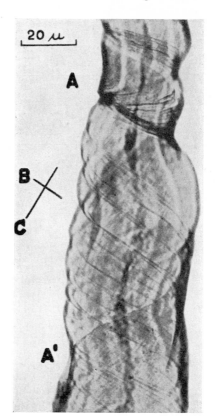

KERR (1947) could show that in
fresh hairs the primary wall may easily be shifted over the secondary wall (by
scraping). From the secondary wall
that became exposed in this way, and
in which after swelling the striation
became visible, he has made fine photographs, one of which is reproduced
in fig. 141. Here too the spiral in the
S_1 layer appears to have a lower pitch
than that in the other layers. He also
stated that the already long known
spiral-shaped swelling is due to the presence of the S_1 layer, fig. 142. This layer
is apparently split in a direction parallel to that of the microfibrils, but
whether the "spiral lines of weakness"
play a part in this process, is unknown.
The reversals of such a spirally swollen
hair appear to coincide with the reversals in the spiral structure (MANGENOT
and RAISON, 1942). KERR further confirms the earlier findings according

Fig. 141. Mature but undried cotton hair,
swollen in cuprammonium. At A and A'
the primary wall, stained with ruthenium
red, is visible; B indicates the orientation
in S_1, C that in S_2 (from KERR, 1946).

to which the direction of the spiral in the S_1 is, as a rule, opposite to that of the
spiral in the S_2, although according to him the reversals in the S_1 and in the S_2

do not always exactly coincide, so that the spirals may over a short distance run parallel to each other. According to KERR too, the spirals in the various lamellae of the S_2 would all be oriented in the same direction, but he has received the impression that they became steeper in the direction of the lumen, and although on account of the swelling his estimations of the speed can not be regarded as reliable, this remark is not entirely irrelevant, as the X-ray diagrams of dry fibres point in the same direction (see below).

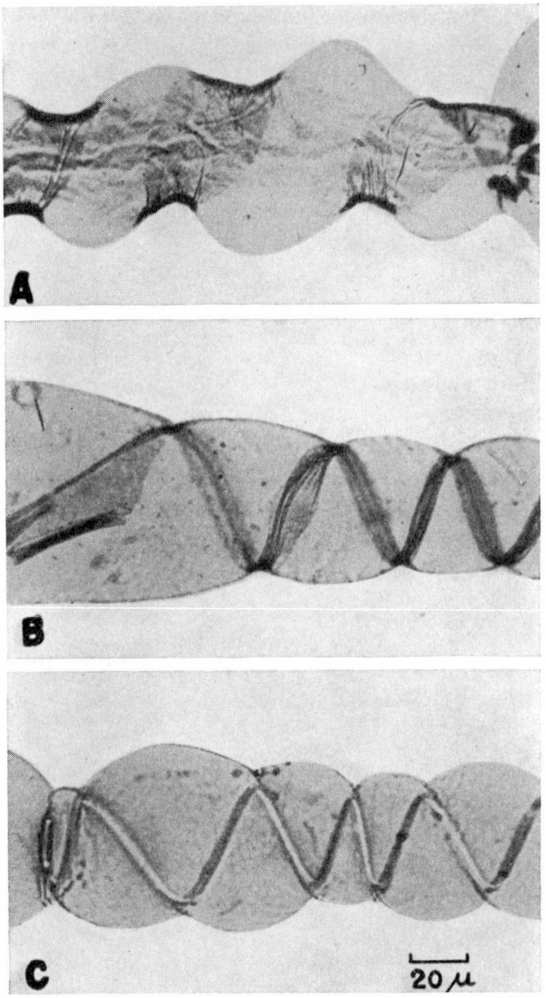

As mentioned in section 211, cotton hairs show, as a rule, ballooning, because the short cylinders in which the primary wall is broken up, are crumpled up by the bulging secondary wall, and form in this way annular constrictions, fig. 26. This is in good agreement with the fact that ballooning is less frequent in hairs that have been treated with alkali, because in that case the non-cellulose has been removed from the primary wall; swelling with spiral constrictions is here more frequent. There are, however, many transitions between ballooning and spiral swelling.

Although normally, certainly no appreciable amounts of non-cellulose are present in cotton, it is known that in some varieties in part of the hairs, the ordinary cellulose lamellae are interrupted by lamellae which do not give cellulose reactions and do not dissolve in cuprammonium,

Fig. 142. Mature but undried cotton hair, swollen in cuprammonium and showing spiral constrictions due to a rupturing of the outer part of the wall consisting of the S_1 layer and the primary wall, the latter coloured with ruthenium red (from KERR, 1946).

though they do in diluted alkali in the heat, and which can be stained with ruthenium-red; they appear to contain a green coloured wax.

It can hardly be denied that the secondary wall of the cotton hair contains also an S_3 layer, by which we mean a layer whose orientation differs from that of the S_2 layer (cf. section 231). In the first place there are indications of its presence in the appearance of striations with an angle of 30–45°, i. e. with a larger angle than that of which undoubtedly belong to the S_2 layer; these striations my be seen in the micrographs of non-swollen hairs near the lumen, e. g. in DENHAM (1923 fig. 1), FARR and CLARK, 1932 (fig. 2), whereas KERR (1946) reports that he has seen an aberrant kind of striations on the inside of the wall. In the older literature too this has been mentioned (LEVINE, 1914). More positive are the descriptions and drawings of MANGENOT and RAISON (1942), who found especially in cotton that had been cleaned with alkali, coarse spiral striations bounding the lumen. In the wall of one hair they even saw three layers with alternating direction of the spiral structure. The birefringence observed in oblique sections is another indication, as we will discuss below, of the presence of S_1 and S_3 layers with a different orientation, cf. fig. P145. That KERR (1946), ROLLINS (1947) and A. HERZOG (1955: 330) found in the innermost layer a different behaviour with regard to stains and some other reagents, is another argument for the assumption that we find here a distinct S_3 layer. It is, of course, not decisive, as this aberrant behaviour may be due to postmortal changes.

Polarization microscopy

The conclusion that the spiral structure in the wall of the cotton hair has in comparison with that in the wall of phloem fibres of the same length a low pitch and that it shows reversals, has not been based on observations with the ordina-

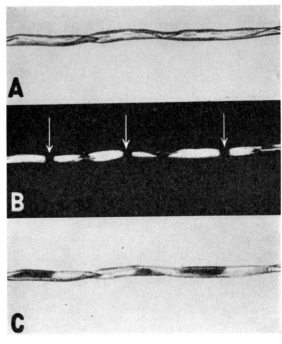

Fig. 143. Dried cotton hair in ordinary light, in which the twists are shown (A), between crossed nicols in orthogonal position, showing that there is extinction only at the three reversals, which are indicated by arrows (B), and like (B), but after insertion of a red I platelet in order to obtain addition and substraction colours as indications of the spiral direction (C), (from HOCK et al., 1941).

ry microscope only, but it has also been arrived at by means of studies with the polarization microscope. As the micelles in the two opposite walls intersect under an angle of circ. 60°, those in the S_1 layer as well as those in the lamellae of the S_2 layer, the cotton hair lights up to some extent even in the orthogonal positions, except at the reversals, which in this position are recognizable as dark transverse zones. If a red I platelet is inserted, the part at one side of the dark zone assumes an addition colour, the part at the other side a substraction colour, which on account of the antagonistic spiral structure is to be expected (section 212). Coloured pictures of this phenomenon have been published by FARR and CLARK (1932). Fig.143 shows in black and white the same hair in ordinary light, between crossed nicols in orthogonal position, and once more after insertion of a red I platelet in order to show the addition and substraction colours. There prove to be three reversals in the fragment which is depicted in this figure.

A. HERZOG (1955) has noted, and our own observations confirm it, that the colours which become visible in the orthogonal positions give us the impression that the whole hair behaves as we might expect that it would do in case the S_1 layer exercised in optical respect a predominating influence. In view of the much greater thickness of the S_2 layer with its orientation in the opposite direction, this is excluded. BALLS (1923), moreover, has shown that the extinction direction found in the single wall proves that it is the S_2 layer that actually exercises a predominating optical influence, cf. fig. 144; (that this observation is irreconcilable with his view that the micelles in the S_1 and in the S_2 layer are oriented in the same direction, was apparently overlooked by him). It may be added that KERR's observation (1946) according to which the place where the reversal in the S_1 layer takes place, does not always coincide exactly with that at which, according to the extinction in the orthogonal position, the reversal in the S_2 layer is found, may be regarded as a confirmation of the conclusion that it is the S_2 layer which exercises a predominating influence.

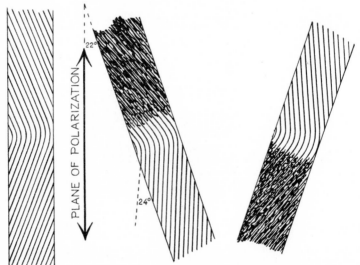

Fig. 144. Extinction positions observed in the single wall of a cotton hair near a reversal; they show that the S_2 layer whose spiral structure is opposite to the direction of the distinct striations in the S_1 layer which are indicated, exercises a predominating influence on the optical behaviour (from BALLS, 1923).

It seems to us that the only way to explain these rather paradoxical results is to assume that each of the layers S_1, S_2, S_2 and S_1 through which the light successively has to pass (the very thin S_3 layers may be left out of consideration), acts as a separate birefringent layer. In that case the N-S position will be the consecutive one for those parts of the hair in which in the S_1 layer a Z-spiral is found, and in these parts therefore we will note an addition colour, as we actually do. If the optical behaviour would be determined by the S_2 layer only, the N-S position would be the alternative one, in which case a substraction colour would appear, and this, as we have seen, does not happen. The correctness of this explanation might be tested by observations on a single wall, and it would therefore be desirable that such observations were made. In a similar way we have tried to explain the difference in optical behaviour shown by flax in comparison with hemp (section 2341). The intricacies with which we are confronted in these cases, teach us that the optical method is not always the most suitable one for determining which layer is the dominant one. Good results are obtained only if the birefringent lamellae, except the dominant one, are so thin that they do not act as separate birefringent objects. A pile of such lamellae acts, even if the individual lamellae have a varying orientation, as one layer with a uniform orientation throughout. FREY-WYSSLING (1941) has treated the matter theoretically. This situation occurs e. g. in latex vessels (section 23453).

Unlike the wall of phloem and xylem fibres, that of the cotton hair is seen to light up as a rule, in transverse sections between crossed nicols with a uniform brightness. This is due to the fact that in the S_1 layer as well as in the thick S_2 layer the spiral angle is circ. 30°. The brightness of these layers mask the birefringence of the S_3 layer and of the primary wall, which are very thin.

Expecting that the S_1 and S_3 layers would become distinguishable in part of the section if the latter was not a transversal one but one cut in an angle of circ. 25° with the cell axis, we have studied thin sections (4μ) of this kind from hairs that were embedded in methacrylate before sectioning . It appeared now that only $3/4$ of the wall lighted up, at least if the sections were studied in an exactly horizontal position. In the part where the S_2 layer does not light up, the microfibrils run vertical to the plane of section, and at such a place one can frequently observe at the margin a very thin positively birefringent layer, presumably consisting of the S_1 layer and the primary wall. Even in these thin sections no indication of a negatively birefringent cuticular layer or cuticle could be observed. At the opposite side of the wall near the lumen, not rarely another birefringent layer, obviously the S_3 layer, could be observed. Although the latter was very thin and only slightly birefringent, we nevertheless succeeded in obtaining some micrographs of it, fig. P145.

In the S_2 layer no lamellar differences in the degree of birefringence could be observed, so that we must assume that there are no differently oriented lamellae in the S_2 layer. We must add, however, that BARROWS (1940) claims to have seen such differences in transverse sections of untreated fresh hairs, and that HOCK et al. (1941) seem to have observed lamellae which did light up more or less, in transverse as well as in longitudinal sections of swollen walls that had been stained with congo-red.

The X-ray analysis of mature cotton hairs did so far not produce any new points of view with regard to the structure of the wall. It is, however, the most suitable method for estimating the average angle between the predominating spiral and the cell axis (cf. fig. 33). The various data that have been obtained in this way show that a lower angle is correlated with a greater fibre length and with a higher tensile force (BERKLEY, 1948). The mean value varies in different varieties between 27 and 35°. The hairs break nevertheless, as a rule, at the reversals where the microfibrils are oriented longitudinally!

In completely thickened hairs the average steepness of the spirals appears to be higher than in incompletely thickened ones (BERKLEY, 1938/39). This might mean that in the younger day-growth-rings the spiral becomes steeper, and this would agree with what KERR (1946) afterwards thought he could see in swollen hairs. The present author, however, found no indications of such a change in his oblique sections (v. supra). Neither the character of the X-ray diagram obtained from a short zone of one hair by ASTBURY (cf. PRESTON 1952: 149), does favour this supposition. In this diagram each of the ordinary sickle-shaped interferences has been replaced by two short arcs, corresponding in orientation to the crystallites in the upper and in the lower wall. This would not have been possible if there had been considerable differences in orientation between the different lamellae of the S_2 layer.

Finally we wish to refer to section 113 where an explanation is given of the mistake made by BERKLEY and KERR (1947) in claiming that the X-ray diagrams of fresh hairs prove that the cellulose does not crystallize before the hair begins to dry, a view which unfortunately has found its way into the textile literature, and which even now is often quoted as a well-established fact.

The study of the secondary wall by means of the electron microscope has for the cotton hair not led to very important results. TRIPP et al. (1951, cf. also ROLLINS and TRIPP, 1954) treated the hairs mechanically in water, and could isolate in this way not only the primary wall (cf. section 2344) but also the S_1 layer, just as this has been done in xylem fibres. Under the microscope and between crossed nicols too, this layer showed a conspicuous striation and in the electron micrographs the latter appeared to be due to an alternation of strips, 0.5–$1.0\,\mu$ in width, which consisted either of densely packed microfibrils aligned parallel to the direction of the strips, or of a network of microfibrils that lay further apart and were oriented more or less transversely to the direction of the strips. In the last-named kind of strips, moreover, narrow bundles of microfibrils were present which ran parallel to the strips and overcrossed therefore the transversely oriented microfibrils, fig. P146. The authors could not make out whether the differently oriented microfibrils occur in the same or in different layers.

This structure is obviously akin to that of the S_1 layer in xylem elements, and it shows also points of resemblance with the structure of the wall in the mature parenchyma cells of *Avena* coleoptiles (cf. section 23451). In the case of the cotton hair too one is inclined to think that the S_1 layer has been extended during the last phase of growth, but this is, in our opinion, irreconcilable with the fact that the primary wall has retained its original structure. Therefore we should like to suggest that the peculiar structure of the S_1 layer is caused by a temporarily changed and more or less abnormal structure of the ectoplasm which was caused by extension just before the deposition of the S_1 layer began. A similar change in the structure of the ectoplasm might account for the crossed structure of the S_1 layer of xylem fibres.

Electron micrographs of fragments of the S_2 layer show, as was to be expected and as several investigators have seen, a dense mass of parallel microfibrils, fig. P147.

KINSINGER and HOCK (1948), KLING and MAHL (1950, 1951, 1952), SIGNER et al. (1951) and TRIPP et al. (1957) studied replicas, and found in this way that the surface of dried hairs is always covered with ridges and grooves, and that the latter in the zones between the reversals make an angle of 20–45° with the cell axis, and are separated from each other by distances of 0.3–0.7 μ. The height of the ridges proves to be very variable, but amounts on the average to circ. 0.5 μ, whereas their length is 10–20 μ and more, cf. fig. 148. They appear to run parallel to the microfibrils in the S_1 layer (TRIPP et al., 1957) and they change their direction therefore at the same place as the microfibrils, fig. 149.

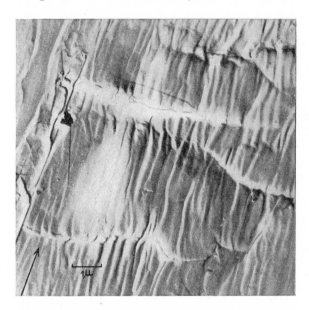

Fig. 148. Electron micrograph of a surface replica of a dry raw cotton hair, showing axial ridges and grooves and slightly oblique dislocations (from TRIPP et al., 1957; official U.S. D.A. photograph).

The dimensions of the ridges and grooves are of such an order of magnitude that with the exception of the smallest ones, they must be visible under the ordinary microscope. This actually is correct; it are apparently the striations which already long ago were observed in non-swollen hairs, i. e. the "pit spirals" or "spirals of the primary wall", and which were probably seen by DENHAM (1923) also in reflected light. As the illumination is not everywhere adequate and as the contrasts may be too weak, they are, with the ordinary microscope, seen only locally. According to our own experience they become easily distin-

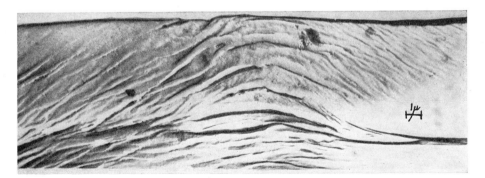

Fig. 149. Surface replica of a dry raw cotton hair, showing a reversal in the direction of the system of ridges and grooves (from TRIPP et al., 1957; official U.S.D.A. photograph).

guishable, in native as well as in bleached cotton, if the surface is shadowed with aluminium, and observed by means of a reflecting microscope (oil-immersion objective 60 ×); the dislocations too can be studied in this way.

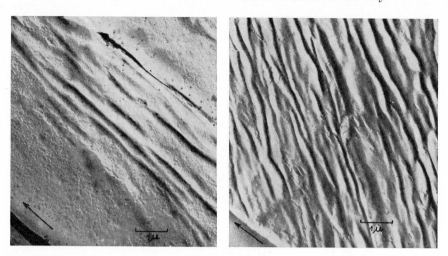

Fig. 150. Surface of untreated mature cotton hair from unopened boll before (left) and after (right) it had been dried for the first time (from TRIPP et al., 1957; official U.S.D.A. photograph).

Fig. 151. Transverse section of a cotton hair which had been swollen in boiling ethylene glycol and underwent a further swelling during the embedding in methacrylate; it shows conspicuous day - growth - rings (made by TRIPP and MOORE; official U.S.D.A. photograph).

The ridges and grooves are not present from the beginning, but arise during the process of drying; at the same time the hairs undergo a considerable decrease in diameter, fig. 150. If the dry hairs are immersed in water, they do not fully regain their original diameter, and they retain their ridges. The latter may owe their origin perhaps to the contraction of the interfibrillar substance, a process whereby the strips of densely packed microfibrils occurring in the S_1 layer probably obtain a more prominent position than the strips with a more open structure, which would result in the development of wrinkles at the surface.

KLING and MAHL (1952) ascribed the origin of the wrinkles to the presence of fissures between the bundles of microfibrils in the S_2 layer, but this seems to be impossible, as the direction of the wrinkles differs from that of the spiral structure in that layer. In this connection it is noteworthy that at an earlier occasion (1950) these authors had observed fissures which ran in a direction opposite to that of the wrinkles, and they had assumed that these fissures found their origin in a deeper layer. In our opinion it is questionable whether the very conspicuous bundles and fissures that are visible in the replicas of their transverse sections, may be regarded as natural, as there is no indication of the presence of day-growth-rings. The authors explain the absence of the latter by deformation as a result of desiccation, but this looks unlikely to us.

MAERTENS et al. (1956) too had little success in their search for day-growth-rings in electron micrographs. TRIPP and GIUFFRA (1954) found that the rings were not distinguishable in ordinary ultra-thin sections, but that they became visible if the sections were cut from acetylated hairs that had been embedded in methacrylate, a medium in which they undergo a marked swelling. Better results were obtained if the swelling was enhanced by a pretreatment with boiling glycerol or ethylene glycol, cf. fig. 151.

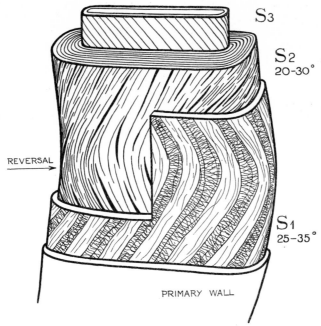

Fig. 152. Schema of the structure of the secondary wall of a mature dry cotton hair; the wrinkles on the surface have been omitted.

Fig. 152 schematically represents the structure of the secondary wall of the cotton hair. The structure of its primary wall has been discussed in section

2271. The number of day-growth-rings in the S_2 layer is 20–40, whereas only 8 lamellae are drawn; the figures refer to the spiral angles between the reversals. The spiral angle of the S_3 layer is unknown. The hair is supposed to be dry since it is ribbon-shaped. At the edges the two "spiral lines of weakness" would occur, but they are not shown as their presence requires confirmation. The ridges and grooves in the surface which follow the direction of the strips in the S_1 layer, are not shown either.

23442. Other epidermal cells

In *other hairs* the structure of the secondary wall has hardly been investigated. We know, however, for a number of hairs, how on the average the cellulose micelles are oriented with regard to the cell axis. DIPPEL (1898: 335) reports a number of cases with Z- and with S-spiral structure, and states that the spiral angle may vary in the same hair between less than 45° and more than 45°, which means that the same hair in light which traverses it perpendicular to the surface, may appear either positively or negatively birefringent, and, of course, also isotropic. This was confirmed in recent times by FREYTAG (1954a) for the hairs of *Lamium galeobdolon:* in the latter the Z-structure is predominant, and the orientation of the striations agrees with this structure. A. FREY (1926) drew the attention to the cuneiform hairs found on the mericarps of *Erodium gruinum:* the wall of these hairs too shows a spiral structure, but on account of the slight degree of orientation of the cellulose micelles they show for their thickness a comparatively slight birefringence.

In connection with the presence of day-growth-rings in the wall of the cotton hair, it is worth mentioning that in the climbing-hairs of *Humulus lupulus*, according to FRANZ (1935), on some days several lamellae are deposited, on other days none, and in the hairs of *Echium vulgare* the number of lamellae that are deposited daily, is, according to WECKERLING (1949), so large that their total number varies in the end between 200 and 300.

KERPEL (1938) has made some observations on the cell-wall structure of the hairs of *Ceiba pentandra*. The drying twist shows that in most of the hairs either an S-structure in the cell or an S-overcrossing in the single wall is mechanically predominating. The present author made similar observations, and could confirm this conclusion by a study of the optical properties. In the other hairs a Z-structure may predominate, or no spiral structure is revealed at all. This of course does not imply absence of spiral structure since spirals of opposite direction might be present in the single wall. According to KERPEL, a striation may sometimes be seen which includes an angle of less than 10° with the cell axis and as a matter of fact the major part of the hairs is positively birefringent. In the thickened basal part of the hair a spiral with a low pitch is found and in this part the wall is always negatively birefringent. In transverse sections the walls are positively birefringent; although the lipid content is not low (see table 1), no trace of a negatively birefringent cuticle is detectable.

What is known of the structure of the cellulose in the cell-wall of mature hairs from the stamens of *Tradescantia virginica* has already been mentioned in section 2271, as this is in reality a primary wall.

On the structure of *the non-cutinized layer of non-capilliform epidermal cells* too but little information is available. Here too the cellulose micelles prove to be oriented in the plane of the wall. In cells that seen from the outside are nearly as long as wide, there is no preference for a definite orientation in the tangential walls, the latter are isotropic in surface view. In cells that are longer than wide, the cellulose micelles in these walls show preference for axial orientation and these walls are therefore positively birefringent in surface view. With regard to the occurrence of spiral orientation and of differences in orientation in the successive layers in epidermal cells, no optical data are available.

That the outer wall of the epidermal cells consists in many plants of several layers, was already known to the older microscopists. GENEAU DE LAMAR-LIÈRE (1906) showed, moreover, that the outer wall contains pectin, and that the largest amount of this substance is to be found in the outer layer of the non-cutinized part; in the direction of the cell lumen the concentration decreases.

FREY-WYSSLING (1926) found that in the leaves of *Clivia nobilis* the central part of the cellulose layer in the outer epidermal wall shows the strongest birefringence, although the concentration of the cellulose reaches its highest value in the innermost layer, cf. fig. 166. It seems that this can not be due to the presence of a negatively birefringent substance, as wax seems to be absent, and as the slight absorption of U. V. light shows that this part of the wall is not cutinized either. ANDERSON (1928) thinks that this unexpected result may be due to a higher water content of the innermost layer, but this is no more than a supposition. It might in our opinion also be explained by assuming that the cellulose micelles in this layer were to a lesser degree oriented in the plane of the section. ANDERSON (l. c.) proved that in *Clivia nobilis* the differentiation of the wall in lamellae rests on the alternation of layers that are rich in cellulose and poor in pectin, with layers with little cellulose and much pectin. He too found that the cellulose content increases and the pectin content decreases towards the cell lumen, cf. fig. 166. Where the non-cutinized part of the wall borders on the cuticular membrane, there is a layer which consists entirely or almost entirely of pectin; this layer, at least, stains strongly with ruthenium-red, and gives no cellulose reaction, dissolves in diluted acid as well as in ammonia and other alkaline liquids, is decomposed by H_2O_2, and is easily attacked by bacteria.

Since that time several other investigators observed that the cuticle and the cuticular membrane may in many plants be detached from the rest of the cell-wall by a treatment with soda, H_2O_2 or enzymes, which proves that the presence of a layer with a very high pectin content between the cuticular membrane and the rest of the cell-wall, must be very common. In several instances the cuticle is detached in the normal course of events (cf. KÜSTER, 1956: 697).

The deposition of the cellulose in lamellae was beautifully confirmed by MÜHLETHALER (1953a) in the epidermis of the hyacinth leaf by means of the electron microscope, fig. P153. The outer wall appears to contain circ. 50 lamellae. The author is of opinion that the orientation of the micelles varies in these layers, and this is indeed clearly visible. We should realize, however, that the differentiation may be due to the collapse of rows of microfibrils in different directions. For this reason a confirmation of this isolated case, e. g. by means of tangential sections, is therefore desirable.

The very thick walls of the guard-cells of stomata too contain a large number of lamellae. In fig. 154, reproduced from MÜHLETHALER (1953a), the magnification is not high enough to show the microfibrils. The latter, however, may be seen in fig. 155, which shows a section through a stoma of an *Avena* coleoptile. As the guard-cells are not yet full-grown, the wall is in this case a primary one, and accordingly rather thin. The lamellar structure stands out very clearly as

16*

the non-cellulose has been removed. With regard to differences in orientation in the various lamellae nothing is as yet known.

The thick-walled palissade cells in the testa of *Gleditschia triacanthos* have been studied polarization optically and electron optically by CAVAZZA (1950). The so-called linea lucida is characterized by a higher density of the cellulose microfibrils.

Striations in the non-cutinized part of the outer epidermal wall when this is observed in surface view, have been described already by NAEGELI, STRASBURGER and CORRENS. They become especially conspicuous if the walls are trea-

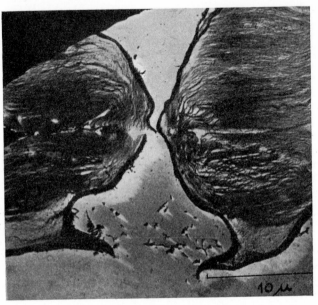

Fig. 154. Transverse section through the guard-cells in a leaf of *Hyacinthus orientalis* (from MÜHLETHALER, 1953a).

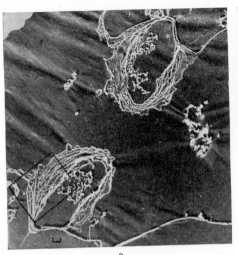

a

b

Fig. 155. Transverse section through young guard-cells in an *Avena* coleoptile; the rectangle indicated in (a) is shown under a higher magnification in (b), (from SETTERFIELD, 1957).

ted with chlor-zinc-iodine, and they are often oriented perpendicular to the longitudinal axis, although they may run in every possible direction. B. J. D. MEEUSE (1938, 1941) has discussed the literature and has added observations of his own; he is of opinion that these striations are comparable to the dislocations that have been observed in the walls of fibres, and that it are therefore artefacts that owe their origin to mechanical causes, especially during the cutting of the sections. They have been observed in parenchyma and collenchyma cells too.

The presence of pores and plasmodesmata in the outer wall of the epidermal cells has been described already long ago (cf. e. g. DIPPEL, 1898: 320; GARDINER, 1897; SCHUMACHER and HALBSGUTH, 1939). B. J. D. MEEUSE (1941) pointed out that in sections through epidermal cell-walls having dislocations, plasmodesma-like structures may be imitated, but it can now no longer be doubted that plasmodesmata really may be present (SCHUMACHER, 1942; LAMBERTZ, 1954; SCHUMACHER and LAMBERTZ, 1956). Their presence has been confirmed by means of the electron microscope by HUBER et al. (1956) and by SCHUMACHER (1957) in sections, and by SCOTT et al. (1957) in surface view.

2345. Other kinds of cells

23451. Parenchyma cells

In the wall of isodiametric parenchyma cells the cellulose micelles are always oriented in the way indicated in fig. 32 g, whereas in the wall of prismatic parenchyma cells a predominantly axial orientation (fig. 32 d) as well as a transverse orientation (fig. 32 f) and even spiral orientations (fig. 32 c and e) may occur. This depends upon the ratio length to diameter, and presumably also upon the thickness of the wall. In cells of the same length the chance that the micelles will be oriented either transversely or in a spiral with a low pitch, and that the wall therefore will be negatively birefringent in surface view, will increase with the diameter of the cell and with the thinness of the wall. Long, narrow and thick-walled cells have, as a rule, a more axial cell-wall structure, i. e. an orientation of the cellulose micelles in steeper spirals.

Only one of these presumable correlations has so far been confirmed by measurements on parenchyma cells, viz. the relation between steepness of the spiral and the ratio length to diameter. The measurements were carried out on mature parenchyma cells in *Avena* coleoptiles (PRESTON, 1938). In some of the cells there would be an S-spiral, in other ones a Z-spiral, and the angle of the spiral with the longitudinal axis would vary between 30 and 75°, with a mean value of 55°. The same author and his collaborators found this correlation also in the secondary wall of tracheids and in fibres of bamboo; other authors found it in other Monocotyledones and in cotton hairs; this has been mentioned already in previous sections.

PRESTON (1. c.) was of opinion that his measurements on *Avena* cells referred to the primary wall, although his coleoptiles had been grown constantly in diffuse light and had nevertheless reached a length of 35 mm, which means that they must have been rather old; he chose moreover for his measurements cells in the basal and middle part of the coleoptile. FREY-WYSSLING (1942a) already pointed out that PRESTON had studied the secondary wall, and in collaboration of this view he referred to observations made by K. and M. WÜHRMANN-MEYER (1939), who observed that in growing parenchyma cells of *Avena* coleoptiles the originally negative birefringence of the wall decreases and passes finally into a positive birefringence. They conclude from their observations that in the basal part of the coleoptile secondary thickening of the cell-wall begins already after three days, and that it spreads rapidly in the direction of the tip.

BÖHMER (1958) on the other hand, although confirming these observations, could not find any secondary thickening in his electron micrographs, and he explains the observations therefore in another way. The change of the negative birefringence into a positive one is according to him entirely due to the increase in the number of axially oriented microfibrils in the outer part and in the edge-thickenings of the primary wall (cf. section 2271).

The question if there may or may not occur secondary thickening in *Avena* coleoptiles has been settled by SETTERFIELD and BAYLEY (1958), who did observe secondary thickening in electron micrographs of cell-wall sections of these coleoptiles, fig. 156.

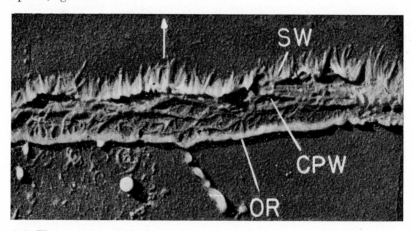

Fig. 156. Electron micrograph of a transverse section through a single parenchyma cell-wall; the latter had been obtained from an *Avena* coleoptile that had reached a length of 50 mm and had ceased to grow two days before. OR, outer rib; CPW, continuous primary wall; SW, secondary wall with bundles of more or less axially oriented microfibrils (from SETTERFIELD and BAYLEY, 1958).

WARDROP and CRONSHAW (1958) too describe secondary thickening in *Avena* coleoptiles that had completed their growth. In fig. P157 part of a parenchyma cell that had been cleaned and was subsequently stained with congo-red, is shown between crossed nicols. The walls clearly show a crossed spiral structure, and such a structure has never been observed in the walls of growing parenchyma cells. Such full-grown cells have also been described and depicted by MÜHLETHALER (1950), who in this connection speaks of a secondary thickening in which fissures had arisen as a result of axial extension.

Electron micrographs of the walls of similar cells are given in figs. P158 and P159. The former micrograph shows on the inner side of the primary wall what appears to be the early stage of a helical secondary thickening; the primary wall lies on top since the cell is observed from the outside, and in this layer transversely oriented microfibrils still prevail. In the other micrograph we see a crossed fibrillar structure which, according to the authors, would occur in the single wall.

It is very striking that BÖHMER (1958 and private confirmation) could not find any sign of secondary thickening in old coleoptiles by means either of the polarization microscope or of the electron microscope. The present author too looked in vain for cells like the one shown in fig. P157 in cell macerates of very old coleoptiles that had been coloured either with congo-red or with benzo-azurin and that were observed between crossed nicols. The cultural conditions or perhaps varietal differences may be responsible for these discrepancies in the observations.

It seems worth while to draw the attention to the rather striking resemblance in structure that we observe in comparing the structure of the secondary wall of older *Avena* coleoptiles with that observed by SCOTT et al. (1956) in roots of *Allium cepa* and with that of the S_1 layer in tracheids, xylem fibres and cotton hairs.

Electron micrographs of the cell-walls of mature parenchyma cells from the apple, the *Dahlia* tuber and the potato have been published by WARDROP (1954a, 1954b, 1955). It is not certain whether these micrographs show the walls from the outside or from the inside, but as the material was obtained by macerating disks or cubes of tissue and not by disintegrating cells, they probably show the primary wall, and it would therefore have been more proper if they had been dealt with in section 2271. They show an isotropic network consisting of micro-fibrils or of bundles and even wide strips of the latter, alternating with pits of various dimensions. Only in the cell-wall obtained from the *Dahlia* tuber a more or less crossed structure is distinguishable with a preference for a definite direction. The thickness of the wall is sometimes so considerable that it seems reasonable to assume that the secondary wall too is included in the micrograph. However, the secondary wall is apparently not fundamentally different from the primary one, a condition that was to be expected in isodiametric cells.

It can not be doubted that the walls in the mature parenchyma cells from the centre of the root of *Beta vulgaris var. saccharifera* that were studied by VAN DER POEL et al. (1958) by means of the carbon-replica method, have been photographed from the inside. Fig. P160 shows a cell-wall that had merely been washed with water of 78° C; nevertheless the microfibrils are in this micrograph very clearly distinguishable. This is because the cell-walls in the parenchyma of the sugar beet contain only a minor quantity of true hemicelluloses but a large amount of pectin and of water-soluble polyoses, a circumstance that is rather annoying to the sugar manufacturer. In fig. P160 on the inside of a wall a layer with more or less transverse structure is shown, whereas underneath the latter a more axial structure is visible. The micrographs of some other cell-walls reproduced in the same publication show an isotropic network. One of these is fig. P11 which we discussed in section 114 in connection with a possible apical growth of the microfibrils.

As in the secondary wall of thick-walled parenchyma cells several investigators have noted a lamellar structure, it is not improbable that such a structure is a general feature of the secondary wall in parenchyma cells. A detailed description of the deposition of a number of lamellae in the walls of the medullary parenchyma of *Clematis vitalba* has been given by DIPPEL (1898: 552).

Well-known is the lamellar structure in the wall of sclereids. In those from the medulla of *Hoya carnosa* and in those from the mesocarp of the pear too, the walls are stratified but their sections show no differences in birefringence, so that we must assume that the lamellae show here no difference in orientation or in cellulose content (FREY-WYSSLING, 1942b). In other objects a lamellar deposition of lignin has been supposed (DAUPHINÉ, 1941).

According to VAN DER HOUVEN VAN OORDT-HULSHOF (1957) the secondary wall in the parenchyma cells of the stems of *Saccharum officinarum* consists like that of the perivascular fibres, of more than three lamellae; the micelles in these lamellae are oriented in a Z-spiral, but the pitch of the latter is alternatively high and low. A similar situation will probably be present in the wall of the parenchyma cells of bamboo, *Pandanus* and other Monocotyledones, where, however, so far a lamellar structure is known only from the fibres. An electron micrograph reproduced by VAN DER HOUVEN VAN OORDT-HULSHOF (l. c.) shows the inside of a wall from a parenchyma cell of *Saccharum;* the micelles prove to be oriented in a Z-spiral with an angle of 45°.

In wood-parenchyma cells too the structure of the wall has been studied. RITTER (1949) reports that in the wall of the wood ray parenchyma, which reach their largest dimension in the radial direction, the cellulose micelles are mainly oriented perpendicular to that direction; this could be concluded from the optical behaviour of the wall and from the stronger swelling in the radial direction. WARDROP and DADSWELL (1952a) found in ordinary wood parenchyma as well as in ray parenchyma of a number of deciduous trees and of conifers, a spiral structure whose angle with the longitudinal cell axis varied between 30 and 60°. In some species the secondary wall showed no lamellar structure, but in others, e. g. in *Dialium laurinum*, some lamellae with alternatively strong and slight birefringence could be distinguished. In thickened, sclerosed parenchyma cells of this tree and of *Persoonia lanceolata*, fig. P 161, a large number of such layers with differences in orientation proved to be present.

Lamellar structures are apparently not rare in the wall of wood-parenchyma cells. RIBI (1953) noticed differences in orientation between the various layers which are recognizable in the walls of this kind of cells in *Populus tremuloides*, but it is not excluded that this were the normal S_1, S_2 and S_3 layers. FREI et al. (1957), however, noted a large number of lamellae in the wall of ray-parenchyma cells of *Pinus radiata*, cf. fig. P 162. Although part of the differences in orientation that appear in this micrograph, will have to be ascribed to a collapse in various directions of rows of microfibrils, it seems likely that a transverse orientation alternates in the successive lamellae with a more or less axial one or with a steep spiral. This is confirmed by the study of more or less oblique sections, such as the one shown in fig. P 163.

23452. Collenchyma cells

DE BARY has already in 1877 drawn the attention to the remarkably high degree of shrinkage and swelling in the radial direction that the thickened parts of the wall of collenchyma cells undergo if these cells are dried and if the dried cells are moistened. There are, as a rule, no intercellular spaces in the collenchyma, and the swelling may easily proceed so far that the lumen of the cells disappears almost entirely. Various authors, quoted e. g. by ANDERSON (1927a), have measured these changes, and so did PRESTON and DUCKWORTH (1946). The last-named authors noted in collenchyma from the petioles of *Petasites vulgaris* that the wall showed an increase in thickness of 100–150 % if the sections were transferred from alcohol (presumably 96 %) to water, whereas the increase in length amounted at the most to 0,5 %. COHN found a water content varying between 165 and 245 % of the dry weight (62–71 % of the fresh weight), i. e. an even somewhat higher water content than was found by us in the primary wall. AMBRONN noted in 1881 that the plasticity (irreversible extensibility) of the walls of fresh collenchyma cells is higher than that of phloem fibres, though far less than that of the primary wall (cf.FREY-WYSSLING, 1952).

It can not be doubted that there exists a connection between these peculiarities and the high amounts of pectin and hemicelluloses that are present in these walls. In the collenchyma of *Petasites* we found 45 % pectin and 35 % hemicellulose, so that the cellulose content is at most 20 %, which means that it is here even lower than it is in the primary wall. PRESTON and DUCKWORTH too found circ. 45 % pectin.

The collenchyma of *Solanum lycopersicum* was studied by ANDERSON (l. c.), that of *Heracleum sphondylium* by MAJUMDAR and PRESTON (1941), and that of *Petasites* by PRESTON and DUCKWORTH (1946). All these investigators used sections that had been swollen e. g. by a treatment with sulphuric acid, after which the pectin was stained with ruthenium-red, and the cellulose with iodine, and from their results it appears that the walls, or at least their angular thickenings, contain 7–20 lamellae, which are alternately poor and rich in cellulose, and which, in the same way as the lamellae in the epidermal wall, become more rich in cellulose as they approach the cell lumen. In *Petasites* this lamellar structure is somewhat less easily observable than in the two other species.

Just as in the walls of the epidermal cells, the lamellar structure becomes even more conspicuous if the non-cellulose is dissolved, e. g. by the aid of chromic acid, of H_2O_2, or of ammonia and acid, and if the cellulose is stained. The cellulose lamellae become also easily distinguishable if the material is treated with a fungal enzyme preparation or after a spontaneous attack by bacteria; the cells are in this way macerated, and the walls show a strong swelling, which is due to the enzymatic depolymerization of the non-cellulose. For this reason the behaviour of these cell-walls may even be used as a reaction on the presence of poly-galacturonase (SLOEP, 1928).

The lamellar structure can also be observed in transverse as well as in longitudinal sections between crossed nicols, as the birefringence of the lamellae appears to be alternately stronger and less strong. This has been described by various authors, but no good pictures are as yet available.

Electron micrographs of full-grown collenchyma cells are not available either. Presumably the lamellar structure of the secondary wall will not be very different from that of the primary wall since the thickening had already started before the deposition of the secondary wall began. This has been described in section 2274, and is depicted in fig. 93. The lamellation is already very conspico uus and the thickening considerable.

Collenchyma cells appear to be the only cells where it is unknown which part of the wall was deposited during the period of longitudinal growth, and which part after the latter had been completed. It is therefore impossible to say where in these cells the primary wall ends and where the secondary wall begins. Nor is there in transverse sections a more strongly birefringent S_1 layer by which it might be possible to locate the boundary line.

MAJUMDAR and PRESTON (l.c.) obtained in the collenchyma of *Heracleum*, typical ballooning and also spiral swelling. The last-named phenomenon suggests, in our opinion, the possibility that there is a peripheral layer with helical structure that might be comparable to the S_1 layer in fibres. These authors also observed a thin inner layer that might be compared to the S_3 layer found in the secondary wall of various kinds of fibres. In transverse section its birefringence appears to be stronger, in longitudinal section less strong than in the rest of the cell-wall. MAJUMDAR and PRESTON were of opinion that this behaviour could only be explained by assuming that in this layer, the angular dispersion reaches a higher value, but PRESTON (1952: 146) afterwards admitted that it may also be caused by the presence of a spiral structure with a rather low pitch.

In studying the extinction position in the cell-walls of the collenchyma of *Petasites* and *Heracleum*, PRESTON and his collaborators came to the conclusion that the cellulose micelles are in the main, axially oriented. The X-ray diagram makes it clear that their orientation has reached a high degree of regularity, for the angular dispersion does not exceed a value of circ. 10° in *Petasites* and a value of 14° in *Heracleum* (MAJUMDAR and PRESTON, 1941; PRESTON and DUCK-WORTH, 1946; ROELOFSEN and KREGER, 1951). Whether the micelles in the cellulose layers are arranged in a steep spiral or not, and whether there are differences in orientation in the various strata is unknown. The S_1 and S_3 layers if present, might form an exception, but as they are in any case very thin, this need not be visible in the X-ray diagram.

The pectin too is according to ROELOFSEN and KREGER (1951) axially oriented, partly crystalline and to some extent fibrillar (fig. P20). In the pectin skeletons that were obtained by dissolving the cellulose and probably also the greater part of the hemicellulose by the aid of cuprammonium, they noted a weak negative intrinsic birefringence; in water, however, a positive rodlet-birefringence prevailed. In comparison with the rodlet-birefringence of the cellulose micelles, that of the pectin is, however, very weak. This is so far the only object in which a birefringent pectin with fibrillar and crystalline properties has been found (section 151).

According to ANDERSON and MOORE (1937) the lamellar wall structure is found also in the collenchyma of plants that have been grown in continuous light and in constant temperature (cotton and potato).

23453. Vessels

The general aspect of xylem vessels, sieve tubes and latex vessels has often been described, but little attention has so far been paid to the finer structure of their secondary wall. Apart from the pits and from the various kinds of thickenings, there is but one submicroscopical structural feature of the secondary wall that is known with sufficient certainty, viz. that here, just as in the primary wall, on the whole a transverse structure such as is schematically shown in fig. 32f and c, predominates. It is at once recognizable by the position of the slit-like pits and also by the behaviour of the wall in polarized light, and it is therefore no wonder that it has been known already for a long time (for literature cf. DIPPEL, 1898: 291).

In the *xylem* the same *vessel* may show a transverse orientation of the micelles as well as an orientation in an S- or a Z-spiral with a low pitch. PRESTON (1939) described this for the vessels of six different kinds of trees. In wider vessels and in the wider parts of a vessel, the pitch of the spiral is, as a rule, lower. According to this author the angular dispersion of the cellulose micelles would be but slight in the wall of the various kinds of xylem vessels, and just as in the wall of the fibres, the micelles therefore would run nearly parallel to each other.

So far as is known at present, the secondary wall of the xylem vessels does not show conspicuous differences in orientation in the successive layers, but in *Sassafras officinale* and in some of the vessels of *Fraxinus americana*, a number of layers are recognizable which differ in the nature of their birefringence; in *Fraxinus* there are usually three of these layers, in *Sassafras* a larger number.

That differences of this kind are really present, is proved already by the fact that it is impossible to find a position in which these walls show, in surface view, complete extinction. In *Fraxinus* the differences in orientation appear also in the curious changes which the direction of the split-like pit canals undergoes in different distances from the surface. The pit canals show here the same corkscrew shape as those did which NAEGELI (1864a) observed in the wall of phloem fibres. The orientation of the split changes rather suddenly, sometimes once and sometimes twice in the single wall, which points to the presence of two, respectively three layers with a different orientation, each of them of sufficient thickness to cause such an effect. If there are three layers in the single wall, the helical structure of the central one often has the lowest pitch.

In the successive layers the sign of the spirals not rarely alternates. In the xylem vessels of *Fraxinus* they sometimes ran in the same sense and sometimes in opposite ones, and there were also vessels in which no layers at all were observable.

It should further be noted that the corresponding split-like pits in the double wall between two adjoining cells always differ in direction which is easily comprehensible as the spirals in the single walls too are of opposite direction.

In the thickenings on the longitudinal walls and in the bars of the perforated transverse septa, the micelles are on the average oriented parallel to the longitudinal direction of these structures. PRESTON (1935) concluded from the values found for the birefringence shown by the bars in the transverse septa of the xylem vessels of *Helianthus*, that the cellulose micelles are oriented to a very high degree, cf. fig. 32 k.

In section 2273 it has already been reported that the first indications of the thickenings become noticeable before the cell has completed its growth, and that at first they are nearer together than afterwards. HEPTON et al. (1956) made electron micrographs of sections cut through the thickenings on the wall of xylem vessels of *Cucurbita*, and they noted that these thickenings consist of a very large number of lamellae, each of them only a few hundreds Å thick. These lamellae presumably represent growth-rings; theoretically, however, there is another possibility, viz. that they have been differentiated by periodical changes in the lignification which set in after the whole mass of cellulose had been deposited, cf. fig. P 164.

Electron micrographs of *the sieve plates in full-grown sieve tubes* have been published by VOLZ (1952). The development of the sieve plates has been studied by FREY-WYSSLING and MÜLLER (1957) in sieve tubes of *Cucurbita*; their results were discussed already in section 2274. HEPTON et al. (1955) noticed in sections through these plates that the pits themselves are, as a rule, completely filled with protoplasm. The walls of the sieve plates are not homogeneous; it seems that they consist of two different substances, but more definite data are as yet not available. The chemical nature of callose has been discussed in section 141.

The *latex vessel of Euphorbia splendens* was one of the first cells in which a typical tubular texture (fig. 32 f) was found, viz. by A. FREY (1926). Since PRESTON had, in several papers between 1934 and 1939, questioned the existence of tubular texture in any plant cell and instead had assumed the general occurrence of a flat spiral structure (fig. 32 c), FREY-WYSSLING later (1942a) presented which by himself as well as by others, was considered as a final proof of the existence of tubular texture in these cells. However, in 1956 MOOR (unpublished, quoted by FREY-WYSSLING, 1959: 28), appears to have shown electron optically that in reality the walls in question consist of a great number of very thin lamellae having a flat spiral structure, but with alternating S- and Z-spiral direction. Apparently this is a most striking example of the phenomenon, also studied by FREY-WYSSLING (1941, 1959: 251), that a packet of birefringent lamellae with crossed major extinction directions acts as one homogeneous thick layer, provided the birefringence of the individual lamellae is very slight.

23454. Endosperm cells

The shape of the endosperm cells and especially that of the pits by which they are perforated, have repeatedly been studied by means of the microscope. With regard to the structure of the wall itself the only investigation that deserves our attention, is that of MEIER (1958) carried out on the endosperm of *Phytelephas macrocarpa* and of *Phoenix dactylifera*. It is since long known that the innermost layer of the wall stains blue with chlor-zinc-iodine, and for this reason it has always been assumed that the rather more than 6% cellulose found by chemical analysis, must have its seat in that part of the wall. MEIER, however, points out that mannan B too, stains blue with chlor-zinc-iodine, and that this conclusion therefore is not justified.

In *Phytelephas* all the layers of the wall show in surface view, according to the data which he obtained by the aid of the polarization microscope and of the electron microscope, an isotropic structure, except around the circular pits where the usual concentric orientation of the micelles is found. In *Phoenix* this applies only to the layer which is contiguous with the non-birefringent middle lamella; the remaining part of the cell-wall possesses a tubular texture.

In section 1332 we have already called attention to the remarkable circumstance that the mannan B fraction would be fibrillar and amorphous and the mannan A fraction granular and crystalline.

235. ON THE THEORIES THAT HAVE BEEN PROPOSED FOR EXPLAINING THE ORIENTATION OF THE CELLULOSE IN THE SECONDARY WALL

The oldest theory ascribes the orientation of the cellulose in the secondary wall to the action of the streaming protoplasm. The latter was supposed to exercise its influence on particles that are visible under the microscope, e. g. on STRASBURGER'S microsomes, or else on submicroscopical micelles. At present we would have to assume that it acts on the microfibrils, but this is a point of minor importance. CRÜGER (1855) introduced this theory in order to explain the relation which he had observed between the position of the bars of streaming protoplasm and that of the wall thickenings that subsequently were differentiated. He had studied this relation especially in the velamen of the aerial roots of an orchid, where the cell-walls show spiral thickenings. At the green top of these roots, where the cells are still increasing in size, the parietal protoplasm shows a uniform aspect, but as soon as they cease growing, a definite pattern of plasma streams becomes noticeable, and this pattern even remains visible if the cells are plasmolysed and their protoplasts therefore contract. The wall thickenings subsequently develop underneath these bars of protoplasm. The latter disappear as soon as the wall thickenings are fully developed.

In 1868 DIPPEL (see 1898: 557) has published exactly corresponding descriptions and even more convincing drawings of this process, which he himself studied in the sporogonium wall and in the elaters of two different *Marchantiaceae* and in the xylem vessels of *Balsamina* and *Impatiens*, fig. 165.

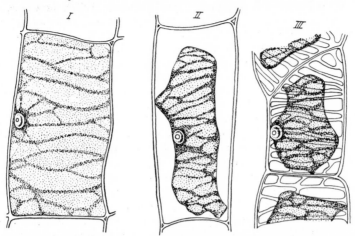

Fig. 165. Successive stages in the development of the spiral thickenings in a xylem vessel of *Impatiens noli-tangere* in relation to the previously formed bars of protoplasm. In I and II only the latter are visible, in I before and in II after plasmolysis; in III the development of the thickenings has just set in; they are shown here in a plasmolysed cell (after DIPPEL).

That not only the direction of the thickenings corresponds with that of the protoplasmic streaming, but that the larger refractive index of the cellulose in the thickenings too is in agreement with the latter, was not unknown to DIPPEL either. It is an indication that there must be a relation either direct or indirect, between the direction of the protoplasmic streaming and that of the micelles of the cellulose, a point that was emphasized especially by VAN ITERSON (1927).

SCHMITZ (1880) confirmed CRÜGER's observations with regard to the development of the spiral thickenings in the velamen cells of orchid roots, whereas STRASBURGER (1882) made similar observations on the origin of the spiral thickenings in the xylem vessels of *Bryonia* and *Impatiens*, in the tracheidal cells of the *Sphagnum* leaf and in the hypodermal cells of the anther wall. Another observation made by STRASBURGER deserves special attention, viz. that in the young tracheids of *Pinus*, where no wall thickenings are present, the direction of the protoplasmic streaming appears to correspond exactly with that of the striation observed in the S_1 layer of the cell-wall in the mature tracheids; both appear to be oriented in an angle of circ. 45° with the cell axis.

Not so very long ago the correlation found by CRÜGER between the direction of the wall thickenings and that of the plasma bars was once more confirmed by SINNOTT and BLOCH (1945), this time for reticulate thickenings that appeared in traumatic tissue of *Coleus*. These authors stated that in contiguous cells the wall thickenings are often also contiguous; this may also be seen in fig. 165 from DIPPEL. In all these wall thickenings the microfibrils of the cellulose appear to be oriented to a high degree parallel to the longitudinal axis of the thickenings.

DENHAM (1923) observed in young cotton hairs the presence of a spirally streaming protoplasm, and he correlates the latter, but without adducing proofs, with the spiral structure of the secondary wall. In corroboration of this view the author referred to an apparently similar situation occurring in the hairs on the *Tradescantia* stamens, where he noted a quite distinct relation between the steep spiral in which the striations of the cell-wall are oriented, and the direction of the protoplasmic streaming. VAN ITERSON (1937), however, rightly pointed out that in the latter case the relation can at any rate not be regarded as a direct one, as the striations are found in the cuticle, whereas in the rest of the wall no such striations are present, and as the cellulose micelles show a transverse orientation. MARTENS (1940) studied the movement of the inclusions of the protoplasm, and found in this way that the direction of the protoplasmic streaming was not fully constant, and that it agreed only approximatively with the average direction of the cuticular striation. His findings with regard to the direction of the protoplasmic streaming were not new, for that the individual streams may change their course to some extent, and that they even may fuse and once more separate, was known already in 1867 to HOFMEISTER. MARTENS agreed with VAN ITERSON that the relation between the direction of the cuticular striation and that of the protoplasmic streaming could not be a direct one, but that they are both probably due to the action of an agent which determines the growth of the cell-wall in a definite direction.

AMBRONN (1925) observed in the epidermal cells of the seedcoat of *Cobaea scandens* that the development of the spirally coiled cellulose threads is preceded by the development of a spiral structure in the protoplasm.

In the sporangiophore of *Phycomyces* the presence of a correlation between the direction of the protoplasmic streaming and the orientation of the chitin micelles in the secondary wall, was observed by OORT and ROELOFSEN (1932), and confirmed by CASTLE (1936a), POP (1938) and MARTENS (1940). KIRCHHEIMER (1933), however, found little or no correlation.

It should, on the other hand, not be forgotten that the direction in which the cellulose micelles are oriented does by no means always correspond with the direction of the protoplasmic streaming. We have mentioned already the discrepancy that was noted between the two in the case of the hairs on the *Tradescantia* stamens. In the secondary wall of the *Nitella* cells, an object that is known for its very conspicuous protoplasmic streaming, there is also a marked difference between the direction of the latter and that of the cellulose micelles, cf. section 2413.

In many instances, however, the presence of a correlation between the development of the wall thickenings and a corresponding accumulation of protoplasm, and less obviously, also between the orientation of the cellulose micelles in these thickenings and the direction in which the protoplasm in these accumulations is streaming, seems to be undeniable. Several investigators have tacitly assumed that there exists a causal relation between these phenomena, viz. that the streaming protoplasm determines the direction in which the molecules or micelles are deposited, but in the third decennium of this century this idea had to be abandoned, as it was then generally recognized that the outermost layer of the protoplasm did not share in the movement of the inner part, but that it was firmly united with the wall. VAN ITERSON, for instance, was at first of opinion that the streaming would orient the cellulose micelles (1927, 1937), but afterwards (1942) he ascribed the orientation of these micelles to an anisotropic structure of the ectoplasm, but in what way the latter would effect the orientation, remains up to now an open question.

Another open question is that of the way in which the anisotropism of the ectoplasm is brought about. It can hardly be denied that in some cases, e. g. where such structures as wall thickenings and bordered pits are developed, the ectoplasm must have assumed this character autonomously, but according to VAN ITERSON (1936a) the anisotropism may in some other instances be due to extension. In a cell that is growing in length, the extension is strongest in the axial direction, and for that reason the ectoplasm, and consequently the cellulose in the secondary wall also, would be more or less axially oriented. In the successive layers in the cell-wall of *Valonia* the direction in which the micelles are oriented undergoes every time a change of circ. 90° (cf. section 2411); here too, he ascribes the orientation to an extension of the ectoplasm, which therefore would undergo corresponding changes in direction.

Several authors (e. g. FREY-WYSSLING, 1953; PRESTON and ASTBURY, 1937) have raised objections against the view that the extension of the ectoplasm would be the decisive factor, although they admitted that it might be one of the determining factors. In their opinion the theory does not take into account that the *Valonia* cells, for instance, do not alternately grow in diameter and in length, but that they extend simultaneously in all directions, as follows from the fact that they are all the while retaining their globular shape. Neither does it pay attention to the circumstance that the protoplasm of a tubular cell apparently does not react in this way to the extension during the greater part of the period of growth; the supposition that it does so in the final stage involves therefore the assumption that the character of the protoplasm undergoes at that particular moment an essential change. ROELOFSEN (1950a) has tried to solve this difficulty by assuming that during the initial stages of the cell's growth the ectoplasm might retain its transverse structure because the intussusception of protein with a similar orientation is as yet fully adequate. However, as soon as this surface growth of the plasmatic membrane would become insufficient to compensate the extension in the axial direction, a re-orientation would set in. This would happen in the final stage of the cell's growth. In one of the previous sections such a change in the structure of the ectoplasm has been suggested as a possible cause of the particular structure shown by the S_1 layer in xylem elements and in cotton hairs.

Still another objection that has been raised against VAN ITERSON's theory, is that in the secondary wall of fibres and of some kinds of parenchyma cells, three or even more than three layers with a different orientation may be present; as these layers have been deposited after the cells have completed their growth, their orientation must be due to an autonomous activity of the protoplasm. In order to explain the production of local wall thickenings and of cellulose threads that are more or less free from the cell-wall, the assumption of an autonomous activity of the protoplasm also seems unavoidable.

The protoplasm does not only determine the orientation of the cellulose micelles in the wall, but obviously also the place where the latter grows, and in this way the shape of the cell. In what manner this influence is exercised, is also unknown; it is clear, however, that the protoplasm must be able to regulate the adhesion between the individual microfibrils.

A correlation of an entirely different kind, viz. that between the speed of the spiral in which the micelles are oriented, and the length, or better the quotient length/diameter, of the cells in which they occur, was studied by PRESTON, as we have discussed already in sections 2342 and 23431. He studied it first and most extensively in the tracheids of various kinds of *Coniferae* (1934; 1947; 1948; with WARDROP, 1949a), further in the parenchyma cells of the *Avena* coleoptile (1938), in xylem vessels (1939), in bamboo fibres (PRESTON and SINGH, 1950) and in sisal fibres (PRESTON and MIDDLEBROOK, 1949). A summary of these studies is given in PRESTON's book (1952). The same correlation has been found also in the fibres of other *Monocotyledones* (A. D. J. MEEUSE, 1938) and in cotton hairs (BERKLEY, 1948). A corresponding correlation exists between the pitch of the spiral thickenings in tracheids and the length of the latter (WARDROP and DADSWELL, 1951).

It is noteworthy that the speed of the helix may vary in different parts of one cell, e. g. in the tangential and in the radial walls of tracheids. Even more conspicuous is the difference between the inner tangential wall and the outer one in the hypodermal fibres found in the beak of the fruits of *Anemone pulsatilla*. In the first-named walls the helical structure has a pitch of a few degrees only, whereas a pitch of circ. 54° is found in the outer tangential wall (SEYFRIED, 1954). This structure explains the twisting of the beak when the water content changes.

PRESTON thought at first that the differences in the speed of the spiral were due to differences in the degree of extension to which the spiral structure in the wall and in the protoplast of the cambium initials had been subjected during the period of growth, but this hypothesis, which was already untenable in view of various data on the cell-wall structure reported in the older literature, was dropped by him when he too recognized that the same wall may contain layers with a spiral structure of different speed and direction (1947). So the explanation of the correlation mentioned above, became to him too an open question.

Afterwards WARDROP and PRESTON (1950) found in tracheids of a given length a negative correlation between the speed of the spiral and the rate of growth of the cells from which they developed. The deeper cause of this correlation too is an open question. As WARDROP and DADSWELL (1951) found in cells with spiral thickenings a larger number of turns per cell if the length of the cells increases, they are of opinion that these thickenings can not owe their origin to extension of a preformed "plasmatic spiral", because in that case all the descendants of the same cambial initial would have to contain the same number of turns, irrespective of differences in length.

For theories with regard to the orientation of cellulose and chitin microfibrils in growing walls we refer to the sections 22825 and 22827.

236. THE STRUCTURE OF INCRUSTATED AND ADCRUSTATED CELL-WALLS

2361. Lignified cell-walls

What is known with regard to the structure of lignin, has already been discussed in section 16. Apart from its chemical and physical properties, its presumable biogenesis and the way in which it is attacked by microphytes, we have described in that section its localization in the cell-wall and in the space between the microfibrils of the cellulose; this incrustation was illustrated also by means of electron micrographs (fig. 22 and 23). Further, the increase in thickness which the cell-wall undergoes on account of the lignification, and the decrease in thickness which is noticed when the lignin is removed, were discussed.

In xylem elements the radial walls appeared to be more strongly lignified than the tangential ones, which, according to Bosshard (1956b), explains why wood shows a stronger shrinkage in the tangential direction. It was also mentioned that by far the strongest lignification is met with in the middle lamella and in the primary wall, and that the lignification starts at the cell edges, from where it proceeds first in the middle lamella of the tangential walls and then in that of the radial ones (Wardrop, 1957a). This happens more or less during the time that the S_1 layer is deposited; this layer itself becomes lignified when the deposition of the S_2 layer is in progress. It was also mentioned that in the lamellae of the S_2 layer the degree of lignification may show alternately an increase and a decrease; this is illustrated by the micrographs reproduced in section 23433.

2362. Cutinized cell-walls and cuticles

Some information with regard to the chemical structure of cutin and wax, the substances that are always present in the cuticle and in the cutinized cell-wall, has already been given in section 17. The degree of development of the cutinized cell-wall and the different forms which this wall may assume in various kinds of epidermal cells, will not be dealt with, because these aspects of the problem are considered in works dealing especially with the structure of the epidermis (cf. Linsbauer, 1930; Küster, 1956). At this place we will confine our attention in the main to the ultramicroscopical structure of the cutinized cell-wall.

It has been known already for a long time (literature e. g. in Fritz, 1935; van Wisselingh, 1925) that the outermost periclinal (i. e. tangential) wall of the epidermal cells is coated with a thin layer of cutin, and that in this layer no cell-wall polysaccharides are present. This cutin layer extends in the form of a very thin membrane via the stomata into the intercellular spaces; this was observed by several investigators (Geneau de Lamarlière, 1906; Arzt, 1933, 1936, 1937; Priestley, 1943; Häusermann, 1944; Scott, 1950 and Küster, 1956: 700).

In the epidermis of hygrophytes the layer underneath the cutin layer contains cellulose but no cutin. In many mesophytes and in the xerophytes, on the other hand, it contains not only cellulose, and presumably pectin, but also cutin, and in these plants this layer may often reach a considerable thickness.

The outermost layer which, as we have seen, contains cutin but no cellulose, we will call in the usual way "cuticle" or "cuticle proper", the next layer, at least if it contains not only cellulose but also cutin, the "cuticular layer". The cuticle proper owes its origin to the secretion of cutin or of precursors of the latter, a process for which Sitte (1955) coined the term "adcrustation". Following the terminology as used by Esau (1953: 142), adcrustation of cutin is to be called "cuticularization". The cuticular layer, however, is formed by the deposition of cutin in spaces in the outermost layer of the cell-wall; as this is an incrustation, it is called "cutinization".

In order to obviate confusion, we will not use the term "cuticle" for the combination of the cuticle proper and the cuticular layer, but we will call this complex, as we have proposed at an earlier occasion (1952), the "cuticular membrane". In many plants the outer epidermal wall consists therefore of this cuticular membrane and an inner, non-cutinized part.

Theoretically the distinction of the various layers by the aid of these definitions looks easy enough, but in reality the boundaries are but seldom sharply distinguishable. This is due to the fact that the cellulose and the other constituents of the cutinized layer are so completely enveloped by cutin that they no longer give the ordinary microchemical reactions, and so it is, as a rule, difficult to make out in this way where in radial sections of cuticular membranes, the cutinization ends and cuticularization begins. In radial sections of walls from which the cutin wax has been extracted, the transition may be marked by a change in optical behaviour, as the cellulose-containing cuticular layer may then have become positively birefringent with reference to the plane (tangent) of the wall, whereas the cuticle may have stayed isotropic or nearly so. However, the amount of cellulose is sometimes so small, especially in the outermost part of the cuticular layer, that its birefringence may be masked by that of traces of residual wax.

As a means to determine the boundary between cuticle and cuticular layer it is often assumed that with reference to the plane of the wall the cuticle is always optically isotropic and that the cuticular layer so long as the cutin wax has not been removed, is always negatively birefringent. However, the presumably isotropic cuticle may, as we will see, in reality show a small negative birefringence and, more important, it has so far never been proved that cellulose really occurs in all parts that exhibit a more conspicuous negative double refraction.

Although it is therefore most uncertain where the cuticle exactly ends and the cuticular layer begins, there need not be any uncertainty with regard to the presence or absence of a cuticular layer. As the cutinized cellulose of this layer is protected against solvents, it is quite easy to isolate this cellulose. To this end the non-cutinized part of the cell-wall is dissolved e. g. in concentrated sulphuric acid and cuprammonium. The remaining part, i. e. the cuticular membrane, may then be decutinized, e. g. by means of hot alcoholic alkali. If the whole membrane dissolves, this means that no cellulose was present, and in that case there was, of course, no cuticular layer. The question of the presence or absence of a cuticular layer may also be decided by using sections that have partly been decutinized, and that are subsequently treated for a long time with chlor-zinc-iodine, which enables us to localize the cellulose. However, as decomposition products of suberin too are known to stain violet with this reagent, though weakly, it is not entirely excluded that the decomposition products of cutin might give this reaction too; this, however, has not yet been experimentally verified.

In turning our attention towards the main publications dealing with the ultra-microscopical structure of the cuticular membrane, we meet in the first place a paper by AMBRONN (1888), in which it is shown that the negative birefringence that, as was known already at that time, is observed in sections through the cuticular membrane and through the wall of cork cells, disappeared if the preparation, which was embedded in glycerol, was heated to 100°C, and that it returned when the preparation was allowed to cool. On account of the fact that in cork the birefringence was known to disappear also if the preparation was extracted with chloroform, or if it was treated with alkali, and also on account of experiments with crystallized fats, AMBRONN supposed that this behaviour was due to the melting of fat- or wax-like substances in the cuticular membrane, which on cooling once more crystallized.

A. FREY (1926) has measured the birefringence in various layers of the epidermal wall in the petiole of *Aucuba japonica* and in the leaf of *Clivia nobilis*. His results were summarized in a figure that is reproduced here in fig. 166. In both objects the negative birefringence reaches its highest value in the middle of the cuticular membrane. The cuticle of *Clivia* is said to be isotropic, whereas in *Aucuba* the outermost layer would be positively birefringent, which is exceptional and as yet unexplained.

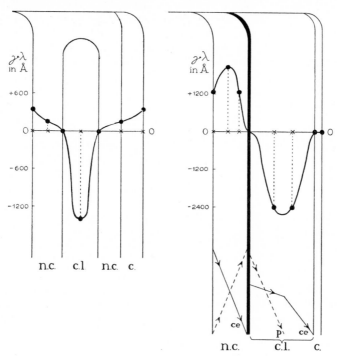

Fig. 166. Birefringence in different parts of a section through the outer epidermal wall of, at the left: *Aucuba japonica* (petiole, transverse), and at the right: *Clivia nobilis* (leaf, radial); n.c.: non-cutinized layer; c.l.: supposed cuticular layer; c: supposed cuticle proper (from A. Frey, 1926). Anderson's view (1928) with regard to the content of cellulose and pectin in the cuticular layer in *Clivia* is given in the lower part of the right-hand drawing; p.: pectin; ce. cellulose (see, however, the text and the view of Meyer, 1938).

According to this author the epidermal wall of *Aucuba* would contain cuticular plates that end in the cell edges, as shown in the figure. In our own transverse sections we found a similar delimitation of the birefringent part, but this did not apply to the part that gave cutin reactions. The absence of birefringence at the cell edges may therefore be due to differences in the orientation of the micelles or to differences in the concentration of the birefringent constituent (wax). Fritz (1935) too could not fully confirm Frey's observations on the structure of the epidermal wall in *Aucuba*.

Anderson's conclusions (1928) with regard to the constitution of the cuticular membrane are rather hypothetical. He thought that he might regard the faculty of the cuticular membrane to stain with ruthenium-red and with magdala-red as proof of the presence of pectin, and concludes that in *Clivia* the greatest amount of this substance is present in the innermost part of the cuticular layer, and that the concentration in the central part of the latter has already decreased to zero, fig. 166. However, it is to be expected that these cation stains will be bound not only by the carboxyl groups of the pectin but also by those of the acids that presumably function as precursors of cutin (cf. section 171).

ANDERSON's supposition that the cellulose content too decreases towards the periphery, though less rapidly, is not improbable, but it is not supported by experimental evidence, and this applies also to his supposition that the cutin content increases in that direction, which rests merely on the supposition that the other constituents undergo a decrease.

That the negative birefringence reaches its highest value in the central part of the cuticular layer, would, according to ANDERSON, be due to the circumstance that the concentration of the "birefringent cutin" (it appeared afterwards that the birefringence is not due to the presence of cutin but to that of wax) increases towards the periphery, but that the orientation of the birefringent particles decreases in that direction, since it would be correlated with the number of orienting cellulose micelles. The cuticle proper would be isotropic, because in this part of the cell-wall there is no orientation at all. However, all this is pure hypothesis.

FRITZ (1935) gives a valuable survey of the literature. He himself studied especially species of *Aloë* and *Gasteria armstrongii*, later (1937) also the pericarp of *Convallaria*, *Smilacina* and *Asparagus*. By decutinizing sections completely or partly by means of concentrated alkali, or by treating them with 20 % chromic acid, or else by exposing them to the attacks of rotting bacteria, he could

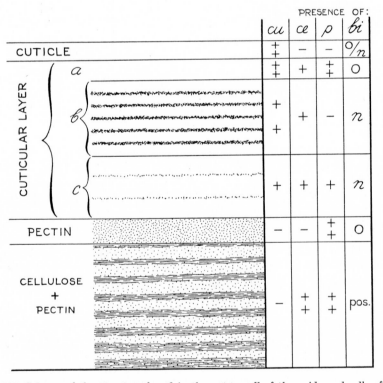

Fig. 167. Schema of the structure found in the outer wall of the epidermal cells of *Aloë* species; cu: cutin; ce: cellulose; p: pectin; bi: birefringence, (n)egative, (pos)itive or nil (o). (Mainly based on a drawing and description of FRITZ, 1935).

demonstrate by means of chlor-zinc-iodine, ruthenium-red or other stains, that the cuticular layer consists without doubt of several layers and lamellae, fig. 167.

The outermost lamella (a) of the cuticular layer is very poor in cellulose but rich in cutin, and is supposed to contain also a large amount of pectin. The inner and much thicker part contains more cellulose; in *Gasteria* it is homogeneous, but in *Aloë* it appears to consist of two parts, viz. an outer part (b) with about 6 lamellae that are rich in cutin, alternating with 5 lamellae that are rich in cellulose, and an inner part (c) with a lower cutin content, but consisting also of several lamellae, which would differ in their pectin content. However, it is noteworthy that according to the author the substance which gives the pectin reactions, was not removed by a treatment with concentrated potassium hydro-xyde, so that it can not be pectin. We suppose that it is a decomposition pro-duct of cutin. FRITZ himself (1937) too is dubious with regard to the value that is to be attached to the staining of the cuticular layer with ruthenium-red. The presence of pectin in the non-cutinized part of the wall is absolutely certain.

The highest number of lamellae found in the cuticular layer was in *Aloë* 20 and in the pericarp of *Asparagus* even 65. A very large number of lamellae may be distinguished without any previous treatment in the cuticular layer of seve-ral other plants, e. g. in *Eucalyptus* and in *Viscum* (LINSBAUER, 1930).

The outermost lamellae of the cuticular layer extend throughout the whole epidermis, the inner ones are at the cell edges deflected into the anticlinal walls. PRIESTLEY (1943) supposes that the first set is deposited in the period of growth, the second set after the latter has been completed. At any rate, it is clear that the cuticular layer is nothing more than a cutinized part of a normal wall.

FRITZ describes also radial structures occurring in the cuticular layer, espe-cially in *Gasteria*, and discusses the older literature on this subject. These parts differ from the rest in cutin content. FRITZ illustrates his findings with se-veral drawings, and at another place he gives also a micrograph (cf. KÜSTER, 1956: 693). Abnormal cutinization and regeneration of the cuticular layer are also dealt with.

M. MEYER (1938) has carried out a most elucidating investigation into the cause of the negative birefringence found in the cuticular layer of *Clivia*, *Gaste-ria*, *Yucca* and *Dasylirion*. The changes in the birefringence of the various layers observed in sections are summarized by her in the schema reproduced in fig. 168.

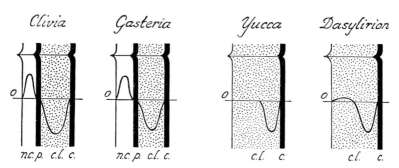

Fig. 168. Schema of the differences in birefringence shown by the successive layers in the outer epidermal wall in the leaves of four different kinds of plants after M. MEYER (1938); interpretation of the abbreviations as in fig. 166.

The outermost layer, the cuticle proper, is according to her always isotropic. The next one, i. e. the cuticular layer, is always negatively birefringent. In *Gasteria* and *Clivia* the latter passes on the inside into a non-cutinized layer with positive birefringence, whereas in **Dasylirion** and *Yucca* this layer too proves to be cutinized; it is, however, either slightly positively birefringent or isotropic.

After extracting the material for a long time with fat-solvents (presumably at boiling temperature or in a Soxhlet apparatus), the negative birefringence is no more visible. As the cutin is not removed in this way, this proves that the latter can not be responsible for the negative birefringence, but that this phenomenon is caused by presence of soluble lipids, as AMBRONN already had supposed. However, except in *Clivia*, the cuticular layer became isotropic only in the outermost part; the inner part became positively birefringent or, if it was already positively birefringent, it became more strongly so. The staining effected by a long continued treatment with chlor-zinc-iodine proved that this is due to the presence of tangentially oriented cellulose. The latter appeared to be deposited in the form of lamellae.

In *Clivia* a slight degree of dichroism appearing after the treatment with chlor-zinc-iodine, proved that a small amount of cellulose was present, but that it was too small to cause a clear positive birefringence. In the outermost part of the cuticular layer the cellulose was not recognizable at all, and MEYER assumed therefore that it was actually absent; she differs therefore in this respect from ANDERSON. Although admitting that MEYER's conclusion is probably right, we wish to point out that the absence of cellulose in this part of the cuticular layer can nevertheless not be regarded as fully certain, as slight amounts of this substance may escape the attention and further that if cellulose really was absent in this part, the latter ought to be included in the cuticle proper, not in the cuticular layer, notwithstanding the fact that its negative double refraction in the non-extracted condition was considerable.

Because the wax she had extracted, proved to be positively birefringent (with regard to the molecule axis), and also because the cuticular layer after the extraction showed form-birefringence, MEYER came to the conclusion that this layer must be incrustated with flat wax crystallites, and that the latter are oriented more or less tangentially in the periclinal walls, and radially in the anticlinal ones. The wax molecules are oriented normal to the plane of the crystallites. The latter would occupy lamellar spaces in the cutin. Fig. 169 shows this schematically.

FREY-WYSSLING (1953a) has suggested that the cutin would act as intermediary between the hydrophilic cellulose and the hydrophobic wax.

As we do not intend to devote a special section to the question of the orientation of the wax crystallites in the non-cutinized cell-wall, it seems worth while to draw at this place the attention to the conclusion at which K. and M. WÜHRMANN-MEYER (1939) arrived with regard to the nature of the *wax crystallites* that are found in the *walls of the parenchyma cells* of the growing *Avena* coleoptile. On account of their optical properties they believe that these crystallites can not have the form of slabs, but are rod-like, and that the rods are oriented parallel to the microfibrils of the cellulose; in the present case therefore, on the average more or less transverse to the cell axis. In these rodlets the molecules would occupy a radial position, which means that the rodlets would have in transverse section a more or less sphaeritic structure. FREY-

WYSSLING (e. g. 1953a) prefers a somewhat different interpretation of the results of these authors, viz. that the wax molecules would be oriented radially with regard to the microfibrils of the cellulose, i. e. that these microfibrils would form the axis of the rodlets.

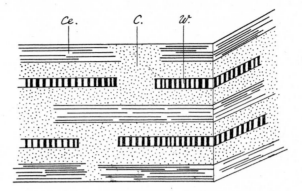

Fig.169.Schema of the structure supposed to be present in the cuticular layer in the epidermal cells of *Clivia* leaves; it would contain cellulose lamellae (ce) and wax platelets (w) embedded in cutin (c); after M. MEYER (1938).

It seems to us that neither of these interpretations is very probable. FREY-WYSSLING ascribes an orienting influence to the cellulose, but it is difficult to imagine that the affinity between the hydrophilic cellulose and the hydrophobic wax would be sufficient to allow the first to exercise an orienting influence on the molecules of the latter, and that the microfibrils of the cellulose therefore could function as axis for a rodlet that for the rest would consist of wax. The wax from the cuticular layer on the other hand would, according to FREY-WYSSLING (l. c.), have no affinity to the cellulose and for this reason in this layer cutin would have to act as intermediary. This would mean that the wax in the walls of the meristematic cells would chemically be quite different from that in the cuticular layer, but of such a difference nothing is known.

Next we wish to point out that the crystallinity of the two suggested types of sphaeritic structure (there are X-ray interferences, see below) is inexplicable if we assume that in the rodlets the molecules are radially oriented since in a crystal structure the molecules must be parallel. We would therefore have to assume that the molecules are combined into rod-like crystallites, and that the latter are the radially oriented building stones of the supposed sphaeritic structures. Such crystal aggregates, however, would not be of submicroscopic size, but would become distinguishable under the microscope, like some of the wax rodlets with which in some plants the cuticle is covered (KREGER, 1948). This evidently is out of the question.

The observations of K. and M. WÜHRMANN-MEYER (l. c.), moreover, form in our opinion no reliable foundation, as the results obtained in different coleoptiles varied too much, and also because of the shrinkage caused by the extraction of the wax. However, even if we were prepared to overlook these shortcomings, we will have to admit that these results can be explained as well if we do not assume a sphaeritic structure for the wax particles, but a slab-like form comparable to that of the wax inclusions in the cuticular layer and a similar orientation of these platelets, viz. parallel to the surface of the wall. If these platelets occupy positions which deviate slightly from the plane of the surface, they may cause birefringence in surface view of the wall, and this birefringence may be positive or negative with reference to the cell axis according to the direction of the deviation that predominates. The other observations of K. and

M. WÜHRMANN-MEYER too can be explained in this way. Before a final judgment can be given, we will therefore have to await further information.

The observations that so far have been reported, do not, as a matter of fact, justify the conclusion that the cuticular layer or the meristematic cell-walls contain wax crystallites, as the birefringence and the latter's disappearance when the material is heated, can also be explained by assuming molecular birefringe of wax molecules that are adsorbed to the cutin in a position normal to the wall surface. However, from young cotton hairs and from hairs found on the seed-coat of other plants and also from epidermal cells, GUNDERMANN, WERGIN and HESS (1937) had already obtained X-ray interferences of wax. At that occasion it was also found out that they had at an earlier occasion already been observed by two of them and also by other investigators, although their true nature was not recognized, viz. in cotton hairs by CLARK (1930) and in the epidermis of *Avena* coleoptiles and other objects by HEYN (1934). Although the latter noted that the X-ray interferences disappeared after extraction with alcohol, he did not express an opinion with regard to the identity of the substance to which they were due.

These investigations proved that the cell-wall must contain somewhere wax crystallites, but not that they occurred for the greater part in the cuticular membrane. This was proved in 1950 by BANGE in the author's laboratory for the cuticular membrane of *Clivia*. Previously extracted as well as not extracted cuticular membranes were folded into small multi-layered packets and then X-ray diagrams were made by directing the beam either normal or parallel to the plane of the cuticular membranes. No interferences were obtained from cellulose, although the latter was doubtless present, but wax interferences were clearly distinguishable, and a very vague ring represented the amorphous cutin. If the beam of X-rays traversed the membrane perpendicularly, the interferences were not oriented, but they were distinctly oriented when the beam traversed the latter in a tangential direction, no matter whether they did this longitudinally or transversely, fig. P170. This confirms the correctness of MEYER's conclusions. The presence of so-called long-spacings shows that the wax platelets must be at least 4 times as thick as the molecules are long, presumably therefore at least 150 Å.

The present author(1952) has made a few supplementary observations on epidermal cells of the same plant species which had been investigated by M. MEYER (l. c.) and also in those of *Aloë*. If cuticular membranes of *Clivia* from which the freely exposed cellulose and hemicellulose had been removed by means of cuprammonium, acid and ammonia, were decutinized with hot alcoholic alkali, a frail cellulose skeleton was obtained in which the microfibrils were oriented as indicated schematically in fig. 171. This structure too is in perfect agreement with the idea that the cuticular layer is a cutinized but for the rest entirely normal cell-wall layer. In some (unpublished) electron micrographs of these preparations the microfibrils of the cellulose were clearly distinguishable, although they were still to a considerable degree polluted. The reaction with chlor-zinc-iodine was nevertheless already quite distinct.

It appeared furthermore that in all these objects the cuticle proper is not isotropic, as it was so far said to be, but that it shows a slight negative birefringence with reference to the tangential plane. That this is due to the presence of wax, appeared from the fact that it disappeared after extraction, and that the cuticle in this way even began to show a slight positive birefringence. It is noteworthy that the supposed isotropism of the cuticle proper has led to the generally accepted conclusion that this layer contains no wax (PRIESTLEY, 1943). Even if it really were isotropic, this conclusion would not be justified, as the wax molecules or crystallites might be distributed at random.

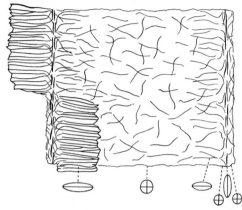

Fig. 171. Orientation of the micelles and optical properties of the cellulose skeleton obtained from the cuticular layer in a part of the wall of an epidermal cell from a leaf of *Clivia nobilis*, to the left with a flattened ridge, representing the anticlinal wall, to the right without ridge (from ROELOFSEN, 1952).

Between the cuticle and the strongly birefringent layer for which the name cuticular layer is used, there is in *Clivia* and in many other objects a thin isotropic layer (a in fig. 167).

We found furthermore that even if an extraction in the heat with various wax solvents, was continued for a very long time, the cuticular layer still showed a slight negative birefringence. This was ascribed to wax molecules that are adsorbed to the cutin in a radial position, although oriented monomers of the cutin too might cause the phenomenon. These wax molecules were supposed to line the lamellar pores that were originally filled with wax platelets. In insect cuticles too, non-extractable oriented lipids have been found (HURST, 1950), and in cork a similar situation seems to be present (see later).

A more detailed study of the form-birefringence present in extracted cuticular membranes of *Clivia* demonstrated the presence of spaces, presumably left by the removal of the wax platelets, that actually are flattened and that are oriented in such a way that the flat side runs parallel to the surface of the cell-wall; seen from the surface it appears that they are on the average in the axial direction of the cell shorter than in the transverse direction. From the fluctuations in the birefringence observed in surface view in flattened non-extracted cuticular membranes, it may furthermore be concluded that these lamellar pores are not absolutely flat but more or less undulating.

Fig. 172 indicates schematically how the birefringence (T) of the cuticular membrane rests on that of the wax platelets (W), of the residual wax (R) and of the cellulose (C), and on form birefringence (F).

In the cuticular membrane of the staminal hairs of *Tradescantia* too, it is according to ROELOFSEN and HOUWINK (1951) impossible to destroy or even to diminish by extraction the intrinsic negative birefringence with reference to the tangential plane, so that here too we must assume the presence of oriented wax molecules that are strongly adsorbed to the cutin or else a birefringence of the cutin itself. As in this cuticular membrane no cellulose was present, it could not be regarded as a cuticular layer, but had to be interpreted as the cuticle proper. If this layer was embedded in a medium with a refractive index below 1.4 or above 1.6, it showed positive birefringence with reference to the plane because the form birefringence had become stronger than the intrinsic one.

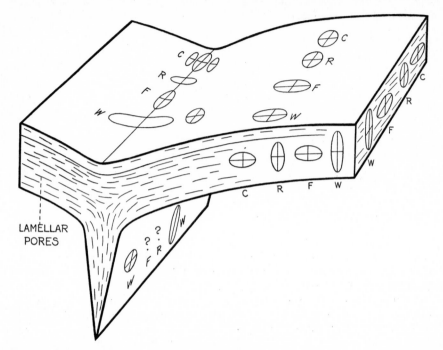

Fig. 172. Schematical representation of the way in which the birefringence in various parts of the non-extracted cuticular layer of *Clivia nobilis* rests on that of the wax platelets (W) of the residual wax (R) and of the cellulose (C) as well as on form birefringence (F) (according to ROELOFSEN, 1952).

FREYTAG (1954b) found in the hairs of the cecidia caused by an aphid on the petioles of *Populus*, that the lamellar spaces in the cuticular layer in which the wax is deposited, are also tangentially oriented, and that they have, like those found in the cuticular layer of *Clivia*, a more or less undulating shape.

In glandular hairs of *Matricaria chamomilla*, FREYTAG (1957) found that the cuticle, which forms here the outer wall of the space which contains the secretion, as well as the part of the cell-wall which encloses this space on the inside, are negatively birefringent. Already after a short extraction with chloroform in the cold, both layers become positively birefringent, and he arrives therefore at the conclusion that the negative birefringence is not due to the presence of wax but to that of more easily soluble constituents of the secretion.

In the glandular hairs of some other plants the corresponding layers were already positively birefringent with reference to the tangential plane before they were extracted; this might be due to the presence of a smaller amount of lipid or perhaps to the presence of another kind of lipid. The positive birefringence which he found in extracted cuticles, he regarded partly as form birefringence and partly as the result of the presence of cellulose, so that these layers are in his opinion no true cuticles but cuticular layers. The presence of cellulose, however, was not proved.

Already since 1951 we have tried to obtain by means of the electron microscope confirmation of the presence of the tangentially oriented lamellar spaces
filled with wax, which on account of the study of the optical properties and of
the X-ray diagrams were supposed to be present in the cuticular layer; but only recently we succeeded in obtaining sections, thin enough to show a delicate
periclinal striation that might be due to layers of wax of less than 100 Å thickness, fig. P 173. The sections were obtained from cuticular membranes that had
been stained with osmium tetroxide and that had been embedded in methacrylate. Sections of membranes from which the wax had been extracted and that had
been shadowed after removal of the methacrylate, so far did not show the expected lamellar pores.

Recently, HILKENBÄUMER (1958) observed a somewhat more conspicuous
periclinal lamellation in the cuticular membrane of apples; the lamellae were
about 60 Å thick, fig. P 174.

If the observed lamellae really correspond to the wax-filled pores in the cutin,
these pores can not have contained true crystallites, but only monomolecular
or bimolecular layers of wax molecules, since we know that the latter must be
oriented radially and have a length of about 40 Å in case it are paraffins, alcohols or acids and about 70 Å in case it are esters. However, in that case the origin
of the interference of the long spacing in fig. P 170 becomes difficult to explain
since there must be at least four molecules placed end to end to obtain an interference.

When eventually present deposits of wax have been removed, *the surface of
the cuticle* as seen under the microscope, is often smooth, but it may also be
granular or plicate. The folds often show some relation to the direction of
growth or of the growth during a previous stage of development (MARTENS,
1934; 1940). The surface has repeatedly been studied by means of the electron
microscope. Sometimes replicas have to be made, viz. if the cuticular membrane proves to be too thick, but in other objects the membranes themselves may be used (BOCK, 1955) .The surface of untreated cotton hairs and also
of hairs that, by means of a treatment with alcohol, had been deprived of superficial wax, has often been figured, e. g. by TRIPP et al. (1954, 1957) and by
KLING and MAHL (1951, 1952). In the objects studied so far with the electron
microscope, the surface of the cuticle did not show special structures, except a
uniform granulation that varied from fine to coarse in different objects and
that was also different on the two sides of a leaf.

GESSNER and VOLZ (1951) and VOLZ (1952) found in the cuticle of water plants,
especially in the hydropotes of *Nymphaea* and *Nelumbo*, pore-like structures,
which, however, were no openings but very thin spots. Such structures were
found also in the cuticle of nectaries, which according to the older literature
would be provided with pores.

The cuticle of the moss *Physcomitrium acuminatum* was studied by BAUER
(1956). Its outer surface was finely granular, the inner one coarsely granular,
and it consisted of two lamellae, of which the outer one was locally fissured and
occasionally even detached and turned over, but this was probably an artefact;
pores were absent; and whether one of the lamellae contained cellulose and
might be regarded therefore as a cuticular layer, is unknown.

On account of the secretion of wax on the outside of the cuticle, and especially if this wax was present in the form of radially arranged rodlets, it was

not unnatural to assume that the cuticle would contain radial pores. One of the investigators who claimed to have seen these pores under the microscope, was Dous (1927), and experiments on the permeability of the cuticle were said to have proved their presence too. Recent observations and experiments, however, did not confirm these findings (Volz, l. c.; Sitte, 1954; Skoss, 1955; Bock, 1955). Experiments on the permeability carried out by Bange in our laboratory, also had a negative result, although they were partly made with the cuticle of *Cotyledon gibbiflora*, in which Dous claimed to have seen very distinct pores. Under the microscope it in fact proved to be marked with light dots, but the electron micrographs show a uniform surface, possibly with some thinner spots. A uniform granular cuticle surface was also found in leaves of *Typha latifolia* and of *Colocasia antiquorum*; in both species the cuticle is known to be covered with wax rodlets. Scott et al. (1957) arrived at the same conclusion in their study of the cuticle of the onion leaf, although in this case in the cellulose layer underneath the cuticle, pores were actually present (cf. section 23442) .Mueller et al. (1954) found in the cuticle of *Musa* no pores either, though shallow depressions were actually present, and in the latter the greater part of the wax rodlets, though not all of them, were developed, fig. P 175.

In section 171 we have made mention of the hypothesis according to which the cuticle owes its origin to the polymerization of monomers that are secreted by the epidermal cells. This would be in harmony with an observation reported by Martens (1934), viz. that it looks as if the cuticle is at first rather weak and that it hardens later on; in full-grown staminal hairs of *Tradescantia* it is rather easily torn if it is stretched. There are more indications of changes on ageing (Linskens, 1952). In some instances we will have to assume that the cuticle retains its elasticity, e. g. in the strongly elongating filaments of the *Gramineae*.

2363. The sporoderm

The development of the spore membrane has been investigated by Fitting (1900) and Lyon (1905) in *Isoëtes* and *Selaginella*, by Wentzel (1929) in *Hepaticae*, and in pollen grains especially by Strasburger and, more recently, by Mühlethaler (1953b, 1955) and Sitte (1953).

The membrane of spores and pollen grains proves to consist of an intine which contains cellulose, an exine which consists mainly of sporopollenine and sometimes on the outside of the latter a perine which is formed by the periplasmodium. The exine is probably a secretion product comparable to the cuticle (Sitte, 1953). The relief of the exine is of taxonomical and palynological importance, and has therefore been described extensively (Erdtman, 1943; 1952; 1954; 1956).

The recent literature on the *submicroscopical structure* has been discussed by Steffen (1955), Erdtman (1956a) and Sitte (cf. Treiber, 1957: 443). Sporopollenine is like cutin an amorphous substance. Labouriau and Cardoso (1948, cf. Steffen l. c.) noted very weak X-ray interferences. The exine shows no intrinsic birefringence, but only a weak form birefringence, and in very thin sections it reveals, when very strongly magnified, a granular structure and sometimes in addition a conspicuous lamellation; this is shown in fig. P176 (Afzelius et al., 1954; Afzelius, 1956; Erdtman, 1956a).

The granules measure about 65 Å and are supposed to be molecules of sporopollenine. The space between the lamellae are locally greatly enlarged as a result of swelling. According to Afzelius (1956) the presence of the lamellar structure could, contrary to the expectation, not be demonstrated by means of the small-angle X-ray scattering method.

The surface of spores has repeatedly been investigated by means of replicas (SITTE, 1953; MÜHLETHALER, 1955), and with a strong magnification it always proves to be granular with the granules arranged in definite patterns. With regard to the submicroscopical structure these replicas do not enlighten us.

2364. The suberized cell-wall

We will confine our attention here to the walls of true cork cells, and mention only in passing that thin suberized layers occur, according to SCOTT et al. (1948) and SCOTT (1950), also in the middle lamellae and on the inner surface of the wall in most of the other kinds of cells. Of the chemical nature of the substance of which this layer consists, we know only that it is a lipid which does not dissolve in wax-extracting liquids and is like suberin resistant against sulphuric and chromic acid. The endodermis cells do have suberized cell walls, but the submicroscopic structure of the latter has not yet been studied.

A concise but well-documented survey of the literature on the structure of the suberized wall has been given by SITTE (cf. TREIBER, 1957: 421). The microscopical structure of the suberized wall has been studied thoroughly, especially by VAN WISSELINGH (1925: 145). Several of the older authors like VON HÖHNEL who described in 1877 many observations made with the micro-scope, had assumed that suberin was deposited in a similar way as lignin bet-ween the cellulose of the secondary wall, but by carefully removing the suberin and the cork wax by which the latter was accompanied, VAN WISSELINGH could prove that the suberin forms a distinct lamella on the inside of a thin layer which contained cellulose and for which he used the name "primary wall"; the ex-traction was carried out either with concentrated KOH in the heat, with al-coholic alkali or with fat or glycerol at a temperature of $300°C$, and the cellu-lose was identified by staining with chlor-zinc-iodine. (With regard to VAN WISSELINGH's use of the term "primary wall", we wish to point out here that he did not prove that this layer consists only of the meristemic wall, and that he did not intend to say this; at that time, as we have remarked at an earlier occasion, this term was used in another sense; it is not excluded that his "primary wall" contained also a secondary thickening comparable to the S_1 layer).

On the inside of the suberin layer he found a thin membrane which contains cellulose and in sections the latter lies, after the removal of the suberin, in the form of an isolated ring in the lumen of the cell; this was called the "tertiary layer". The cork cells which VAN WISSELINGH studied, were obtained from *Laburnum vulgare, Quercus suber, Betula alba, Ilex aquifolium*, and some other species. The "tertiary layer" may occasionally be absent, but in the cork of *Quercus* it was, according to VAN WISSELINGH, actually present, which, how-ever, was contradicted by the results of SITTE ,which we will discuss below. The middle lamella and the "primary wall" are always lignified, the "tertiary layer" too is often lignified; these layers never contain suberin and the suberin layer is never lignified. In several instances, e. g. in *Laburnum*, the suberin layer shows a lamellate structure. One of the products that are formed when suberin is saponified, assumes, according to GILSON, a violet colour when it is treated with chlor-zinc-iodine, and this would, according to VAN WISSELINGH, explain why VON HÖHNEL thought that the suberin layer contained cellulose.

It was known already for a long time that the walls of the cork cells are just like the cuticular layer, isotropic in surface view, but negatively birefringent in sections; this negative birefringence, however, disappears according to KÜG-LER and DIPPEL after a treatment with chloroform or with alkali, and is replaced by a positive one, which was ascribed to the presence of cellulose. AMBRONN (1888) discovered that the negative birefringence disappears also when the material is heated in water or in glycerol to 100°C or to a higher temperature, but that in this case it reappears when the material is allowed to cool down. AMBRONN compared this behaviour and the effect of the extraction methods with the behaviour of fat crystals, and suggested that the negative birefringence of these cell-walls must be due to the presence of fat- or wax-like substances which melt on heating and recrystallize on cooling.

MADER (1954) was the first to investigate the birefringence of the various layers of the suberized cell-wall before as well as after the extraction of the wax with pyridine; he did this in the cork cells of *Laburnum watereri*. As indicated in the schematical fig. 177, he found in suberized cell-walls that had not been extracted, an isotropic "middle lamella", with which term he means the entire meristematic wall. This is covered by a thick layer of suberin showing a centripetally decreasing negative birefringence and finally passing into a positively birefringent inner layer, which apparently corresponds to the "tertiary", cellulose containing layer described by VAN WISSELINGH. He also noted that the cell still shows a slight growth after the suberin layer has been deposited. This makes it improbable that between the latter and the primary wall a remnant of the secondary wall would be present. The walls of older cork cells were found to be less strongly birefringent than those of the younger ones.

Extraction with pyridine affects according to MADER the suberin layer only, fig. 177, right part. As a rule the latter shows after the treatment a thin isotropic layer on the outside and a thicker positively birefringent one. Bordering on the primary wall, occasionally a thin negatively birefringent layer is found.

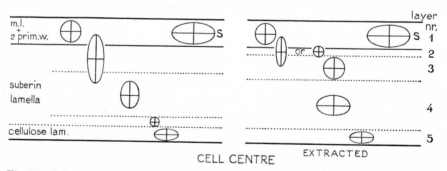

Fig. 177. Schematical representation of the optical behaviour in the various layers that are distinguishable in a transverse section of a suberized cell-wall, e. g. of *Laburnum watereri*, before and after the extraction of the wax with pyridine, after MADER (1954); according to SITTE (cf. TREIBER, 1957: 424) the primary walls are not isotropic, but positively birefringent; the index ellipses marked with an S refer to this view.

With regard to these observations it seems worth while to point out that the expected positive birefringence of the primary wall (layer 1) was not noticed by MADER, not even after the extraction. It may be that a wax-like substance is present that is less easily removed, so that the birefringence of the cellulose can not manifest itself. Next, the negative birefringence of layer 2 indicates that, just as in the cuticular membrane, it is apparently very difficult to remove the wax entirely. That layer 4 becomes positively birefringent, must, in our opinion, be due to form birefringence, at least if we accept MADER's view that this layer contains no cellulose. In this respect he agrees with VAN WISSELINGH, and the study of bottle cork by the aid of the electron microscope has subsequently confirmed this view. If this is right, the isotropism of layer 3 may rest on a compensation of the form birefringence by the negative birefringence of residual wax. In bottle cork SITTE (unpublished, cf. TREIBER, 1957: 426) actually found this form birefringence. According to him, layer 1 is in bottle cork not isotropic, as MADER found it in the *Laburnum* cork, but positively birefringent.

SITTE (1955; see also TREIBER, 1957: 425) has studied *bottle cork* also *by the aid of the electron microscope*. He used to this end sections as well as fragments of: untreated cork, cork that had been exposed to oxidizing agents, and cork that had partly been saponified by means of alkali and that subsequently was extracted with pyridine. As indicated in the schematical figure 178, each pair of cork cells possesses a common wall, which contains cellulose and which SITTE calls the primary wall, as it apparently contains no layers that have been deposited after the cell ceased to grow. The microfibrils of the cellulose in this layer form a network without, or with a slight degree of orientation, which is the normal condition in the primary as well as in the secondary wall of isodiametric cells. In untreated fragments this network remains invisible because of the presence of non-cellulose, but it becomes distinguishable after the walls have been purified with alkali, fig. P179.

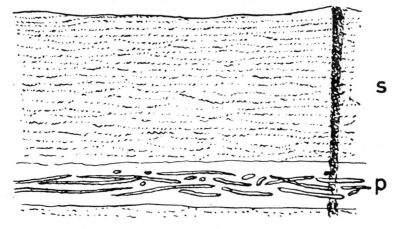

s

p

Fig. 178. Schema of the structure found in the cell-walls of bottle cork (according to SITTE, 1955); p: part of the wall which contains cellulose (middle lamella with the two primary walls); s: suberin layer, showing a lamellate structure. A pit canal traversing the whole thickness of the wall is shown too.

The suberin layer becomes very easily detached from the rest of the cell-wall, and contains no microfibrils. In fragments that have been treated with alkali often lamellae are distinguishable, which make that the preparations look as if they consist of terraces, fig. P180. According to SITTE there are about 60 lamellae, each with a thickness of 70–100 Å. This would mean that if the layer thickens by apposition every day quite a number of lamellae are deposited. That the lamellae often become visible after a treatment with alkali, indicates, according to SITTE, that the wax is localized between these lamellae, but as in sections never interlamellar spaces are noticed, but only striations, necessarily in very thin layers. As aliphatic wax molecules have a length of 40–80 Å, there would, in SITTE's opinion, be no sufficient space for the deposition of platelets, but only for a monomolecular or, at the most, for a bimolecular layer in which the molecules are oriented perpendicular to the suberin layers. He finds a confirmation of this view in the light blue fluorescence of the cork, which, according to him (see, however, MADER, 1954), would be due to the presence of wax. This light blue fluorescence is not shown by wax crystals, which emit a greyish light, but only in wax solutions. A similar situation is known to exist in chlorophyll.

SITTE furthermore found pit canals, usually in groups and traversing the entire thickness of the wall. They appeared to be clogged by a substance, presumably deposited after the death of the cells ,which dissolved in the oxidizing purifiers which were used by him. He found in bottle cork on the inside of the suberin layer no layer which contained cellulose. This does not agree with what VAN WISSELINGH reported on the cork of this species. Such a layer was found by SITTE in the cork of the potato, which in other respects closely resembles that of the cork oak.

The study with the electron microscope therefore produced an admirable confirmation of VAN WISSELINGH's view with regard to the presence of an entirely cellulose-free suberin lamella, and it showed that the latter, just like the cuticle, does not owe its origin to incrustation of a pre-existing layer, but that it is separately deposited. SITTE proposed for this process the term "adcrustation". Whether the suberin layer increases in thickness by apposition or by intussusception, is unknown, but on account of the lamellate structure it is generally assumed that it does so by apposition.

The optical properties of cork do not prove that the wax in the suberin layer is crystalline, no more than those of the cuticular membrane prove this for the wax in the cutin. PRINS (1934), to whom we owe the first *X-ray diagram of bottle cork*, found a diffuse diffraction ring, which he ascribed to the long aliphatic chain in the amorphous suberin, but he did not see interferences indicating the presence of a crystalline substance. RIZZOLI, who made X-ray diagrams for SITTE (1955), on the other hand, did find interferences of this kind, but he ascribed them to the presence of cellulose. KREGER (1958) found no interferences of cellulose, but besides the strong diffuse ring from suberin, weak interferences of aliphatic as well as of cyclic wax, those of the latter corresponding with those given by friedelin. The aliphatic fraction of the cork wax was only for a small part in the crystalline state, the cyclic one to a high extent. The position of the interferences obtained by rays that passed the suberin layer in compressed cork in a tangential direction, indicated that the molecules of both fractions must be oriented with their longitudinal axis perpendicular to the plane of the wall. This is in good agreement with the conclusion drawn from the optical properties.

The absence of conspicuous lamellar spaces between the suberin lamellae suggests that the reason why such a small part of the aliphatic wax is crystalline, is to be sought in the absence of sufficient space in the direction in which the chains are oriented. The molecules of the cyclic wax have much shorter chains (only circ. 14 Å), and here the development of crystals is therefore more easy.

It might be asked why the molecules in the wax lamellae are oriented perpendicular to the plane of the latter, and not in the plane itself, which would seem to be a more plausible position. In the band-shaped crystals of cork wax that according to SITTE (1955) are occasionally found in the lumen of the cork cells, the molecules are, as the positive birefringence of these crystals indicates (cf. SITTE in TREIBER, 1957: 426), actually oriented in an axial direction, i. e. in the plane of the band. As all sides of a cork cell are similar, it is hardly possible to assume that the orientation of the wax molecules is determined by the direction of the cell axis. It seems more plausible to suppose that the suberin in the wall of the lamellar spaces exercises an orienting influence on the wax molecules. In the cuticular membrane a similar part might be ascribed to the cutin molecules.

24. The Structure of the Wall of some Algae and Fungi

Our survey will be confined to the cell-wall structures found in macroscopically visible *Algae* and *Fungi* and in a few microscopical representatives of these groups, like the yeasts. The greater part of the microscopic and microchemical observations that have been made on the cell-walls of these organisms are of a more or less reconnoitring kind. For this reason we will restrict our attention to a few examples in which the microscopic observations have subsequently been augmented by dates obtained by means of the polarization microscope, by X-ray analysis or by the aid of the electron microscope.

241. GREEN ALGAE

A survey of the literature, especially with regard to the chemical composition of the cell-wall of the Green Algae, but also including some microscopical observations, has been given by NICOLAI and PRESTON (1952). They themselves studied the X-ray diagrams of dried, but non-purified cells taken from a large number of representatives of this group in order to obtain data with regard to the chemical composition. As a result of this study they provisionally distinguished three groups; the first group comprised the Green Algae that gave a cellulose-I diagram (mainly *Valoniaceae* and *Cladophoraceae*); the second group those that gave a diagram resembling that of cellulose II (e. g. *Halicystis* and *Spongomorpha*), whereas the last group gave diagrams that could not yet be identified. It can not be doubted that there are in the last group Algae whose walls indubitably contain cellulose, but where the latter did not reveal its presence in the diagrams because there was too much non-cellulose, e. g. *Spirogyra* (KREGER, 1957b), *Hydrodictyon* (KREGER, 1958a), *Chara* (AMIN, 1955) and *Nitella* (HOUGH et al., 1952). As the diagrams show a wide range of variability and as their serviceability, moreover, is impaired to some extent by the circumstance that all weak reflections are masked it will be clear that these diagrams give in most cases but little information. For these reasons the study of the X-ray diagram usually has to be supplemented by a chemical investigation.

With regard to the wall structure the only supplementary investigation carried out by NICOLAI and PRESTON (l. c.) concerns *Cladophora:* this will be discussed further on.

2411. *Valoniaceae*

Of this family the genus *Valonia* has, especially since 1930, received a good deal of attention. Its cells are multinuclear, and reach a large size. In *V. ventri-*

cosa volumes of 30 ml have been registered, and although they are, as a rule, much smaller, it is quite easy to cut a piece out of the cell-wall, and to treat such a piece in the desired way. *V. macrophysa* and *V. utricularis* too have often been studied, and the same applies to the related genus *Dictyosphaeria*, much less so to *Chamaedoris*, *Microdictyon* and *Siphonocladus*, genera which also belong to the *Valoniaceae*. In all these Algae the cell-wall contains a considerable amount of cellulose. This can be demonstrated by means of the usual staining and dissolving reagents, but it follows also from the X-ray diagram; in *Valonia* the analysis by means of the X-ray diagram was carried out already in 1930 (SPONSLER, 1930, 1931), in *Dictyosphaeria* and *Siphonocladus* only a few years ago (NICOLAI and PRESTON, 1952). In *Halicystis* the wall shows a different structure, and it does certainly not contain cellulose I, as that of the genera mentioned above, but another substance, which may be cellulose II.

24111. *Valonia and genera with similar cell-wall structure*

We will discuss the literature in the main in a chronological sequence, and we will start with the publications dealing with *Valonia* and with related genera showing a similar wall structure, and then we will pass on to those dealing with *Halicystis*.

AGARDH (1852) was the first to describe microscopically visible striations on the wall of Algae, but it seems that in the *Valoniaceae* they were discovered by NAEGELI (1864). The latter saw in the cell-walls of *Valonia utricularis*, *Microdictyon* and *Chamaedoris annulata* two sets of striations, the one almost axial and nearly perpendicular (or, to be more precise, in an angle of circ. 80°) to the other; the striae of this second set ascended in spirals with a low pitch. In *Valonia* and *Microdictyon* he saw, as a rule, a third, much less distinct set of striations, and in *Chamaedoris* there were one or two of such extra sets. In *Valonia* too, a fourth set was noted, but only once.

CORRENS (1893), who studied mainly species of *Cladophora* and *Chaetomorpha*, mentions for *Valonia utricularis*, *Dictyosphaeria favulosa* and *Chamaedoris annulata*, as a rule, two very distinct and one faint set of striations, in the last-named species sometimes four sets. By focussing on different levels, he saw that the various sets were situated in different lamellae. As these observations were illustrated by drawings only, we reproduce a photograph of a *Valonia* cell-wall that was published at a much later date, viz. by PRESTON and ASTBURY in 1937, fig. P181.

By means of maceration and mechanical division, CORRENS succeeded in isolating the separate lamellae of which the cell-wall of these Algae consists, and by studying the birefringence of these lamellae he found out in what way the cellulose micelles were oriented. It appeared that the orientation always agreed with that of the striation. In transverse sections of *Cladophora*, *Chaetomorpha*, *Chamaedoris* and *Dictyosphaeria*, he saw that the wall consisted of several lamellae which showed alternately a stronger and a weaker birefringence, according to the way in which their micelles were oriented with regard to the plane of the section. When he studied these lamellae with the highest magnification he had at his disposition, it appeared that they were slightly undulating. These undulations explained in his opinion the presence of the striations that appeared in surface view (but this proved afterwards to be an error).

By the study of the birefringence he arrived at the afterwards entirely confirmed conclusion that the orientation of the cellulose micelles in the two main sets of lamellae differs nearly 90°, and that the orientation in the outermost lamella is nearly identical with that in the other lamellae with an uneven number, whereas that in the second lamella agrees more or less with that in the other lamellae with an even number; the deviations amounted at the most to a few degrees. This orientation, he says, is apparently determined by the protoplasm, and in one and the same lamella it undergoes no change on account of the extension caused by the growth of the cell.

He shortly mentioned that in *Valonia* and *Dictyosphaeria* as well as in *Caulerpa* the wall shows in surface view between crossed nicols and with a platelet of red I inserted, a mosaic of addition and substraction colours, a phenomenon that was afterwards studied by PRESTON (1931).

CORRENS also noticed the easiness with which the lamellae could be split in the direction parallel to the striation, and reported that in the beginning the two parts remain sometimes in contact with each other by means of S-shaped connections; the latter therefore bridge the fissures. WILSON (1951), who was unacquainted with the work of CORRENS, described this phenomenon afterwards once more and illustrated it by good pictures.

It lasted until 1930 before the study of the cell-wall structure of *Valonia* was resumed. This was done by SPONSLER (1930, 1931), who demonstrated the presence of cellulose in this wall by means of the X-ray diagram, and who even chose the *Valonia* cell-wall, because it was so easy to manipulate, for his investigation into the crystal structure of the cellulose. He cut meridional (axial) sectors out of the wall of the ovoid cell of *Valonia ventricosa*, made a pile of them, taking care that they retained as much as possible their original orientation, dried this pile, and irradiated it from various sides by X-rays. He found in this way that one of the crystal planes (101) always ran parallel to the surface (orientation of the microfibrils of the cellulose due to shrivelling, cf. section 113). The reflections of the other strongly reflecting crystal planes (002 and $10\overline{1}$) were distributed more or less at random, which proved, in his opinion, that the way in which the microfibrils were oriented with reference to the cell axis, varied in different parts of the cell-wall; the latter, therefore would be comparable to a patch-work quilt. This conclusion was not very plausible, as it was difficult to reconcile with the constant direction of the striations but this the author overlooked.

The next investigation was that of PRESTON (1931), who, likewise without being acquainted with the work of NAEGELI and of CORRENS, described for the cell-wall of *Valonia ventricosa* and of *V. utricularis* the mosaic which becomes visible between crossed nicols. The individual spots have on the average a size of 0.001 square mm, and the direction of their major extinction is quite irregular. PRESTON stated that the phenomenon was not due to folding or crinkling of the wall and based his interpretation entirely on the erroneous picture that SPONSLER had given of the cell-wall structure, viz. that it consists of patches which differ in the way in which the microfibrils are oriented in them. This was, in his opinion, in agreement with what he saw when he studied sections through the wall between crossed nicols, viz. that the birefringence showed in the longitudinal direction periodical changes in degree. In the radial direction it remained the same, which led him to the conclusion that there would be in that direction no differences between the lamellae as far as the direction of the cellulose is concerned. Like SPONSLER, PRESTON was apparently unaware of the presence of striations which, as we have heard, are everywhere oriented in the same direction. As he embedded his objects in Canada balsam, it is easily conceivable that this escaped his attention.

That this conception of the wall structure could not be right, appeared when ASTBURY et al. (1932) studied the X-ray diagram of a single cell-wall, for the reflections that they observed in a preparation of this kind, indicated that there were only two different orientations. As the surface that was irradiated, far exceeded the size of two "patches", a much larger number of orientations ought to have been present. Moreover, even when different parts of the cell-wall were irradiated, the two orientations remained nearly the same with respect to the cell axis. When a micrograph of a piece of the cell-wall which PRESTON had made for them, was compared with the X-ray diagram of the same piece, the two orientations appeared to agree with the direction of the two sets of striations, a correlation that was subsequently confirmed by SISSON (1938a), cf. fig. 34. The presence of this correlation was once more demonstrated, and if possible still more convincingly, by PRESTON and RIPLEY (1954a) and by HONJO and WATANABE (1957) by comparing electron micrographs showing the direction of the microfibrils with electron-diffraction diagrams of the same piece of wall. However, it is only fair to repeat that the presence of a correlation between the striation and the orientation of the cellulose had already been proved by the observations which CORRENS had made by means of the polarization microscope.

ASTBURY and his collaborators confirmed the conclusion at which SPONSLER already had arrived with regard to the 101 plane, viz. that it is in the dried wall tangentially oriented. They also noted that sometimes weak interferences were present, indicating that part of the cellulose chains were oriented in a third direction; in this way they confirmed the observations of NAEGELI and of CORRENS, which were unknown to them, with regard to the presence of the weak third set of striations.

That SPONSLER had obtained so much more reflections in his diagrams, might, according to ASTBURY and his collaborators, be due either to the circumstance that the wall sectors which were assembled by him in a pile, were not all cut out in exactly the same direction, or that they had not been assembled with sufficient care, or else to the presence of small differences in the orientation of the cellulose in remote parts of the cell-wall.

The finding that only two, or occasionally three, different kinds of orientation are present, made it necessary to find another explanation for the mosaic that is observed when the wall is studied in surface view between crossed nicols. They suggested, as CORRENS already had done, that this phenomenon might be due to local differences in the proportion in which the two differently oriented sets of cellulose micelles are present in different parts of the cell-wall. The possibility to explain this phenomenon in another way, will be discussed further on.

In 1933 VAN ITERSON published a paper in which he drew the attention to the observations of NAEGELI and of CORRENS on the cell-wall of *Valonia* and other *Algae*, observations that were fully confirmed by him, and in which he described some observations of his own on the cell-walls of *Valonia utricularis* and *V. macrophysa*. In sections of the circ. 10μ thick cell-walls he counted 20 lamellae (PRESTON had recorded the presence of 40 lamellae), and confirmed the observation of CORRENS that the latter are not flat but more or less undulating. Looking at the cell-wall in surface view he noted by focussing on different levels that the three sets of striations occurred in different lamellae, but that the third set was met less often, from which he concluded that it occurred in a smaller number of lamellae. He succeeded in isolating single lamellae and in splitting the latter up in bundles of microfibrils, of which he determined the refractive indices at 1.533 and 1.598. Contrary to the findings of his predecessors he noted the presence of an outermost lamella which did not consist of cellulose (this lamella is probably present in young cells only, see further on). The conspicuous iridescence of the cell-wall may, according to him, be due to its lamellate structure.

ULLRICH (1935) was apparently not acquainted with the publications of ASTBURY et al. and of VAN ITERSON, but he knew the "patch-work quilt" explanation given by PRESTON. He did not reject this explanation, but remarked that the patches at any rate can not be distributed entirely at random, as he found that the top of the cell seen in surface view behaves between crossed nicols like a sphaero-crystal. He published a picture of this phenomenon, but it is not so good as the one that was published afterwards by WILSON (1955), fig. P189. ULLRICH did not give an explanation of what he had seen ,but this was provided by the investigations of PRESTON and ASTBURY (1937) to which we will now pass on.

PRESTON and ASTBURY studied by means of the X-ray diagram the two main orientations of the cellulose in a single cell-wall of *Valonia ventricosa*, and they confirmed once more that the orientation of the two sets of microfibrils corresponds to the direction of the two main striations.

There are with respect to the striations, two "poles" one of which lies in the region of the rhizoidal attachment, the other one near, but not necessarily in the morphological tip of the cell. One set of cellulose chains forms very slow S-spirals which converge to the pole, whereas the other set extends meridian-like from pole to pole. As the work of VAN ITERSON (1933) had now acquainted them with the observations of CORRENS, they investigated microscopically the localization of the differently oriented cellulose micelles, and in this way they too confirmed the alternating orientation in subsequent lamellae. The presence of a third direction was not unknown to them, and appears even in one of their micrographs (fig. P181), but is not mentioned in this paper. As it is not mentioned either in some of their well-known publications that since then have appeared, including PRESTON's book of 1952, several students of this subject have got the impression that only two directions are present. The fact that X-ray diagrams tend to minimize the effect of minor quantities of a differently oriented substance, probably explains to some extent why these investigators payed so little attention to the orientation in the third direction.

Starting from the explanation given by ASTBURY et al. (l. c.) of the mosaic which appears between crossed nicols, PRESTON and ASTBURY suggest here that the supposed local differences in the proportion between the micelles with different orientation, might be due to a difference in the joint thickness of the lamellae with the meridional orientation and of the lamellae with the orientation in the S-spiral, a difference that might perhaps be caused by the loss of parts of the cracked outermost lamellae. Such a loss of parts of the outer layers is a phenomenon that has been known for a long time, not only from *Valonia*, but also from quite a number of other Algae (NOLL, 1887).

Although the explanation given in the paper of 1937 is repeated in PRESTON's book (1952), and although it is presented there more or less as a matter of course, it seems desirable to draw attention to the fact that this need not be the sole cause since there is another possibility. In the first place we wish to point out that the phenomenon is known also from *Cladophora* (ASTBURY and PRESTON, 1940), although in this Alga no parts of the outermost layer become detached. It has also been described from *Halicystis* (VAN ITERSON, 1936), and here too no parts of the outermost lamellae are rejected, and there are in this Alga probably not even differently oriented lamellae, at least the presence of the latter could not be demonstrated. In these cases and, of course, in *Valonia* too, the phenomenon can be explained if the cell-wall parts that were studied by means of the polarization microscope were not flat but more or less undulating, which means that if the cell-wall is studied in surface view, its surface will not everywhere be perpendicular to the axis of the microscope. A flat cell-wall that in surface view is isotropic, will become anisotropic if it is brought in a sloping position with regard to the axis of the microscope, and under such circumstances it will show a major extinction in a direction parallel to the contour-line of the slope. This phenomenon will be met with in membranes with an irregular orientation of the microfibrils (foliar texture) as well as in membranes like the cell-wall of *Valonia*, but in the latter case the change in the optical behaviour will become especially conspicuous if by change the position of one of the two orientations of the cellulose happens to coincide with the contour-line of the slope.

The explanation given in the preceding paragraph finds support in van ITER-SON's statement that in *Halicystis* the wall is undulating, and that it looks as if it contains on the slopes of the waves a larger amount of the substance by which the birefringence is caused than it does on the crest of the waves. That the phenomenon is not shown by all *Valonia* cell-walls (ASTBURY et al. 1932), means perhaps that the walls are not always undulating; in the walls of turgescent cells the undulations will probably be entirely lacking.

A paper by SISSON (1941), the next one in the chronological sequence, tells us that the two main orientations of the cellulose are already observable in young cells with a diameter of only one twelfth of the final one, and that the angle between the two spirals is in these cells the same as in mature ones.

The presence of lamellae with alternating direction of the cellulose in the cell-walls of *Valonia* was confirmed by PRESTON et al. (1948) by the aid of *electron micrographs*. The latter were made from replicas that were obtained from the outer surface of the cell-wall of *Valonia ventricosa* and also from the surface of detached lamellae. The very thin lamellae with crossed orientation of the microfibrils are clearly visible (fig. 7). They also reported that a third orientation could be observed more frequently than they had expected on account of the studies with the X-ray method.

WILSON (1951) also published some electron micrographs of single lamellae that had been isolated by him, but as they were not shadowed, they showed but little detail (fig. 8). However, they demonstrate very clearly the S-shaped connections which were found to bridge the fissures in the lamellae and which were known already to CORRENS. The striation that is observed under the microscope is obviously explained by the presence of these fissures and not by that of the undulations, as CORRENS thought. WILSON states that when the wall is dissected, it readily breaks up in 10–15 layers, which each of them consists of 2–4 lamellae. It seems therefore as if there are groups of lamellae, a phenomenon which, as we will see in section 2412, plays a much more prominent part in the cell-wall of the *Cladophoraceae*. It is perhaps worth while to point out that the number of lamellae that is actually observed, is not the total number that has been produced, as the peripheral lamellae are gradually thrown off.

Interesting is WILSON's figure of the hyphae of a fungus that were found in a cell-wall, and which show in their growth a distinct preference for the two directions in which the microfibrils are oriented. A similar phenomenon, although on a much larger scale, was known already from hyphae growing in textile fabrics (for literature on this subject cf. ROELOFSEN, 1956).

WILSON noted not rarely three sets of striations in *Valonia*. In *Dictyosphaeria* this is the rule, and in this Alga they are all three almost equally conspicuous, even in very young cells. Most enlightening is his figure of a "pole" (i. e. the apex of a cell) as it looks between crossed nicols; in this "pole" the three sets of striations, which in the bright fields are easily recognizable, meet each other. These bright fields separated from each other by a dark cross, had already been observed by ULLRICH (l. c.), and that the image of such a sphaeritic structure was to be expected, follows from what the X-ray analysis of PRESTON and AST-BURY (1937) had revealed with regard to the orientation of the microfibrils.

Excellent electron micrographs of the cell-wall of *Valonia* were obtained by PRESTON and KUYPER (1951) by detaching thin layers from the surface, and by shadowing these layers. In these micrographs we recognize also the cracks and the signs of disintegration that are to be expected in the outermost layers. As a rule, only the two main orientations are visible, but occasionally the third one is present too. Halfway between the outer and the inner surface of the wall, the number of fissures in the lamellae is but small and they are narrow, and in some parts the fissures may even be entirely absent. The orientation of the microfibrils in the innermost layer appeared to be irregular in these cells, which had been preserved in formaldehyde; it is said to be associated in a conspicuous manner with cytoplasmic flocculae.

Electron micrographs of the inner side of the wall that were made by PRESTON, NICOLAI and KUYPER (1953), this time of cells of *Valonia macrophysa* that in fresh condition had been freeze-dried, showed, however, a very clear parallel orientation in this part of the wall, even of the innermost microfibrils (fig. P 182), a difference with their earlier findings to which the authors, remarkably enough, paid no attention. The cytoplasm was repeatedly seen to adhere to the microfibrils, and looks under these circumstances as if it is itself oriented. In one case the whole outermost layer of the cytoplasm exhibited a conspicuous orientation almost at a right angle to that of the cellulose in the innermost lamella, although it was itself entirely devoid of cellulose micelles, fig. P 183. This suggests that the outermost layer of the cytoplasm is re-oriented, each time a new lamella is to be deposited.

For the sake of completeness we mention a paper by ZIEGENSPECK (1953), who succeeded in making the lamellae with their alternately different orientation better visible microscopically; he studied them to this end under certain precautions between crossed nicols.

Particularly fine were the electron micrographs by means of which STEWARD and MÜHLETHALER (1953) demonstrated the development of the cell-wall in the aplanospores of three *Valonia* species and of *Dictyosphaeria;* these Algae were grown in the laboratory. Entirely as in the primary wall of the isodiametric cells of the Anthophytes, the first-formed cellulose wall appeared to be a felt-like mass of cellulose microfibrils embedded without any definite orientation in amorphous non-cellulose. This wall, however, remains intact only during the first growth phase. At first the microfibrils may slip one past the other, but this apparently comes soon to a stop, and then this primary wall cracks and is split up in fragments that are successively rejected. In the meantime a new layer is formed, and in this one the microfibrils show a somewhat more orderly arrangement, although they are as yet far from parallel. In the subsequently formed layers the parallelism becomes more pronounced, and the direction is changed in every new layer, fig. P184.

The third set of striations was present regularly or at least more often in the cell-walls that were studied by STEWARD and MÜHLETHALER than in those that had been studied by other investigators, and in their material the angle between the two main ones was smaller. We suppose that this was no mere coincidence, but the expression of a true correlation, as NAEGELI (1864) has reported a similar correlation from *Chamaedoris*. In fig. P185 the three directions are in surface view as well as in section easily distinguishable, and this figure shows also that one of the sets is less well developed. The direction of the strands in successive layers was reported to turn through about 60°, but in their schema we actually measure 76° between the two main sets and 59 and 47° between the latter and the third set.

STEWARD and MÜHLETHALER are of opinion that the presence of three regularly alternating orientations is the rule, whereas according to them in the publication of PRESTON and ASTBURY (1937) but two alternating systems would have been reported. As may be seen from what we have related above, and also from what PRESTON and ASTBURY (1954) have adduced in a paper in which they defended themselves, STEWARD and MÜHLETHALER's representation of the findings of these authors is in this respect not right, although it is true that the latter often did not mention the presence of the third orientation, presumably because X-ray diagrams tend to minimize the effect of minor orientations, and do therefore no justice to wall constituents that are present in minor amounts. In this way the X-ray method has also led to the denial of the presence of a differently oriented S_1 layer in the Anthophytes (section 234).

The flat strands of microfibrils and the fissures which cause the microscopically visible striations are also well shown in fig. P185. The fissures are especially frequent in the outermost lamellae, and they are therefore probably due to the extension caused by the growth of the cell. The innermost lamella is always just as well oriented as the older ones; this is shown also by the electron micrographs of PRESTON, NICOLAI and KUYPER (l. c.).

STEWARD and MÜHLETHALER doubt the presence of a pole at the apex of the vesicles, but in our view this had been put beyond doubt, both by the work of PRESTON and ASTBURY (1937) and by that of WILSON (1951).

In very young as well as in older cells of *Valonia ocellata* and *V. macrophysa* the same cell-wall structure was found as in *V. ventricosa;* the only difference was that the third orientation of the microfibrils proved to be much weaker in *V. ocellata*, and that it might even be entirely absent in *V. macrophysa*. However, the experience with *V. ventricosa* reported in the preceding paragraphs indicates that this difference need not be of fundamental importance, but that it may be due to accidental circumstances.

The cell-walls in the pluricellular thallus of *Dictyosphaeria* are very thick and consist of a considerable number of lamellae. In transverse sections (fig. P186) as well as in surface view three almost equally well represented orientations were recognizable, which intersected in the form of an almost exactly equilateral triangle.

WILSON (1955) has once more given figures of the "poles" where in *Valonia* and *Dictyosphaeria* the various spiral structures meet, as they look in surface view between crossed nicols. A very instructive image was obtained from a single lamella of *Dictyosphaeria* in which the microfibrils were oriented in the nearly transverse direction; it is reproduced in fig. P187.

The latest publication on the cell-wall of *Valonia ventricosa* is that of CRON-SHAW and PRESTON (1958). By means of X-ray analysis, electron microscopy and electron diffraction diagrams, they re-examined adult cells with particular reference to the criticism of STEWARD and MÜHLETHALER (l. c.) on the work of PRESTON and ASTBURY (l. c.). In the material studied by them they did not find a regular repeat of lamellae oriented in two directions as had been suggested by PRESTON and ASTBURY, nor the regular three-lamella repeat as described by STEWARD and MÜHLETHALER, but a two-lamella repeat, occasionally interrupted by a much thinner and more loosely packed lamella with strands running in a steep Z-spiral, usually bisecting the obtuse angle between the two major directions (on the average 97°, mean deviation 3.5°). The three directions converge in the two poles. We may add that the irregular occurrence of one of the three types of lamellae had already been noticed incidentally by VAN ITERSON (1933) by means of light microscopy.

We will close this survey of the kind of cell-wall structure that is found in *Valonia* with a discussion of some opinions with regard to the mode of origin of this structure. As we have mentioned already, VAN ITERSON (1936) suggested that the changes in orientation in the successive lamellae would be due to changes in the orientation of the outermost layer of cytoplasm, which in their turn would be due to the circumstance that the cell does not expand equally in all directions, but that everytime a lamella has been deposited, it expands a little more in a direction perpendicular to that of this layer.

The suggestion given by VAN ITERSON did not find favour with any of the investigators who subsequently have turned their attention towards this problem. In the main the following three objections were brought forward. Although it was generally admitted that the principle might be applicable to cell-walls consisting of one or two layers, it seemed difficult to imagine that it would apply also to a wall consisting of a considerable number of lamellae. It was also admitted that in this way a reorientation in a direction perpendicular to the first might be explained, but that it seemed impossible to explain in this way a reorientation in a direction which made an angle of 60° with the preceding one. The third objection was that the electron micrographs proved that the change was every time completely abrupt, whereas with a reorientation of the plasma structure on account of stretch a more or less gradual transition was to be expected. That nevertheless the deposition of a new lamella with a different orientation is preceded by a reorientation of the cytoplasm, is according to the findings of PRESTON, NICOLAI and KUYPER (1953) undeniable, fig. P183. The fact that at the boundary between the successive lamellae no transitions in orientation are found, also makes it in our view impossible to assume that the orientation of the microfibrils, once they have been deposited, would undergo a change on account of an anisotropic expansion of the cell, as it does in the case of multinet growth. It seems, that at this moment, the opinions with regard to the cause of the varying microfibrillar orientation agree in that it must reside in some obscure way in the cytoplasm.

FARR (1949) thought that she had seen in *Valonia* under the microscope coiled microfibrils of cellulose in the interior of the chloroplasts that were nearest to the wall, and she believed that disintegrated plastids were deposited layer by layer by the outer surface of the cytoplasm upon the inner surface of the cell-wall. In *Halicystis*, which in contrast to *Valonia* has a granular cell-wall, granules of cellulose were thought to be present in the chloroplasts.

STEWARD and MÜHLETHALER (l. c.) could find no support for this view in their study of *Valonia*.

24112. Halicystis

The cell-wall structure of *Halicystis* has less often been studied than that of *Valonia*, and our knowledge of this cell-wall is still very incomplete. In *Halicystis ovalis* and *H. osterhoutii* the structure of the wall seems to be the same.

In the cell-walls of *H. osterhoutii* neither by VAN ITERSON (1936) nor by the earlier investigators that were quoted by him, striations were seen, but in sections through the wall the latter appears to have like *Valonia*, a lamellate structure. In non-swollen sections he saw underneath the thin and isotropic outermost layer, which is strongly stained by ruthenium-red, a strongly birefringent layer, and between the latter and the inside of the wall a thick, less strongly birefringent layer. In swollen sections the latter appeared to consist of 50–60 lamellae. Both with stains that are used for the identification of callose and with stains used for detection of amyloid, this layer reacted positively. The central layer showed these staining reactions to a lesser degree. Both layers could moreover be stained with chlor-zinc-iodine. VAN ITERSON supposed that the outermost layer contains pectin, the strongly birefringent central one perhaps cellulose, and the inner layer with its numerous lamellae an amyloid-like substance. Although he saw no striations in surface view, he supposed that the cellulose layer would consist, in the same way as in *Valonia*, of lamellae in which the microfibrils are oriented in two directions, one perpendicular to the other, so that they compensate each other's optical activity; this would explain why the wall is in surface view isotropic. More recent findings are as we will discuss, at variance with this supposition.

However, the wall of *Halicystis* is in surface view not everywhere isotropic. VAN ITERSON noted that it showed between crossed nicols the same mosaic as was already known from the wall of *Valonia*. He ascribed this in both genera to the same cause, viz. to local variations in the orientation of the cellulose in the plane of the wall. This is therefore a similar explanation as PRESTON (1931) had originally proposed for the mosaic of *Valonia*, but which afterwards had to be abandoned. As VAN ITERSON records the presence of undulations perpendicular to the plane of the wall, it seems to us, as we have expounded in our discussion of the corresponding phenomenon in *Valonia*, that the mosaic phenomenon must be due to the presence of these undulations.

FARR (1949) was apparently unacquainted with the publication of VAN ITERSON. She too noted the lamellate but non-fibrillar structure of the wall, and the amyloid reaction. She thought that the chloroplasts contained cellulose in a granular form, but as this author had already at another occasion been mistaken as to a granular structure of cellulose, her finding requires, in our opinion, in this case too confirmation.

SISSON (1938; 1938a) discovered that the X-ray diagram of the untreated cell-wall of *Halicystis* differed in two ways from that of *Valonia*. In the first place no orientation could be detected if the wall was placed in a position perpendicular to the irradiation, and in the second place the interferences did not correspond to those of cellulose I, but to those of cellulose II. Just as in *Valonia* the interferences of the 101 crystal plane proved to be oriented parallel to the surface of the cell-wall, a situation that is commonly found in a dried layer of ordinary or of regenerated cellulose (cf. section 113). Another indication of the presence of cellulose II is to be seen in the circumstance that with potassium tri iodide it gives the amyloid reaction (the callose reaction remains unexplained). SISSON further found a diffraction corresponding to an interplanar spacing of 12.5 Å ,which is unusual in cellulose and was ascribed therefore to the presence of an unknown substance. However, this is not supported by the fact that the diffraction appeared only in those diagrams that showed the 101-plane, which means that the corresponding crystal plane is also oriented parallel to the surface, just like the 101-plane of the alleged cellulose II.

By using dried walls of an unidentified *Halicystis* species, ROELOFSEN, DALITZ and WIJNMAN (1953) could confirm most of these röntgenographic data; they found in addition that the same reflections were obtained after a treatment with hot alkali, and that they were in this case even more conspicuous. However, as in a hydrolysate of the cell-wall, no matter whether the latter has been treated with alkali or not, besides the expected dextrose, always a constant amount of xylose was found, which can not have been produced by the hydrolysis of xylan, as the latter is easily soluble in alkali, they suggested the possibility that the cell-wall may not contain cellulose II, but a xylo-glucan, that would give all the interferences observed. This would explain in a more satisfactory way why the 101 plane and the plane with the 13 Å spacing were behaving in a similar way. Our supposition gains in significance, and our scepsis with regard to the presence of cellulose II increases in the same measure, when we take into account the results obtained by CRONSHAW et al. (1958) in their study of the cell-walls of *Rhodophyceae* and *Phaeophyceae*, and the important conclusion at which these investigators arrived, viz. that various cell-wall constituents may give almost identical X-ray diagrams, a conclusion that carries the more weight as it comes from a side where in the past the diagnostic value of the X-ray diagram was certainly not underestimated.

The microscopical observations made by ROELOFSEN, DALITZ and WIJNMAN (l. c.) on the same material as had been used by VAN ITERSON, once more con-

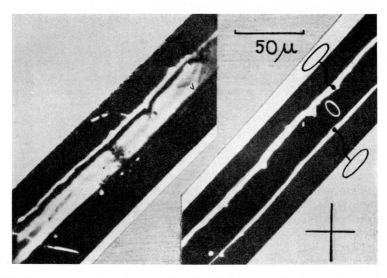

Fig. 189. Transverse section of a dry cell-wall of *Halicystis ovalis;* the section is embedded in methyl benzoate and viewed between crossed nicols without (on the left) and with (on the right) compensation of the negative birefringence in the central layer (from ROELOFSEN, DALITZ and WIJNMAN, 1953).

firmed the lamellate structure, fig. P188, but in their study of sections they arrived at a different and somewhat enigmatic result, viz. that between crossed nicols three birefringent layers could be distinguished, of which the outer and the inner one showed the normal positive birefringence, whereas the central and thicker layer was negatively birefringent, fig. 189.

Electron micrographs made by these authors from replicas of the outer and inner surface of a cell-wall of *H. osterhoutii* that had been treated with hot alkali, by which treatment 60 % of the dry weight was removed, showed a mass of microfibrils without any definite orientation and still a good deal of non-fibrillar material. This lack of orientation is in line with the X-ray data.

Therefore, although neither the chemical constitution nor the structure of the cell-wall of *Halicystis* can be regarded as sufficiently known, it is clear that it differs considerably from that of *Valonia*. This fact may be regarded, as NICO-LAI and PRESTON (1952) have pointed out, as an argument in favour of the view that *Halicystis* should be referred to a separate family.

2412. *Cladophoraceae.*

The cell-wall of the *Cladophoraceae* consists, just as that of many other Algae, of two layers, an outer one which extends over more than one cell and has been deposited by a succession of mother-cells, and an inner one which surrounds the individual cells of the last generation and is deposited by these cells themselves.

In the principal genera of this family, viz. *Cladophora* and *Chaetomorpha*, the microscopic and submicroscopic structure of the wall has been studied rather thoroughly; less well investigated is that of the wall of *Rhizoclonium*. The wall structure shows in these three genera a marked resemblance with that of *Valonia*, which, however, does not mean that there are no differences. As we will expound further on, here too on account of the microchemical reactions and as a result of the X-ray analysis the presence of cellulose I may be regarded as well-established. However, the genus *Spongomorpha* seems to occupy in this respect an isolated place in the family, just like *Halicystis* does in the *Valoniaceae*.

In Algae the presence of microscopically distinguishable striations in the cell-wall was first observed by AGARDH in 1852 in the genera *Chaetomorpha* and *Cladophora* (and in *Codium*, a genus belonging to an entirely different group). A year later MOHL described in the first-named Alga the presence of two sets of striations, one nearly perpendicular to the other. This was confirmed by NAEGELI (1864). The first set intersects the longitudinal cell-axis at an angle of 13–27°, the second set ascends from the other side and intersects the longitudinal axis at an angle of 69–89°, and the angle between the two sets themselves varied between 78 and 86°. By way of exception he saw a third, very weak striation, but this has apparently never again been observed.

CORRENS (1893) mainly used species of *Cladophora* and *Chaetomorpha* for his extensive study of the cell-wall structure of the Algae. He too noted the two sets of striations, the first ascending in an S-spiral at an angle of 20–30°, the second in a Z-spiral at an angle of 60–70°. When the microscope was successively focussed on deeper levels, he observed in surface view a regular alternation of the two directions; the two directions themselves, however, varied in the different depths but a few degrees. In most of the species the cell-walls showed in surface view a positive birefringence with reference to the longitudinal axis of the cells, but in some of them they were isotropic or even negatively birefringent.

In transverse sections (presumably swollen ones) he counted on the average 30 lamellae; between crossed nicols isotropic lamellae were seen to alternate with birefringent ones, and among the latter the degree of birefringence was alternately higher and lower; this he regarded as a confirmation of the view that there is an alternating change in the orientation of the micelles. Both kinds of birefringent lamellae increased in thickness in the direction of the cell lumen. Perpendicular to the plane of the wall they showed a slight undulation (the wall will probably have undergone a contraction because of the loss of turgor).

With iodine and sulphuric acid the walls showed in the sections a strong increase in thickness (the surface shrinks in all directions), and under these circumstances the lamellae that had been struck by the knife in a direction perpendicular to that of the striations, appeared to show a very strong undulation, whereas the lamellae in between, which were struck parallel to the direction of the striations, proved to be flat. In a transverse section therefore one of the two sets of lamellae proved to be undulating, in a longitudinal section the other set. These phenomena are now easily explainable on account of intrafibrillar swelling and of fibrillar contraction (cf. section 211).

Further CORRENS mentions that in the section which had been stained by means of iodine and sulphuric acid, the strongly undulating lamellae became blue, the other ones violet, and that the same lamellae assumed therefore in the transverse section another colour than they did in a longitudinal one. This phenomenon, for which CORRENS could find no satisfactory explanation, has since then not been studied or explained by other investigators. It is very probably due to dichroism, which in non-polarized light too affects the colour of birefringent objects that are viewed in different directions.

BRAND (1906; 1908) too studied a number of *Cladophora* species, but not so much the structure of the cell-wall as the cell-growth. The latter takes place mainly at the top, but to some extent also in other parts. Contrary to what happens in many other Algae, the outermost layer of the cell-wall does not peel off.

In *Chaetomorpha linum* NICOLAI and FREY-WYSSLING (1938) have made other important microscopic observations. They found among other things a strong staining with ruthenium-red, a negative reaction on amyloid, a positive one on cellulose with iodine, and sulphuric acid. With chlor-zinc-iodine staining occurred only when the material had previously been treated with cuprammonium (though not so long that all cellulose is dissolved). In surface view the whole cell-wall appeared to be negatively birefringent, although the outermost layer which is common to all cells, proved to be positively birefringent. Like CORRENS they found that the birefringent lamellae were separated from each other by isotropic ones, and they could prove that the latter contained no cellulose, so that the lamellae which did contain cellulose, could easily be separated from each other by maceration.

Contrary to CORRENS they found that in wall sections the birefringence of the lamellae which contained the cellulose, did not undergo regularly alternating changes in degree, but that it was everywhere nearly the same, although the striations and the X-ray diagram did indicate the presence of two different orientations among the microfibrils of the cellulose. They explained the absence of differences in the degree of birefringence by assuming that each lamella consists of thin sub-lamellae with two different orientations. These sub-lamellae would be comparable to the many lamellae in the cell-wall of *Valonia*, which in sections are also not separately distinguishable with the microscope. In this connection we wish to remind the reader of the probability that in *Valonia* too the lamellae are combined into groups (WILSON, 1951), but as the layers consisting of non-cellulose are in that Alga less well developed, in sections no alternation of birefringent and isotropic layers is recognizable. The situation found in *Chaetomorpha* is schematically represented in fig. 190, which has been designed according to the description given by NICOLAI and FREY-WYSSLING (l. c.).

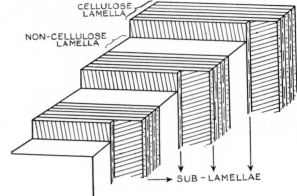

CELLULOSE
LAMELLA

NON-CELLULOSE
LAMELLA

SUB – LAMELLAE

Fig. 190. Schematical structure of the cell-wall of *Chaetomorpha*, according to the description given by NICOLAI and FREY-WYSSLING (1938).

The remarkable spiral shape shown by some of the filaments that become detached from the lamellae when sections are made through the wall, plead, according to these authors, for their assumption of sub-lamellae with different orientation. It may further be mentioned that, just as in *Valonia*, in the dried cell-wall the 101 plane appears to be oriented parallel to the surface.

How it is to be explained that the outer layer of the wall as a whole is positively birefringent, and the inner layer as a whole negatively birefringent, is still unknown. The difference may be related with the cell growth. As there are no indications that the outermost layers are gradually rejected, we will have to assume either that all lamellae grow by intussusception or else that the outermost ones are stretched.

Cladophora prolifera has been studied for the first time after the investigations of CORRENS and BRAND by ASTBURY and PRESTON (1940). In several respects the results agreed with those obtained with *Chaetomorpha*. Here too the microchemical reactions as well as the X-ray diagram indicate the presence of cellulose, but it is so completely enveloped by non-cellulose that the reactions are slow. In opposition to *Chaetomorpha*, *Cladophora* is ramified, fig. 191. The way in which the cells grow, was in its main lines already known, but it was studied now in more detail. The filaments appeared to grow mainly at the top, and in the cells in the vicinity of the latter, growth goes on for some time in the apical part.

The direction of the two sets of striations that can be seen under the microscope has in the specimen shown in fig. 191, been determined and is indicated in the picture. The two sets of striations intersect each other everywhere at an angle of 80–90° (on the average 83°), but their direction changes gradually and simultaneously from the basal part of the cell to the apical part; in the latter, one of the sets appears to be oriented almost axially, the other one nearly transversely. The transverse striation is often invisible, but that the lamellae with this kind of orientation must nevertheless be present, follows from the fact that the wall is in surface view isotropic; if the wall consisted in this part of the cell only of the layer with the almost axial orientation, it would be positively birefringent.

It is noteworthy that we find in *Cladophora* once more the correlation between the rate of growth and the steepness of the spiral which we have met already in various kinds of elongated cells occurring in the Anthophytes.

In *Cladophora gracilis* and in most of the fresh-water species (NICOLAI and PRESTON, 1952) the striations show in all parts of the cell-wall the orientation that in *C. prolifera* is found at the top of the cell only. Fig. P192 shows that in *C. gracilis* the striation in the common outer layer of two adjoining cells undergoes no change when it passes from the basal part of the one to the top of the other. It is rather curious that at the base of a ramification the transverse striation of the mother filament is converted into an axial one and the longitudinal striation into a transverse one, but that in the inner layer the situation remains unchanged, fig. 193.

The X-ray diagram of the single wall appeared to agree entirely with that of *Valonia* (fig. 34), and proved that in *Cladophora* the direction of the striations coincides, in the same way as in *Chaetomorpha* and *Valonia*, with the orientation of the cellulose, and that here too the many lamellae, no matter in what part of the wall, are arranged into two groups, each with a definite orientation. Here too in the (dried!) wall the 101 planes appeared to be oriented parallel to the surface.

The mosaic that in the cell-walls of *Valonia* and *Halicystis* appears when they are studied between crossed nicols, was observed in *Cladophora* too, although somewhat less clearly. Here the mosaic areas tend to take the form of transverse bands. It is noteworthy in this connection that in contrast to *Valonia* there is no peeling off of the peripheral layers. For explanations of the mosaic phenomenon we refer to what has been said on this topic in connection with its occurrence in *Valonia*.

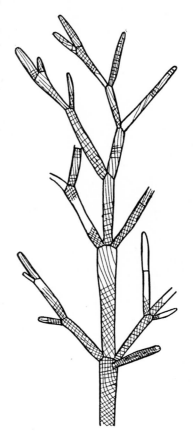

Fig. 191. *Cladophora prolifera.* Diagram of a branching filament showing the orientation of the striations. Where the two sets of striations are both or one of them invisible, this isdue to the opaque cell contents (from ASTBURY and PRESTON, 1940).

According to ASTBURY and PRESTON the outermost lamella of the *Cladophora* cell-wall, which looks more or less like a cuticle, would contain chitin. They conclude this from the X-ray diagram, which, however, is not reproduced in their paper. In support of their conclusion they report that they obtained a positive result with the VAN WISSELINGH test (the violet colour of chitosan that appears when a cell-wall containing chitin is treated first with alkali and then with an acidified solution of iodine in potassium iodide), but this reaction can not be regarded as specific (cf. section 123). As R. FREY (1950) did not succeed in finding chitin by means of the X-ray analysis, and as this substance, moreover, has never been found in organisms that produce cellulose, and is known so far only from Fungi and animals, the conclusion of ASTBURY and PRESTON is probably wrong.

In *Cladophora rupestris* not only cellulose but also a sulphate-containing polysaccharide was found (cf. sections 143 and 144).

For the sake of completeness we mention a paper by H. and H. ZIEGENSPECK (1952, see also 1953). These authors studied the wall of *Cladophora glomerata* by the aid of special microscopic methods and of special media for mounting,

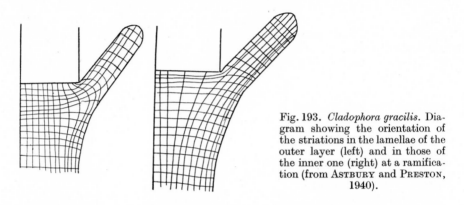

Fig. 193. *Cladophora gracilis*. Diagram showing the orientation of the striations in the lamellae of the outer layer (left) and in those of the inner one (right) at a ramification (from ASTBURY and PRESTON, 1940).

and claim that they have demonstrated in this way for the first time the presence of bundles of microfibrils. Their statement that the outer layer of the wall, which they call the primary wall, has a transverse structure, and the inner layer, which they call the secondary wall, a longitudinal one, does not look acceptable either.

NICOLAI and PRESTON (1952) give figures of the wall of *Cladophora prolifera* as it looks between crossed nicols, in surface view as well as in sections. The latter show the usual birefringent and isotropic lamellae. Here too it appeared that it were the same lamellae which lighted up or remained dark in the transverse and in the longitudinal section; they behaved therefore in the same way as the lamellae that NICOLAI and FREY-WYSSLING (1938) had observed in the cellwall of *Chaetomorpha*. We must assume therefore that here too the birefringent lamellae consist of sub-lamellae with different orientation, and that the compound lamellae are separated from each other by lamellae consisting of non-cellulose.

Since in the cell-wall of cotton hairs (cf. section 23441) no visible daygrowth rings are formed if temperature and light are kept constant, NICOLAI and PRESTON (1953) have tried to find out what influence continuous light would have on the structure of the cell-wall in *Cladophora* species and in *Rhizoclonium*. They do not mention whether the lamellate structure disappeared or not, but with regard to the orientation they report that it was affected in most of these Algae but slightly or not at all; only in *Cladophora rupestris* X-ray analysis as well as the study of the optical behaviour showed that the amount of cellulose which was oriented in a spiral with low pitch, became relatively more important. In surface view the cells became in the main more strongly negatively birefrin-

gent, though a part of the cells remained positively birefringent. The ratio
length/width proved to increase somewhat in continuous light.

In the same way as STEWARD and MÜHLETHALER (1953) had used aplanospores in order to investigate the development of the cell-wall in *Valonia*, NI-
COLAI (1957) used the swarmers of *Cladophora melagonium* for a study of the
wall in subsequent stages of development by means of electron micrographs
and X-ray diagrams. As soon as the swarmer settles down, a wall is formed,
and just as in *Valonia* and *Dictyosphaeria* this appears to consist of a network
of microfibrils without a definite orientation.

The pear-shaped cell shown in fig. P 194 has a pole opposite the sprouting end.
The microfibrils in the outermost network tend to radiate from this pole and to
converge towards the sprouting end, where the microfibrils are still arranged at
random. Underneath these microfibrils coarse bands of microfibrils are found
which encircle the pole, ascend in a flat spiral and assume an almost transverse
direction at the sprouting end. Later a layer of nearly axially oriented bands is
deposited underneath that with the more or less transversely oriented ones, and
this layer is followed in its turn by one with a more or less transverse orientation, and so on. X-ray analysis shows that the microfibrils in the walls of these
young cells too consist of cellulose. In the youngest stages there are in addition
reflections, not belonging to cellulose I. It is clear therefore that the wall develops in a similar way as it does in the young cells of the *Valoniaceae*, where its
development had already been described.

The only observations by means of the electron microscope made on mature
parts of *Cladophora* and *Chaetomorpha*, are those of CRONSHAW et al. (1958).
Cell-wall fragments of *Cl. rupestris* and *Ch. melagonium* showed the same thin
lamellae with a crossed structure as had been found in the cell-wall of *Valonia*,
but only two different orientations could be distinguished. The microfibrils are
said to be 70–100 Å thick and 250–300 Å wide. Here too the presence of cellulose
was confirmed by means of the X-ray diagram. Hydrolysates obtained from
the water-soluble fraction and from the hemicellulose that had been extracted
by means of alkali, proved to contain in *Chaetomorpha* a large amount of arabinose and a smaller amount of galactose, and in *Cladophora* also xylose, dextrose
and uronic acid. It is noteworthy that the cellulose which was left after the
extraction with alkali, the so-called α-cellulose therefore, appeared to contain a
considerable amount of other substances.

In *Rhizoclonium*, an Alga that has also been referred to the *Cladophoraceae*,
no very detailed investigations on the structure of the cell-wall have been
carried out. Here too the wall shows the characteristic crossed striations and
here too it proves to contain cellulose (NICOLAI and PRESTON, 1952). This Alga
has been used in order to demonstrate that the cellulose is already crystallized
in the fresh wall (PRESTON, WARDROP, NICOLAI, 1948). That the 101 plane
would already be tangentially oriented at that time, as these authors report,
seems dubious to us (cf. section 113).

Just as among the *Valoniaceae*, *Halicystis* shows a cell-wall constitution of
a deviating kind, so among the *Cladophoraceae* does *Spongomorpha* (NICOLAI
and PRESTON, 1952); in dried material its X-ray interferences resemble those of
cellulose II. *Acrosiphonia* is said to be another aberrant member of this family
(NICOLAI, 1957).

2413. Other green Algae

Nitella

CORRENS (1893) reported that he had seen in the wall of *N. syncarpa* and in that of *N. opaca* the two sets of striations that had been observed previously by VON MOHL, and that they occurred at a different level. One of the sets appeared to be oriented in a very flat Z-spiral, whereas the other ascended in an almost axial direction; occasionally a third, oblique, striation was recognizable. With chlor-zinc-iodine the striations became darker, and in sections that had been treated with this reagent, he could distinguish three layers, of which the central one appeared to contain the lamellae that had assumed the dark colour. If the cells were burst he could see that the axial and transverse striations occurred in different lamellae.

In mature cells the wall appeared to be negatively birefringent in surface view.

CORRENS assumed that the cell-wall contained cellulose, and this was confirmed by HOUGH et al. (1952), but according to NICOLAI and PRESTON (1952) the X-ray diagram of the untreated dry walls appeared to be too poor in diffraction arcs to allow a decision.

ZIEGENSPECK (1953), who by the aid of his special method of microscopic investigation had seen the striations in *Valonia* very clearly, reports that he had not been able to see the latter in the cell-wall of *Nitella flexilis*. We too looked in vain for them in *Nitella axillaris*, even in preparations that had been stained with iodine in the manner described by CORRENS.

GREEN and CHAPMAN (1955) studied the cell-wall of *N. axillaris* in the hope to find a correlation between the spiral growth and the structure of the wall. They do not mention the study of CORRENS, and did not see the striations which the latter had observed in the two *Nitella* species that he had used for his study. It is possible, of course, that the wall structure is similar in all *Nitella* species, but that the striations are in some of them very difficult to detect. The only "striations" that are mentioned by GREEN and CHAPMAN, are the two well-known spiral streaks that in the living cell mark the boundary between the ascending and the descending stream of protoplasm; these streams are also recognizable between crossed nicols. Some of their other microscope observations too appear to differ from those of CORRENS. In sections, neither in ordinary light nor between crossed nicols lamellae were found; in judging the value of this statement, it should, however, be taken into consideration that they did not use chlor-zinc-iodine, as CORRENS had done. Attempts to split the wall into lamellae and to isolate single lamellae had no success. The only point in which their microscopic observations agree with those of CORRENS, is their finding that the cells are in surface view negatively birefringent.

Electron micrographs of transverse and longitudinal sections through the walls of growing cells showed no trace of lamellation, and created the impression that the microfibrils are throughout the whole thickness of the wall more or less transversely oriented.

Electron micrographs of replicas made by GREEN (1958a) from the inside of the wall of growing internodial cells, show a predominantly transverse orientation of the microfibrils. A minor part of the microfibrils are scattered in other directions, and the latter, as may be seen in fig. P195, appear to be less straight; they look as if they were not subjected to tension (section 22823). The structure of the outer side of the wall is still unknown.

In the wall of a full-grown internodial cell, the inner surface shows fields consisting of nearly parallel microfibrils but varying in the mean direction of the latter. These fields may overlap one another or they merge one into the other by gradual curving of the microfibrils, fig. P196. It is quite obvious that there exists no relation whatever between the orientation of the microfibrils and the direction in which the protoplasm circulates, and that this applies just as well to growing cells as to mature ones.

On the inner surface of the wall of very old cells GREEN sometimes noted peculiar "ring" and "star" structures, fig. P197 and P198. The latter remind us of the structures that were found by PRESTON and RIPLEY in cambium cells (fig. 12) and that might in these cells represent islands of cellulose synthesis. In the opinion of GREEN they do not represent typical islands of synthesis in *Nitella*.

In connection with the spiral growth of these cells GREEN and CHAPMAN (l. c.) tried to find out whether the single wall would show oblique extinction, but the direction of the major extinction proved to be exactly transverse, just as in the double wall. Form birefringence contributes 11–19 % to the total retardation. The observations made by GREEN (1954) on the growth of the cells in length as well as in diameter, and on the rotation of the free tip, showed that so long as the cells are growing in length as well as in diameter, the direction of the rotation is anticlockwise (seen from above). It becomes clockwise when the increase in diameter ceases, and it remains so as long as the growth in length continues. The latter movement tends to untwist the cell, but when it ceases there is still a net anticlockwise turn amounting to several hundred degrees, as appears from the course of the two Z-helical lines in full-grown cells. The spiral growth is evenly distributed over the whole length of the cell, and the pitch of the two spiral lines too is everywhere the same. In very young cells the latter ascend in an angle of about 15° with the cell axis; the angle increases to about 40° during the period of anticlockwise rotation, and it decreases during the last period of growth to a low value. When full-grown cells were compressed, the spiral angle was not noticeably altered; this, however, does in our opinion not imply that no rotation did occur.

In contrast with the findings in *Nitella axillaris*, PROBINE and PRESTON (1958) found that in *Nitella opaca* the major extinction position of the single wall is not transverse, but follows a flat S-helix with a pitch of 0–10°; the longer the cells, the lower the pitch. The streaming direction of the protoplasm follows, as in *Nitella axillaris*, a steep Z-helix; it tends to intersect the major extinction direction at a right angle.

The various attempts to explain the relation between the spiral growth and the wall structure have been discussed in section 22827.

Our knowledge of *the cell-wall structure in other green Algae* not belonging to the *Valoniaceae* and the *Cladophoraceae*, is but fragmentary. We have mentioned already that NICOLAI and PRESTON (1952) made X-ray diagrams of the cellwalls of a number of them. Apart from this in most cases nothing is known; in a few instances it is known whether the cell shows in surface view a positive or a negative birefringence, but as this does not mean much so long as no other information is available, it does not seem worth while to record these observations.

We will make some exceptions for Algae that have been investigated in somewhat more detail. The first is *Hydrodictyon reticulatum*. CORRENS (l. c.) found no striation in the wall of this species. DIEHL et al. (1939) report that the double wall of the cylindrical cells of which the nets consist, remain in surface view negatively birefringent throughout the whole period of growth.

Unpublished observations that were made some ten years ago in the laboratory of the present author on the single wall of these cells, showed that the major extinction is always exactly transverse. Obliquely crossed striations were observed when the cell-wall was studied between crossed nicols; they are presumably due to undulations perpendicular to the surface of the wall which owe their origin to the shrinkage caused by loss of turgescence; a similar phenomenon has been observed e. g. in young cotton hairs (section 225) and in *Phycomyces* sporangiophores (section 2431).

After a treatment of sections with ruthenium-red, congo-red and chlor-zinc-iodine, 2–3 layers were visible, and after swelling, e. g. in chloral hydrate, the inner layer moreover appeared to consist of several lamellae. On account of these results and of the dichroism that is observed after staining with congo-red, it was assumed that the cell-wall contained cellulose.

NICOLAI and PRESTON (1952) could not confirm the presence of cellulose by means of the X-ray diagram of the cell-wall of *H. reticulatum*; the latter appeared to show unknown reflections. In another species, however, the diagram indicated the presence of cellulose II. KREGER (1958a), on the other hand, succeeded in demonstrating beyond all doubt the presence of cellulose in the wall of *H. reticulatum* by means of the X-ray diagram, provided that the material had previously been purified with diluted acid in the heat. According to this author the wall consists almost entirely of a mixture of cellulose and mannan, but these substances are both so slightly crystalline that they produce only weak reflections notwithstanding the fact that they are present in fairly high amounts; these reflections are too indistinct to allow positive conclusions with regard to the nature of the substances. The much stronger reflections that were obtained after heating with diluted acid, showed that cellulose II had been formed and that also mannan had passed into the crystalline state. Before the treatment they were apparently present in an amorphous molecular mixture, which must have been separated in one way or another into the component parts by means of the treatment with acid, after which they crystallized. This interpretation is in agreement with the fact that the two substances do not dissolve in alkali unless the cell-wall has previously been treated with acid. They may to some extent be separated from each other by fractioned precipitation from the solution in alkali. Investigations by means of the electron microscope have not yet been carried out with the cell-wall of *Hydrodictyon*.

Of the cell-wall of *Spirogyra* too a little more is known. This wall consists of an outer layer which stains with ruthenium-red, and an inner layer which strongly swells in cuprammonium, but remains enclosed in the outer layer and fills the cell lumen (KINZEL, 1950). As so often in cell-walls that contain but little cellulose, a positive reaction with chlor-zinc-iodine is obtained only after pre-swelling (NICOLAI and PRESTON, l. c.). NICOLAI and PRESTON found X-ray reflections which resembled those of cellulose I, but which showed various anomalies. KREGER (1957b), however, obtained a quite clear diagram of cellulose I after dissolving the constituents which contain galactose and xylose by means of hot acid. Remarkable enough a crystal lattice plane differing from the usual one (101) became oriented parallel to the surface when the material was dried (cf. section 113). Unpurified material shows in addition the reflections of $BaSO_4$, which originally was present in the cell itself (KREGER, 1957a).

The presence of microfibrils in the cell-wall of *Spirogyra* was demonstrated by Vogel in 1950 by means of the electron microscope; reproductions of his micrographs were published by Frey-Wyssling (e. g. 1953: 128). Nicolai and Preston (l. c.) too stated that microfibrils were present, but in contrast to those in the fragments photographed by Vogel, they showed a slight degree of orientation.

Ulva lactuca and *Enteromorpha* gave X-ray diagrams from which Nicolai and Preston (l. c.) could draw no conclusions. The X-ray analysis was tried once more by Cronshaw et al. (1958), but it allowed no other conclusion than that cellulose I was absent. By means of the electron microscope these authors noted in cell-wall fragments before as well as after purification with hot water and alkali, the presence of a network of microfibrils.

Recently the cell-walls of *Chlorella pyrenoidosa* have been isolated, analysed chemically and photographed electron optically by Northcote et al. (1958). They contain only about 15 % crude cellulose, 31 % hemicellulose, 27 % protein and 9 % lipid materials. The hydrolysate of this crude cellulose contained several hexoses and pentoses in addition to glucose. In the electron microscope microfibrils of 30–50 Å thickness were visible both in untreated walls (fig. P 199) and in walls that had been extracted with alkali. The authors state the presence of two layers with a different fibrillar orientation, but in our opinion there seems to occur random orientation both on the outer and the inner surface of the wall. The latter is visible at the breakage of the cell in fig. P 199.

For literature on and recent investigations of the cell-wall in other green algae we refer to the publications of Nicolai and Preston (l. c.), R. Frey (1950, *Vaucheria, Cystococcus, Hypnomonas, Tribonema*), Brandenberger and Frey-Wyssling (1947, *Chlorochytridion*), Moner (1955, *Pediastrum*), Sponsler and Bath (1950, *Ankistrodesmus*).

242. OTHER ALGAE

The chemical constitution of substances that can be isolated out of the cell-walls of *Phaeophyceae* and *Rhodophyceae* is comparatively well-known. Of the structure of the cell-wall, however, we know but little.

2421. *Rhodophyceae*

The literature on the microscopic structure shown by the cell-wall of the *Rhodophyceae* has been surveyed by Kylin (1937), Fritsch (1945: 399), Mori (1953), and Kinzel (1956). From these surveys the following points come to the fore.

Apart from a cuticle-like lamella on the outside, the wall consists, as a rule, of two distinct layers. Of these two layers the outer one is thinner than the inner one, and extends continuously over the whole alga. It stains deeply with ruthenium-red and methylene-blue, and contains acidic polysaccharides that are partly or completely soluble in hot water; chemically these polysaccharides are of a constitution that is typical for the *Rhodophyceae* (cf. section 143). The inner layer is confined to the individual cells. On account of the way in which it behaves with regard to various staining techniques, it is generally assumed that it contains cellulose. In *Antithamnion* Kinzel (1956) observed that the inner layer stains more deeply with methylene-blue than the outer one, which indicates a higher content of acidic polysaccharides, but it nevertheless gives cellulose reactions too, and this the outer layer does not do. Dilute acid as well as some fungal enzyme preparations, cause a heavy swelling of the whole wall. The lamellate structure that becomes visible in these swollen walls, is especially clear in the inner layer. In sections the latter appears to be positively birefringent with reference to the wall surface, whereas the outer layer is isotropic.

The blue colour which the walls of some of these *Rhodophyceae* (*Cystoclonium*, *Gelidium*, *Laurencia*) assume when they are treated with potassium triiodide, and which has been ascribed to the presence of "amyloid", may be due as well to e. g. the presence of cellulose II or of amorphous cellulose.

The presence of a conspicuous stratification has repeatedly been noted in the cell-wall, especially in some *Ceramiaceae*. Such walls have been used for illustrations in some of the classical studies on apposition, the best-known example being that of *Bornetia*, which was studied by BERTHOLD. On the inside of the wall of a growing cell, successively new layers are deposited, whereas on the outside the layers burst and are rejected. Transverse walls are formed by a growth process that starts from an annular zone in the longitudinal wall and proceeds in a centripetal direction; the nuclear spindle is not involved in this process.

In *Griffithsia* and *Antithamnion* the wall is known to undergo an enormous increase in volume, merely as a result of the death of the protoplasm. It is probably due to the loss of strain in the cell-wall on account of the elimination of the turgor pressure and which permits a greatly increased imbibition (KÜSTER, 1956; KINZEL, 1956).

In the *Corallinaceae* and in some other *Rhodophyceae* the wall becomes calcified. Both wall layers are involved in this process. In the *Corallinaceae* calcite is deposited, in the other *Rhodophyceae* arragonite. In old thalli some magnesium carbonate is usually present in addition.

According to CORRENS (1893) the cell-wall of the *Rhodophyceae* shows, as a rule, no striation ,but in *Polysiphonia* he noted a striation in a longitudinal direction. In sections he observed lamellae which stained with chlor-zinc-iodine.

BAAS BECKING and WAYNE GALLIHER (1931) studied the wall of *Corallina officinalis* and of *Amphiroa dorbigniana*. The wall of the genicular fibres, which does not contain calcite, as well as the decalcified wall of the articular fibres, are in longitudinal sections positively birefringent with reference to the cell axis, and isotropic in transverse sections. This positive birefringence was partly form birefringence, but if the sections were studied in water, the main part proved to be intrinsic; the minimum of the form birefringence curve corresponded to a refractive index of 1.48 in the medium.

BAAS BECKING and WAYNE GALLIHER came to the conclusion that the wall of the fibres consists of elongated lamellae that are axially oriented and whose flat sides are parallel to the surface of the wall, and that these lamellae are interspersed with interstices which evidently are also flat and tangentially oriented. To this concept we must object that it is at variance with the isotropy that was observed in the transverse sections, as this must mean either that the lamellae and the interstices have no definite orientation in the tangential plane or else that there are no lamellae and flat interstices at all but either rodlets or microfibrils that are oriented axially. The conclusion that the constituent parts of the wall must possess the shape of lamellae, was based only on the inclination of the symmetry axis in the form-birefringence curve, and it is not certain whether this may be accepted as a convincing ground (see McCLUNG, 1950). As the X-ray diagram only revealed the presence of calcite, the chemical con-

stitution of the elongated cell-wall constituents remained unknown. The calcite crystals are barely visible under the microscope; they are arranged with a
perpendicular to the plane of the wall.

An investigation of the cell-wall structure of the *Rhodophyceae* by the aid of
modern methods has been planned by PRESTON. Two papers have already appeared. The first describes the results obtained with *Griffithsia flosculosa* (MYERS,
PRESTON and RIPLEY, 1956), and additional information on this species is given
in the second one (CRONSHAW, MYERS and PRESTON, 1958).

In surface view no striation is visible under the microscope; in sections a
lamellate structure is observed. In longitudinal (and presumably also in transverse) sections the birefringence appears to be positive, but it is absent or slightly negative in surface view.

Electron micrographs made of fragments of untreated walls revealed the
presence of a network of microfibrils, which were stated to be about 200 Å
wide and 100 Å thick. In thin sections it was clearly visible that the outer layer
had a more compact structure, and that the inner one was conspicuously lamellate, fig. 200. The authors suppose that this structure rests on an alternation
of periods in which the material is deposited in a more compact form and periods in which it is deposited more loosely.

Study of the X-ray diagram led in the first paper to the conclusion that the
main constituent of the cell-wall is cellulose II, and in support of this conclusion it was pointed out that the material can be converted into cellulose IV

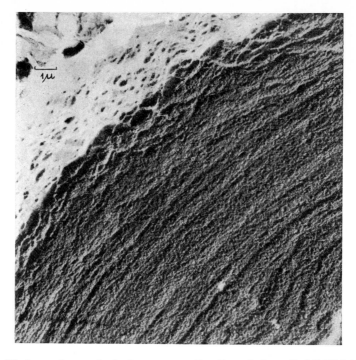

Fig. 200. Electron micrograph of a transverse section through the wall of *Griffithsia flosculosa;* it shows a more compact structure in the outer layer and a distinct lamellation in the
thick inner one (from MYERS, PRESTON and RIPLEY, 1956).

by boiling in glycerol. In the flattened walls of dried material, the 101 plane again proved to be oriented tangentially.

In the second paper the conclusion was formulated more vaguely, for here it was not said that the main constituent was cellulose II, but merely that it could not be cellulose I. The reason for this greater caution was not stated. We presume it was probably twofold. In the first place the circumstance had to be taken into account that in the meantime from the cell-walls of Algae that certainly do not contain cellulose, nevertheless X-ray diagrams had been obtained which resembled those of cellulose II, and in the second place there was the fact that if the residue (22 %) that was left after the *Griffithsia* cell-wall material had been washed first with hot water, which dissolves 42 %, then with 4 N alkali at 25°C, which dissolves another 14 %, and finally with sodium chlorite, which dissolves 22 %, was hydrolysed, the hydrolysate appeared to contain in addition to glucose also some galactose and xylose. If these were the grounds for not upholding the conclusion arrived at in the first paper, we should take in consideration that in the cell-walls of the *Anthophytes* too, a rather tenacious contamination of the cellulose with other polysaccharides is a common feature, and that the same authors observed a contamination of a similar nature in the cell-wall of *Chaetomorpha* which certainly does contain cellulose. The circumstance that the ration between the concentration of the dextrose and that of the two other sugars in the hydrolysates underwent a change during the subsequent stages of the purification process, is, in our opinion, an indication that the latter were present in the form of a contamination and not as a part of a heteropolymer that for the rest consisted of dextrose. The results of the second paper are therefore in our view not irreconcilable with the conclusion at which the authors had arrived in the first, viz. that cellulose II is present.

In two other *Rhodophyceae*, viz. *Ptilota* and *Rhodymenia*, CRONSHAW et al. (l. c.) found that microfibrils were present in the residue obtained by means of the purification with hot water, alkali and chlorite that was mentioned above. Hydrolysis of this residue, which in the first case amounted to 24 % and in the second to 7 %, yielded in addition to much glucose, either xylose, or xylose and galactose. The fraction that dissolves in alkali, seems to consist entirely of xylan; in the case of *Rhodymenia* this was already known (PERCIVAL and CHANDA, 1950).

In an unidentified species of *Porphyra* CRONSHAW et al. (l. c.) observed in untreated cell-walls as well as in the residue that was left after a treatment with hot water and that was estimated at 51 % of the original amount, a network of microfibrils. They appeared to be thinner than those that were observed in other *Rhodophyceae*, and they dissolved in alkali. After the substance that dissolved in alkali had been precipitated, it was hydrolysed; the hydrolysate proved to contain xylose and smaller amounts of galactose and mannose. Glucose was never found. After the treatment with alkali the residue was reduced to 3.5 %; it was of a granular texture, and appeared to consist of mannan, although it gave an X-ray diagram which showed a strong resemblance to those obtained from the cell-walls of *Rhodophyceae* that probably contain cellulose II. The authors come to the conclusion that in this Alga glucose is replaced as basic structural unit of the microfibrils by mannose, but on what grounds this conclusion rests, is not clear to us. It is difficult to reconcile with the fact that the main constituent of the hydrolysate obtained from the microfibrils that had been dissolved in alkali, was not mannose, but xylose. JONES (1950) had already isolated a mannan from the cell-wall of *Porphyra umbilicalis*.

Of general interest is the conclusion reached by CRONSHAW, MYERS and PRESTON (l. c.) with regard to the suitability of the X-ray diagram for the identification of polysaccharides, viz. that it should be used with caution. Their investigations had revealed that polysaccharides of different chemical constitution may give identical diagrams, at least as to the main interferences that in such cases are distinguishable.

2422. *Phaeophyceae*

For a review of the older literature dealing with the cell-wall of the *Phaeophyceae* we refer to FRITSCH (1945 : 24). On account of the results obtained with staining and dissolving agents, the conclusion was arrived at that there was, just as in the *Rhodophyceae*, an outer layer with little or no cellulose and an acid reaction and an inner layer with cellulose as the main constituent. The outer layer stains yellow with reagents that contain iodine, just as in the *Rhodophyceae*. Its main constituent is a polymannuronic acid, viz. alginic acid, which is characteristic for the *Phaeophyceae*. It further contains the sulphate-containing fucoidin (section 143). The presence of cellulose I was demonstrated in species of *Laminaria* by means of chemical reactions and X-ray analysis (PERCIVAL and ROSS, 1949).

It seems that the first observations on the optical properties of the cell-wall of the *Phaeophyceae* were published in 1955, viz. by ANDERSEN. The outer layer with its high content of alginic acid is just like the layer which contains the cellulose, in transverse as well as in longitudinal sections, positively birefringent with reference to the plane of the section; the outer layer, however, is less markedly birefringent than the inner one. When the sections are immersed in acid, the birefringence of the outer layer undergoes an increase. The author compares this behaviour with that shown by gels of calcium or copper alginate, and ascribes it to the substitution of metal ions by those of hydrogen; this would cause a shrinkage of the gel and an orientation of the molecules in the latter. That the outer layer actually contains a high amount of alginic acid was confirmed by washing the acidified sections with water and immersing them in a solution of sodium citrate; in this solution the layer is seen to swell considerably, and herein it finally dissolves; the layer which contains the cellulose, remains unchanged under these circumstances.

CRONSHAW et al. (1958) extended their study of the cell-wall of the *Rhodophyceae* also to seven *Phaeophyceae*. It appeared that 50–70 % of the cell-wall material dissolved in hot water, that a subsequent treatment with alkali removed another 16–30 %, and one with sodium chlorite once more 1–13 %, so that finally 1.5–20 % of the original amount was left. This might have been cellulose, but it did not give all the reflections that are characteristic for either cellulose I or II, and it appeared furthermore that a hydrolysate of this substance did not consist of dextrose alone. The authors are of opinion that the residue can not consist of cellulose I. They doubt the validity of the grounds that led PERCIVAL and Ross (l. c.) to a different conclusion.

The electron micrographs showed that in all stages of the cleaning process fragments with a random orientation of the microfibrils were present, but that the incrusting amorphous material is gradually removed, so that in the end a pure preparation of microfibrils is left. The latter were found to be 40–130 Å thick and 100–250 Å wide.

243. FUNGI

The greater part of the studies that in recent times have been carried out on the cell-wall of the Fungi are, exactly as in the case of the Algae, confined to the chemical nature of the cell-wall constituents. The literature has been reviewed e.g. by van Wisselingh(1925), R. Frey(1950), Roelofsen and Hoette(1951), Northcote and Horne (1952) and Kreger (1954). We may refer also to the sections of this work which deal with chitin, yeast glucan and yeast mannan (12, 1333 and 1332). The presence of cellulose was proved only for Oömycetes; its presence in one of the Chytridiaceae and in some Monoblepharidaceae is doubtful. If we leave the case of Rhizidiomyces bivellatus (Nabel, 1939), which is also very dubious, out of consideration, cellulose and chitin have never been found together, a confirmation of an old maxim of von Wettstein. All other Fungi that have been examined, appeared to be free of cellulose, but to be provided with chitin, although the latter is nowhere the main constituent of the cell-wall, as is often supposed (Norman and Peterson, 1932; Falcone and Nickerson, 1956; Blank, 1953 and 1954; Blumenthal and Roseman, 1957). In pressed yeast the wall consists for about one third of glucan and for one third of mannan (Northcote and Horne, 1952; Roelofsen, 1953). Schizosaccharomyces is the only genus in which neither cellulose nor chitin was found (Roelofsen and Hoette, 1951; Kreger, 1954).

With regard to the structure of the cell-wall the studies were so far almost entirely restricted to Phycomyces blakesleeanus and the yeasts. The curious spiral growth shown by the sporangiophores of the first-named Fungus, has been the object of several investigations; it was discussed in section 22827.

2431. *Phycomyces blakesleeanus*

The papers on the cell-wall structure of this Fungus will be dealt with, as far as possible, in a chronological sequence.

The abbé Carnoy (1870) had found in Rome on human excrements a Fungus which he called *Mucor romanus*, but which according to his accurate descriptions and drawings must have been *Phycomyces blakesleeanus*. He grew this Fungus on fruits, and saw, among other things, that the sporangiophores were covered with a thin layer, which impeded the penetration of reagents, but which dissolved in' alkali; he called this the cuticle. In the "membrane cellulosique", which lay beneath this cuticle and which proved to be resistant to alkali, he observed already without any further measures, but more conspicuously after a treatment with chlor-zinc-iodine, the presence of three layers, viz. a thin outer and inner layer and a comparatively thick central one. In the growing tip he found only the outer one. An immersion in a "solution concentré de potasse" during eight days caused a strong swelling; at the same time the outer layer became detached in some places. Especially if subsequently strong sulphuric acid was added, 12–20 lamellae became visible; the latter would be confined to the outer and the central layer; the inner one would be simple. In the sporangiophores of *Pilobolus* and *Rhizopus nigricans* he observed this lamellate structure of the cell-wall too, be it that the number of lamellae was smaller, viz. 7–10; in what he called *Mucor caninus* and *M. vulgaris* only 2–3 layers were visible, and even these were not very clear.

Errera and especially Laurent (1885) studied in the *Phycomyces* sporangiophore the localization of the region of growth, which is found at the tip, and in the stage in which the sporangium is mature, immediately below the latter. The second author also made interesting observations on the shortening which the region of growth underwent in cases of turgor loss. These authors, however, did not enter into the structure of the cell-wall. Information with regard to the latter, in the species itself as well as in the var. *piloboloides*, was given for the first time after CARNOY by OORT and ROELOFSEN (1932).

Like CARNOY, whose work was at that time unknown to them, they described the presence of a cuticle and of three further layers, of which the outer one appeared to be confined to the growing region; this layer we will indicate as the primary wall.

The cuticle shows in and below the region of growth a thin striation, which ascends in a steep spiral, and in the growth region sometimes in addition transverse undulatory striae.

The primary wall in the region of growth, and fragments of this wall that in the older parts of the wall may sometimes project in places where the wall is torn apart, appear to be nearly isotropic in surface view. However, if the birefringence is enhanced by the aid of congo-red or of chlor-zinc-iodine, especially if the wall has previously been cleaned with hot alkali, the primary wall appears to be negatively birefringent in surface view with reference to the cell axis. If the region of growth was dissected in such a way that locally parts of a single wall could be observed, the direction of the major extinction was stated to be Z-helical with a very low pitch, almost perpendicular to the direction of the longitudinal growth, fig. 201. According to OORT (1931) the latter takes place in a very steep spiral which makes an angle of only 6° with the cell axis. (Further on we will expound that regarding the Z-spiral in the primary wall the present author (1951 c) arrived at a less positive conclusion when he repeated the measurements with the polarization microscope).

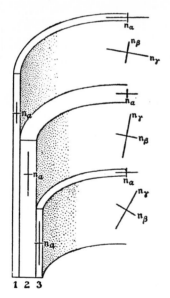

As the tubular texture which afterwards proved to be of general occurrence in growing tubular cells, seems to have been observed in growing cells for the first time in this object, we will insert here the reproduction of a figure which proved this texture (fig. 202). It shows a sporangiophore that was pushed over a thin glass thread, and which, after it had been cleaned and stained, was photographed in a diagonal position between crossed nicols. Owing to the circumstance that the original cylindrical form had been restored by the introduction of the glass thread, the isotropic zones which are typical for the tubular texture (fig. 32 c and f) are easily recognizable in the region of growth (a). There is apparently no relation between the wall structure and the streaming of the protoplasm, as the latter shows in the region of growth no preference for a definite direction.

The thick central layer, which appears for the first time in the zone that has just ceased to grow, and which therefore belongs to the secondary wall, showed a distinct positive birefringence, somewhat masked since the layer contains a slightly dichroitic substance of a slate-blue colour. The major extinction in

Fig. 201. Diagram showing the optical properties of the three layers in the wall of the sporangiophore of *Phycomyces blakesleeanus* (from OORT and ROELOFSEN, 1932).

this layer is usually oriented in the direction of a steep S-spiral. The latter proved to agree in its course more or less with three other spirals, viz. 1° the striation of the cuticle, 2° the protoplasmatic bands that are visible in the living cell and the streaming in the latter, the streaming in these bands is both acropetal and basipetal, 3° the presumable growth spiral.

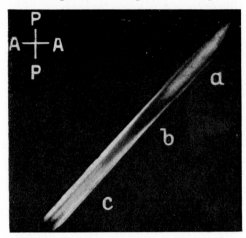

Fig. 202. Optical behaviour in the apical part of a sporangiophore of *Phycomyces blakesleeanus* which had been pushed over a thin thread of glass; it shows negative birefringence in the region of growth (a), lower down positive birefringence caused by the presence of secondary thickening (c), and between the two an isotropic zone (from OORT and ROELOFSEN, 1932).

Exceptionally, instead of an S-spiral a Z-spiral is found, and reversions in the direction of the spiral have occasionally been observed too. The birefringence of the secondary wall predominated strongly in the mature wall; if the wall was stained dichroitically the double refraction became so strong that the double wall did not extinguish in orthogonal but in somewhat oblique position and showed a conspicuous quadrant dichroism.

A distinct inner layer was confined to the mature wall, and became visible only in places where the other layers had been removed for the greater part by laceration. The micelles would here be oriented in an S-spiral with a less steep pitch than is found in the central layer; there would therefore be no agreement with the direction in which the protoplasm streams. (The present author is of opinion that the impression created by the inner layer may have been false. The striations were only observed between crossed nicols, and since the fragments on which the observations were made, were thin, they may have been wrinkled to some extent, in which case the striation may have been produced in the same way as was observed in young cotton hairs, section 225, and in the growth zone of the sporangiophore, vide infra).

It was further noted that an increase of the internal pressure caused a rotation of the tip, and that, if the pressure became too high, there appeared in the region of growth as well as immediately below the latter, a split in the axial direction (why the wall splits in this direction, was explained afterwards by CASTLE, 1937).

In the var. *piloboloides* the cell-wall shows the same structure. The curious swelling which the upper part of the sporangiophore undergoes in this variety and from which it derives its name, would not be accompanied by a rotation of the tip. However, in view of the observations published by BURGEFF (1915), which had been overlooked by the authors, this looks improbable. BURGEFF has irrefutably shown that the swelling is on the contrary accompanied by a very strong torsion, and that during this time the protoplasmic streaming takes place in a flat spiral. KIRCHHEIMER (1933), to whom we owe a large number of observations with regard to the protoplasmic streaming in *Phycomyces blakes-leeanus*, noted that the pitch of the spiral in which the protoplasm is oriented, decreased in this way also in sporangiophores that showed an increase in diameter on account of external causes. CASTLE (1936a), POP (1938) and MARTENS (1940) too occupied themselves with the protoplasmic streaming.

HEYN (1936) used piles consisting of the flattened walls of sporangiophores, all oriented in the same direction, and irradiated them from different sides with X-rays. He concluded from the diagrams that he obtained in this way, that the chitin chains are not only longitudinally oriented, but that they show, in the same way as the cellulose in dried walls of other plants, a preferential orientation in other directions too (cf. section 122). His diagrams do not prove, but are consistent with the view that the spiral structure in the secondary wall makes an angle of at the most $13.5°$ with the cell axis. Starting from this structure, he suggested a theory on the cause of the spiral growth, overlooking the fact that in the region of growth itself, a quite different cell-wall structure is present. Reflections due to the presence of waxes are not mentioned.

CASTLE (1938) confirmed the observation made by OORT and ROELOFSEN (l. c.) according to which the primary wall retains its transverse orientation after the deposition of the secondary wall. He further mentions that the cuticle melts if the sporangiophores are heated to $100°C$, and that if the molten substance is allowed to cool, crystals appear in small pools of "oil". In the growing tip the cuticle shows transversely oriented ridges, which were supposed to be drawn out in a longitudinal direction during the period of growth, whereby they passed through an equi-dimensional stage. Differential staining of the primary wall with a cold solution of congo-red, revealed the presence of a striation with an axial or steeply helical orientation. He ascribed this striation to the presence of an unidentified substance which did not belong to the cuticle; it was insoluble in hot alkali, but dissolved in hot acid; if stained, its birefringence proved to be positive and to predominate over that of the chitin in the region of growth.

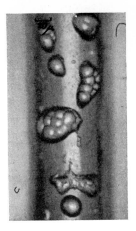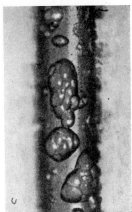

Fig. 203. Sporangiophores with exuded droplets; the latter are included between the cuticle and the rest of the cell-wall (from ROELOFSEN, 1950b).

The present author (1950b; 1951c) afterwards devoted a more detailed study to the structure of the wall. The cuticular striations observed in the region of growth in 1932, and which were oriented in a steep spiral, appeared to be caused by the presence of ridges that could be seen in turgescent sporangiophores when the latter were studied in light that struck them from above; however, they were even more clearly distinguishable in replicas made by the aid of gelatin from non-turgescent cells. The transverse cuticular ridges which CASTLE had seen, appeared only after the sporangiophore had lost its turgescence, and are due to axial shrinkage, which, indeed, is considerable, for it amounts to 15–20 % (LAURENT, 1885; ROELOFSEN, 1950a).

The well-known droplets of liquid that are exuded by the sporangiophores, were shown to be situated between the cuticle and the rest of the cell-wall, and their irregular shape and uneven surface show that the cuticle varies locally in extensibility, fig. 203. In electron micrographs the cuticle appeared as a tenuous membrane in which no structure could be detected (ROELOFSEN, 1951c).

Although we tried in various ways to catch a glimpse of the lamellate structure which, according to CARNOY, would be present in the greater part of the cell-wall, we had no success at all.

When a large number of sporangiophores were pulled to pieces, in three of them, from the partly ruptured cell-wall in the region of growth, narrow strips were seen to unwind in Z-spiral fashion. This pleads for the view that the microfibrils are in the primary wall oriented in a flat Z-spiral. This is also strongly indicated by the rotation of the tip when the internal pressure in the sporangiophore is increased by squeezing (ROELOFSEN, 1950a and b). The unwinding of these strips is shown in fig. 204.

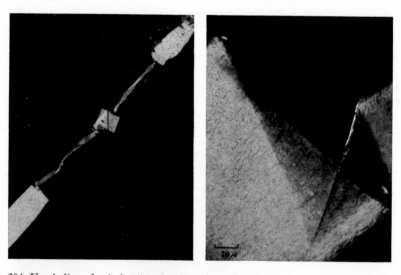

Fig. 204. Unwinding of spiral strips that have been detached by tearing the wall in the region of growth in two pieces; in b the strip is being torn off from the underlying wall of the cell (from ROELOFSEN, 1950b).

However, when we once more estimated the extinction angle in the region of growth in walls that had been cleaned and stained in the usual fashion, we obtained results that in contrast with the earlier ones, did not confirm the presence of a spiral structure. If the walls were cleaned with alkali and acid (cf. CASTLE, 1938) before we treated them with congo-red in order to increase the degree of birefringence still more, only in 9 out of the 29 sporangiophores the wall in the region of growth proved to have an extinction angle which indicated the presence of a Z-spiral, whereas in the remaining ones the extinction in the region of growth took place in a nearly transverse position; nevertheless all of them had shown the normal spiral growth. The reason why the spiral structure had practically disappeared, was sought in the shrinkage which the cell-wall had undergone on account of the treatment with chemicals, and which had reached a value of no less than 30 %.

At a later date (1958) the author pointed out that spiral growth and rotation when the turgor pressure is changed, might even take place if but a small part of the microfibrils were obliquely oriented; this part might be so small that it need not find expression in an oblique extinction (cf. section 22827).

Electron micrographs of cleaned sporangiophores published by FREY-WYSSLING and MÜHLETHALER (1950) and by the author (1951c) revealed, as a rule, in those parts of the cell-wall that remained well within the region of growth, the presence of an isotropic fibrillar structure at the outer surface, fig. P 205a.

Below the region of growth a slight preference for a more axial orientation was noted in the outermost microfibrils; this is shown in fig. P 205b, which is a replica made from the outer surface a good distance below the region of growth.

As the primary wall is negatively birefringent in the region of growth as well as below the latter, the inner part must possess a transverse structure. This is shown in fig. P 206. We find in these walls therefore a similar multinet structure as is present in those of many growing cells of the higher plants (cf. section 22823).

FREY-WYSSLING and MÜHLETHALER (l. c.) found that the fibrillar structures in the primary walls were sometimes transversely oriented and sometimes crossed, fig. P 207, but as the fragments that were studied by them, were obtained by disintegration by means of a blender, it is not known whether it was found on the outer or on the inner surface. The structure resembles the one found e. g. in growing cotton hairs (fig. P 60) and in the S_1 layer of other cells.

Just below the optically isotropic transition zone a more or less axially oriented fibrillar structure was found on the inside; this is apparently the first indication of a secondary thickening, fig. P 208. Towards the base of the sporangiophore this layer showed a denser structure.

HOUWINK has made electron micrographs of the cell-wall of hyphae from shake cultures of *Phycomyces* and of *Aspergillus*, but they have not been published. The outer surface of the hyphae always shows an isotropic network of microfibrils, fig. P 210. These walls had been so thoroughly cleaned csuccessively for half an hour at a temperature of 100°C with acid perhydrol, 2 % sulphuric acid, and 2 % NaOH), that they will have consisted of almost pure chitin (cf. KREGER, 1954).

MIDDLEBROOK and PRESTON (1952) too published a few supplementary observations. Their X-ray diagrams of the secondary wall were consistent with the assumption of a maximum spiral angle of roughly 9°; in the region of growth they too observed a transverse structure. The authors make no mention of interferences caused by the presence of lipids, but the latter are nevertheless probably recognizable in their X-ray diagrams. However, these lipids are presumably derived from the cell contents, as mechanically cleaned cell-walls do not show reflections that might be ascribed to lipids (see further on).

Electron micrographs made by these authors of the inner surface of non-cleaned sporangiophores showed no details of the wall structure.

Inconsistent with the results of previous investigations was the outcome of their determination of the major extinction direction in the primary wall in the region of growth. As they feared that a rigorous chemical cleaning and the staining with congo-red, which is applied in order to accentuate the birefringence, might exercise a distorting influence, they resorted to means, enabling them to study the weak birefringence of the untreated wall. They used a very strong illumination and a narrow diaphragm, and tried to eliminate the effect of light reflecting surfaces by the use of an oil immersion. In this way they found in the untreated primary wall of the region of growth, extinction angles indicating the presence of an S-spiral with a pitch of 11–15°.

As these optical results did not agree with those which we had obtained at an earlier occasion (1951c), we repeated the experiments, this time using the same method as these authors had applied, but without success. Like CASTLE (1953) we are therefore of opinion that their observations cannot be regarded as convincing. When measuring such extremely faint optical effects, we should realize that a very slight birefringence caused by strain in the optical system, even if it is so small that it would hardly be perceptible under normal circumstances, is apt to create a false impression. It is, moreover, questionable whether the use of uncleaned cell-walls may really be regarded as preferable above that of thoroughly cleaned ones, like those that were used by us. The uncleaned cell-wall contains a grey-blue dichroitic substance and, as CASTLE (l. c.) and KREGER (1954) have shown, also lipids and other material which may interfere with the birefringence of the oriented chitin, which is the sole component of the cell-wall which in this respect is of importance to us.

The exposition given by CASTLE (1953), which we have quoted already more than once, contains a valuable survey of the literature, and summarizes facts and theories that may throw some light on the problem of the spiral growth (section 22827).

Finally we will mention some facts that have been brought to light by a preliminary X-ray analysis carried out by KREGER, but which have only partly been published (1954). After the protoplasm had been removed by washing with water, the sporangiophore cell-wall appeared to contain circ. 30 % chitin, as much as 25 % lipids and some chitosan (in the mycelium the walls contain 10 % chitosan). In untreated walls no reflections of lipids were seen, but in walls that had been treated either with acid or with alkali and acid, they were actually present and even so conspicuous that it looked as if the treatment with acid had liberated lipids from a compound that was insoluble in alkali, and as if these liberated lipids had subsequently crystallized.

2432. Yeasts

Important studies by means of the ordinary microscope or of the polarization microscope on the structure of the cell-wall of yeasts are unknown to us. By means of the electron microscope the wall of *Candida tropicalis* and of baker's yeast was studied by HOUWINK (HOUWINK and KREGER, 1953), and in the last-named object also by NORTHCOTE and HORNE (1952) and by AGAR and DOUGLAS (1955). Sections have been studied by the last-named authors only.

In both species the outer surface of walls that had been freed from cytoplasm by mechanical disintegration of the cells and subsequent washing, appears to be smooth and structureless (fig. P211), except for the presence of several bud scars and one birth scar. These scars form circular rims on the surface, in the interior of which a concentric arrangement of fibrillar and granular material is found, fig. P212.On the inner surface of the wall and of the scars tiny microfibrils are visible (fig. P211).

The scars are already visible under the ordinary microscope, as had been detected by BARTON (1950). The latter even could distinguish bud scars from birth scars; seen from the outside the first are convex and the latter concave. This difference was confirmed by electron micrographs that had been made of sections through cells of baker's yeast, fig. P213. In these sections the wall appears to consist of a thin layer (0.05μ) of dense structure, and a thicker one (0.2μ) of a less dense structure; the latter proved to be subdivided by very thin lamellae of a higher density, and to be lined on the inner side by a network of microfibrils, which seem to be identical with those seen on the inner surface in fig. P211. In good agreement with this two-layered structure is the observation made by NORTHCOTE and HORNE (l. c.) according to which the cell-wall tends to split into two layers, especially at the bud scars, where the wall is thick and more clearly two-layered than elsewhere. HOUWINK and KREGER (l. c.), on the other hand, found no indication whatever of the presence of layers.

AGAR and DOUGLAS (l. c.) reported that the outer layer which in the electron micrographs showed a denser structure, disappeared when the cells were disintegrated with the aid of the apparatus by means of which the other investigators had obtained their cell-wall fragments. This observation suggests the possibility that the outer surface depicted in fig. P211, might not be the original one; however, this is unlikely, as in that case one would expect to see side by side cells or areas with and cells or areas without the outer layer with the denser structure.

Boiling with dilute alkali removes two thirds of the dry weight, and leaves a thinner wall with a minutely granular surface, and bud scars in which the microfibrils are more clearly distinguishable, fig. P214. The microfibrils consist most probably of glucan. In the cell-wall of baker's yeast, chitin forms at the most 2% of the whole mass; it can be obtained as a residue by boiling the cell-wall with acid and alkali. This chitin is granular, and seems to be accumulated in the bud scars. In *Candida* the chitin contains besides granules also short microfibrils, fig. P215.

Finally we wish to point out that HURST (1952) has made electron diffraction diagrams of parts of yeast cells, and that these diagrams prove that the lipid molecules in the walls of these cells are oriented in the same way as in the cell-walls of the Anthophytes, viz. perpendicular to the surface.

Bibliography

ABITZ, W., GERNGROSS, O. & HERRMANN, K., 1930. Z. physik. Chem. **10,** 371.
ACKER, L., DIEMAIR, W. & SAMHAMMER, E., 1955. Z. Lebensm.-Untersuch. u. Forsch. **100,** 180.
ADAM, J., 1951. Nature **167,** 78.
AFZELIUS, B. M., 1956. Grana palynologica N. S. **1,** 22.
AFZELIUS, B. M., ERDTMANN, G. & SJÖSTRAND, F. S., 1954. Svensk Botan. Tidskr. **48,** 155.
AGAR, H. D. & DOUGLAS, H. C. ,1955. J. Bacteriol. **70,** 427.
AGARDH, J. G., 1852. De cellula vegetabili febrillis tenuissimis contexta, Lund.
ALDABA, V. C., 1927. Am. J. Botany **14,** 17.
ALEXANDROV, W. G. & DJAPARIDZE, L. I., 1927. Planta **4,** 467.
ALLSOPP, A. & MISRA, P., 1940. Biochem. J. **34,** 1078.
AMBRONN, H., 1888. Ber. deut. botan. Ges. **6,** 226.
—, 1925. Kolloid-Z., Zsigmondy Festheft, 119.
AMBRONN, H. & FREY, A., 1926. Das Polarisationsmikroskop.
A. O. A. C., American Ass. of Official Agricultural Chemists. 1955. Official Methods of Analysis.
AMIN, E. S., 1955. J. Chem. Soc., 281.
ANDERSEN, G., 1955. cf. Braarud and Sörensen. 1956.
ANDERSON, D. B., 1927a. Sitzber. Akad. Wiss. Wien, Math. naturw. Kl. Abt. I **136,** 429.
—, 1927b. Am. J. Botany **14,** 187.
—, 1928. Jahrb. wiss. Botan. **69,** 501.
ANDERSON, D. B. & KERR, Th., 1938. Ind. Eng. Chem. **30,** 48.
ANDERSON, D. B. & MOORE, J. H. 1937., Am. J. Botany **24,** 503.
ANDREWS, P., HOUGH, L. & JONES, J. K. N. ,1952a. J. Am. Chem. Soc. **74,** 4019.
—, —, —, 1952b. J. Chem. Soc., 2744.
—, —, —, 1953. J. Chem. Soc., 1186.
—, —, —, 1954. J. Chem. Soc., 806.
ARNOLD, K., 1956. Naturwiss. **43,** 233.
ARZT, Th., 1933. Ber. deut. botan. Ges. **51,** 470.
—, 1936. Ber. deut. botan. Ges. **54,** 247.
—, 1937. Ber. deut. botan. Ges. **55,** 347.
ASBECK, F., 1955. Naturwiss. **42,** 632.
ASPINALL, G. O., HIRST, E. L., PERCIVAL, E. G. V. & WILLIAMSON, I. R., 1953. J. Chem. Soc., 3184.
ASPINALL, G. O., HIRST, E. L. & WARBURTON, M., 1955. J. Chem. Soc., 651.
ASPINALL, G. O. & MAHOMED, R. S., 1954. J. Chem. Soc., 1731, 1734.
ASPINALL, G. O., RASHBROOK, R. B. & KESSLER, G., 1958. J. Chem. Soc., 215.
ASPINALL, G. O., & WILKY K. C. B., 1956. J. Chem. Soc., 1072.
ASTBURY, W. T., MARWICK, T. C. & BERNAL, J. D., 1932. Proc. Roy. Soc. (London) **109,** 444.
ASTBURY, W. T. & PRESTON, R. D., 1940. Proc. Roy. Soc. (London) B**129,** 54.
ASTBURY, W. T., PRESTON, R. D. & NORMAN A. G., 1935. Nature **136,** 391.
ASUNMAA, S., 1955. Svensk Papperstidn. **58,** 308.
ASUNMAA, S. & LANGE, P. W., 1952. Svensk Papperstidn. **55,** 936.
—, —, 1954. Svensk Papperstidn. **57,** 501.

BAAS BECKING, L. G. M. & WAYNE GALLIHER, E., 1931. J. Phys. Chem. **35,** 469.
BAILEY, A. J., 1936. Ind. Eng. Chem., Anal. Ed. 8, 389.
BAILEY, I. W., 1938. Ind. Eng. Chem. **30,** 43.
—, 1954. Contribution to plant anatomy (Waltham).
—, 1957. Am. J. Botany **44,** 415.
BAILEY, I. W. & BERKLEY, E. E., 1942. Am J. Botany **29,** 231.
BAILEY, I. W. & KERR, Th., 1934. J. Arnold Arboratum **15,** 327.

BAILEY & KERR, 1935. J. Arnold Arboratum **16**, 273.
—, —, 1937. J. Arnold Arboratum **18**, 261.
BAILEY, I. W. & VESTAL, M. R., 1937a. J. Arnold Arboratum **18**, 185.
—, —, 1937b. J. Arnold Arboratum **18**, 196.
BALASHOV, V. & PRESTON, R. D., 1955. Nature **176**, 64.
BALASHOV, V., PRESTON, R. D., RIPLEY, G. W. & SPARK, L. S., 1957. Proc. Roy. Soc. (London) B**146**, 460.
BALL, D. H., 1956. Tappi **39**, 438.
BALLS, W. L., 1919. Proc. Roy. Soc. (London) **90**B, 542.
—, 1923. Proc. Roy. Soc. (London) **95**B, 72.
BALLS, W. L. & HANCOCK, H. A., 1922. Proc. Roy. Soc. (London) **93**B, 426.
—, —, 1926. Proc. Roy. Soc. (London) **99**B, 130.
BANGE, G. G. J., 1950. unpublished graduate work in author's laboratory.
BANNAN, M. W., 1950. Am. J. Botany **37**, 511.
—, 1956. Can J. Botany **34**, 175.
BARNES, R. B. & BURTON, C. J., 1943. Ind. Eng. Chem. **35**, 120.
BARROWS, F. L., 1940. Contr. Boyce Thompson Inst. **11**, 161.
BARTON, A. A., 1950. J. Gen. Microbiol. **4**, 84.
BAUER, L., 1956. Z. Naturforsch. 11b, 673.
BAYLEY, S. T., 1955. Biochim. Biophys. Acta **17**, 194.
BAYLEY, S. T., COLVIN, J. R., COOPER, F. P. & MARTIN-SMITH, C. A., 1957. J. Biophys. Biochem. Cytol. **3**, 171.
BAYLEY, S. T. & SETTERFIELD, G., 1957. Ann. Botany, N. S. **21**, 633.
BECHERER, G. & VOIGTLAENDER–TETZNER, G., 1955. Naturwiss. **42**, 577.
BECKER, W. A., 1938. Botan. Rev. **4**, 446.
BEER, M. & SETTERFIELD, G., 1958. Am. J. Botany **45**, 571.
BELFORD, D. S., MYERS, A. & PRESTON, R. D., 1958. Nature **181**, 1251.
BELL, D. J. & NORTHCOTE, D. H., 1950. J. Chem. Soc., 1944.
BENNET, A. H., JUPNIK, H., OSTERBERG, H. & RICHARDS, O. W., 1951. Phase contrast microscopy, Wiley, New York.
BEREK, M., 1953. Anleitung zu opt. Untersuch. mit dem Polarisationsmikroskop.
BERGMAN, S. I. & JOHNSON, M. M., 1950. Tappi **33**, 586.
BERKLEY, E. E., 1938–1939. Textile Research **9**, 355.
—, 1942. Am. J. Botany **29**, 416.
—, 1948. Textile Research J. **18**, 71.
BERKLEY, E. E. & KERR, Th., 1946. Ind. Eng. Chem. **38**, 304.
BERKLEY, E. E. & WOODYARD, O. C., 1948. Textile Research J. **18**, 519.
BERNHEIM, F., BUNN, C. & WILBUR, K. M., 1951. Am. J. Botany **38**, 458.
BION, F., 1928. Helv. Phys. Acta **1**, 165.
BISHOP, C. T., BAYLEY, S. T. & SETTERFIELD, G. ,1958.Plant physiology **33**, 283.
BJÖRKMAN, A., 1956. Svensk Papperstidn. **59**, 477.
BJÖRKMAN, A. & PERSON, B., 1957. Svensk Papperstidn. **60**, 158.
BJÖRKQUIST, K. L., JÖRGENSEN, L. & WALLMARK, A., 1954. Svensk Papperstidn. **57**, 113.
BLACK, R. A., ROSEN, A. A. & ADAMS, S. L., 1953. J. Am. Chem. Soc. **95**, 5344.
BLACK, W. A. P., 1948. J. Soc. Chem. Ind. **67**, 165.
BLAND, D. E. & GATLEY, F. M., 1954. Nature **173**, 32.
BLANK, F., 1953. Biochim. Biophys. Acta **10**, 110.
—, 1954. Can. J. Microbiol. **1**, 1.
BLOUT, E. R., 1953. Advances in Biol. and Med. Phys. Vol. III.
BLOUT, E. R. & WEISSBERGER, A. 1954. Vol. I, 2179.
BLUMENTHAL, H. J. & ROSEMAN, S., 1957. J. Bacteriol. **74**, 222.
BOCK, L., 1955. Kutikularstrukturen im Elektronenmikroskop, Thesis München.
BÖHMER, H., 1958. Planta **50**, 461.
BOLAM, F., 1958. Trans. Symposium 1957 on Fundamentals of Papermaking Fibres, Techn. Sect., Brit. Paper and Board Makers' Assoc.
BONDI, A. & MEYER, H., 1948. Biochem. J. **43**, 248.
BONNER, J., 1935. Pringsh. Jahrb. wiss. Botan. **82**, 377.
BOS, J., 1957. see BOLAM, F., 1958.
BOSSHARD, H., 1952. Ber. schweiz. botan. Ges. **62**, 482.
—, 1956a. Schweiz. Z. Fortstw. **107**, 1.
—, 1956b. Holz: Roh- u. Werkstoff. **14**, 285.
BRAARUD, T. & SÖRENSEN, N. A., 1956. Second Intern. Seaweed Symp. 1955, Pergamon Press, London.

BRADING, J. W. E., GEORG-PLANT, M. M. T. & HARDY, D. M., 1954. J. Chem. Soc., 319.
BRAND, F., 1906. Ber. deut. botan. Ges. 24, 64.
—, 1908. Ber. deut. botan. Ges. 26, 114.
BRANDENBERGER, E. & FREY-WYSSLING, A., 1947. Experientia 3.
BRANDENBERGER, E. & SCHINZ, H. R., 1944. Ber. schweiz. botan. Ges. 54, 255.
BRAUNS, E. ,1952. The Chemistry of Lignin, New York.
BREMEKAMP, C. E. B., 1944. Verh. Ned. Akad. v. Wetenschap. 2e ser. 41, 24.
BRIAN, P. W., 1949. Ann. Botany 13, 59.
BROWN, S. A. & NEISH, A. C., 1955. Nature 175, 689.
BRUNSWIK, H., 1921. Biochem. Z. 113, 111.
BUCHER, H., 1953. Die Tertiärlamelle von Holzfasern u. i. Erscheinungsform bei Coniferen, Attisholz, Solothurn, Switzerland.
—, 1955. Bull. Assoc. Techn. Inst. Pap. 4/5, 95.
—, 1957a. Holzforschung 11, 1.
—, 1957b, Holzforschung 11, 97.
BURGEFF, H., 1915. Flora 108, 353.
BURRI, C., 1950. Das Polarisationsmikroskop, Birkhäuser, Basel.
CAMPBELL, F. W., 1929. Ann. Entomol. Soc. Am. 22, 401.
CARLQUIST, S., 1956. Am. J. Botany 43, 425.
CARLSTRÖM, D., 1957. J. Biophys. Biochem. Cytol. 3, 669.
CARNOY, J. B., 1870. Bull. soc. roy. botan. Belg. 9, 157.
CASTLE, E. S., 1936. J. Gen. Physiol. 19, 797.
—, 1936a. J. Cellular Comp. Physiol. 7, 445.
—, 1937. J. Cellular Comp. Physiol. 10, 113.
—, 1938. Protoplasma 31, 331.
—, 1953. Quart. Rev. Biol. 28, 364.
—, 1955. Proc. Nat. Acad. Sci. 41, 197.

CAVAZZA, L., 1950. Bull. soc. botan. suisse 60, 596.
CHANDA, N. B., HIRST, E. L. & MANNERS, D. J., 1957. J. Chem. Soc. 1951.
CHESTERS, C. G. C., TURNER, M. & APINCI, A., 1955. cf. Braarud and Sörensen 1956.
CHIPPELLE, F. L. & PUTT, F. A., 1951. Stain Technology 26, 51.
CHOLODNY, N., 1922. Ber. deut. botan. Ges. 40, 326.
CLARK, G. L., 1930. Ind. Eng. Chem. 22, 481.
—, 1940. Applied X-rays, McGraw Hill.
CLARK, G. L., FARR, W. K. & PICKETT, L. W., 1930. Ind. Eng. Chem. 22, 481.
CLARK, G. L. & SMITH, A. F., 1936. J. Phys. Chem. 40, 863.
CLARK, G. L. & TREFORD, H. C., 1955. Anal. Chem. 27, 888.
COLVIN, J. R., 1957. Arch. Biochem. Biophys. 70, 294.
COLVIN, J. R., BAYLEY, S. T. & BEER, M., 1957. Biochim. Biophys. Acta 23, 652.
COOKE, W. B., 1957. Tappi 40, 301.
COPPICK, S. & FOWLER, W. F., 1939. Paper Trade J. 109, nr. 11, 81.
CORRENS, C., 1892. Jahrb. wiss. Botan. 23, 254.
—, 1893. Zimmermann's Beitr. Morph. Physiol. Pflanzenzelle 1, 260
COSLETT, V. E., ENGSTRÖM, A. & PATTEE, H. H., 1957. X-ray Microscopy and Microradiography, Ac. Press.
COTÉ, W. A., 1958. Forest Products J. 8, 296.
CRAMER, C., 1890. Denkschr. Allg. schweiz. Ges. Naturw. 30, 1.
—, 1891. Denkschr. Allg. schweiz. Ges. Naturw. 32, 1.
CROCKER, E. C., 1933. Botan. Gaz. 95, 168.
CRONSHAW, J., MYERS, A. & PRESTON, R. D., 1958. Biochim. Biophys. Acta 27, 89.
CRONSHAW, J., & PRESTON, R. D. 1958. Proc. Roy. Soc. (London) B148, 137.
CRÜGER, H., 1855. Botan. Ztg. 13, 601, 617.
DAFERT, F. W. & MIKLAUZ, R., 1912. Denkschr. kaiserl. Akad. Wiss. 87, 143.
DARMON, S., & RUDALL, K. M. 1950. Disc. Faraday Soc. 9, 251.
DAUPHINÉ, A., 1941. Compt. Rend. Acad. Sci. Paris 213, 739.
DEARING, G. G., 1957. Nature 179, 579.
DEBAUN, R. M. & NORD, F. F., 1951. Arch. Biochem. Biophys. 33, 314.
DEMAIN, A. L., & PFAFF, H. J. 1957. Wallerstein Lab. Communic. 20, 119.
DENHAM, H. J., 1922. J. Textile Inst. 13, 19.
—, 1923. J. Textile Inst. 14, T87.
DEUEL, H. & NEUKOM, H., 1949a. Makromol. Chem. 3, 13.
—, —, 1949b. Makromol. Chem. 4, 97.
—, —, 1954. Advances in Chem. Ser. 11, 51.

DEUEL, H. & STUTZ, E., 1958. Advances in Enzymol. **20,** 341.

DIEHL, J. M. & ITERSON, G. v., 1935. Kolloid-Z. **73,** 142.

DIEHL, J. M., GORTER, C. J., ITERSON, G. v. & KLEINHOONTE, A., 1939. Rec. trav. botan. néerl. **36,** 709.

DIPPEL, L., 1878. Die neue Theorie über die feinere Struktur der Zellhülle, betrachtet an der Hand der Thatsachen, Frankfurt.

—, 1898. Das Mikroskop und seine Anwendung (first ed. 1867–1869).

DOLMETSCH, H., 1955. Holz: Roh- u. Werkstoff. **13,** 85.

DORÉE, C., 1950. The Methods of Cellulose Chemistry. Chapman, London.

DOUS, E., 1927. Botan. Arch. **19,** 461.

DRAKE, N. L., CARHART, H. W. & MORZINGO, R., 1941. J. Am. Chem. Soc. **63,** 617.

DRAWERT, H. & METZNER, I., 1956. Ber. deut. botan. Ges. **69,** 291.

DUFF, R. B., 1952. J. Chem. Soc., 2592.

ECKLING, K. & KRATKY, O., 1930. Z. physik. Chem. B**10,** 367.

EHRENTHAL, I., MONTGOMERY, R. & SMITH, F., 1954. J. Am. Chem. Soc. **76,** 5509.

ELLIOT, E., 1951. Nature **168,** 1089.

EMERTON, H. W., 1955. Proc. Techn. Sect. Brit. Paper and Board Makers' Ass. **36,** 595.

—, 1957a. Tappi **40,** 542.

—, 1957b. see Bolam, F. 1958.

EMERTON, H. W. & GOLDSMITH, V., 1956. Holzforschung **10,** 108.

EMERTON, H. W., PAGE, D. H. & WATTS, J., 1956. Proc. Techn. Sect. Brit. Paper and Board Makers' Ass. **37,** 103.

ERDTMANN, G., 1943. Introduction to pollen analysis, Waltham.

—, 1952. Pollen Morphology and Plant Taxonomy, Uppsala.

—, 1954. Svensk Botan. Tidskr. **48,** 471.

—, 1956. Svensk Botan. Tidskr. **50.**

—, 1956a. Grana palynologica **1,** 127.

ERSKINE, A. J. & JONES, J. K. N., 1956. Can. J. Chem. **34,** 821.

ESAU, K. ,1953. Plant Anatomy, New York.

ESCHRICH, W., 1954. Planta **44,** 532.

—, 1956. Protoplasma **47,** 488.

—, 1957. Planta **48,** 578.

FÅHRAEUS, G., 1958. see Ruhland Vol. VI. 1958, 305.

FALCONE, G. & NICKERSON, W. J., 1956. Science **124,** 272.

FARR, W. K., 1949. J. Phys. & Colloid Chem. **53,** 260.

FARR, W. K. & CLARK, G. L., 1932. Contribs. Boyce Thompson Inst. **4,** 273.

FIERZ-DAVID, H. E. & ULRICH, C., 1945. Experientia **1,** 160.

FISHER, I. S. & PERCIVAL, E. C., Second Seaweed Symposion 1955, Pergamon Press, London 1956.

FITTING, H., 1900. Botan. Ztg. **58** I, 107.

FLINT, E. A., 1950. Biol. Revs. **25,** 414.

FRAENKEL, G. & RUDALL, K. M., 1940. Proc. Roy. Soc. (London) B**129,** 1.

FRANZ, H., 1935. Flora **129,** 287.

FREI, A., PRESTON, R. D. & RIPLEY, G. W., 1957. J. Exptl. Botany 8, 139.

FREUDENBERG, K., 1954. Fortschr. Chem. org. Naturstoffe **11,** 43.

—, 1955. Naturwiss. **42,** 29.

FREUDENBERG, K., ZOCHER, H. & DUER, W., 1929. Ber. deut. chem. Ges. **62,** 1814.

FREUND, H., 1952. Handb. Mikroskopie in der Technik II, 1.

FREY, A., 1926. Jahrb. wiss. Botan. **65,** 195.

FREY-WYSSLING, A., 1928. Ber. deut. botan. Ges. **46,** 444.

—, 1930. Z. wiss. Mikrosk. **47,** 1.

—, 1934. Z. wiss. Mikrosk. **51,** 29.

—, 1935. Die Stoffausscheidung der Pflanzen, Springer.

—, 1936. Protoplasma **25,** 261.

—, 1937a. Protoplasma **27,** 372.

—, 1937b. Protoplasma **27,** 563.

—. 1937c. Protoplasma **27,** 402.

—, 1939. Verhandl. schweiz. naturforsch. Ges. **67.**

—, 1941. Protoplasma **35,** 527.

—, 1942a. Jahrb. wiss. Botan. **90,** 705.

—, 1942b. Cellulosechemie **20,** 55.

—, 1945. Arch. Julius Klaus-Stift. **20,** 381.

—, 1947. J. Polymer Sci. **2,** 314.

FREY-WYSSLING, 1950. Ann. Rev. Plant Physiol. **1**, 169.
—, 1951. Holz **9**, 333.
—, 1952. Deformation and flow in biological systems, North Holl. Publ. Co., Amsterdam.
—, 1953. Submicroscopic morphology of protopplasm. Elsevier's Publ. Co., Amsterdam.
—, 1953a. Experientia **9**, 181.
—, 1954. Science **119**, 80.
—, 1955. Biochim. Biophys. Acta **18**, 166.
—, 1957. Macromolecules in cell structure, Harvard Univ. Press.
—, 1959. Die pflanzliche Zellwand, Springer.
FREY-WYSSLING, A., BOSSHARD, H. H. & MÜHLETHALER, K., 1956. Planta **47**, 115.
FREY-WYSSLING, A., EPPRECHT, W. & KESSLER, G., 1957. Experientia **13**, 22.
FREY-WYSSLING, A. & MÜHLETHALER, K., 1949. Mikroskopie **4**, 257.
—, —, 1950. Vierteljahresschr. naturforsch. Ges. Zürich **95**, 45.
—, —, 1951. Zechmeister's Fortschr. 14, Naturst. VIII.
—, —, 1951. Mikroskopie **6**, 28.
FREY-WYSSLING, A., MÜHLETHALER, K. & MOOR, H., 1956. Mikroskopie **11**, 219.
FREY-WYSSLING, A., MÜHLETHALER, K. & WYCKOFF, R. W. G., 1948. Experientia **4**, 475.
FREY-WYSSLING, A. & MÜLLER, H. R., 1957. J. Ultrastruct. Res. **1**, 38.
FREY-WYSSLING, A. & SCHOCH-BODMER, H., 1938. Planta **28**, 257.
FREY-WYSSLING, A. & SPEICH, H., 1936. Helv. Chim. Acta **19**, 900.
FREY-WYSSLING, A. & STECHER, H., 1951. Experientia **7**, 410.
—, —, 1954. Z. Zellforsch. **39**, 515.
FREY, R., 1950. Ber, schweiz. botan. Ges. **60**, 199.
FREYTAG, K., 1954a. Protoplasma **43**, 253.
—, 1954b. Ber. oberhess. Ges. Natur- u. Heilk. **26**, 21.
—, 1957. Planta **50**, 41.
FRITSCH, F. E., 1935, 1945. Structure and reproduction of the algae I, II, Cambridge Univ. Press.
FRITZ, F., 1935. Jahrb. wiss. Botan. **81**, 718.
—, 1937. Planta **26**, 693.

GARDINER, W., 1897. Proc. Roy. Soc. (London) **62**, 100.
GARZULY-JANKE, R., 1940. Zentr. Bakteriol. Parasitenk. **102**, 361.
GEERDES, J. D. & SMITH, F., 1955. J. Am. Chem. Soc. **77**, 3572.
GEITLER, L., 1934. Österr. Botan. Z. **83**, 284.
—, 1937. Planta **27**, 426.
GENEAU DE LAMARLIERE, L., 1906. Rev. gén. botan. **18**, 289.
GESSNER, F. & VOLZ, G., 1951. Planta **39**, 171.
GEZELIUS, K. & RÅNBY, B. G., 1957. Exptl. Cell Research **12**, 265.
GILLES, K. A. & SMITH, F., 1956. Cereal Chem. **33**, 29.
GLASER, L., 1957. Biochim, Biophys. Acta **25**, 436.
GLASER, L. & BROWN, D. H., 1957 Biochim. Biophys. Acta **23**, 449.
GORDON WHALEY, W., MERICK, L. W. & HEIMSCH, C., 1952. Am. J. Botany **39**, 20.
GORHAM, P. R. & COLVIN, J. R., 1957. Exptl. Cell Research **13**, 187.
GOTTLIEB, S. & PELCZAR, M. J., 1951. Bacteriol. Rev. **15**, 55.
GRAFF, J. H., 1942. Pulp & Paper Microscopy, Inst. Paper Chem. Appleton, Wisc.
GREEN, P. B., 1954. Am. J. Botany **41**, 403.
—, 1958. Am. J. Botany **45**, 111.
—, 1958a. J. Biophys. Biochem. Cytol. **4**, 505.
GREEN, P. B. & CHAPMAN, G. B., 1955. Am. J. Botany **42**, 685.
GRIFFIOEN, K. J., 1935. Planta **24**, 584.
GROSS, S. T. & CLARK, G. I., 1938. Z. Krist. **99**, 357.
GUINIER, A. & FOURNET, G., 1955. Small angle scattering of X-rays, Chapman & Hall, London.
GUNDERMANN, J., WERGIN, W. & HESS, K., 1937. Ber. deut. chem. Ges. **70**, 517.

HABERLANDT, G., 1887. Über die Beziehungen zwischen Funktion und Lage des Zellkernes bei den Pflanzen, Jena.
HÄGGLUND, E. 1951. Chemistry of Wood. Acad. Press.
HALL, C. E., 1953. Introd. to electronmicroscopy, McGraw Hill.
HALL, D. A., LLOYD, P. F., SAXL, H. & HAPPEY, F., 1958. Nature **181**, 470.
HALLER, R., 1935. Helv. Chim. Acta **18**, 50.
HALLIWELL, G., 1958. Biochem. J. **68**, 605.
HARADA, H., MIYAZAKI, Y. & WAKASHIMA, T., 1958. Govt. Forest Exp. Sta., Tokyo, bull. 104.

HARRIS, E. E., 1953. Tappi **36**, 402.

HARTSHORNE, N. H. & SHOART, A., 1950. Crystals and the polarizing microscope, E. Arnold, London.

HÄUSERMANN, E., 1944. Ber. schweiz. bot. Ges. **54**, 541.

HAYASHI, K. & MIZUNO, T., 1952. J. Chem. Soc. Japan **26**, 569.

HEATH, M. A. & JOHNSON, M. M., 1950. Tappi **33**, 386.

HEIKENS, D., HERMANS, P. H., VAN VELDEN, P. F. & WEIDINGER, A., 1953. J. Polymer Sci. **11**, 433.

HEIKENS, D., HERMANS, P. H. & WEIDINGER, A., 1958. Verhandlungsber. Kolloid-Ges. **18**, 15.

HENGLEIN, F. A., 1958. cf. Ruhland, Vol. VI 1958, 405.

HENGLEIN, F. A., KRÄSSIG, H. & STEIMMIG, A., 1949. Makromol. Chem. **4**, 78.

HENGSTENBERG, J. & MARK, H., 1929. Z. Krist. Mineral. **69**, 271.

HEPTON, C. E. L., PRESTON, R. D. & RIPLEY, G. W., 1955. Nature **176**, 868.

—, —, —, 1956. Nature **177**, 660.

HERGERT, H. L. & KURT, E. F., 1952. Tappi **35**, 59.

HERMANS, P. H., 1949. Physics and chem. of cell. fibers, Elsevier Publ. Co., Amsterdam.

—, 1949a. J. Polymer Sci. **4**, 145.

HERMANS, P. H., DE BOOYS, J. & MAAN, C. J., 1943. Kolloid-Z. **102**, 169.

HERZOG, A., 1926. Die Unters. d. Flachs. u. Hanffaser, Springer, Berlin.

—, 1955. Mikrophotogr. Atlas der techn. wichtigen Pflanzenfasern, Akademie Verlag, Berlin.

HERZOG, R. O., 1926. J. Phys. Chem. **30**, 457.

HERZOG, R. O. & GONELL, H. W., 1924. Naturwiss. **12**, 1153.

HERZOG, R. O. & JANCKE, W., 1920. Z. Physik **3**, 196.

HESS, K. & LÜDTKE, M., 1928. Ann. Chem. **466**, 18.

HESS, K., MAHL, H. & GÜTTER, E., 1957. Kolloid-Z. **155**, 1.

HESS, K., TROGUS, C. & WERGIN, W., 1936. Planta **25**, 419.

HESS, K., WERGIN, W., KIESSIG, H., ENGEL, W., & PHILIPPOFF, W., 1939. Naturwiss. **27**, 622.

HESSLER, L. E., MEROLA, G. V. & BARKLEY, E. E., 1948. Textile Research J. **18**, 628.

HESTRIN, S. & SCHRAMM, M., 1954. Biochem. J. **58**, 345.

HEYN, A. N. J., 1933. Protoplasma **19**, 78.

—, 1934. Protoplasma **21**, 299.

—, 1936. Protoplasma **25**, 372.

—, 1949. Textile Research J. **19**, 163.

—, 1950. J. Am. Chem. Soc. **72**, 5768.

—, 1955. J. Appl. Phys. **26**, 519, 1113.

—, 1957. Textile Research J. **27**, 449.

HIBBERT, H. & BARSHA, J. 1931. Can. J. Research **5**, 580.

HIGUCHI, T., 1955. J. Japan. Forestry Soc. **37**, 298.

—, 1956. J. Japan. Forestry Soc. **38**, 31.

—, 1957. Physiol. Plantarum **10**, 356, 621, 633.

HILKENBÄUMER, F., 1958. Z. Naturforsch. **13**b, 666.

HILPERT, R. S., BECKER, D. & ROSSER, W., 1937. Biochem. Z. **289**, 179.

HIRST, E. & JONES, J., 1939. J. Chem. Soc., 452.

HIRST, E. L., PERCIVAL, E. G. V. & WYLAM, C. B., 1954. J. Chem. Soc., 189.

HOCK, C. W., 1942. J. Research Nat. Bur. Standards **29**, 41.

—, 1947. Textile Research J. **17**, 423.

HOCK, C. W., RAMSAY, R. C. & HARRIS, M., 1941. J. Research Nat. Bur. Standards **26**, 93.

HODGE, A. J. & WARDROP, A. B., 1950. Australian J. Sci. Research B **3**, 265.

HONJO, G. & WATANABE, M., 1957. J. Electronmicroscopy **5**, 59 (see also: 1958. Nature **181**, 326.)

HOPMANN, O., 1930. Diss. Münster.

HOTTENROTH, B., 1951. Die Pektine und ihre Verwendung, München.

HOUGH, L., JONES, J. K. N. & WADMAN, W. H., 1952. J. Chem. Soc., 3392.

HOUVEN VAN OORDT-HULSHOF, B. VAN DER, 1957. Acta Botan. Neerl. **6**, 420.

HOUWINK, A. L. & KREGER, D. R., 1953. Antonie van Leeuwenhoek **19**, 1.

HOUWINK, A. L. & ROELOFSEN, P. A., 1954. Acta Botan. Neerl. **3**, 385.

HUBER, B., KINDER, E., OBERMÜLLER, E. & ZIEGENSPECK, H., 1956. Protoplasma **46**, 380.

HUELIN, F. E. & GALLOP, R. A., 1951. Australian J. Sci. Research **34**, 526.

HULL, 1917. Phys. Rev. **10**, 661.

HURST, H., 1950. J. Exptl. Biol. **27**, 238.

HURST, 1952. J. Exptl. Biol. **29**, 30.
HUSEMANN, E. & CARNAP, A., 1943. J. makromol. Chem. **1**, 16.
—, —, 1944. Naturwiss. **32**, 79.

INOUE, S. & HYDE, W. L., 1957. J. Biophys. Biochem. Cytol. **3**, 831.
ITERSON, G. VAN, 1927. Chem. Weekblad **24**, 166.
—, 1933. Chem. Weekblad **30**, 2.
—, 1935. Proc. 6th Intern. Botan. Congr. II, 294.
—, 1936. Proc. Koninkl. Akad. Wetenschap. **39**, 1066.
—, 1936a. Nature **138**, 364.
—, 1937. Protoplasma **27**, 190.
—, 1942 in V. J. KONINGSBERGER, Leerboek der Alg. Plantkunde, part 2, chapt. 8.
ITERSON, G. VAN, MEYER, K. H. & LOTMAR, W., 1936. Rec. trav. chim. Pays-Bas **55**, 61.
ITERSON, W. VAN. 1958. Gallionella ferruginea in a different light, North Holl. Publ. Co., Amsterdam.
JAYME, G. & HARDERS–STEINHÄUSER, M., 1947. Holzforschung **1**, 33.
JAYME, G. & HUNGER, G., 1958. Mikroskopie **13**, 24.
JAYME, G. & NEUSCHÄFFER, K., 1955. Naturwiss. **42**, 536.
—, —, 1957. Naturwiss. **44**, 62.
JENSEN, A. & SUNDE, I., 1955. see BRAARUD and SÖRENSEN 1956.
JENSEN, W., 1950. Paper & Timber **32**, 261, 291, 293.
JENSEN, W. & OSTMAN, R., 1954. Paper & Timber **36**, 427.
JENSEN, W. & RINNE, P., 1954. Paper & Timber **36**, 32.
JENSEN, W. & TINNIS, W., 1957. Paper & Timber **39**, 237.
JERMYN, M. A. & TOMKINS, R. G., 1950. Biochem. J. **47**, 437.
JOHANSEN, D. A., 1940. Plant Microtechnique, McGraw Hill.
JONES, J. K. N., 1950. J. Chem. Soc., 3292.
JONES, W. J. M. & PEAT, S., 1942. J. Chem. Soc., 225.
JOULIA, R., 1938. Rev. gén. botan. **50**, 261.

KANAMARU, K., 1934. Helv. Chim. Acta **17**, 1047.
KARIYONE, T. & HASHIMOTO, J., 1953. Experientia **9**, 136.
KATZ, I. R. see HESS, R., 1928. Chemie der Cellulose, Leipzig.
KAUSHAL, R., WALKER, T. K. & DRUMMOND, D. G., 1951. Biochem. J. **50**, 128.
KELANEY, M. A. EL & SEARLE, G. O., 1930. Proc. Roy. Soc. (London) **106**, 357.
O'KELLEY, J. C., 1953. Plant Physiol. **28**, 281.
O'KELLEY, J. C. & CARR, P. H., 1954. Am. J. Botany **41**, 261.
KERPEL, D. A., 1938. Ann. Jard. botan. Buitenzorg **48**, 173.
KERR, T., 1937. Protoplasma **27**, 229.
—, 1946. Textile Research J. **16**, 249.
KERR, T. & BAILEY, I. W., 1934. J. Arnold Arboretum **15**, 327.
KERTESZ, Z. I., 1951. The pectic substances, Interscience, New York.
KESSLER, G., 1958. Ber. schweiz. bot. Ges. **68**, 5.
KHOUVINE, Y. 1932. Compt. Rend. Acad. Sci. Paris **195**, 396.
KINSINGER, W. G. & HOCK, C. W., 1948. Ind. Eng. Chem. **40**, 1711.
KINZEL, H., 1950. Mikroskopie **5**, 89.
—, 1956. Compt. Rend. Acad. Sci. Paris.
KIRCHHEIMER, F., 1933. Planta **19**, 574.
KISSER, J., 1939. Abderhalden, Hdb. Biol. Arb. M. XI. T4, 1, 391.
KISSER, J. & SKUHRA, H., 1952. Mikroskopie **7**, 160.
KLEIN, G., 1931–1933. Handb. Pflanzenanalyse I–III.
KLING, W. & MAHL, H., 1950. Melliand Textilber. **31**, 407.
—, —, 1951. Melliand Textilber. **32**, 131.
—, —, 1952. Melliand Textilber. **33**, 32, 328, 829.
KOHL, G., 1889. Kalksalze und Kieselsäure in der Pflanze, Marburg.
KOOIMAN, P., 1954. Biochim. Biophys. Acta **13**, 338.
—, 1957. Nature **179**, 107.
—, 1957a. Nature **180**, 201.
—, 1959. Onderzoek van amyloid uit zaden, Thesis Delft.
KOOIMAN, P. & KREGER, D. R., 1957. Biochim. Biophys. Acta **26**, 207.
KRABBE, G., 1887. Pringsh. Jahrb. wiss. Botan. **18**, 346.
KRAJCINOVIC, M., 1954. Acta Histochem. **1**, 76, (Chem. Abstr. **49**, 11782, 1955).
KRATKY, O., 1951. Kolloid-Z. **120**, 24.
KRATKY, O. & POROD, G., 1949. J. Colloid Sci. **4**, 35.
KRATKY, O. & SCHOSSBERGER, F., 1938. Z. physik Chem. (B)**39**, 145.

KRATKY, O., SEKORA, A. & TREER, R., 1942. Z. Elektrochem. 48, 587.
KRATZL, K. & BILLEK, G., 1957. Holzforschung 10, 161.
KREGER, D. E., 1948. Rec. trav. botan. néerl. 41, 603.
—, 1954. Biochim. Biophys. Acta 13, 1.
—, 1957a. Nature 180, 867.
—, 1957b. Nature 180, 914.
—, 1958. J. Ultrastr. Research 1, 247.
—, 1958a. in preparation.
—, 1958b. see RUHLAND. 1958. Handb. Pflanzenphysiol. Bd X, 249.
KREGER, D. R. & MEEUSE, B. J. D., 1952. Biochem. Biophys. Acta 9, 699.
KRIEG, W., 1907. Beih. botan. Centr. 21, I, 245.
KUNDU, B. C. & PRESTON, R. D., 1940. Proc. Roy. Soc. (London) B128, 214.
KURSANOV, A. L. & VYSKREBENTSEVA, 1952. Biokhimiya 17, 480, (ref. 1953. Chem. Abstr. 47, 859).
KÜSTER, E., 1956. Die Pflanzenzelle, Jena.
KYLIN, H., 1937. LINSBAUER's Handb. Pflanzenanatomie VI 2 Bg.
—, 1946. Kgl. Fysiograf. Sällskap. Lund, Förh. 16, 102, (ref. 1947. Chem. Abstr. 41, 6605).

LAMBERTZ, P., 1954. Planta 44, 147.
LANGE, P. W., 1950. Svensk Papperstidn. 53, 749.
—, 1954. Svensk Papperstidn. 57, 525, 563.
LANGE, P. W. & KJAER, A., 1957. Norsk Skogsind. 11, 425.
LANNING, T. C., PONNAIYA, B. W. X. & CRUMPTON, C. F., 1958. Plant Physiol. 33, 339.
LAURENT, E., 1885. Bull. Acad. Roy. Belg. 55, 3e série 10, 57.
LAUTENSCHLAGER–FLEURY, D., 1955. Ber. schweiz. botan. Ges. 65, 343.
LAVES, F. & ERNST, TH., 1943. Naturwiss. 31, 68.
LEE, B., 1925. Ann. Botany 39, 755.
LEE, B. & PRIESTLEY, J. H., 1924. Ann. Botany 38, 525.
LEGG, V. H. & WHEELER, R. V., 1925. J. Chem. Soc. 127, 1412.
—, —, 1929. J. Chem. Soc., 2444, 2449.
LEVINE, B. S., 1914. Science 40, 906.
LIESE, W., 1957a. Ber. deut. botan. Ges. 70, 21.
—, 1957b. Naturwiss. 44, 240.
—, 1958. (Private communication).
LIESE, W. & HARTMANN–FAHNENBROCK, M., 1953. Biochim. Biophys. Acta 11, 190.
LIESE, W. & JOHANN, I., 1954. Planta 44, 269.
LINDBERG, B. & MEIER, H., 1957. Svensk Papperstidn. 60, 785.
LINDEBERG, G., 1948. Physiol. Plantarum 1, 198, 401.
LINDGREN, P. H., 1958. Arkiv Kemi 12, 9.
LINSBAUER, K., 1930. Handb. Pflanzenanatomie, Bd. IV.
LINSKENS, H. F., 1952. Planta 41, 40.
LOTMAR, W. & PICKEN, L. E. R., 1950. Experientia 6, 58.
LUNDEGÅRDH, H., 1946. Arkiv. Botan. 33A, 1.
LUNIAK, B., 1953. The Identification of Textile Fibres, Pitman, London.
LYON, F., 1905. Botan. Gaz. 40II, 285.
LYR, H., 1958. Planta 50, 359.

MAAS GEESTERANUS, R. A., 1941. Proc. Koninkl. Akad. Wetenschap. Amsterdam 44, 481.
McCLUNG, R., 1950. Handbook of Microscopical Technique, Hoeber.
McCOMB, E. A. & McCREADY, R. M., 1952. Anal. Chem. 24, 1630, 1986.
McCREADY, R. M. & REEVE, R. M., 1955. J. Agr. Food Chem. 3, 260.
MacDOWELL, R. M., 1955. cf. Braarud and Sörensen, 1956.
MacLARTY, D. H., 1941. Bull. Torrey Botan. Club 68, 75.
MADER, H., 1954. Planta 43, 163.
MAERTENS, C., RAES, G. & MEERSCHE, G. VAN DER, 1956. Proc. Conf. on Electr. Microsc. Stockholm, 292.
MAJUMDAR, G. P. & PRESTON, R. D., 1941. Proc. Roy. Soc. (London) B130, 859.
MANGENOT, F., 1953. Bull. Soc. Sci. Nancy 12, 10.
MANGENOT, G., & RAISON M., 1942. Rev. cytol. et cytophys. végétales 6, prt. I, (translated in Botan. Rev. 17, 556, 1951).
MANN, J. & MARRIMAN, H. J., 1956. Trans. Faraday Soc. 52, 481.
MANTELL, C. L., 1947. The water soluble gums, Reinhold, New York.
MARK, H. & SUSICH, G., 1929. Z. physiol. Chem. (B)4, 431.
MARTENS, P., 1931. La Cellule 41, 17.

MARTENS, 1933. Bull. soc. roy. botan. Belgique **66,** fasc. 1.

—, 1934. Protoplasma **20,** 484.

—, 1937. La Cellule **46,** 357.

—, 1938. La Cellule **47,** 247.

—, 1940. La Cellule **48,** 249.

MASON, H. S. & CRONYN, M., 1955. J. Am. Chem. Soc. **77,** 491.

MATIC, M., 1956. Biochem. J. **63,** 168.

MEEUSE, A. D. J., 1938. Rec. trav. botan. néerl. **35,** 288.

—, 1941. Rec. trav. botan. néerl. **38,** 20.

MEEUSE, B. J. D., 1938. Proc. Koninkl. Akad. Wetenschap. **41,** 965.

—, 1941. Ber. deut. botan. Ges. **59,** 122.

MEIER, H., 1955. Holz: Roh- u. Werkstoff. **13,** 323 (Thesis Zürich, E. T. H.).

—, 1956. Proc. Confer Electr. Microsc. Stockholm.

—, 1957. Holzforschung **11,** 41.

—, 1958. Biochim. Biophys. Acta **28,** 229.

MEREWETHER, J. W. T., 1957. Holzforschung **11,** 65.

MERICLE, L. W & GORDON WHALEY, W., 1953. Botan. Gaz. **114,** 382.

METZNER, I., 1955. Arch. Mikrobiol. **22,** 45.

METZNER ,P., 1930. Planta **10,** 281.

MEVIUS, W., 1923. Ber. deut. botan. Ges. **41,** 237.

MEYER, K. H., HUBER, L. & KELLENBERGER, E., 1951. Experientia **7,** 216.

MEYER, K. H. & MARK, H., 1929. Z. physik. Chem. (B)**2,** 115.

—, —, 1953. Makromolekulare Chemie, Akad. Verlag, Leipzig. (or MEYER, K. H., 1950. Natural and synthetic high polymers, Interscience).

MEYER, K. H. & MISCH, L., 1937. Helv. Chim. Acta **20,** 232.

MEYER, K. H. & PANKOW, G. W., 1935. Helv. Chim. Acta **18,** 589.

MEYER, K. H. & WEHRLI, H., 1937. Helv. Chim. Acta **20,** 111.

MEYER, M., 1938. Protoplasma **29,** 552.

MIDDLEBROOK, M. J. & PRESTON, R. D., 1952. Biochim Biophys. Acta **9,** 32.

MIGITA, N., KANDA, T. & FUHINAMI, R., 1951. J. Japan. Forestry Soc. **33,** 424, (ref.: 1952. Chem. Abstr. **26,** 13237).

MOEHRING, E., 1922. Wiss. u. Ind. I, 68.

MOLISCH, H., 1923. Mikrochemie der Pflanze.

MONER, J. G., 1955. Am. J. Botany **42,** 802.

MONTGOMERY, R. & SMITH, F., 1955. J. Am. Chem. Soc. **77,** 2834, 3325.

MORI, T., 1953. Advances in Carbohydrate Chem. **8,** 315.

MOSS, B. L., 1948. Ann. Botany, N. S. **12,** 267.

MUELLER, L. E., CARR, P. H. & LOOMIS, W. E., 1954. Am. J. Botany **41,** 593.

MÜHLETHALER, K., 1949a. Biochim. Biophys. Acta **3,** 527.

—, 1949b. Biochim. Biophys. Acta 3, 15.

—, 1950a. Biochim. Biophys. Acta **5,** 1.

—, 1950b. Ber. schweiz. botan. Ges. **60,** 614.

—, 1950c. Exptl. Cell Research **1,** 341.

—, 1953a. Z. Zellforsch. u. mikroskop. Anat. **38,** 299.

—, 1953b. Mikroskopie **8,** 103.

—, 1955. Planta **46,** 1.

—, 1956. Am. J. Botany **43,** 673.

MÜHLETHALER, K. & LINSKENS, H. F., 1956. Experientia **12,** 253.

MUKHERJEE, S. M. & WOODS, H. J., 1953. Biochim. Biophys. Acta **10,** 499.

MÜLLER, R., 1956. Mikroskopie **11,** 36.

MYERS, A., PRESTON, R. D. & RIPLEY, G. W., 1956. Proc. Roy. Soc. (London) B**144,**450.

NABEL, K., 1939. Arch. Mikrobiol. **10,** 515.

NAEGELI, C., 1864. Sitzber. bayer. Akad. Wiss. **1,** 282.

—, 1864a. Sitzber. bayer. Akad. Wiss. **2,** 115.

NAEGELI, C. & SCHWENDENER, S., 1877. Das Mikroskop.

NAKAMURA, Y., 1937. Cytologia (Tokyo) Vol. 482.

NAKAMURA, Y. & HESS, K., 1938. Ber. deut. chem. Ges. **71,** 145.

NETOLITZKY, F., 1929. LINSBAUER's Handb. Pflanzenanatomie Bd. 3, Ia (Lief. 25).

NEWMAN, S. B. & RIDDELL, H. F., 1954. Textile Research J. **24,** 113.

NICOLAI, E., 1957. Nature **180,** 491.

NICOLAI, E. & FREY-WYSSLING, A., 1938. Protoplasma **30,** 401.

NICOLAI, E. & PRESTON, R. D., 1952. Proc. Roy. Soc. London B**140,** 244.

—, —, 1953. Proc. Roy. Soc. London B**141,** 407.

NIKLOWITZ, W. & DREWS, G., 1956. Arch. Mikrobiol. **24,** 134.
NISHIKAWA, S. & ONO, S., 1913. Phys. Math. Soc. Japan, 20 Sept. Tokyo.
NODDER, C. R., 1922. J. Textile Inst. **13,** 167.
NOLL, F., 1887. Exper. Unters. Wachstum der Zellmembranen, Würzburg.
NORMAN, A. G. & PETERSON, W. H., 1932. Biochem. J. **26,** 1946.
NORTHCOTE, D. H., GOULDING, K. J. & HORNE, R. W., 1958. Biochem. J. **70,** 391.
NORTHCOTE, D.H. & HORNE, R. W., 1952. Biochem. J. **51,** 232.

OHARA. 1933. Sci. Papers Inst. Phys. Chem. Research (Tokyo) **21,** 211.
O'KELLEY, J. C., 1953. Plant Physiol. **28,** 281.
O'KELLEY, J. C. & CARR, P. H., 1954. Am. J. Botany **41,** 261.
OORT, A. J. P., 1931. Proc. Roy. Acad. Sci. Amsterdam **34,** 564.
OORT, A. J. P. & ROELOFSEN, P. A., 1932. Proc. Roy. Acad. Sci. Amsterdam **35,** 898.
ORGELL, W. H., 1955. Plant Physiol. **30,** 78.
OSHIMA, K., 1931. Bull. Agric. Chem. Soc. Japan **7,** 332.
OSTER, G. & POLLISTER, A. W., 1956. Physical techniques in biological research I–III.
OTT, E. & SPURLIN, H. M., 1954–1955. Cellulose and cellulose derivates, I–III, Interscience.
OVERBECK, F., 1934. Z. Botan. **27,** 129.
OZAWA, J. & OKAMOTO, K., 1952. Rept. Ohara Inst. Agr. Research **40,** 103. (Chem. Abstracts 1953, **47,** 10070).
OZTIG, O. F., 1940. Flora **134,** 105.

PAECH, K. & TRACEY, M. V., 1955. Modern methods of plant analysis II.
PALMER, K. J. & HARTZOG, M. B., 1945. J. Am. Chem. Soc. **67,** 2122.
PALMER, K. J., MERRILL, R. C., OWENS, H. S. & BALLANTYNE, M.,1947. J. Phys. & Colloid Chem. **51,** 710.
PEAT, S., WHELAN, W. J. & LAWLEY, H. G., 1953. Biochem. J. **54,** XXXIII.
—, —, —, 1955. Chem. & Ind. (London), 35.
PEIRCE, F. T., 1946. Trans. Faraday Soc. **42,** 545, 560.
PEISER, H. F., ROOKSBY, H. P. & WILSON, A. J. C., 1955. X-ray diffraction by polycrystalline materials, London.
PERCIVAL, E. G. V. & CHANDA, S. K., 1950. Nature **166,** 787.
PERCIVAL, E. G. V. & ROSS, A. G., 1949. J. Chem. Soc. 3041.
PETITPAS, T. & MERING, M. J., 1956. Compt. Rend. Acad. Sci. Paris **243,** 47.
PFEIFFER, H. H., 1949. Das Polarisationsmikroskop, Vieweg.
PIA, J., 1934. Beih. botan. Zentralbl. **52A.**
PICKEN, L. E. R. & LOTMAR, W., 1950. Nature **165,** 599.
POEL, P. W. VAN DER, LE POOLE, J. B., SPIT, B. J. & WATERMAN, H. I., 1958. De Ingenieur **70,** Ch: 7, cf. 1958. Sugar **53,** 261.
POLANYI, M., 1921. Naturwiss. **9,** 288.
POLANYI, M. & WEISSENBERG, K., 1922. Z. Physik **9,** 123.
POLGLASE, W. J., 1955. Advances in Carbohydrate Chem. **10,** 283.
POP, L. J. J., 1938. Proc. Koninkl. Akad. Wetenschap. Amsterdam **41,** 661.
PREECE, I. A. & MACKENZIE, K. G., 1925. J. Inst. Brewing **58,** 353.
PRESTON, R. D., 1931. Proc. Leeds Phil. Lit. Soc. **2,** 185.
—, 1934. Phil. Trans. Roy. Soc. London B**224,** 131.
—, 1935. Proc. Leeds Phil. Lit. Soc. **3,** 102.
—, 1938. Proc. Roy. Soc. (London) B**125,** 372.
—, 1939. Ann. Botany, N. S. **3,** 507.
—, 1941. Proc. Roy. Soc. (London) B**130,** 103.
—, 1946. Proc. Roy. Soc. (London) B**133,** 327.
—, 1947. Proc. Roy. Soc. (London) **134,** 202.
—, 1948. Biochim. Biophys. Acta **2,** 370.
—, 1951. Discussions Faraday Soc. **11,** 165.
—, 1952. Molecular architecture of plant cell walls, Chapman & Hall, London.
PRESTON, R. D. & ALLSOPP, A., 1939. Biodynamica **53,** 1.
PRESTON, R. D. & ASTBURY, W. T., 1937. Proc. Roy. Soc. (London) B**127,** 76.
— —, 1954. Nature **173,** 203.
PRESTON, R. D. & CLARK, C. S., 1944. Proc. Leeds Phil. Lit. Soc. **4,** 201.
PRESTON, R. D. & CRONSHAW, J. 1958. Nature **181,** 248.
PRESTON, R. D. & DUCKWORTH, R. B., 1946. Proc. Leeds Phil. Lit. Soc. 4, (5) 345.
PRESTON, R. D., HERMANS, P. H. & WEIDINGER, A., 1950. J. Exptl. Botany.
PRESTON, R. D. & KUYPER, B., 1951. J. Exptl. Botany **2,** 247.
PRESTON, R. D. & MIDDLEBROOK, M., 1949. J. Textile Inst. **40,** T715.

PRESTON, R. D., NICOLAI, E. & KUYPER, B., 1953. J. Exptl. Botany **4**, 40.
PRESTON, R. D., NICOLAI, E., REED, R. & MILLARD, A., 1948. Nature **162**, 665.
PRESTON, R. D. & RIPLEY, G. W., 1954. J. Exptl. Botany **5**, 410.
—, —, 1954a. Nature **174**, 76.
PRESTON, R. D. & SINGH, K., 1950. J. Exptl. Botany **1**, 24.
—, —, 1952. J. Exptl. Botany **3**, 162.
PRESTON, R. D. & WARDROP, A. B., 1949. Biochim. Biophys. Acta **3**, 549.
—, —, 1949a. Biochim. Biophys. Acta **3**, 585.
PRESTON, R. D., WARDROP, A. B. & NICOLAI, E., 1948. Nature **162**, 957.
PRIESTLEY, J. H., 1943. Botan. Rev. **9**, 593.
PRIESTLEY, J. H. & SCOTT, L. I., 1939. Proc. Leeds Phil. Lit. Soc. **3**, 532.
PRINS, A., 1934. Physica **1**, 752.
PROBINE, M. C. & PRESTON, R. D., 1958. Nature **182**, 1657.

RÅNBY, B. G., 1952a. Fine structure and reactions of cellulose, Thesis Uppsala, (see 1952. Tappi **35**, 53.)
—, 1954. Makromol. Chem. **13**, 40.
RÅNBY, B. G. see 1958. RUHLAND VI: 268.
RAYNAUD, M., FISCHER, G., PREVOT, A. R. & BIZZINI, B., 1956. Ann. inst. Pasteur **91**, 267.
REEVE, R. M., 1946. Am. J. Botany **33**, 191.
REEVES, R. E., 1951. Advances in Carbohydrate Chem. **6**, 108.
REIMERS, H., 1921. Textilber. **2**, 367, 381, 420.
—, 1922. Angew. Botan. **4**, 70.
—, 1922a. Mitt. Forschungsinst. Textilst. Karlsruhe, 109.
REZNIK, H., 1955. Planta **45**, 455.
REZNIK, H. & URBAN, R., 1956. Planta **47**, 1.
RIBAS–MARQUES, I., 1952. Chim. & Ind. (Paris) **68**, 333.
RIBI, E., 1953. Exptl. Cell Research **5**, 161.
RIGBY, G. W., 1936. U. S. Patent 2.040.879.
RITTER, G. J., 1949. Tappi **32**, 11.
ROELOFSEN, P. A., 1949. Biochim. Biophys. Acta **3**, 518.
—, 1950a. Rec. trav. botan. néerl. **42**, 72.
—, 1950b. Biochim. Biophys. Acta **6**, 340.
—, 1951a. Biochim. Biophys. Acta **7**, 43.
—, 1951b. Textile Research J. **21**, 412.
—, 1951c. Biochim. Biophys. Acta **6**, 357.
—, 1952. Acta Botan. Neerl. **1**, 99.
—, 1953. Biochim. Biophys. Acta **10**, 477.
— 1954. Biochim. Biophys. Acta **13**, 592.
—, 1954. Acta Botan. Neerl. **3**, 154.
— 1956. Holz **14**, 208.
—, 1958. Acta Botan. Neer.l **7**, 77.
ROELOFSEN, P. A., DALITZ, V. CH. & WIJNMAN, C. F., 1953. Biochim. Biophys. Acta **11**, 344.
ROELOFSEN, P. A. & HOETTE, I., 1951. Antonie van Leeuwenhoek **17**, 27.
ROELOFSEN, P. A. & HOUWINK, A. L., 1951. Protoplasma **40**, 1.
—, —, 1953. Acta Botan. Neerl. **2**, 218.
ROELOFSEN, P. A. & KREGER, D. R., 1951. J. Exptl. Botany **2**, 332, see also 1954. **5**, 24.
ROLLINS, M. L., 1945. Textile Research J. **15**, 65.
—, 1947. Botan. Gaz. **108**, 495.
ROLLINS, M. L. & TRIPP, V. W., 1954. Textile Research J. **24**, 345.
ROMANO, A. H. & NICKERSON, W. J., 1956. J. Bacteriol. **72**, 478.
RUDALL, K. M., 1955. Symposium Soc. Exptl. Biol. **9**, 49.
RUGE, U., 1938. Ber. deut. botan. Ges. **56**, 165.
RUHLAND, W., 1957–1958. Encyclopedia of Plant Physiology, Springer.
RUNKEL, R. O. H., 1942. Holz: Roh- u. Werkstoff. **5**, 413.
—, 1951. FREUND's Handb. Mikroskopie in der Technik V 2, 540.
RUNKEL, R. O. H. & LÜTHGENS, M., 1956. Holz **14**, 424.
RUSKA, H. & KRETSCHMER, M., 1940. Kolloid Z. **93**, 163.

SAKOSTSCHIKOFF, A. P. & KORSCHENIOVSKY, G. A., 1932. Faserforschung **9**, 249.
SALTON, M. R. G., 1953. Biochim. Biophys. Acta **10**, 512.
SCARTH, G. W., GIBBS, R. D. & SPIER, J. D., 1929. Proc. Roy. Soc. Can. 3rd ser. **23**, 269.
SCHLUBACH, H. H. & HOFFMANN–WALDECK, H. P., 1949. Markromol. Chem. **4**, 5.

SCHMIDT, W. J., 1936. Z. Zellforsch. u. mikroskop. Anat. **25**, 181.
SCHMITZ, F., 1880. Sitzber. Ges. Natur u. Heilk. Bonn **159**, 250.
SCHOCH–BODMER, H., 1938. Flora **133**, 69.
SCHOCH–BODMER, 1939. Planta **30**, 168.
—, 1945. Ber. schweiz. botan. Ges. **55**, 154.
SCHOCH–BODMER, H. & HUBER, P., 1951. Ber. schweiz. botan. Ges. **61**, 377.
—, —, 1952. Proc. Leeds Phil. Lit. Soc. **6**, I, 25.
SCHOLTEN, G., 1951. unpublished graduate work in author's laboratory.
SCHRAMM, M., GROMET, Z. & HESTRIN, S., 1957. Biochem. J. **67**, 669
SCHRAMM, M. & HESTRIN, S., 1954. Biochem. J. **56**, 163.
SCHUBERT, W. J. & NORD, F, F,. 1955. Proc. Nat. Acad. Sci. U. S. **41**, 122.
—, —, 1957. Advances in Enzymol. **18**.
SCHUMACHER, W., 1942. Jahrb. wiss. Botan. **90**, 530.
—, 1957. Ber. deut. bot. Ges. **70**, 335.
SCHUMACHER, W. & HALBSGUTH, W., 1938. Jahrb. wiss. Botan. **87**, 324.
SCHUMACHER, W. & LAMBERTZ, P., 1956. Planta **47**, 47.
SCHWARZ, E. R., 1934. Textiles and the Microscope.
SCOTT, F. M., 1950. Botan. Gaz. **111**, 378.
SCOTT, F. M., HAMNER, K. C., BAKER, E. & BOWLER, E., 1956. Am. J. Botany **43**, 313.
—, —, —, —, 1957. Science **125**, 399.
SCOTT, F. M., SCHROEDER, M. R. & TURRELL, F. M., 1948. Botan. Gaz. **109**, 381.
SEARLE, G. O., 1924. J. Textile Inst. **15**, 370.
SEN, J., 1956. Botan. Rev. **22**, 343.
SEN, M. K. & ROY, S. C., 1954. Nature **173**, 298.
SETTERFIELD, G., 1957. Can. J. Botany **35**, 791.
SETTERFIELD, G. & BAYLEY, S. T., 1957. Can. J. Botany **35**, 435.
—, —, 1958. J. Biophys. Biochem. Cyt. **4**, 377.
—, —, 1958a. Exptl. Cell Research **14**, 622.
SEYFRIED, L., 1954. Z. Botan. **42**, 437.
SIEGEL, S. M., 1955. Physiol. Plantarum **8**, 20.
SIGNER, R., PFISTER, H. & STUDER, H., 1951. Makromol. Chem. **6**, 15.
SINNOTT, E. W. & BLOCH, R., 1939. Proc. Natl. Acad. Sci. U. S. A. **25**, 248.
—, —, 1945. Am J. Botany **32**, 151.
SISSON, W. A., 1935. Ind. Eng. Chem. **27**, 51.
—, 1936. J. Phys. Chem. **40**, 343.
—, 1937. Contr. Boyce Thompson Inst. **8**, 389.
—, 1938. Science **87**, 350.
—, 1938a. Contr. Boyce Thompson Inst. **9**, 381.
—, 1938b. Contr. Boyce Thompson Inst. **9**, 239.
—, 1941. Contr. Boyce Thompson Inst. **12**, 31, 171.
SITTE, P., 1953. Mikroskopie **8**, 290.
—, 1954. Thesis Innsbruck.
—, 1955. Mikroskopie **10**, 178.
SIU, R. G. H. & REESE, E. T., 1953. Botan. Rev. **19**, 377.
SKOSS, J. D., 1955. Botan. Gaz. **117**, 55.
SLOEP, A. C., 1928. Onderzoekingen over pektinestoffen, Thesis Delft.
SÖDING, H. J., 1932. Jahrb. wiss. Botan. **77**, 627.
—, 1934. Jahrb. wiss. Botan. **79**, 231.
SONNTAG, P., 1909. Flora **99**, 201.
—, 1911. Jahresber. Ver. angew. Botan. **9**, 140.
SPEARIN, W. E. & ISENBERG, I. H., 1947. Science **105**, 214.
SPONSLER, O. L., 1926. J. Gen. Physiol. **9**, 221, 677.
—, 1930. Nature **125**, 633.
—, 1931. Protoplasma **12**, 241.
SPONSLER, O. L. & PATH, J. D., 1950. Am. J. Botany **36**, 756.
STACEY, M., 1954. Advances in Enzymol. **15**, 301.
STECHER, H., 1952. Mikroskopie **7**, 30.
STEENBERG, B., 1947. Svenska Träforskn. Inst. Medd. 20.
STEFFEN, K., 1955. Z. Botan. **43**, 346.
STEINBRINCK, C., 1906. Biol. Zentr. **26**, 657.
STEMSRUD, F., 1956. Holzforschung **10**, 69.
STERLING, C., 1957a. Acta Botan. Neerl. **6**, 458.
—, 1957b. Biochim. Biophys. Acta **26**, 186.

STERLING, C. & SPIT, B. J., 1957. Am. J. Botany **44**, 851.
STERN, F., 1957. J. Textile Inst., Transact. **48**, T21.
STEVENS, F. J. DE & NORD, F. F., 1951. J. Am. Chem. Soc. **73**, 4615.
STEWARD, T. C. & MÜHLETHALER, K., 1953. Ann. Botany, N. S. **17**, 295.
STOCKAR, G. K., 1948. Thesis Zürich.
STRASBURGER, E., 1882. Über den Bau u. das Wachstum der Zellhäute, Fischer, Jena.
STRASBURGER, E. & KOERNICKE, M., 1923. Das botanische Praktikum.
SUBRAHMANYAN, V., BAINS, G. S., MATARAJAN, C. P. & BHATIA, D. S., 1956. Arch. Biochem. Biophys. **60**, 27.
SVENSSON, A. A., 1956. Arkiv Kemi **10**, 239.
SWANN, M. M. & MITCHISON, J. M., 1950. J. Exptl. Biol. **27**, 226.

TÄUFEL, K. & THALER, H., 1935. Z. Untersuch. Lebensm. **69**, 152.
TAMMES, T., 1908. Der Flachsstengel, Naturk. Verh. Holl. Mij Wetenschap. Haarlem, Ser. III, reeks VI, 4e stuk.
TARKOW, H., 1950. Tappi **33**, 595.
THALER, H., 1957. Z. Lebensm.-Untersuch. u. -Forsch. **106**, 128.
THIMANN, K. & BONNER, J., 1933. Proc. Roy. Soc. (London) B**113**, 126.
THOMAS, R. C., 1928. Am. J. Botany **15**, 537.
—, 1942. Ohio J. Sci. **42**, 60.
—, 1943. Ohio J. Sci. **43**, 135.
TIMELL, T. & JAHN, E. J., 1951. Svensk Papperstidn. **24**, 831.
TIMELL, T. E. & TYMINSKI, A., 1957. Tappi **40**, 519.
TOWERS, G. H. N. & DARNLEY GIBBS, R., 1953. Nature **172**, 25.
TRACEY, M. V., 1953. Biochem. Soc. Symposia no. 11.
—, 1955. Biochem. J. **61**, 579.
TRAYNARD, PH. & AYROUD, A. M., 1952. Rev. gén. botan. **59**, 561.
TRAYNARD, PH., AYROUD, A. M., EYMERY, A., ROBERT, A. & COLIGNY, S. DE. 1954. Holzforschung **8**, 42.
TREIBER, E., 1953. Österreich. Papierzeitung **59**, 23.
—, 1957. Die Chemie der Pflanzenzellwand ,Springer.
TRIPP, V. W. & GIUFFRA, R., 1954. Textile Research J. **24**, 757.
TRIPP, V. W., MOORE, A. T. & ROLLINS, M. L., 1951. Textile Research J. **21**, 886, (see also 1952. Anal. Chem. **24**, 1721).
—, —, —, 1954. Textile Research J. **24**, 956.
—, —, —, 1957. Textile Research J. **27**, 419.
TUNMANN, O. & ROSENTHALER, L. 1931. Pflanzenmikrochemie.
TUPPER–CAREY, R. M. & PRIESTLEY, J. H., 1923. Proc. Roy. Soc. (London) B**95**, 109.

ULLRICH, H., 1935. Planta **23**, 147.
ULLRICH, J., 1955. Ber. deut. botan. Ges. **68**, 93.

VELDKAMP, H., 1955. Meded. Landbouwhogeschool Wageningen **55**, 127.
VIEL, G., 1939. Compt. rend. Acad. Sci. Paris **208**, 532.
VIRTANEN, A. I., 1946. Nature **158**, 795 (cf. 1946. Suomen Kemistilehti **19**B, 3).
VLIET, W. F. VAN. 1954. Biochim. Biophys. Acta **15**, 211.
VOGEL, A., 1950. unpublished work at E. T. H. Zürich.
—, 1953. Makromol. Chem. **11**, 111.
VOLZ, G., 1952. Mikroskopie **7**, 251.
VRIES, M. A. DE. 1948. Thesis Leiden.

WÄLCHLI, D., 1945. Die Einlagerung von Kongorot in Zellulose. Diss. Zürich.
WARD, K., 1955. Chemistry and Technology of Cotton, Interscience.
WARDROP, A. B., 1949. Nature **164**, 366.
—, 1952. Nature **170**, 329.
—, 1952a. Text. Res. J. **22**, 288.
—, 1954a. Australian J. Botany **2**, 165.
—, 1954b. Holzforschung **8**, 12.
—, 1954c. Biochim. Biophys. Acta **13**, 306.
—, 1954d. Australian J. Botany **2**, 154.
—, 1955. Australian J. Botany **3**, 137.
—, 1956. Australian J. Botany **4**, 193.
—, 1957a. Tappi **40**, 225.
—, 1957b. Holzforschung **11**, 102.
WARDROP, A. B. & CRONSHAW, J., 1958. Australian J. Botany **6**, 89.

WARDROP, A. B. & DADSWELL, H. E., 1950. Proc. Australian Pulp & Paper Ind. Techn. Ass. **4**, 198.
—, —, 1951. Nature **168**, 610.
—, —, 1952. Australian J. Sci. Research B**5**, 385.
—, —, 1952a. Australian J. Sci. Research B**5**, 223.
—, —, 1953. Holzforschung **7**, 33.
WARDROP & DADSWELL, 1955. Australian J. Botany **3**, 177.
—, —, 1957. Holzforschung **11**, 33.
WARDROP, A. B. & PRESTON, R. D., 1947. Nature **160**, 911.
—, —, 1950. Biochim. Biophys. Acta **6**, 36.
—, —, 1951. J. Exptl. Botany **2**, 20.
WARTH, A. H., 1956. The chemistry and technology of waxes, New York.
WEBER, E., 1942. Ber. schweiz. botan. Ges. **52**, 111.
WECKERLING, G., 1949. Ber. oberhess. Ges. Natur- u. Heilk., N. F. Naturw. Abt. **24**, 151.
WEISSBERGER, A., 1949–1954. Physical Methods in Organic Chemistry, Vol. I.
WENTZEL, R., 1929. Inaug. Diss. Marburg.
WERGIN, W., 1937. Naturwiss. **25**, 830.
WEURMAN, C., 1954. Acta Botanica Neerl. **3**, 108.
WHISTLER, R. L. & CORBET, W. M., 1955. J. Am. Chem. Soc. **77**, 6318.
WHISTLER, R. L. & KERBY, K. W., 1959. Hoppe Seyler's Z. physiol. Chem. **314**, 46.
WHISTLER, R. L. & SAARNIO, J. ,1957. J. Am. Chem. Soc. **79**, 6055.
WHISTLER, R. L. & SMART, C. L., 1953. Polysaccharide Chemistry, Acad. Press. Inc. New York.
WHITE, E. V. & RAO, P. S., 1953. J. Am. Chem. Soc. **75**, 2617.
WIELER, A., 1943. Botan. Arch. **44**, 285.
WIESNER, J., 1892. Die Elementarstruktur u. d. Wachstum der lebenden Substanz, Wien.
WIJK, A. J. A. VAN DER & MEYER, K. H., 1947. J. Polymer Sci. **2**, 583.
WIJK, A. J. A. VAN DER & SCHMORAK, J., 1953. Helv. Chim. Acta **36**, 385.
WILLIAMS, W. T., PRESTON, R. D. & RIPLEY, G. W., 1955. J. Exptl. Botany **6**, 451.
WILSON, K., 1951. Ann. Botany, N. S. **15**, 279.
—, 1955. Ann. Botany, N. S. **19**, 289.
—, 1957. Ann. Botany, N. S. **21**, 1.
WIRTH, P., 1946. Ber. schweiz. botan. Ges. **56**, 175.
WISE, L. E. & JAHN, E. C., 1952. Wood Chemistry Vol. I–II, Reinhold Publ. Corp.
WISSELINGH, C. VAN. 1925. LINSBAUER's Handb. Pflanzenanatomie Bd. III, 2.
WOLFF, P. M. DE & HOUWINK, A. L., 1954. Acta Botan. Neerl. **3**, 396.
WÜHRMANN, K. & PILNIK, W., 1945. Experientia **1**, 330.
WÜHRMANN–MEYER, K. u. M., 1939. Jahrb. wiss. Botan. **87**, 642.
—, 1941. Planta **32**, 43.

YUNDT, A. P., 1951. Crystalline hemicellulosis, Tappi **34**, 89.

ZECHMEISTER, L. & TOTH, G., 1939. Fortschr. Chem. org. Naturstoffe **2**, 212.
ZETSCHE, F. see KLEIN Handb. Pflanzenanalyse 1932. III: 205.
ZETZSCHE, F. & LÜSCHER, E., 1938. J. prakt. Chem. **150**, 68, 140.
ZIEGENSPECK, H., 1924. Botan. Arch. **25**, 1.
—, 1953. Mikroskopie **8**, 47.
ZIEGENSPECK, H. & H., 1952. Protoplasma **41**, 15.

Subject Index

Index of Botanical Names

Page references to names in the text in regular type, to illustrations in italics. References to plates at the end of
the book in bold face italics

Index of Zoological Names

Author Index

Numbers with * indicate plates at the end of the book

KLING, W., MAHL, H. **1950.** 238, 241
—, — **1951.** 147, 149, 238, 267
—, — **1952.** 147, 149, 238, 241 ,267
KOHL, G. **1889.** 101
KOOIMAN, P. **1954.** 75
— **1957, 1957ᵃ, 1959.** 62
KOOIMAN, P., KREGER, D. R. **1957.** 62
KRABBE, G. **1887.** 134, 160, 194, 196, 197, 201, 202
KRAJCINOVIC, M. **1954.** 74
KRATKY, O. **1951.** 17
KRATKY, O., SCHOSSBERGER, F. **1938.** 19
KRATKY, O., SEKORA, A., TREER, R. **1942.** 17
KRATZL, K., BILLEK, G. **1957.** 83
KREGER, D. R. **1948.** 96, 122, 263
— **1954.** 40, 41, 44, 46, 59, 62, 95, 298, 303, 304
— **1957ᵃ.** 292
— **1957ᵇ.** 26, 273, 292
— **1958.** 94, 96, 272
— **1958ᵃ** (in prep.). 3, 16, 18, 46, 273, 292
— **1958ᵇ.** 95
KREGER, D. R., MEEUSE, B. J. D. **1952.** 59, 61
KÜGLER. 270
KUNDU, B. C., PRESTON, R. D. **1940.** 138, 140, 199, 200, 203
KURSANOV, A. L., VYSKREBENTSEVA. **1952.** 2
KÜSTER, E. **1956.** 10, 53, 59, 69, 83, 95, 98, 100, 101, 134, 178, 194, 208, 243, 257, 261, 294
KYLIN, H. **1937.** 293
— **1946.** 67

LABOURIAU & CARDOSO. **1948** (cf. STEFFEN, K. **1955**). 268
LAMBERTZ, P. **1954.** 245
LANGE, P. W. **1950.** 84, 109, 123
— **1954.** 76, 84, 109, 123
LANGE, P. W., KJAER, A. **1957.** 109
LANNING, T. C., PONNAIYA, B. W. X., CRUMPTON, C. F. **1958.** 102
LAUE. **1912.** 11
LAURENT, E. **1885.** 298, 302
LAUTENSCHLAGER-FLEURY, D. **1955.** 89
LAVES, F., ERNST, TH. **1943.** 110

LEE, B. **1925.** 87
LEE, B., PRIESTLEY, J. H. **1924.** 88
LEGG, V. H., WHEELER, R. V. **1925, 1929.** 87, 88
LEVINE. **1914.** 235
LIESE, W. **1957ᵃ, ᵇ.** 226, 227
— **1958.** 220, 221, 222
LIESE, W., HARTMANN-FAHNENBROCK, M. **1953.** 226, 227, 39* 41*
LIESE, W., JOHANN, I. **1954.** 226, 227, 40*
LINDBERG, B., MEIER, H. **1957.** 57
LINDEBERG, G. **1948.** 84
LINDGREN, P. H. **1958.** 122
LINSBAUER, K. **1930.** 257, 261
LINSKENS, H. F. **1952.** 88, 268
LOTMAR, W., PICKEN, L. E. R. **1950.** 43
LÜDTKE. 203
LUNDEGÅRDH, H. **1946.** 133
LUNIAK, B. **1953.** 40, 102
LYON, F. **1905.** 268
LYR, H. **1958.** 84

MAAS GEESTERANUS, R. A. **1941.** 138, 146
McCLUNG, R. **1950.** 110, 113, 294
McCOMB, E. A., MacCREADY, R. M. **1952.** 73
McCREADY, R. M., REEVE, R. M. **1955.** 71, 74
MacDOWELL, R. M. **1955.** 74, 76
MacLARTY, D. H. **1941.** 40
MADER, H. **1954.** 93, 270–272
MAERTENS, C., RAES, G., MEERSCHE, G. VAN DER. **1956.** 204, 241
MAJUMDAR, G. P., PRESTON, R. D. **1941.** 70, 126, 138, 140, 177, 192, 249, 250
MANGENOT, F. **1953.** 40
MANGENOT, G., RAISON, M. **1942.** 104, 107, 233, 235
MANGIN. **1889.** 74
MANN, J., MARRINAN, H. J. **1956.** 18
MANTELL, C. L. **1947.** 59, 65, 75
MARK, H., SUSICH, G. **1929.** 11, 25
MARTENS, P. **1931.** 139
— **1933.** 88, 89
— **1934.** 187, 267, 268
— **1937.** 129, 135

— **1938.** 129, 139
— **1940.** 254, 267, 301
MASON, H. S., CRONYN, M. **1955.** 83
MATIC, M. **1956.** 87, 88, 91
MÄULE. **1900.** 85
MEEUSE, A. D. J. **1938.** 138, 205, 256
— **1941.** 134, 138, 201
MEEUSE, B. J. D. **1938.** 135, 245
— **1941.** 135, 245
MEIER, H. **1955.** 76, 77, 214, 217, 224
1956. 56, 57
— **1957** (cf. TREIBER). 227
— **1957.** 190, 213
— **1958.** 55, 57, 252
MERCER. 8
MEREWETHER, J. W. T. **1957.** 78
MERICLE, L. W., GORDON WHALEY, W. **1953.** 74
METZNER, I. **1955.** 3, 68
METZNER, P. **1930.** 80, 89, 93
MEVIUS, W. **1923.** 86
MEYER, K. H., HUBER, L, KELLENBERGER, E. **1951.** 22
MEYER, K. H., MARK, H. **1929.** 11–15, 30
—, — **1953.** 66
MEYER, K. H., MISCH, L. **1937.** 12–15, 25, 26, 30
MEYER, K. H., PANKOW, G. W. **1935.** 42, 43
MEYER, K. H., WEHRLI, H. **1937.** 41, 42, 45
MEYER, M. **1938.** 97, 259, 261–264
MIDDLEBROOK, M. J., PRESTON, R. D. **1952.** 303
MIGITA, N., KANDA, T., FUHINAMI, R. **1951.** 91
MIRBEL. **1835.** 196
MOEHRING, E. **1922.** 11, 44
MOHL, VON. 208, 222, 284, 290
MOLISCH, H. **1923.** 35, 36, 38, 46, 62, 65, 93, 101, 102
MONER, J. G. **1955.** 293
MONTGOMERY, R., SMITH, F. **1955.** 67
MORI, T. **1953.** 64, 293
MOSENTHAL. 232
MOSS, B. L. **1948.** 75
MUELLER, L. E., CARR, P. H., LOOMIS, W. E. **1954.** 268, 51*
MÜHLETHALER, K. **1949ᵃ.** 3, 27, 28
— **1949ᵇ.** 82, 147, 159, 232, 33*, 43*

Errata

page	paragraph (alinea)	line		
10	1	8	read:	„ethers of cellulose"
40	6	1	„ :	„*Chytridiaceae*"
60	6	3	„ :	„Smart"
62	3	3	„ :	„1959" instead of „1958"
63	3	1	„ :	„endosperms" instead of „cotyledons"
102	2	4	„ :	„*Chlorochytridion*"
246	4	7	„ :	„1950 b"
303	8	4	„ :	„cleaned (succes-"

plate 2, Fig. P 16, add: *a* to the left figure, *b* to the right one
  „   9, „ P 48, read: „cell axis indicated by cell-edge".

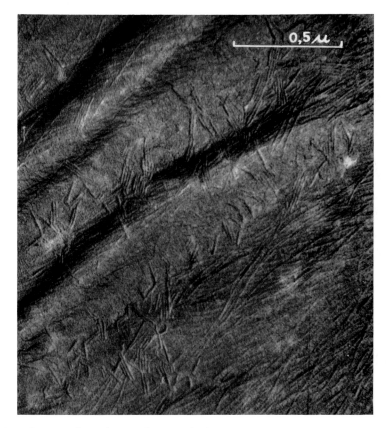

Fig. P 11. Inner surface of parenchyma cell of mature beet root, cleaned with water at 20° C but not otherwise. It is not known whether the short threads are young cellulose microfibrils. Note that the microfibrils in the wall are embedded in amorphous non-cellulose material (from VAN DER POEL et al. 1958).

Plate 2 Fig. P 15, 16

Fig. P 15. Electronmicrograph of a part of a d sintegrated parenchyma cell from the internode of *Vicia faba*; it shows a finely granular layer rich in non-cellulose and a layer containing more cellulose (from WILLIAMS et al. 1955).

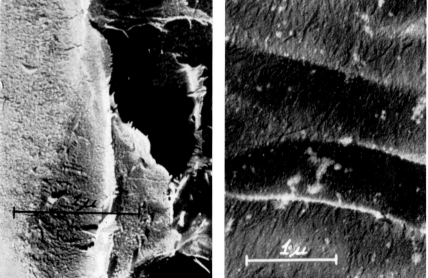

Fig. P 16. Replica of the surface of a delignified tracheid of *Picea excelsa*; a without visible microfibrils (probably a middle lamella); b, with cellulose microfibrils (probably from the primary wall) (from SVENSSON, 1956).

Fig. P 20. Electronmicrograph of the pectin skeleton of a collenchyma cell-wall of *Petasites vulgaris* (ROELOFSEN and KREGER, 1951).

Plate 4   Fig. P 28, 36

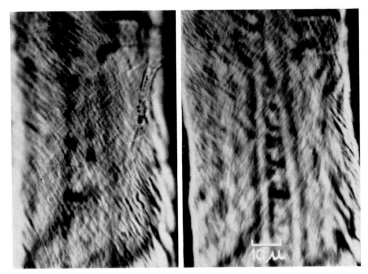

Fig. P 28. Flax fibre swollen in cuprammonium, as seen when the microscope is focussed on the surface (left) or below the latter (right). Three layers are visible, respectively with Z-, S- and Z-helical striation (from ROELOFSEN, 1951 b).

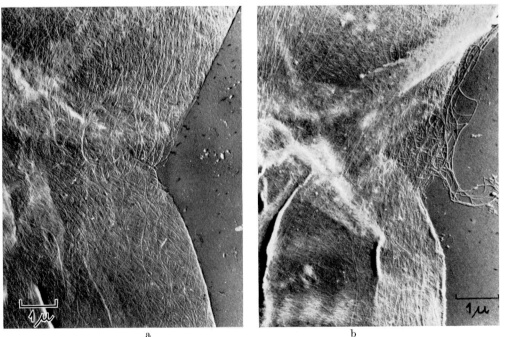

a   b

Fig. P 36. Cell-wall structure in dividing cells of *Avena* coleoptile (from FREY-WYSSLING and MÜHLETHALER, 1951).

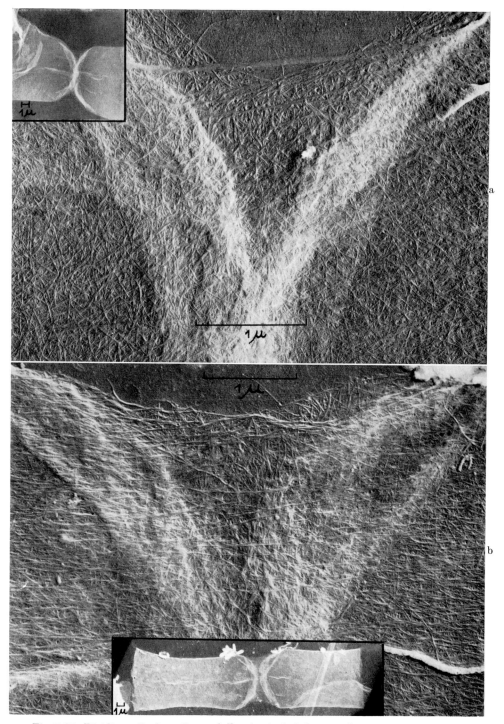

Fig. P 37. Dividing cells from the medulla of a leaf of *Juncus effusus*; a, young, b, older stage, (from HOUWINK and ROELOFSEN, 1954).

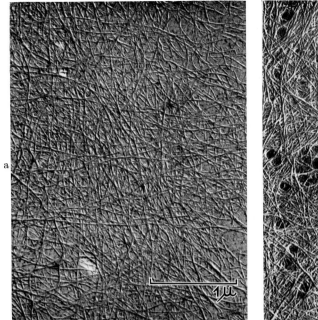

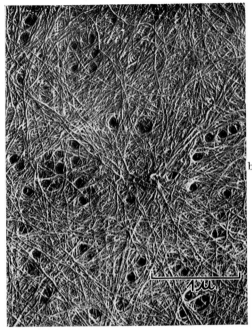

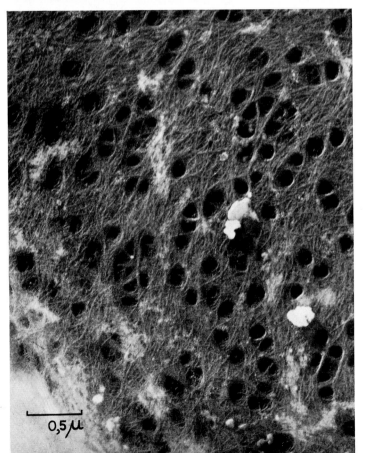

Fig. P 38. Transverse walls of parenchyma cells in the growing apex of a *Cucurbita* shoot; a, initial stage; b, mature stage (from FREY-WYSSLING and MÜLLER, 1957).

Fig. P 39. Partition wall of a fullgrown cell from a hair on a *Tradescantia* stamen; it is uniformly perforated by some 800 plasmodesmata (from ROELOFSEN and HOUWINK, 1951).

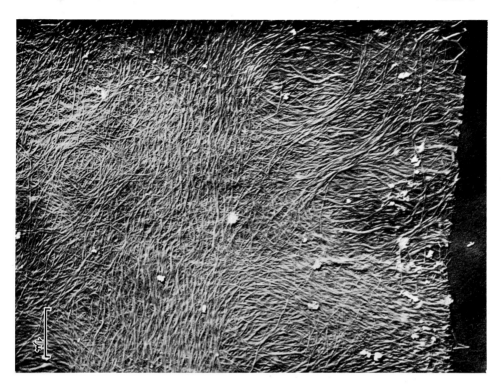

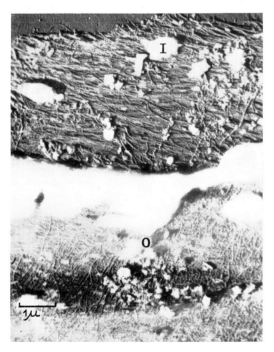

Fig. P 44. Outermost part of the wall of a very young parenchyma cell (20 μ long) from an *Avena* coleoptile. Note the primary pit fields and the thickened rib with its axially oriented microfibrils; compare fig. 43 a, b (from Böhmer, 1958).

Fig. P 45. Outer (O) and inner (I) part of the wall of a parenchyma cell from a 30 mm long *Avena* coleoptile; compare fig. 43 c (from Wardrop, 1956).

Plate 10   Fig. P 49, 50

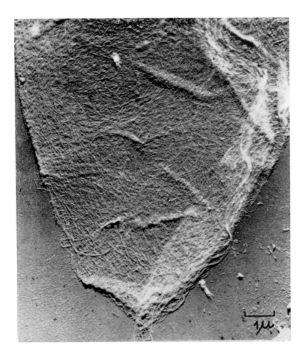

Fig. P 49. Outer part of the wall in the conical tip of an *Avena* coleoptile parenchyma cell situated at the end of a longitudinal file of cells; compare fig. 41 (from MÜHLETHALER, 1950b); in the uppermost part of the tip the wall is evidently crumpled up.

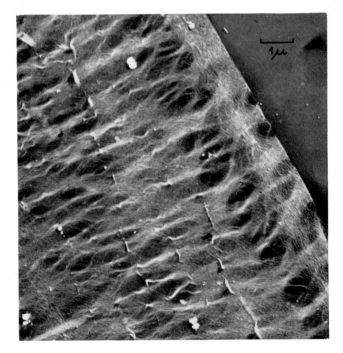

Fig. P 50. Part of the wall of a very young parenchyma cell from a root of *Zea mays*; the primary pit fields appear to be elliptical and the ribs are thikkened (from MÜHLETHALER, 1953a).

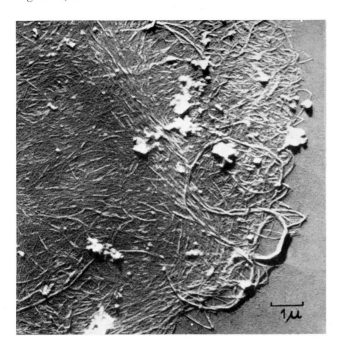

Fig. P 52. Outer part of the wall of a young parenchyma cell from the root of *Zea mays*; the cell just begins to grow in length (from STECHER, 1952).

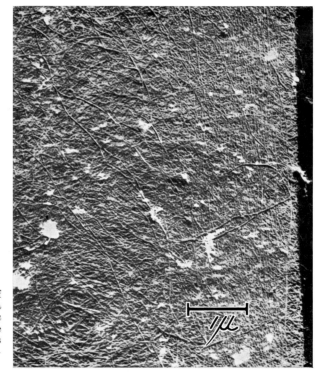

Fig. P 54. Outer part of the wall of a parenchyma cell from a root of *Vicia faba*, 5—8 mm from the tip; direction of cell axis is visible (from WARDROP, 1955).

Plate 12

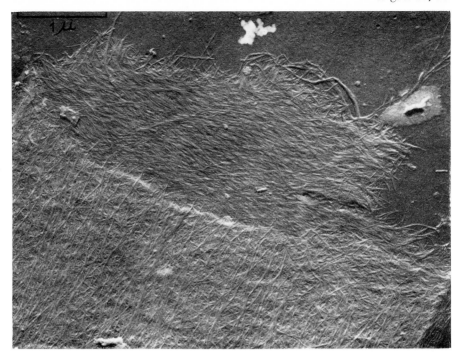

Fig. P 55. Arm of stellate cell from the medulla of *Juncus effusus*, showing the structure of the outer and inner layers of the primary wall; compare fig. P 37 (from HOUWINK and ROELOFSEN, 1954).

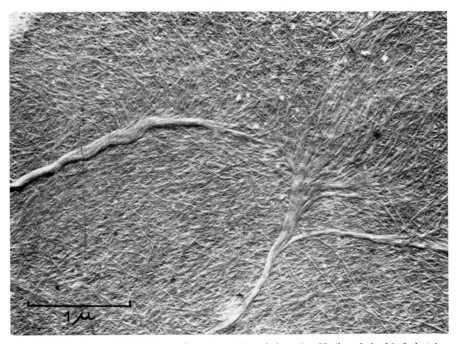

Fig. P 56. Primary wall with irregular orientation of the microfibrils, of the kind that is typical for isodiametric cells; central part of a stellate cell from the medulla of *Juncus effusus*. Note the microfibrils that have been detached from the wall during the maceration, and that are now aggregated into bundles (from HOUWINK and ROELOFSEN, 1954).

Plate 13

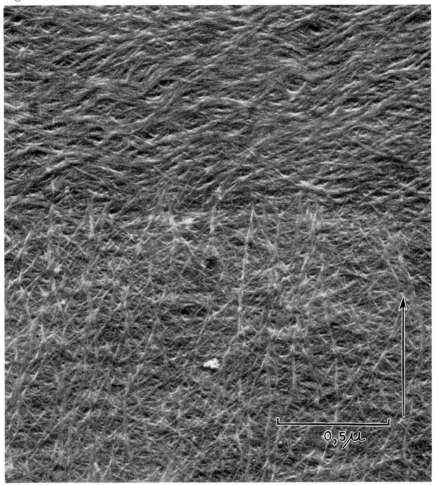

Fig. P 57. Inner side (above) and outer side (below) of the primary cell-wall of a growing cotton hair; the arrow indicates the direction of the axis of the hair (from ROELOFSEN and HOUWINK, 1953).

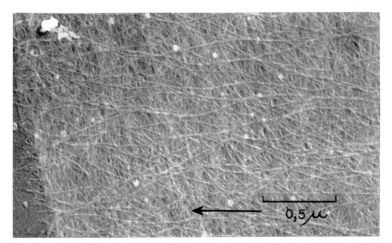

Fig. P 58. Outer side of the primary wall of a growing cotton hair; the arrow indicates the direction of the cell axis (from ROELOFSEN and HOUWINK, 1953).

Plate 14

Fig. P 61

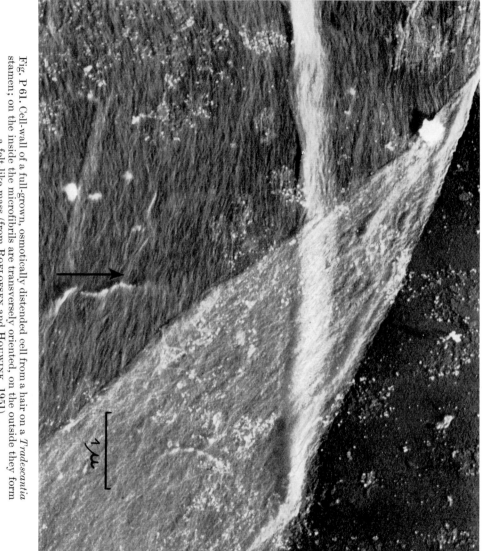

Fig. P 61. Cell-wall of a full-grown, osmotically distended cell from a hair on a *Tradescantia* stamen; on the inside the microfibrils are transversely oriented, on the outside they form a felt-like mass (from ROELOFSEN and HOUWINK, 1951).

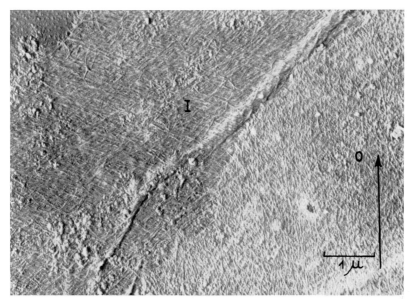

Fig. P 60. Outer (O) and inner (I) side of a shred of the primary wall detached from the wall of a full-grown cotton hair (from TRIPP et al., 1954).

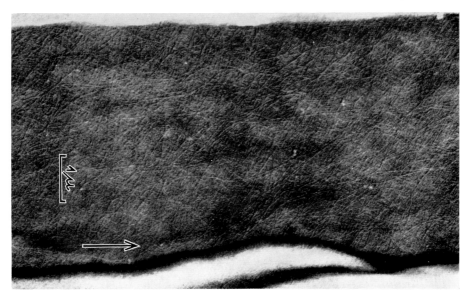

Fig. P 62. Outer layer of a similar cell as shown in fig. P 61; the orientation of the outermost fibrils is here predominantly axial (from ROELOFSEN and HOUWINK, unpublished).

Plate 16

Fig. P 63, 64

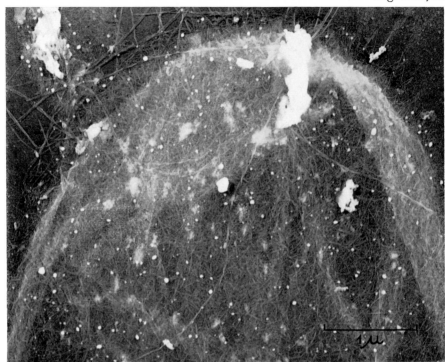

Fig. P 63. Outer face of the cell-wall at the tip of a root hair of *Zea mays* (from HOUWINK and ROELOFSEN, 1954).

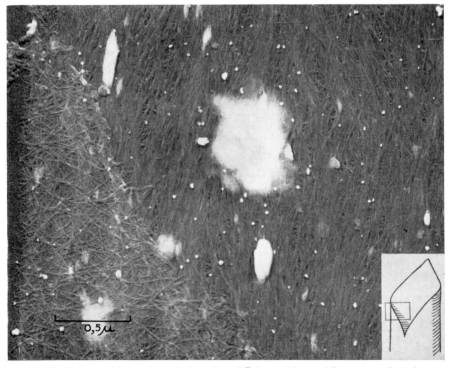

Fig. P 64. Outer and inner face of the cell-wall of a root hair of *Zea mays*; the primary wall appears to be very thin, and its microfibrils show no definite orientation; in the secondary wall they are axially oriented (from HOUWINK and ROELOFSEN, 1954).

Fig. P 68. Cell-wall at the tip of an epidermal cell from an *Avena* coleoptile; at the left the outer wall and at the right the radial wall (from MÜHLETHALER, 1950 b).

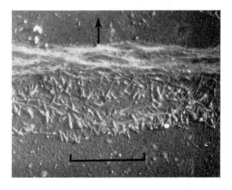

Fig. P 67. Part of the outer wall (above) and radial wall of an epidermal cell from an *Avena* coleoptile (from MÜHLETHALER, 1950 b).

Fig. P 69. Transverse section through the outer wall of an epidermal cell of an onion root; the cell was situated about 1 mm from the tip of the latter; the arrow points towards the centre of the cell (from SETTER-FIELD and BAYLEY, 1957).

Plate 18

Fig. P 72

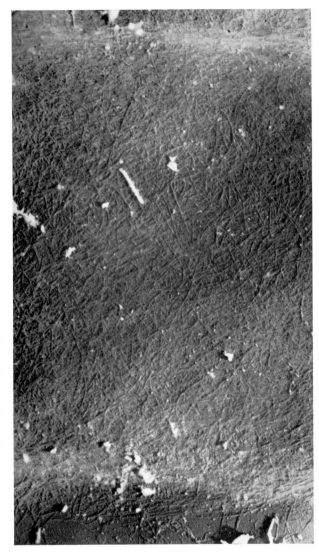

Fig. P 72. Outer face of the primary wall of a young tracheid of *Pinus radiata* with transverse and slightly oblique crossed microfibrils and two thickened axial ribs with axially oriented microfibrils (obtained from WARDROP in 1958).

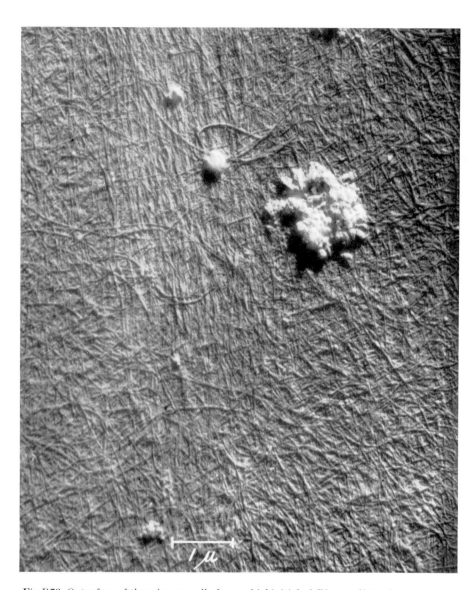

Fig. P 73. Outer face of the primary wall of a cambial initial of *Pinus radiata*; the outermost microfibrils more or less axially oriented, but the other ones all transversely oriented (from WARDROP, 1954 a).

Plate 20

Fig. P 74, 77

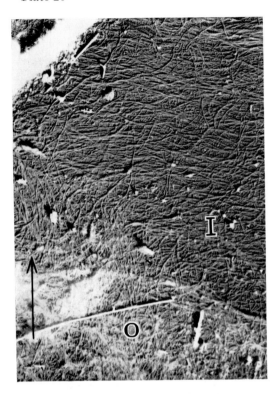

Fig. P 74. Outer (O) and inner (I) surface of a growing tracheid of *Pinus
radiata*; cell axis indicated (micrograph
obtained from WARDROP in 1958).

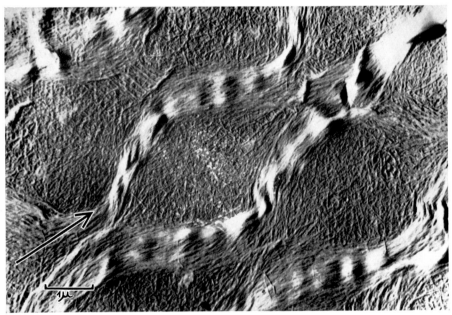

Fig. P 77. Cell of *Fraxinus excelsior* that is going to develop into a segment of a xylem
vessel; the inside of the wall is provided with wavy ridges running in an axial direction;
at this place out of the primary pit field a multiple perforation plate will be formed (from
BOSSHARD, 1952).

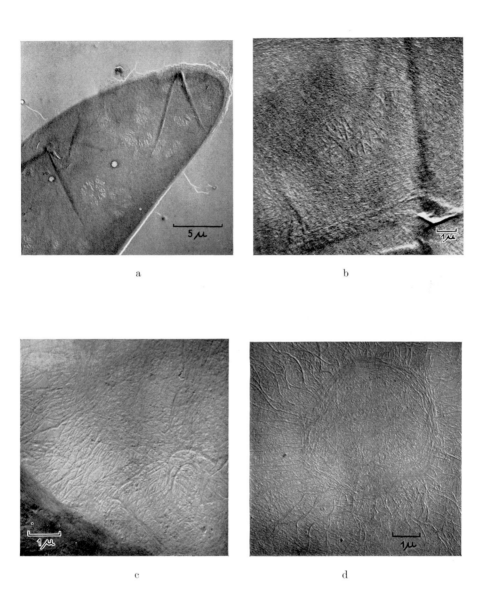

Fig. P 78. Development of pit membrane and torus of a bordered pit in the primary wall of a tracheid of *Pinus sylvestris*; *a* and *b*: show initial bundling of microfibrils, *c* and *d*: the differentation of the torus and of radiating fibril bundles in the annular zone around the latter (from FREY-WYSSLING, BOSSHARD and MÜHLETHALER, 1956).

Plate 22   Fig. P 79, 80

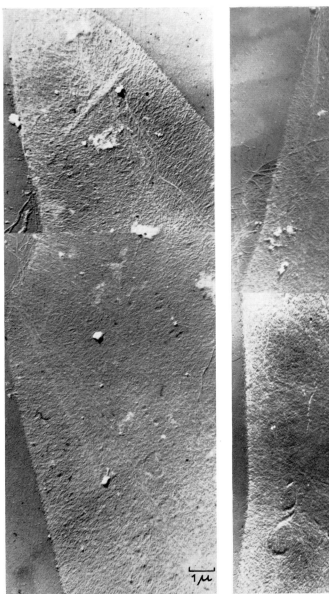

Fig. P 79. Cell-wall of young sieve-tube cell from the tip of a 10 mm long *Avena* coleoptile; it is provided with two thickened ribs (from MÜHLETHALER, 1950b).

Fig. P 80. Cell-wall of older sieve-tube cell from the basal part of a 40 mm long *Avena* coleoptile (from MÜHLETHALER, 1950b).

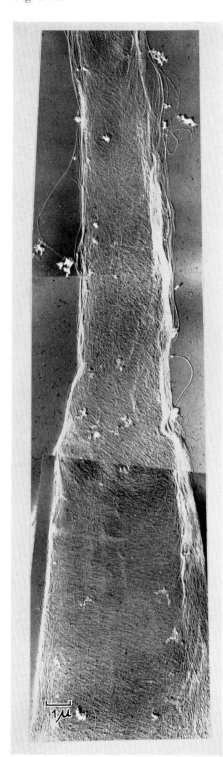

Fig. P 82. Cell-wall in the growing tip of a
pointed sieve-tube cell from an *Avena* coleoptile (from MÜHLETHALER, 1950b).

Plate 24   Fig. P 83

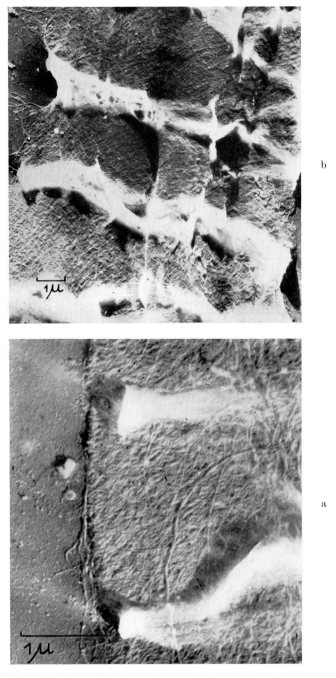

Fig. P 83. Segments of annular vessels from a *Zea* coleoptile (from MÜHLETHALER, 1950 b).

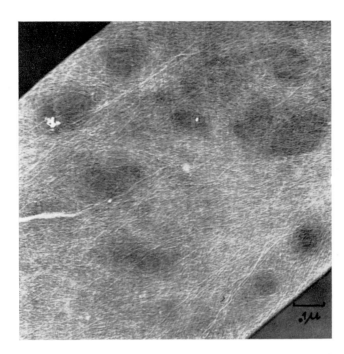

Fig. P 81. Cell-wall
of older sieve-tube
cell from a *Zea* root
(from MÜHLE-
THALER, 1953).

Fig. P 84. Segment
of a spiral vessel from
a *Zea* root (from
MÜHLETHALER,
1953a).

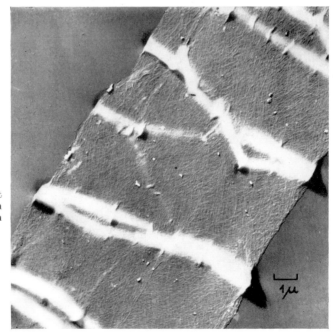

Plate 26   Fig. P 85

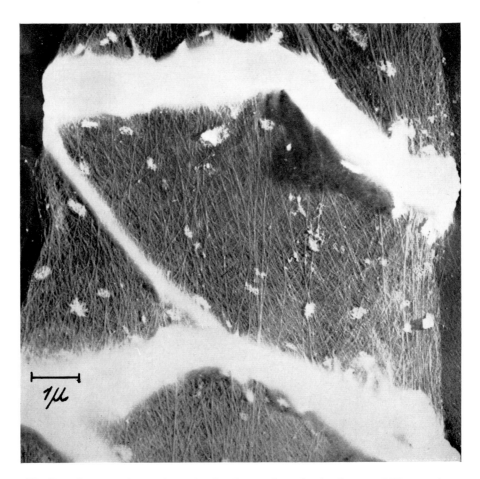

Fig. P 85. Segment of a spiral vessel isolated 8 mm from the tip of a root of *Pisum savitum* (from WARDROP, 1955).

Fig. P 86. The tip of a tracheary element from an *Avena* coleoptile, with at the outside a predominantly axial orientation of the microfibrils (from MÜHLETHALER, 1950b).

Plate 28   Fig. P 87

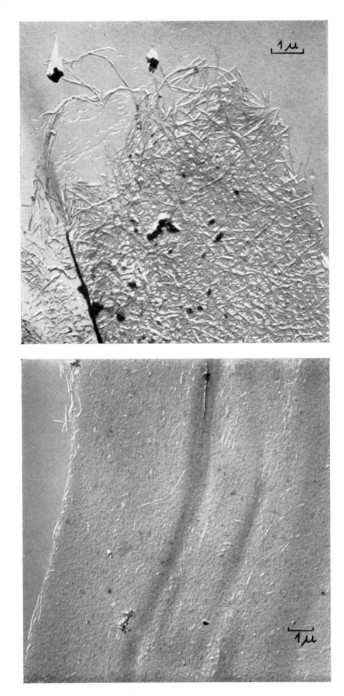

Fig. P 87. Outer side of the cell-wall at the tip (above) and in the middle zone of a *Petunia* pollen-tube grown on agar (from Müh-lethaler and Linskens, 1956).

Plate 29

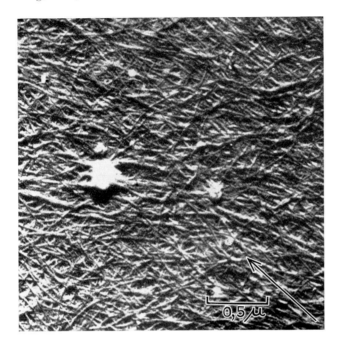

Fig. P 88. Outer side of the cell-wall of a pollen tube of *Tulipa*; cell axis indicated (from VOGEL, 1950).

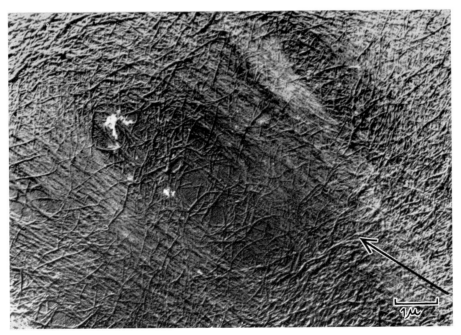

Fig. P 89. Inner surface of the wall of a growing phloem fibre obtained from *Fraxinus excelsior*; inner layer thin and provided with transversely oriented microfibrils, and locally distended; outer layer with axially oriented bands of microfibrils (from BOSSHARD, 1952).

Plate 30   Fig. P 90

a

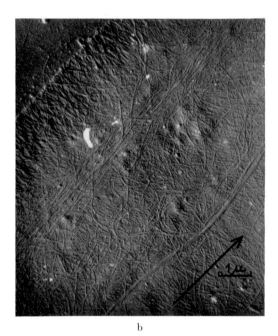

b

Fig. P 90. Outer surface of the wall of cortical fibres
from a young *Asparagus* shoot, *a*: from a zone 5—6 cm,
and *b*: from one 8—9 cm from the tip; cell axis indicated (from STERLING and SPIT, 1957).

Fig. P 91. Cell-wall from the tip of a cortical fibre taken from a zone 8—9 cm below the apex of an *Asparagus* shoot (from STERLING and SPIT, 1957).

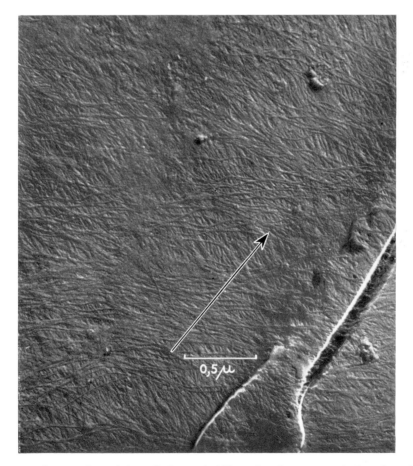

Fig. P 92. Inner surface of the wall of a cortical fibre taken from a zone 5—6 cm from the apex of an *Asparagus* shoot (from STERLING and SPIT, 1957).

Plate 32   Fig. P 104, 105

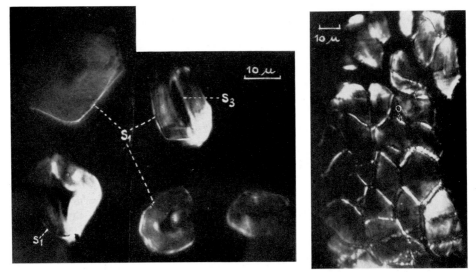

Fig. P104. Thin transverse sections of fibres seen between crossed nicols; a: of *Boehmeria* fibres showing S_1 and S_3 layers; b: of *Cannabis* fibres showing conspicuous S_1 layers, with visible pores, but only occasionally an S_3 layer; in both objects the thick S_2 layers light up evenly (own micrographs).

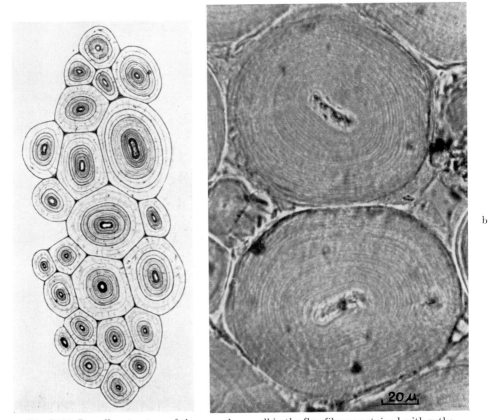

Fig. P105. Lamellar structure of the secondary wall in the flax fibre; a: stained with ruthenium red; b: swollen in cuprammonium and stained with congo red (a: from REIMERS, 1922a, and b: from HOCK, 1942).

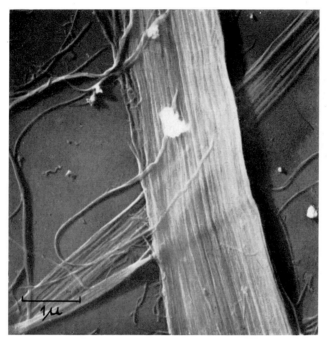

Fig. P107. Electron micrograph of a fragment obtained by disintegrating a non-purified
ramie fibre (from MÜHLETHALER, 1949*b*).

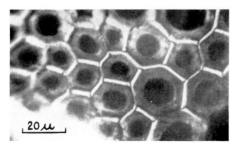

Fig. P109. Transverse section of a fibre bundle of *Musa* (*Ensete*) *textilis* as seen between crossed nicols; the S_1 layers are conspicuous, and occasionally a thin S_3 layer is distinguishable;
the thick S_2 layer lights up evenly but faintly (own micrograph).

Plate 34   Fig. P 110

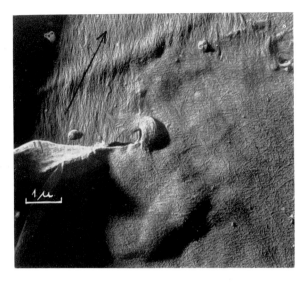

a

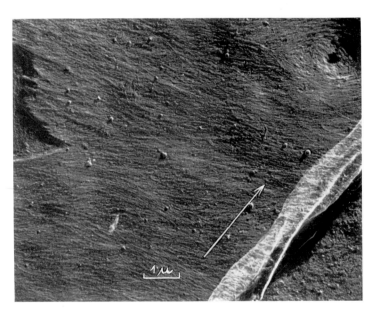

b

Fig. P110. Young cortical fibres of *Asparagus* shoots seen from the inside at the moment the secondary thickening has just set in. In a: a steeply oriented secondary wall is visible through a hole in the upper wall of the fibre (isotropic structure at the surface); in b: a flat spiral structure is shown. From STERLING and SPIT (1957).

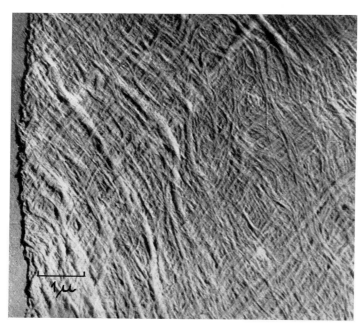

Fig. P116. Crossed fibrillar structure in a wall fragment of a xylem fibre from *Fraxinus excelsior;* such fragments may now be accepted as representing parts of the S_1 layer (from BOSSHARD, 1952).

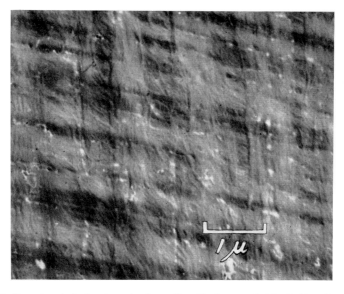

Fig. P117. Cross-banded structure in the cell-wall of a tracheid of *Alstonia spathulata* (WARDROP, 1954a).

Plate 36   Fig. P 118, 119

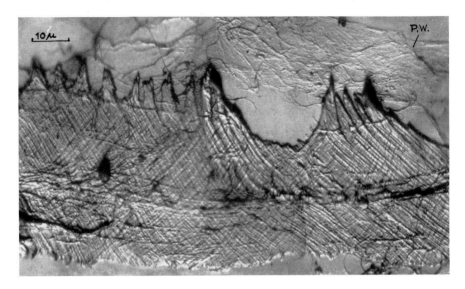

Fig. P118. Crossed fibrillar structure in the S_1 layer of a tracheid of *Pinus patula* as seen with the reflecting microscope in a metal-shadowed cell-wall fragment (EMERTON and GOLDSMITH, 1956).

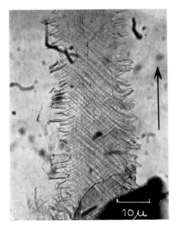

Fig. P119. Fragment of the S_1 layer detached from a delignified tracheid of *Pinus radiata* and stained with congo-red; cell axis indicated (from WARDROP, 1957b).

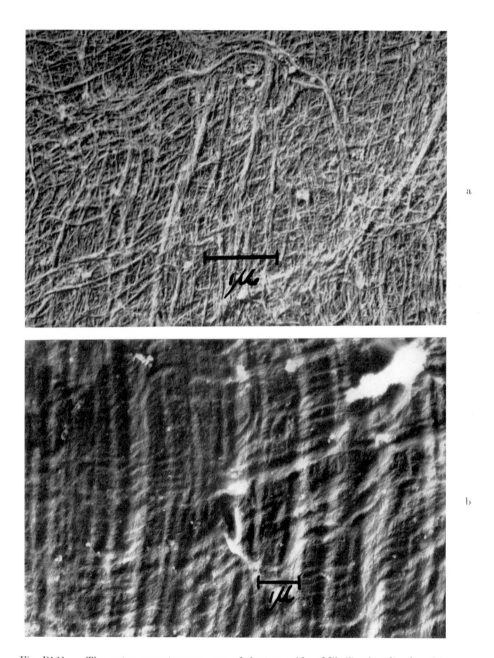

Fig. P121. a: The outer more tenuous one of the two grids of fibrillar bundles found in the S₁ layer of a tracheid of Pinus radiata; b: the inner grid consisting of thicker bundles (from WARDROP, 1957b).

Plate 38

Fig. P 122, 123

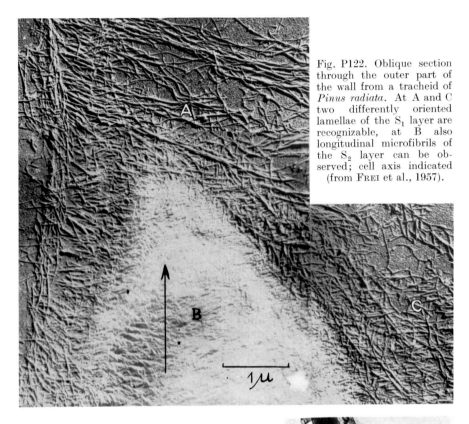

Fig. P122. Oblique section through the outer part of the wall from a tracheid of *Pinus radiata*. At A and C two differently oriented lamellae of the S_1 layer are recognizable, at B also longitudinal microfibrils of the S_2 layer can be observed; cell axis indicated (from FREI et al., 1957).

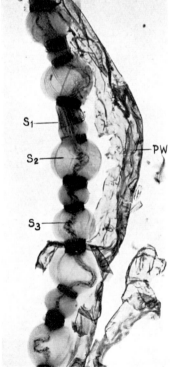

Fig. P123. Balloon swelling of a tracheid of *Pinus insignis*, of which the wall had previously been stained; the primary wall (PW) was split and detached, and the constrictions are caused by the S_1 layer; in the centre stained remnants of the S_3 layer and of the protoplasm occur, the S_2 layer did not stain, but underwent a considerable swelling (from BUCHER, 1957a).

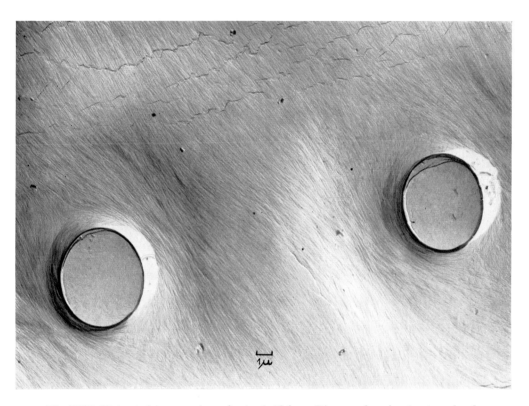

Fig. P134. Untreated inner surface of a tracheid from *Picea excelsa*, showing two closed
bordered pits and a helical structure with deviations in the neighbourhood of the pits
(from LIESE and HARTMANN-FAHNENBROCK, 1953).

Plate 40   Fig. P 135

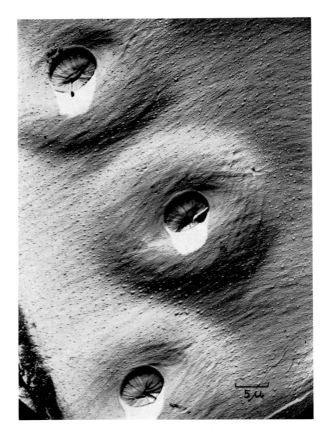

Fig. P135. Untreated inner surface of a tracheid from *Pinus sylvestris*, showing bordered pits and a nearly transversely oriented structure covered by a thin non-fibrillar film provided with warts; cell axis visible, (from LIESE and JOHANN, 1954).

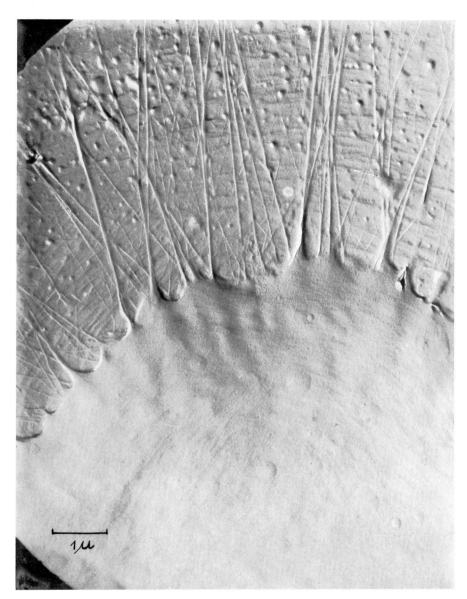

Fig. P137. Torus, perforated pit membrane and inner side of the overhanging margin of a bordered pit of *Pinus sylvestris* (from LIESE and HARTMANN-FAHNENBROCK, 1953).

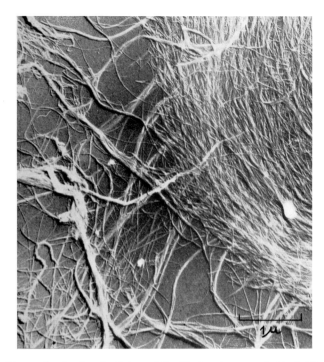

Fig. P138. Torus of a bordered pit in a delignified mature tracheid of *Pinus sylvestris*, showing circular structure and marginal thickening (STEMSRUD, 1956).

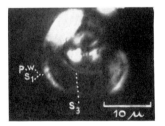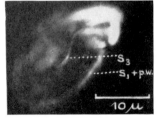

Fig. P145. Oblique sections of cotton hairs cut in an angle of 25° with the cell axis, as seen between crossed nicols. In part of the cell-wall the microfibrils in the S_2 layer have been cut transversally, and here a birefringent outer layer consisting of the S_1 layer and the primary wall is usually visible; sometime also an S_3 layer (own micrographs).

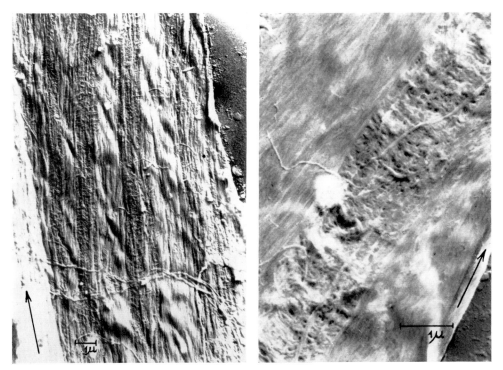

Fig. P146. S₁ layer in the wall of a cotton hair, showing alternating strips consisting either of closely aligned longitudinally oriented microfibrils or of open transversely oriented bundles of microfibrils; arrows indicate cell axis (from ROLLINS and TRIPP, 1954; official U.S.D.A. photograph).

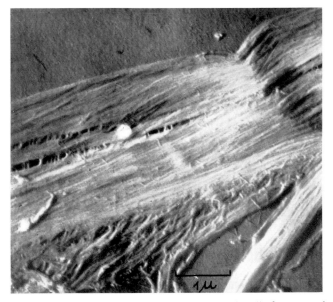

Fig. P147. Fragment of the S₂ layer from the disintegrated wall of a cotton hair, as seen under the electron microscope; it shows densely aligned microfibrils, and also what is thought to be a remnant of a dislocation in the original fibre (from MÜHLETHALER, 1949b).

Plate 44   Fig. P 153, 157

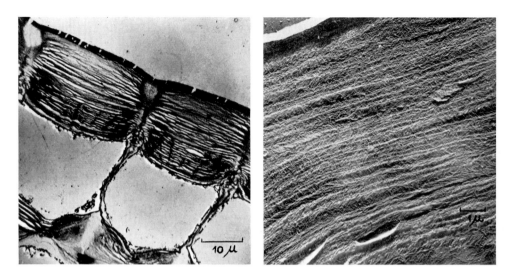

Fig. P153. Section through epidermal cells (a) and through their outer wall (b); the cells were obtained from the leaves of *Hyacinthus orientalis* (from MÜHLETHALER, 1953*a*).

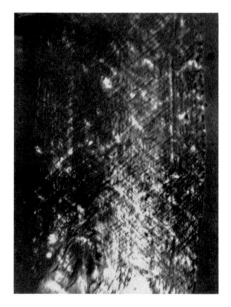

Fig. P157. Part of a parenchyma cell from an *Avena* coleoptile that had completed its growth. The cell had been cleaned and was stained with congo-red, and is seen between crossed nicols. It shows a secondary thickening consisting of crossed helical bundles (from WARDROP and CRONSHAW, 1958).

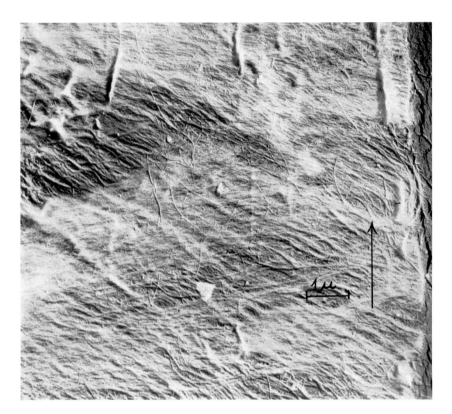

Fig. P158. Outer side of the wall of a parenchyma cell obtained from an *Avena* coleoptile that had completed its growth. Under the transversely oriented microfibrils of the primary wall, obliquely oriented fibrillar bundles are visible; the latter are supposed to represent the early stage of secondary thickening (from WARDROP and CRONSHAW, 1958).

Plate 46 Fig. P 159

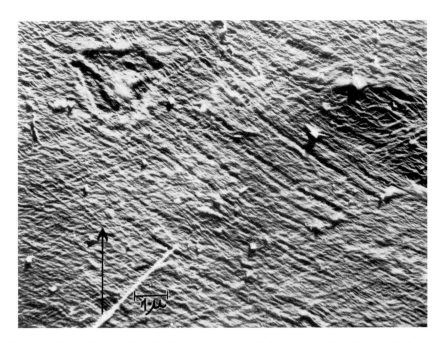

Fig. P159. Probably a single wall of a parenchyma cell of an *Avena* coleoptile that had completed its growth. It shows a secondary thickening with crossed fibrillar texture (from WARDROP and CRONSHAW, 1958).

Fig. P160. Cell-wall of a parenchyma cell from the root of *Beta vulgaris var. saccharifera*, as seen from the inside (from VAN DER POEL et al., 1958).

Fig. P161. Transverse section through a sclerosed cell from the ray parenchyma of *Persoonia lanceolata*, seen between crossed nicols; the wall shows a lamellar structure (from WARDROP and DADSWELL, 1952 *i*).

Plate 48   Fig. P 162, 163

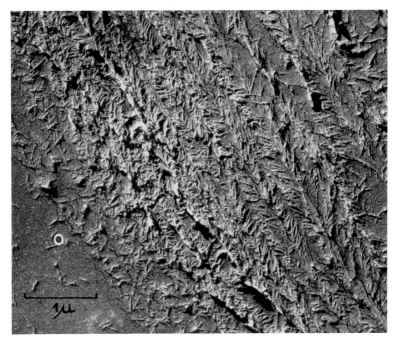

Fig. P162. Part of the wall of a ray-parenchyma cell from *Pinus radiata*, cut in a direction perpendicular to the cell axis; it shows several lamellae oriented alternatively in a transverse and in a nearly axial direction, 0: outer side (from FREI et al., 1957).

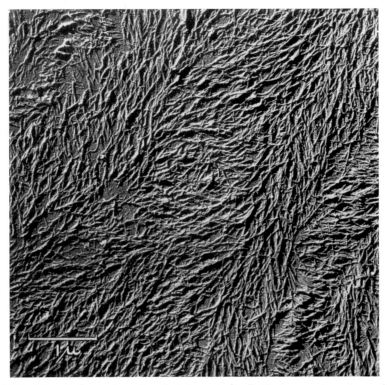

Fig. P163. Cell-wall of a similar cell as that shown in fig. P162; it was cut nearly parallel to the plane of the wall, and shows lamellae with differently oriented microfibrils (from FREI et al., 1957).

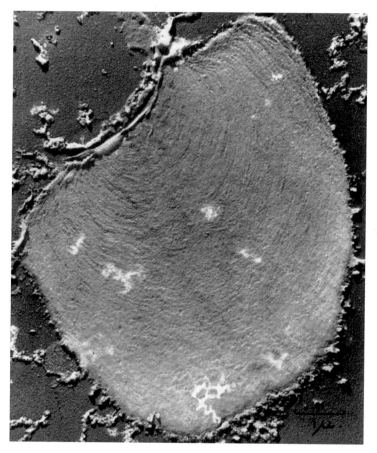

Fig. P164. Section through a spiral thickening on the wall of a protoxylem vessel of *Cucurbita*; it shows numerous lamellae (from HEPTON et al., 1956).

Plate 50   Fig. P 170, 173

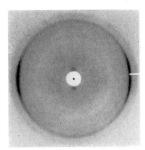

Fig. P170. X-ray diagram of the cuticular membrane from a leaf of *Clivia nobilis*, obtained by rays that traversed the membrane in a direction parallel to the longitudinal axis of the cells. The reflections on the equator are produced by the short side-spacings between the wax molecules, the meridional reflections near the centre by the long-spacings which correspond to the length of the molecules (from BANGE, 1950)

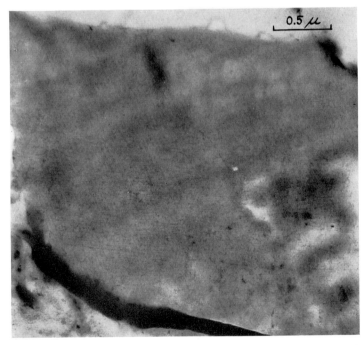

Fig. P 173. Electron micrograph of a section through the cuticular membrane of a leaf of *Clivia nobilis*, showing a fine periclinal striation, that might correspond to the expected lamellar pores filled with wax (made in 1958 by M. SALOME in the author's laboratory).

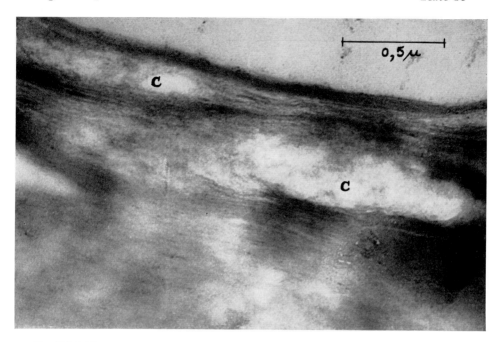

Fig. P 174. Electron micrograph of a section through the cuticular membrane of the apple, showing periclinal lamellation; at c: cavities formed during the embedding in methacrylate (from HILKENBÄUMER, 1958).

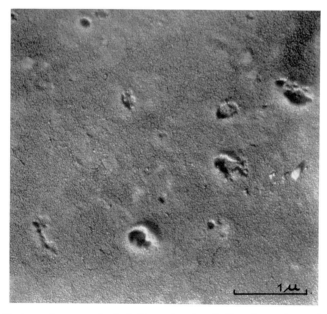

Fig. P 175· Surface of a young leaf of *Musa*, showing shallow depressions, which in older leaves prove to be regions of increased wax production (from MUELLER et al., 1954).

Plate 52   Fig. P 176, 179

Fig. P176. Section through the acetolysed exine of *Lycopodium clavatum*, showing lamellae with a granular structure (from AFZELIUS et al., 1954).

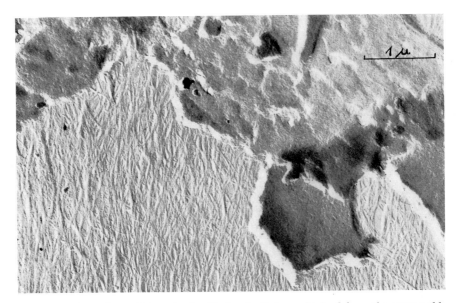

Fig. P179. Network consisting of microfibrils of cellulose, obtained from the presumable primary wall in bottle cork that had been treated with hot alkali; locally parts of the suberin layer are present (from SITTE, 1955).

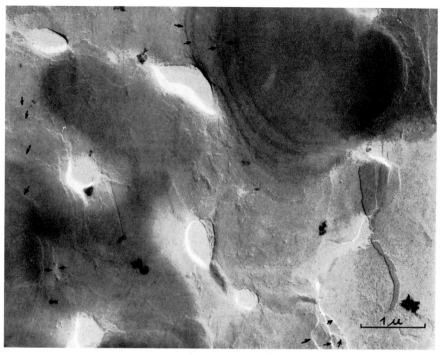

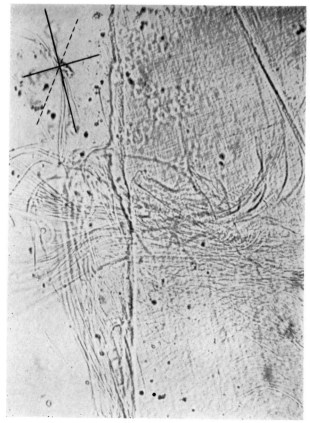

Fig. P 180.
Lamellate structure of
the suberin layer in bot-
tle cork that had been
treated with alkali; the
arrows indicate places
with terrace formation
(from SITTE, 1955).

Fig. P 181. Part of the
cell-wall of *Valonia ventricosa*, showing two distinct and one weak set
of striations, the three
directions are indicated
by lines (from PRESTON
and ASTBURY, 1937).

Plate 54

Fig. P 182. Inner surface of the wall of a cell of *Valonia macrophysa* that had been preserved by freeze-drying; it shows the very first microfibrils of a new lamella, and proves that these microfobrils are deposited exactly parallel to each other, an orientation that they will retain to the end (from PRESTON et al., 1953).

Fig. P 183. Inner surface of the wall with annexed to it the re-oriented outermost layer of the cytoplasm, from a cell similar to that shown in fig. P 182 (from PRESTON et al., 1953).

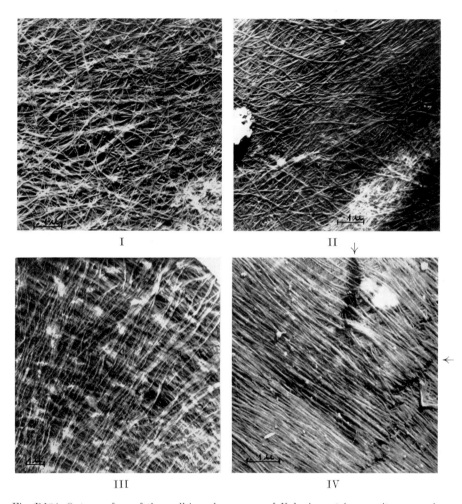

Fig. P 184. Outer surface of the wall in aplanospores of *Valonia ventricosa* as it appears in successive stages of development; I: earliest, IV: latest stage; the arrows in IV indicate cracks (from STEWARD and MÜHLETHALER, 1953).

Plate 56

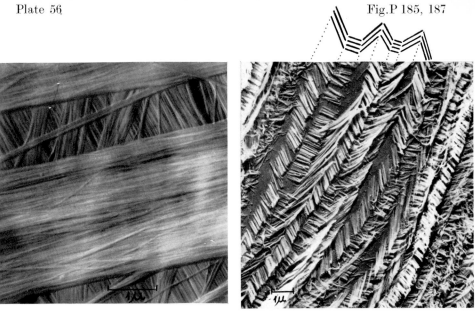

Fig. P 185. Cell-wall of *Valonia ventricosa* in surface view and in transverse section, showing the presence of three different orientations in the successive lamellae (from STEWARD and MÜHLETHALER, 1953).

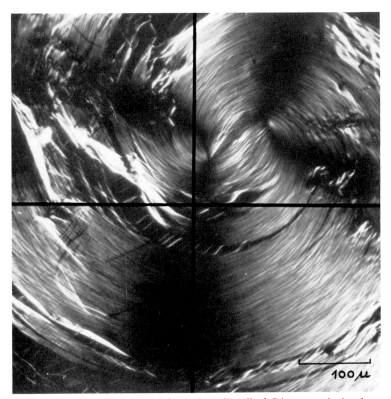

Fig. P 187. A single lamella detached from the cell-wall of *Dictyospaeria favulosa* at the "pole", as it appears between crossed nicols; it shows the spiral with a very low pitch (from WILSON, 1955).

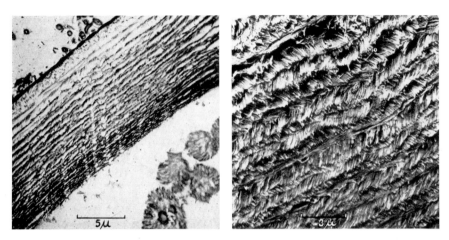

Fig. P186. Transverse sections through the outer wall of the pluricellular thallus of *Dictyosphaeria favulosa*, showing three different kinds of orientation in the successive layers (from STEWARD and MÜHLETHALER, 1953).

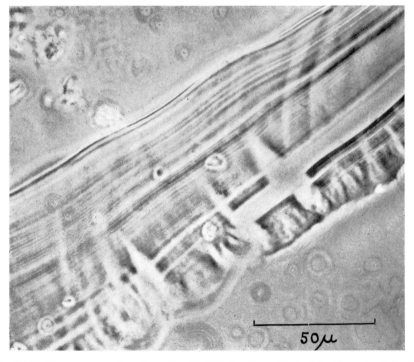

Fig. P188. Transverse section of a cell-wall of *Halicystis ovalis* that had been treated with dilute cuprammonium; it was photographed with phase contrast, and shows numerous lamellae (from ROELOFSEN, DALITZ and WIJNMAN, 1953).

Plate 58   Fig. P 192, 194

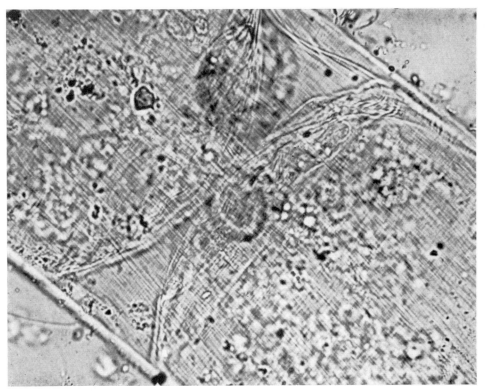

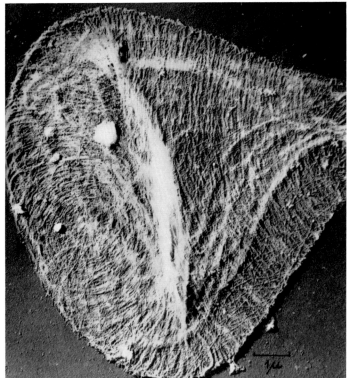

Fig. P 192.
Cladophora gracilis. At the place of a transverse wall the orientation of the striations in the outer layer of the longitudinal wall does not undergo a change, as it does in *C. prolifera* (from Astbury and Preston, 1940).

Fig. P 194.
Fibrillar cell-wall structure in a settled swarmer of *Cladophora melagonium;* the structure shows the presence of a pole opposite the sprouting end (from Nicolai, 1957).

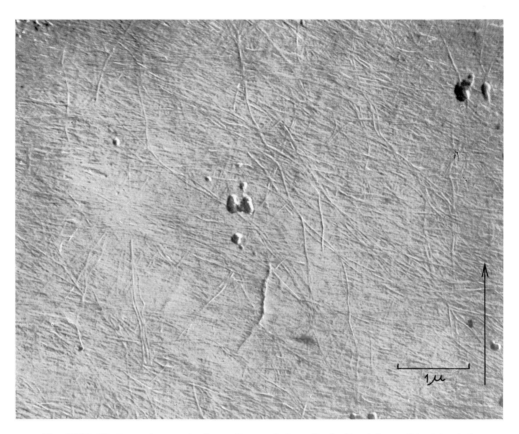

Fig. P 195. Electron micrograph of a replica made from the inside of the wall (not treated chemically) of a growing internodial cell (60 mm) of *Nitella axillaris;* it shows a predominantly transverse orientation of the microfibrils (from GREEN, 1958a).

Plate 60   Fig. P 196, 197

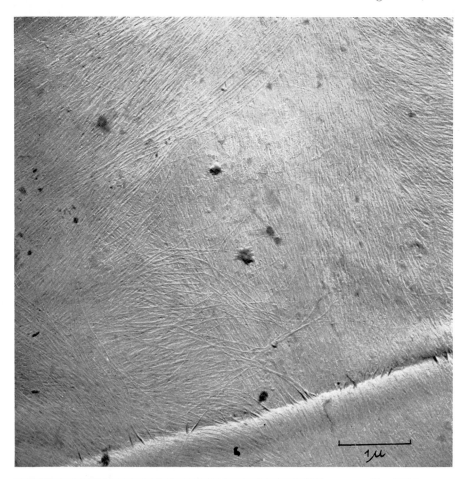

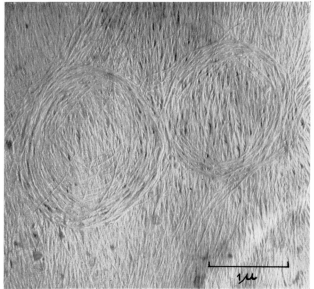

Fig. P 196.
Electron micrograph of
a replica made from the
inside of the wall (not
treated chemically) of a
mature internodial cell
of *Nitella axillaris;* it
shows a patchy arrange-
ment of the microfibrils
(from GREEN, 1958a)

Fig. P 197.
Circular orientation of
the microfibrils at the
inner surface of the wall
in very oldinternodial
cells of *Nitella axillaris*
(from GREEN, 1958a).

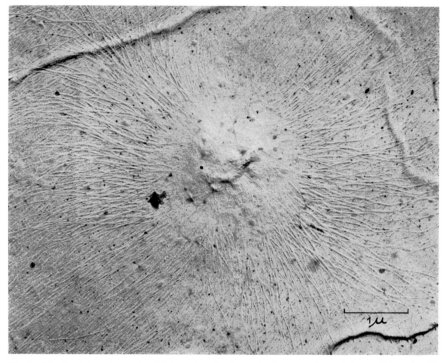

Fig. P 198. Stellate orientation of the microfibrils at the inner surface of the wall in very old internodial cells of *Nitella axillaris* (from GREEN, 1958[a]).

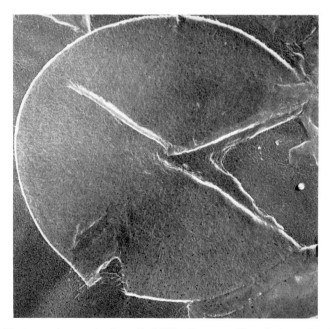

Fig. P 199. Electron micrograph of a cell of *Chlorella pyrenoidosa* that was burst and then cleaned with water at room temperature (from NORTHCOTE et al., 1958).

Plate 62   Fig. P 205

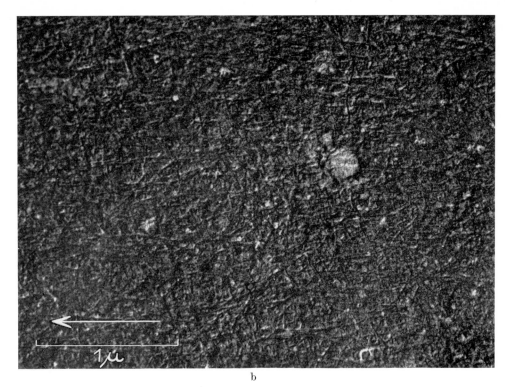

b

a

Fig. P 205. Outer surface of the primary wall in the region of growth (a), and below the latter (b) in a sporangiophore of *Phycomyces blakesleeanus;* arrow indicates position of cell axis (a: from ROELOFSEN, 1951 c; b: unpublished).

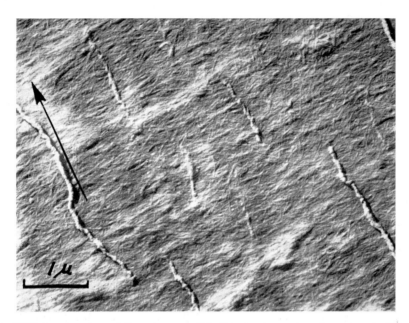

Fig. P206. Inner surface of the primary wall in the growing region of a sporangiophore of *Phycomyces blakesleeanus* (stage with sporangium) ; it shows a transverse fibrillar structure and ridges that are regarded as artefacts; cell axis indicated (from ROELOFSEN, 1951 c).

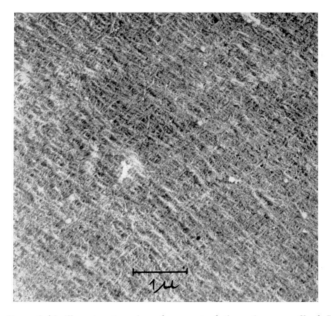

Fig. P207. Crossed fibrillar structure in a fragment of the primary wall of *Phycomyces blakesleeanus* (from FREY-WYSSLING and MÜHLETHALER, 1950).

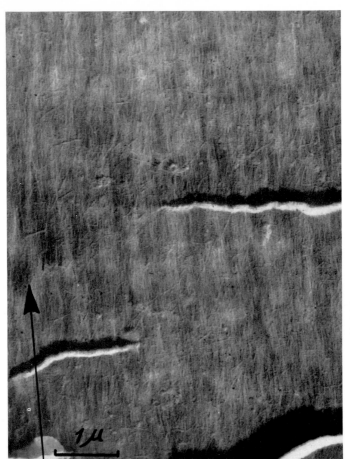

Fig. P 208. Inner surface of the wall of a sporangiophore of *Phycomyces blakesleeanus* at a point 0.2 mm below the optically isotropic zone; it shwos the beginnings of the secondary wall (from ROELOFSEN, 1951 c).

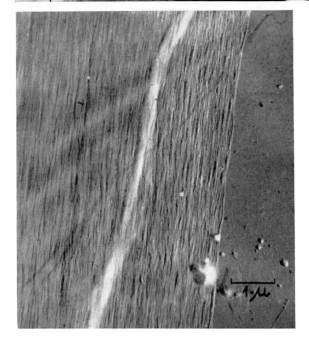

Fig. P 209. Dense fibrillar structure observed in the secondary wall at the base of a sporan giophore of *Phycomyces blakesleeanus* (from FREY-WYSSLING and MÜHLETHLAER, 1950).

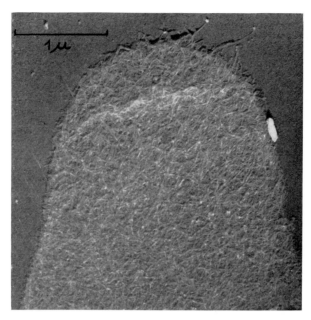

Fig. P210. Network of chitin microfibrils in the tip of a hypha from a shake culture of *Phycomyces blakesleeanus* (electron micrograph made by HOUWINK in 1954).

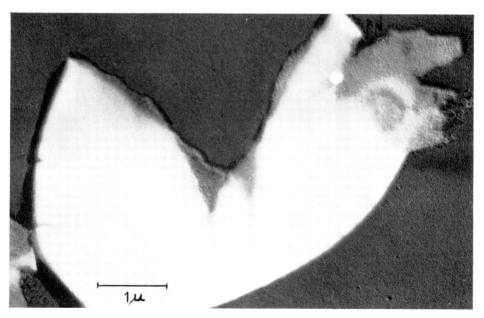

Fig. P211. Washed wall of a disrupted cell of *Candida tropicalis*; it shows a smooth outer surface and the presence of tiny microfibrils on the inner surface (baker's yeast shows a similar structure), (from HOUWINK and KREGER, 1953.)

Plate 66   Fig. P 212

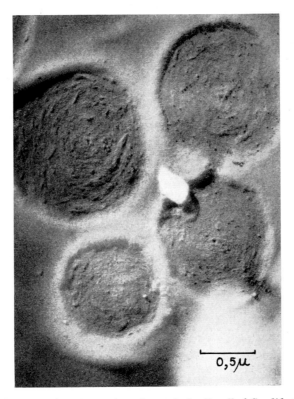

Fig. P212. Bud scars on the outer surface of a washed cell-wall of *Candida tropicalis;* they show a concentric arrangement of wall material surrounded by a rim (from HOUWINK and KREGER, 1953).

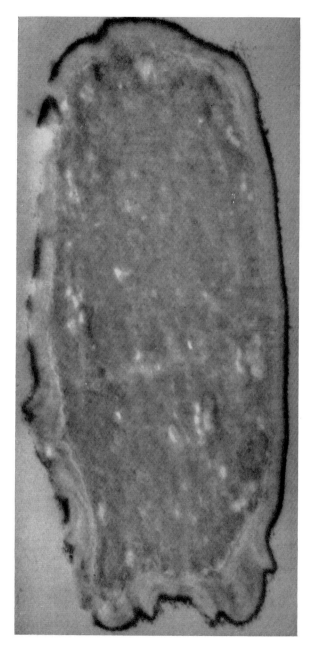

Fig. P213. Longitudinal section through a cell of baker's yeast; it shows a cell-wall with a birth scar at the lower end (centre) with two bud scars annexed; the wall itself shows the presence of an outer layer with a denser structure, and of an inner layer containing micro-fibrils (from AGAR and DOUGLAS, 1955).

Plate 68   Fig. P 214, 215

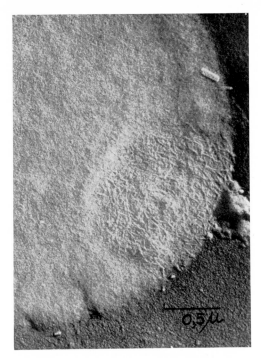

Fig. P214. Cell-wall of *Candida tropicalis*, boiled with alkali; it shows a minutely granular surface and in the scar the presence of microfibrils (from HOUWINK and KREGER, 1953).

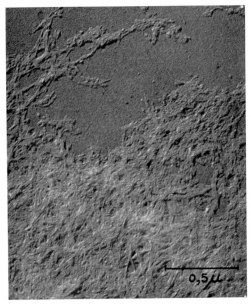

Fig. P215. Chitin granules and microfibrils obtained from the cell-wall of *Candida tropicalis* by boiling the latter with acid and alkali (from HOUWINK and KREGER, 1953).